Human Gene Mutation

Human Gene Mutation

David N. Cooper
Charter Molecular Genetics Laboratory, Thrombosis Research Institute, University of London, London, UK

Michael Krawczak
Abteilung für Humangenetik, Medizinische Hochschule, Hannover, Germany

*β*IOS
SCIENTIFIC
PUBLISHERS

First published in the United Kingdom 1993 by
BIOS Scientific Publishers Limited,
St Thomas House, Becket Street, Oxford OX1 1SJ, UK.
Tel: 01865 726286; Fax: 01865 246823.

Reprinted as paperback 1995.

A CIP catalogue record for this book is available from the British Library.

ISBN 1 85996 055 3

THIS BOOK IS DEDICATED TO
ROSEMARY COOPER
WHOSE BRAVE STRUGGLE AGAINST ILL HEALTH HAS
BEEN A SOURCE OF INSPIRATION

Typeset by Unicus Graphics Ltd, Horsham, UK.
Printed by Information Press Ltd, Eynsham, UK.

Preface

The study of naturally occurring gene mutations is very important for a number of reasons, not the least being that the process of mutational change is fundamental to an understanding of the origins of genetic variation and, as such, plays a vital role in the evolution of all living systems. More specifically, knowledge of the nature, relative frequency and DNA sequence context of different gene lesions promises both to improve our understanding of underlying mutational mechanisms and to provide us with valuable insights into the intricacies of the basic cellular processes of DNA replication and repair. In addition, the drawing up of the ground rules for assessing and predicting the probable relative frequencies and locations of specific types of gene lesion causing human inherited disease may contribute to improvements in both the design and efficacy of mutation search strategies in molecular diagnostic medicine. This notwithstanding, until relatively recently, our knowledge of the nature of artificially induced lesions, resulting from the treatment of cultured cells with exogenous mutagens, far exceeded that pertaining to spontaneous mutations. For these reasons, we have sought to follow the advice of the founder of modern human genetics, William Bateson, who, in the context of collecting plant mutants, exhorted us all to 'treasure our exceptions'.

Within the last 15 years, we have seen remarkably rapid progress in the analysis and diagnosis of human inherited disease and in the characterization of the underlying gene lesions. Recombinant DNA technology with its powerful, methodologically uniform approach has made antenatal and/or pre-symptomatic diagnosis feasible for many disorders that were until very recently refractory to analysis. Whilst known mutations may now be screened for almost on a 'same-day' basis, screening for novel mutations can also be accomplished fairly rapidly, largely thanks to the use of the polymerase chain reaction (PCR) whose advent has revolutionized both the theory and practice of molecular medicine. Indeed, many different types of mutation (single base-pair substitutions, deletions, insertions, duplications, inversions etc) have now been detected and characterized in a large number of different human genes. Although knowledge of the nature of a specific gene defect (the disease genotype) can permit direct detection of carriers of that lesion, such information can sometimes also be used to make prognostic predictions about clinical severity, the age of onset and clinical course of the disease (the disease phenotype). Detailed analysis of the genotype–phenotype relationship promises both to improve the accuracy of prognostic predictions and to increase our understanding of the mechanisms and processes of disease pathogenesis.

It has been known for a long time that the incidence and prevalence of different human genetic diseases are very variable. It has therefore come as no surprise to find that the nature, frequency and location of human gene lesions are also highly non-random; the study of this non-randomness and its underlying causes represents the central and unifying theme of this volume. We now recognize that this non-randomness is very largely sequence-directed; thus, some DNA sequences are not only very much more mutable than others, but these sequences also mutate in very specific ways and at very characteristic frequencies. A major goal therefore for those of us interested in the molecular basis of mutation is to be able to understand the underlying mechanisms responsible for this non-randomness. If these endogenous mechanisms can be deduced and inferred from the sizable spectrum of mutations now available for study, we shall be that much closer to fulfilling our eventual aim of understanding the ultimate causes of pathology associated with inherited disease. Since the frequency of gene mutation is an important determinant of disease prevalence, this must be a key question for human geneticists.

The aim of this volume has been to put together under one cover an empirically-based mechanistic analysis of the nature of human gene mutation causing genetic disease, an assessment of the consequences of mutation both at the level of gene expression and for the complex relationship between genotype and phenotype, an overview of currently available methods for mutation detection and analysis, and a reference source to current diagnostic possibilities in a fast-moving field. As far as the first of these topics is concerned, the emphasis has been placed firmly upon single base-pair substitutions and deletions since these comprise the vast majority of known human gene lesions.

Although we have tried to refer to as many examples of gene mutation as possible in the body of the text, it is virtually impossible to be fully comprehensive. We nevertheless hope that our selection of examples is regarded as both representative and illuminating. Regrettably, it was found to be impossible to cover 'chromosomal disorders' in any depth: thus it was found necessary to largely exclude aneuploidies and chromosome deletion/duplication syndromes from our study. In a single volume, it was also considered impossible to attempt to do justice to the enormous literature on the effects of specific mutations on protein structure and function. Such effects are of course a vital link in the pathway from mutant genotype to disease phenotype. However, our remit has been the study of human gene mutation and the application of nucleic acid-based methodology to molecular diagnostic medicine. With these aims in mind, we have declined to stray too far from the initial source of the mutational event, the gene.

In this reprint of the first edition, we have included an analysis of the mutational spectrum of the TP53 tumour suppressor gene responsible for many human cancers. The remarkable similarity noted between the somatic TP53 spectrum and the germline spectrum derived from other human genes supports the view that many cancer-causing mutations in the soma arise directly or indirectly as a consequence of endogenous cellular mechanisms.

Our genes have evolved slowly, probably via a myriad of meandering and circuitous pathways, 'guided' through the millennia of erratic environmental influences by the moulding force of natural selection. Perhaps this hesitant evolutionary past accounts for present-day genes containing, encoded within their base sequences, the potential seeds of their own destruction. How apt in this context is the poet's description of nature: 'so careful of the type she seems, so careless of the single life' (Alfred, Lord Tennyson, 'In Memoriam A.H.H.', 1850).

David N. Cooper (*London*)
Michael Krawczak (*Hannover*)

Acknowledgements

We wish to acknowledge debts of gratitude to Jörg Schmidtke who introduced us both to the study of human genetic disease and to each other, Ted Tuddenham who suggested the (initially unwelcome!) idea of a volume on human gene mutation, Jochen Reiss, Michael Barfoot and Peter Nürnberg for their many suggestions and for critical reading of parts of the manuscript, David Hames and Jonathan Ray for their help in planning and preparation, Vijay Kakkar for his enthusiastic support and encouragement, John Clayton for his valuable contributions to the interpretation of RFLP/disease associations, Francis Barany for communication of unpublished work, Doug Wallace for communication of mitochondrial DNA sequence data, the Thrombosis Research Trust, Charter Consolidated plc and British–American Tobacco plc for their much appreciated research funding and finally to Margaret McLaughlin and Regina Krawczak who have probably helped in more ways than they will realize.

Contents

Abbreviations

ARE	androgen-responsive element
ARMS	amplification refractory mutation system
ASO	allele-specific oligonucleotide
ASPCR	allele-specific polymerase chain reaction
bp	base-pair
CF	cystic fibrosis
CFTR	cystic fibrosis transmembrane conductance regulator
cM	centiMorgan
CV	consensus value
CVM	mutated splice site consensus value
CVN	wild-type splice site consensus value
DGGE	denaturing gradient gel electrophoresis
DNA	deoxyribonucleic acid
dNTP	deoxyribonucleotide $5'$-triphosphate
HDL	high density lipoprotein
kb	kilobase
LCR	ligase chain reaction
LCR	locus control region
LDL	low density lipoprotein
LDR	ligase detection reaction
LINE	long interspersed repeat element
5mC	5-methylcytosine
MREC	mismatch repair enzyme cleavage
Myr	million years
PAH	phenylalanine hydroxylase
PCNA	proliferating cell nuclear antigen
PCR	polymerase chain reaction
PCU	potential of cryptic splice site utilization
PKU	phenylketonuria
rdm	relative dinucleotide mutability
RFLP	restriction fragment length polymorphisms
RNA	ribonucleic acid
rSSCP	RNA conformation polymorphism
SINE	short interspersed repeat element
snRNA	small nuclear RNA
snRNP	small nuclear ribonucleoprotein particle
SNuPE	single nucleotide primer excision
SSCP	single-strand conformation polymorphism
UV	ultraviolet
VLDL	very low density lipoprotein
VNTR	variable number tandem repeat
YAC	yeast artificial chromosome

A historical view of research into the nature of mutation

What man that sees the ever-whirling wheele
Of change, the which all mortall things doth sway,
But that thereby doth find, and plainly feele
How mutability in them doth play
Her cruel sports, to many men's decay?

[Edmund Spenser, c. 1609; *The Faerie Queene*. Book VII, 'Two Cantos of Mutabilitie', Canto VI (i)]

Mutation may be defined as the process by which a structural change occurs in the genetic material, deoxyribonucleic acid (DNA). It represents the driving force behind evolution, the origin of genetic variation and the ultimate cause of hereditary disease. In order to place present-day mutation research in what we believe is its proper historical context, we present here a short history of thought and experiment which together form the intellectual and conceptual backdrop to our current view of gene mutation. In so doing, we attempt to go back rather further than Hugo de Vries, the 'father of mutation theory', to demonstrate that ideas of mutation and mutability, which in many ways anticipated gene theory, were being promulgated long before the concept of the gene came to be accepted. This new concept, however, was to provide the secure foundations for a new biology which would eventually link recombination in fruit flies to the recognition of DNA as the hereditary material and which would lead inexorably from the elucidation of the structure of DNA to the development of techniques for the direct diagnosis of human genetic disease.

1.1 The ancient Greeks

The ancient Greeks, including the physicians of the Hippocratic school and the philosophers Plato and Aristotle in the 4th and 5th centuries BC, were possibly the first to explore genetic ideas and theories of heredity (Stubbe, 1972; Bartsocas, 1982, 1984). Hippocrates held that a human embryo was reconstituted from parental elements, supplied by the semen into which they were concentrated, and which were representative of all parts of the parental body both healthy and diseased. The Hippocratic view, which implied the inheritance of acquired characteristics, was rapidly shown to be inadequate by Aristotle who noted that children born to mutilated parents did not exhibit the defects of their progenitors. Further, it was Aristotle who first realized that heredity was not based upon the inheritance of concentrated body parts but rather involved the transmission of the information necessary for embryonic development. Although these ideas were largely forgotten for the next 2000 years, the Aristotelian school of thought was remarkably insightful in its day. Thus Aristotle's pupil, Theophrastus of Eresus (c. 372–287 BC), recorded in *De Causis Plantarum*:

> Changes sometimes occur spontaneously in fruits and also, though more rarely, in whole trees. Soothsayers see omens and portents in such variations; and when they occur infrequently, they are generally thought to be contrary to nature, though this is no longer the case when they are found in large numbers.

Theophrastus appears in this passage to draw a subtle distinction between what we now term mutations and polymorphisms. He nevertheless appears to have believed that the causes of this variation lay with environmental variables such as habitat and climate rather than with heredity.

1.2 Early descriptions of genetic variants

By the end of the 16th century, the first detailed description of a novel hereditary variant had appeared: a Heidelberg apothecary named Sprenger discovered a new form of the greater celandine, *Chelidonium majus*, which was subsequently described by Bauhin (1596); its form was constant and it bred true. Two centuries later, Kölreuter described the occurrence of *Missgeburten* (monstrosities) amongst the progeny of plant hybrids (Olby, 1985). D'Azara (1801) described the sudden appearance of a new breed of hornless (mocho) South American cattle which originated from a single isolated individual. By the latter half of the 19th century, many examples of the emergence of new heritable varieties and forms had been documented largely thanks to the attentions of a multitude of amateur naturalists, breeders and horticulturists (reviewed in great detail by Darwin, 1868).

1.3 Early concepts of human inherited disease

Although not yet considered akin to either variation or mutation, concepts of disease also originated in antiquity. Thus, for example, sex-linked haemophilia was first recognized and recorded by Rabbi Simon ben Gamaliel in the second century AD: he gave special dispensation from circumcision to an infant whose three maternal cousins had died from excessive bleeding after the operation (Babilonian Talmud; reviewed by Rosner, 1969). The first modern description of haemophilia was however provided by Otto who, in 1803, recognized its sex-limited mode of inheritance:

males only are affected and all are not liable to it. Though females are free [of it], they are capable of transmitting it to their children.

In 1752, Maupertuis (cited by Motulsky, 1959) published an account of polydactyly in a four-generation German family and demonstrated that this trait could be transmitted through either the mother or the father. He further demonstrated, by employing simple probability calculations, that the familial occurrence of the trait could not be due to chance alone. Meckel (1812) described a number of other hereditary deformities in his *Handbuch der Pathologischen Anatomie.*

In 1814, the English apothecary and physician Joseph Adams published *A Treatise on the Supposed Hereditary Properties of Diseases* which, although at the time largely ignored (see Motulsky, 1959), was remarkably prescient in a number of different respects. Adams distinguished between familial diseases [recessive disorders] which were 'confined to a single generation, to brothers and sisters, the children of the same parent' and hereditary diseases [dominant disorders] which could be 'traced from generation to generation'. He understood that inherited diseases might not be obvious at birth but could still manifest themselves later in life and that intrafamilial correlations of age of onset could be used for the purposes of genetic prognosis. He appreciated the potential deleterious consequences of inbreeding noting that 'endemic peculiarities may be found in certain sequestered districts'. Finally, he hinted at early conceptual links between mutation, disease and selection:

> Those constitutions, which are peculiarly susceptible to such diseases as are excited by climate, fall an early sacrifice; hence, the propagation from such sources gradually lessens, and the disease would cease altogether were it not that parents, free from such susceptibility, occasionally produce an offspring in whom the susceptibility originates.

A number of other early reports of inherited human diseases and traits are cited by Stubbe (1972).

1.4 The 19th century: from Lamarck to Bateson

In the early part of the 19th century, biological science had been largely limited to the descriptive study of the organization of living things. 'Vitalism', a mysterious life force, neither chemical nor physical in nature, was often still invoked to explain biological phenomena. By the late 19th and early 20th centuries, however, the new concepts of cellular organization, evolutionary theory and the study of heredity had permanently altered the intellectual landscape and spawned a tough new reductionist approach. The remarkably rapid transition from a purely observational to a true experimental science, from an essentially passive to an active (and secular) discipline, meant that the study of living processes was no longer necessarily inaccessible and inexplicable. Once the foundations of modern biology had been laid, the emphasis shifted from the descriptive to the explanatory, from simple organization to multiple levels of organization, to the underlying processes and biological laws governing the formation and function of biological structures and of course to the nature of heredity itself, long regarded as the most intractable problem.

The terms 'mutation' and 'transmutation' had both been used as early as 1809 by Lamarck to describe the change of one form of a species into another, albeit through the imagined inheritance of acquired characteristics. Thus, as individuals of a species

> change their situation, climate, and manner of living, they change also, by little and little, the consistence and proportions of their parts, their form, their faculties, and even their organization, in such a manner that everything in them comes at last to participate in the mutations to which they have been exposed.

These terms were subsequently adopted by palaeontologists to describe the change of one species into another. Thus Waagen (1869) [quoted by De Vries (1901)] used mutation to denote the smallest perceptible temporal change in a geological series of ammonites.

Darwin (1859) in his *Origin of Species* was well aware of 'sports' and 'monstrosities' as he termed them, defining these as 'some considerable deviation of structure in one part, either injurious to or not useful to the species, and not generally propagated'. Although it was not at all clear at this time whether these deviations were always heritable, Darwin surmised that whereas 'the laws governing inheritance are quite unknown', 'any variation which is not inherited is unimportant to us' (Darwin, 1859). To what extent Darwin had separated in his own mind the emerging concepts of variation, mutation and inherited disease is unclear. He was certainly aware of many hereditary disorders in man including haemophilia, colour blindness, polydactyly, cataract, diabetes and albinism. Indeed, perhaps with the ill health that dogged his own family in mind, he argued

> When any rare deviation, due to some extraordinary combination of circumstances, appears in the parent — say, once among several million individuals — and it reappears in the child, the mere doctrine of chances almost compels us to attribute its reappearance to inheritance (Darwin, 1859).

As far as the causes of variation were concerned, however, this was 'an extremely obscure subject' (Darwin, 1868). Whilst he noted that 'sports are extremely rare under nature but far from rare under cultivation' (Darwin, 1868), he stopped short of implying that he considered relaxed selection to be the most important underlying cause of this phenomenon. Nevertheless, almost prophetically, and despite his enduring belief in pangenesis, he speculated that

> The causes which induce variability act on the mature organism, on the embryo, and...on both sexual elements before impregnation has been effected (Darwin, 1868).

Perhaps Darwin had been influenced by von Kölliker who in 1864 had proposed a theory of 'heterogeneous reproduction' in which he had stated

> under the influence of a general law of development, living creatures produce from their seeds others which are different.

Bateson (1894, 1913) strongly opposed Darwin's thesis that variability was primarily due to environmental influences. Rather he supposed that 'substantive' variations (changes in the substance of parts as opposed to their number or arrangement) arose from chemical differences, although he was not in a position to speculate as to their nature. Whilst many thinkers of the time saw spontaneous variation purely and simply in terms of its role as the evolutionary fuel for speciation, Bateson drew parallels with disease. Disease, he maintained, presented 'a discontinuity closely comparable with that of many variations' and he speculated that the

> problem of species [may well] be solved by the study of pathology; for the likeness between variation and disease goes far to support the view which Virchow has forcibly expressed, that 'every deviation from the type of the parent animal must have its foundation on a pathological accident'.

Bateson therefore not only coined the term 'genetics' but already in 1894 appears to have appreciated its potential contribution to the study of inherited disease. However, he still considered Mendelian characters to be inherited in an all-or-nothing fashion. Thus

> a dominant character is the condition due to the presence of a definite factor while the corresponding recessive owes its condition to the absence of the same factor.

This principle was deemed 'applicable throughout the whole range of Mendelian phenomena'. Interpreted with hindsight, he appears to have believed that mutant alleles arose through the complete and hence irreversible loss of a gene (the 'presence–absence' hypothesis) despite the improbability that such dramatic alterations could account for evolutionary change. Bateson introduced the terms 'allelomorph' (allele) to denote the alternative factors responsible for a given character difference, 'heterozygote' for an individual carrying two alternative alleles and 'homozygote' for an individual carrying two copies of an identical allele. Bateson (1913) was also the first to distinguish clearly between the inheritance of a pre-existing mutation and the *de novo* occurrence of that mutation. Thus,

> conditions [such] as hereditary cataract or various deformities of the fingers behave as dominants [and] we recognize that those conditions must be due to the addition of some element to the constitution of the normal man. In the collections of pedigrees relating to such pathological dominants there are usually to be found alleged instances of the origin of the condition *de novo*. The *de novo* origin of brachydactylous fingers in a child of normal parents must indicate the action of some new specific cause.

Haeckel (1866) is usually accredited with being the first to appreciate that the cell nucleus contains the material basis of heredity. However, he still believed in the inheritance of acquired characteristics. This vestige of Lamarckism died hard but, with the publication in 1892 of Weismann's *Das Keimplasma: Eine Theorie der Vererbung* [*The Germplasm: a Theory of Heredity* (Weismann, 1893)], the biological role and significance of reduction division could finally be appreciated. The distinction between the germline and the soma had at last

been made and the cell nucleus was recognized as the location of the hereditary material. Biologists were now in a position, at least in principle, to understand how newly generated mutations could be inherited. The emerging new
synthesis of ideas was implicit in Weismann's statement:

> Modifications of the nuclear matter [in the germline] can alone give rise to transfor-
> mations of a hereditary nature in the cell body.

Weismann's theory of heredity invoked 'determinants' (genes?) which were
located in groups on the 'ids' (linkage groups or whole chromosomes). Hereditary variations in certain characteristics were attributed to changes in the
determinants although such changes were held to be brought about by
inequalities of nutrition in the germplasm. Indeed, Weismann speculated that
the human congenital abnormality, supernumerary digits, might be explained
by the doubling of a group of determinants due to 'excessive local nutrition'.

Sudden variations were also studied by Korschinsky (1901) who coined the
term 'heterogenesis' to describe them. Korschinsky believed that heterogenesis
usually appeared spontaneously in a single individual and, with remarkable
foresight, that its causes lay not with the external environment but instead
resulted from unspecified endogenous processes. Thus

> because of unknown circumstances and contrary to the law of inheritance, an
> organism can be formed from the fertilized egg cell so unlike its parents that we can
> consider it a distinct species both in respect of the totality of its external characters
> and of its capacity to transmit them by inheritance.

Although Gregor Mendel studied the inheritance of genetic variants of the
garden pea, *Pisum sativum*, and eventually (1866) deduced the laws of segregation, he was not directly concerned with the origin of the different characters
with which he worked. Like Darwin, he appeared to invoke a role for the
environment in the origins of variation although he went further when he
stated

> by cultivation, the origination of new varieties is favoured and that by man's labour
> many varieties are acquired which under natural conditions would be lost (Mendel,
> 1866).

Although by now familiar with Darwin's theory of natural selection, Mendel
did not seek to explain this observation in terms of relaxed selection. He nevertheless noted that

> were the change in the conditions the sole cause of variability, we might expect that
> those cultivated plants which are grown for centuries under almost identical condi-
> tions would attain constancy. That, as is well known, is not the case.

1.5 De Vries' mutation theory

Mendel's laws of heredity were rediscovered independently by De Vries,
Correns and Tschermak in 1900, and it is to the first of these men that we owe
the emergence of the modern concept of mutation. Hugo De Vries described in
Die Mutationstheorie (1901) his extensive experiments on *Oenothera*

lamarckiana (the evening primrose) and deduced what he termed his 'laws of mutation'. These may be briefly summarized in his own words:

(i) 'New elementary species arise suddenly without transitional forms'.
(ii) 'New elementary species are, as a rule, absolutely constant from the moment that they arise' [i.e. they breed true].
(iii) 'Most of the new forms that have appeared are elementary species and not varieties in the strict sense of the term'.
(iv) 'New elementary species appear in large numbers at the same time or at any rate during the same period'.
(v) 'The new varieties have nothing to do with individual variability' [the new characters are very different from normally observed variation].
(vi) 'The mutations, to which the origin of new elementary species is due, appear to be indefinite, that is to say, the changes may affect all organs and seem to take place in almost every conceivable direction'.
(vii) 'Mutability appears periodically'.

In a sense, De Vries was fortunate in his choice of material since *Oenothera* species are highly variable. He was not however to know that *Oenothera* possesses a highly unusual hereditary mechanism and that the variants observed arose, not from mutational events as he believed, but rather as a result of revealed homozygosity due to recombinational events between chromosomes maintained heterozygous by balanced lethality. Thus, as has so often happened both before and since, correct concepts emerged even although they stemmed originally from the flawed interpretation of observations.

De Vries studied mutants that he found in the wild but he also collected seeds and grew them under favourable conditions of cultivation. His therefore was the first concerted attempt to research the nature of mutation by experimental means — many of his conclusions are still valid today. Although in principle he advocated a clear distinction between mutability and variability (e.g. he considered man immutable), in practice his work succeeded in uniting for the first time the experimental analysis of hereditary factors with theories for the origin of inherited variation. As far as the latter was concerned, De Vries considered that

> an altered numerical relationship of pangenes [hereditary units] already present and the formation of new kinds of pangenes must be the two chief factors of variability.

Probably as a result of the peculiar genetics of *Oenothera*, De Vries believed that newly emerged characters had already been present in latent form (as a 'premutation') which a second mutation had then allowed to become manifest. Mutation was thus regarded as a hereditary, albeit partially latent, character. The origin of premutations, he speculated,

> must be due partly to internal and partly to external causes. The former determine what shall arise; the latter when it arises.

De Vries also considered what he termed 'repeated mutations' (the first hint of the notion of the non-randomness of mutation perhaps!) to be both independent of each other and 'the result of the same inner causes'. Finally, he concluded that

> the analysis of organisms leads us to the hypothesis of units, which are in many respects analogous to the molecules of the chemist. They are, however, of a much more complicated structure and have arisen in a historical way. They cannot be isolated and then subjected to experiment like chemical bodies.

Despite the falsity of the latter assertion, as recently demonstrated with the advent of recombinant DNA technology, these comments presaged the emergence of the concept of a gene which could be understood in molecular terms and which would provide explanations for both the mutation of hereditary factors and their evolution.

Sutton (1903) provided the first clear formulation of the chromosome theory of heredity by pointing out that the random segregation of homologous chromosomes at meiosis mirrored Mendel's independent assortment of factors. Once this view was accepted, the factors became visualized as 'beads on a string'. Mutation was now envisaged as a stable change in the molecular structure of the factor which, since it could be copied when the chromosome was duplicated, could also be inherited.

Mendel's hereditary factors (*Elemente*) and De Vries's pangenes were replaced by the term 'gene', introduced by Johannsen in 1909. From his own vantage point studying continuous variation in French beans (*Phaseolus*), Johannsen drew the first distinction between the gene and its effect, that is between the genotype (the hereditary constitution) and the phenotype (the appearance of the organism resulting from the complex interplay of genes and environment).

1.6 *Drosophila* and the advance of experimental genetics

In the years that followed, T.H. Morgan (1912, 1926) and colleagues made great strides toward understanding the nature of the gene by following the inheritance of eye colour mutants in *Drosophila*. Normally red-eyed, some of the first mutant flies isolated possessed white or eosin-coloured eyes. Since eosin mutants also occasionally emerged from white-eyed fly populations (partial reverse mutation), all these characters could be considered allelic. The existence of multiple interchangeable alleles at this locus implied that genes could mutate in more than one way. Moreover, since eosin could also mutate back to red, mutation at this locus must be a subtle rather than an irreversible change. These observations proved that Bateson's all-or-nothing view of mutation must be wrong since eye colour had been determined by the action of an altered gene rather than by the presence or absence of that gene. Further, mutations were seen to behave as single Mendelian traits since simple segregation patterns could be observed in crosses between the wild-type and mutant forms. De Vries' distinction between variation and mutation was thus shown to be artificial. Perhaps, however, the most important and enduring contribution made by Morgan and his colleague, A.H. Sturtevant (1913), was to chromosome mapping. They recognized that the frequency with which non-allelic mutants were combined or separated in successive generations by genetic recombination could be used to derive linear maps of the corresponding loci on the chromosomes. The gene as a unit of recombination had come of age.

In humans, the first (mutant) gene to be mapped to a specific chromosome was that underlying colour blindness, which was deduced very early on to reside on the X chromosome on account of its characteristic inheritance pattern (Wilson, 1911). In 1937, Bell and Haldane demonstrated close linkage on the X chromosome between the loci for colour blindness and haemophilia. The first autosomal linkage was established by Mohr (1951) between secretor factor and Lutheran blood group but it was not until 1968 that McKusick and colleagues succeeded in chromosomally assigning the first autosomal gene (Duffy blood group to chromosome 1) by demonstrating linkage between the Duffy locus and a chromosome heteromorphism (Donahue *et al.*, 1968).

Studies on *Drosophila* also increased our knowledge of the gene as a unit of mutation: Demerec (1937) described the existence of 'mutator' genes in some *Drosophila* stocks (which appeared to increase the spontaneous mutation rate of other genes) and 'unstable' genes (which exhibited unusually high mutation frequencies) in *Delphinium* (1931) and *Drosophila* (1941). These studies provided further evidence for the non-randomness of spontaneous gene mutation in higher organisms. Subsequent studies (reviewed by Mohn and Würgler, 1972) were soon to provide convincing evidence for the endogenous (as opposed to exogenous) nature of at least some types of mutation in higher animals.

Side by side with mutation analysis, the mathematical consequences of Mendelian inheritance in populations were being worked out. J.B.S. Haldane showed (1932) in his influential book *The Causes of Evolution*, that genetic variation existed within species as well as between them, that most mutations were disadvantageous and that, in haemophilia, 'the rates of production by mutation and elimination by natural selection must about balance'. This work, together with R.A. Fisher's *The Genetical Theory of Natural Selection* (1930), effected the synthesis of Darwinism and Mendelism, and the theory of evolution as we know it today was firmly established. As Haldane (1932) succinctly phrased it:

> The fundamental importance of mutation for any account of evolution is clear. It enables us to escape from the impasse of the pure line.

With the study of spontaneous mutations in *Drosophila* proceeding apace, Morgan's colleague H.J. Muller attempted (1932) a classification of mutations based upon functional considerations; thus, 'hypermorphs' and 'hypomorphs' exhibited increased and decreased gene function respectively, whilst 'amorphs' had lost, and 'neomorphs' had gained, a function. The recognition that genes were capable of reproducing their mutations in successive generations (thus providing the fuel for evolution) had until then perhaps been Muller's (1922) major contribution to theoretical genetics. In his own inimitable style, he proclaimed that

> when the structure of the gene becomes changed...the catalytic property of the gene
> may become correspondingly changed in such a way as to leave it still autocatalytic.

Thus the gene was now perceived not merely as a transmissible unit, but also as a unit of recombination, of mutation and of function capable of fulfilling its role as the chemical substrate upon which evolutionary forces could act. As such, this view of the gene was not so very different from our current picture and provides an indication of the importance of Muller's own contribution.

Muller also introduced the concept of the mutation rate and devised methods of measuring it in *Drosophila* (Muller, 1928). This allowed him to calculate that natural background radiation was too weak to account for the observed frequency of spontaneous mutation (Muller and Mott-Smith, 1930). Making certain assumptions, Haldane (1935) was then able to estimate that the gene for haemophilia (sic!) mutated with a frequency of 1 in 50 000 in humans, a figure not so inconsistent with modern estimates for the factor VIII and IX genes causing haemophilias A and B.

1.7 The artificial induction of gene mutations

Of more immediate practical importance, however, was Muller's pioneering work on the artificial induction of gene mutations in *Drosophila* using X-rays. First reported in 1927, the success of these experiments ensured that mutation research was no longer constrained by the labour-intensive and time-consuming process of searching for spontaneous mutations. Further, it was clear to Muller that

> it should be possible to produce, to order, enough mutations to furnish respectable
> genetic maps...and, by the use of the mapped genes, to analyze the aberrant
> chromosome phenomena simultaneously obtained.

Armed with this powerful new tool, the emphasis of future studies could now shift toward the active generation of specific mutations rather than merely their passive collection. Indeed, X-ray mutagenesis was to dominate genetics for the next two decades and gave rise to the influential but relatively short-lived 'target theory' of mutagenesis, which considered that the number of 'hits' determined the nature of the mutation generated (reviewed by Auerbach, 1976). Chromosome breaks and rearrangements were also generated by radiation treatment. These findings were latched onto by those seeking a unified theory of mutation. In its most extreme form, Goldschmidt (1946) considered that all mutations might be due to rearrangements.

The discovery of chemical mutagens (Auerbach and Robson, 1946) allowed a comparison of the mutational spectra produced by chemicals with those produced by X-rays (reviewed by Auerbach, 1976). However, in the absence of a biochemical model of the gene, the differences observed could not be satisfactorily explained. 'Unstable' genes could be generated by treatment with either X-rays or chemicals; although the underlying 'premutational lesions' could be replicated, speculation as to the nature of the premutation was still premature.

It had been known since the late 19th century (Miescher, 1871) that nucleic acid was a major constituent of the cell nucleus. In 1939, Knapp and Schreiber discovered that the frequency of ultraviolet (UV)-induced mutations in *Sphaerocarpus donnellii* spermatozoids was maximized at a wavelength of 265 nm, corresponding to the absorption peak of nucleic acid. The formal demonstration that the bearer of the genetic information was indeed nucleic acid had however to await the transformation experiments of Avery *et al.* (1944) using *Diplococcus pneumoniae* — the transforming substance was purified and shown to be DNA. This conclusion was further supported by Hershey and Chase (1952) who differentially labelled the DNA and protein of bacteriophage T2 and demonstrated that the infective viral material was DNA. With the elucidation of the double helical structure of DNA by Watson and Crick in 1953, a chemical model for the gene had emerged and the detailed analysis of gene mutations at the DNA level became a more realistic proposition.

In 1955, Benzer discovered that two groups of bacteriophage T4 rII mutants could complement each other in mixed infections, implying that they belonged to independent functional units. The term 'cistron' was thus coined to denote the gene as a unit of function; complementation between mutations implied that they were non-allelic and belonged to different cistrons. Benzer and Freese (1958) studied the effect of 5-bromouracil on the rII cistrons of T4 and demonstrated that the base analogue had a highly non-random mutagenic effect. Brenner *et al.* (1958) carried out similar studies using the mutagen proflavin — a different spectrum of mutations was generated, this time much more randomly distributed. These lesions appeared to abolish the activity of the gene under study, prompting Brenner *et al.* (1961) to propose that they were base insertions or deletions. Freese (1959) demonstrated that the base analogues 2-aminopurine and 5-bromodeoxyuridine could induce reversion of mutants to the wild-type strongly suggesting that these mutagens were responsible for single base-pair substitutions in the DNA. Many other mutagens were tested (Benzer, 1961), again resulting in patterns of mutation both specific to, and characteristic of, the mutagen. Further insight into the non-random nature of induced mutation was provided by Koch (1971), who demonstrated that the frequency with which 2-aminopurine generated a particular type of mutation was dependent on the neighbouring bases.

That mutations artificially generated in the laboratory were indeed comparable to true *in vivo* mutations was confirmed by amino acid sequencing (Henning and Yanofsky, 1962). The discovery of non-random mutational spectra associated with chemical mutagen treatment led very rapidly to the realization that spontaneous mutation was also highly non-random, with certain sites ('hotspots') apparently being particularly prone to mutation (reviewed by Mohn and Würgler, 1972).

1.8 The influence of endogenous DNA replication and repair processes

Kelner (1949) and Dulbecco (1949), working with *Streptomyces griseus* and bacteriophage respectively, demonstrated that short-wave visible light could greatly reduce the lethal effects of short-wave UV light, a phenomenon which became known as photoreactivation. These findings represented the first real evidence for DNA repair. Rupert *et al.* (1958) then showed that an *Escherichia coli* cell-free extract could photoreactivate UV-irradiated *Haemophilus influenzae* (a non-photoreactivable species) transforming DNA *in vitro* in the presence of visible light, indicating the enzymatic nature of photoreactivation. Setlow and Carrier (1964) and Boyce and Howard-Flanders (1964a) demonstrated that a UV-resistant strain of *E. coli* could excise UV-induced thymine dimers from bacterial DNA; this enzymatic activity was not dependent on visible light and appeared to be genetically controlled. Boyce and Howard-Flanders (1964b) subsequently deduced that, in *E. coli*, DNA repair in the dark is controlled by three genes (*uvr*A, *uvr*B and *uvr*C) whose mutation creates UV-sensitive mutants unable to excise thymine dimers. Pettijohn and Hanawalt (1964) then provided direct evidence for the replication repair of UV-irradiated DNA: the repair mechanism appeared to be capable of utilizing the base sequence of the complementary DNA strand as a template.

During the 1950s, considerable interest was shown in the indirect effects of radiation. Thus, for example, it became apparent that, in the presence of oxygen, short-lived oxygen radicals and longer-lived H_2O_2 species produced by ionizing radiation could also contribute to radiation damage (reviewed by Kimball, 1987). The study of these indirect effects gradually led to the realization that radiation or chemical mutagen treatment generated mutations in two distinct stages: the initial induced 'premutational lesion' and its subsequent conversion to a final mutation if either misrepaired or left unrepaired until the next round of DNA replication. It was also realized that the mutagenic effects of radiation could be modified by various post-irradiation treatments (reviewed by Kimball, 1987) and that these effects were consistent with the premutational lesion repair hypothesis.

By 1974, four major DNA repair processes had been recognized in *E. coli*: photoreactivation, excision repair, post-replication repair and SOS error-prone repair (reviewed by Kimball, 1987). Similar DNA repair processes have now been found in mammals (Friedberg, 1985); these are currently being characterized through the genetic analysis of inherited human DNA repair defects (xeroderma pigmentosum, ataxia telangiectasia etc) and cell lines particularly resistant to mutagens, by characterization of the enzymes involved in the repair pathways and the isolation of the genes encoding them. Various genes have been identified which serve not only to control the ability of the cell to repair lesions but which also determine the likelihood that these lesions will be converted to final mutations. Data from humans are consistent with the view that mutational lesions that persist to DNA replication are more likely to cause mutation than those that are repaired by excision. It appears therefore that, although human cells possess complex mechanisms for the repair of DNA damage brought about by the action of both exogenous and endogenous mutagens, these mechanisms are themselves error prone and often give rise to mutations quite spontaneously.

Another consequence of the early genetic studies was the recognition that a substantial proportion of mutational lesions are replication-dependent and hence necessarily endogenous in origin (reviewed by Drake, 1970). Watson and Crick (1953) had originally proposed that mutations might arise by bases shifting transiently to one of their less likely tautomeric forms, which would then lead to misincorporation if coincident with DNA replication. Although no evidence was forthcoming to support this hypothesis, it did have the virtue of being consistent with the general impression, at least in prokaryotes, that the majority of mutations were replication-dependent. Speyer (1965) demonstrated that temperature-sensitive mutations in the T4 DNA polymerase gene (a 'mutator gene' to use Demerec's terminology) could, at the non-permissive temperature, increase the general frequency of both transitions and transversions. This implied that the polymerase normally plays an active role in the selection of bases at DNA replication. DNA replication was also invoked by Streisinger *et al.* (1967) who proposed a physical model to account for the non-randomness of gene deletions: slipped mispairing during DNA replication at runs of identical bases followed by misincorporation. With considerable prescience, these authors speculated that 'the frequency of frameshift mutations at a given site depends on the sequence of bases at that site'. Thus, although no sharp distinction could be drawn between the nature of induced and spontaneous mutations, it was through such studies on DNA replication and repair that the emphasis of research subtly shifted from exogenous to endogenous causes of mutation.

1.9 The emergence of the modern concept of human inherited disease

The equation of pathological traits inherited in Mendelian fashion with defects in genes can in principle be traced back to Bateson and Saunders (1902), who first showed that alkaptonuria was inherited in Mendelian recessive fashion. Garrod (1909) later correctly attributed this inherited defect to the failure to oxidize homogentisic acid as a consequence of an absent or defective enzyme activity. Some of the implications of this work were however already clear to Garrod in 1902. Thus,

> If it be, indeed, the case that in alkaptonuria and the other conditions mentioned [albinism and cystinuria], we are dealing with individualities of metabolism and not with the results of morbid processes, the thought naturally presents itself that these are merely extreme examples of variations of chemical behaviour which are probably everywhere present in minor degrees and that just as no two individuals of a species are absolutely identical in bodily structure, neither are their chemical processes carried out on exactly the same lines.

Garrod (1902) concluded that such 'inborn errors of metabolism' were explicable in terms of a recessive model of inheritance since these disorders were found in sibs but not in parents, and because parents were often related. Weinberg (1912) noted that achondroplasia tended to occur among the last born of a father suggesting both a mutational origin for the condition and the existence of a paternal age effect on mutation frequency. By 1917, Dresel (cited by Faber, 1930) was able to draw up a list of some 30 different diseases whose hereditary nature had been demonstrated statistically through the analysis of a large number of cases. They included examples of dominant, recessive and sex-linked modes of inheritance.

In some ways, the correspondence between Mendelian trait and enzyme defect anticipated the 'one gene–one enzyme' concept of Beadle (1945), which served to define mutation in terms of an alteration in the ability of the cell to carry out a specific biochemical reaction. This latter view soon received strong support from the demonstration that methaemoglobinaemia was caused by the deficiency of the NADH-dependent enzyme required for the reduction of methaemoglobin (Gibson, 1948).

Once techniques of protein purification and analysis had been devised, the stage was now set to examine dysfunctional proteins to determine the nature of the underlying molecular defect. In 1949, using protein electrophoresis, Pauling *et al.* showed that sickle cell anaemia resulted from a subtle alteration in the haemoglobin molecule, making it the first example of a 'molecular disease'. It was later shown that haemoglobins A and S differed from each other as a result of the substitution of a single glutamic acid residue by valine (Ingram, 1957). This was the first description of a genetic disease to be made at the molecular level and confirmed that inborn errors of metabolism are caused ultimately by mutant genes which produce abnormal proteins with altered or absent function. It was soon followed by a report of a different type of gene lesion: Baglioni (1962) showed that, in haemoglobin Lepore, a deletion must have occurred which recombined the β- and δ-globin genes so as to create a hybrid gene encoding a novel polypeptide product with sequence characteristics of both polypeptides. These early findings helped to establish the current axiom that every genetic disease stems from an alteration in DNA structure.

Once the genetic code had been established and it was realized that the nucleotide sequence serves to specify the amino acid sequence of the protein, the nature of mutations at the DNA level responsible for inherited disease could be inferred directly from changes in the amino acid sequence of the protein (Crick *et al.* 1961). Thus Crick (1967) was able to explain known haemoglobin mutations in man in terms of single base-pair substitutions using the genetic code as established for *E. coli.* In similar studies of haemoglobin variants in man (Vogel and Röhrborn, 1965; Fitch, 1967), a significant excess of $C \rightarrow T$ and $G \rightarrow A$ transitions was found, demonstrating that human gene mutation was likely to be as non-random as that found in viruses.

1.10 The new age of recombinant DNA

The advent of recombinant DNA technology in the 1970s resulted in dramatic advances both in the analysis and diagnosis of human inherited disease and in our understanding of the nature of the underlying gene defects at the molecular level. It was the discovery of restriction enzymes, the site-specific bacterial endonucleases that cleave large DNA fragments at defined sites, that beckoned in the new age: the first restriction enzyme was isolated from *E. coli* in 1968 by Meselson and Yuan and, since then, many hundreds of additional enzymes with a multitude of different cleavage specificities have been described. Using DNA fragments cut by restriction enzymes, Jackson *et al.* (1972) demonstrated the use of DNA ligase to join DNA fragments from bacteriophage λ and *E. coli* to SV40 DNA; this recombinant construct was then introduced successfully into mammalian cells. The *in vitro* joining of heterologous DNA molecules (DNA cloning) and the transformation of bacterial cells together provided the means to 'mass produce' specific DNA fragments from the complex genomes of higher eukaryotes so as to provide enough material to permit biochemical analysis. Using these techniques, Shine *et al.* (1977) isolated the first human gene sequence, encoding chorionic somatomammotropin, by DNA cloning. Today, in excess of 2000 different human genes have been cloned and characterized, including many known to be defective or absent in inherited disease states.

The second wave of technical advances included 'Southern blotting' and methods for establishing the sequence of specific DNA molecules. Southern blotting (Southern, 1975) permits the detailed analysis of specific DNA sequences in the genome by challenging restriction fragments, separated by gel electrophoresis and attached to a solid support, with a radiolabelled cloned gene probe. Using this technique, Kan and Dozy (1978a, 1978b) were able to track the inheritance of a neutral DNA restriction site polymorphism within the β-globin gene through the pedigree of a family with sickle cell anaemia/trait; this *indirect* method of analysis yielded the first antenatal diagnosis of a genetic disease using a DNA-based approach. Southern blotting was soon also employed to accomplish the *direct* analysis/detection of a β-globin gene deletion causing β-thalassaemia (Orkin *et al.*, 1978).

The study of the fine structure of genes was finally made possible in 1977 with the publication of two different strategies for sequencing DNA; one was chemically based (Maxam and Gilbert) and the other employed chain terminators (Sanger *et al.*, 1977). More recently, with the invention of the polymerase chain reaction (Saiki *et al.*, 1985) for the *in vitro* enzymatic amplification of specific DNA sequences, we emerge from history to the present day with a formidable battery of very powerful and highly versatile techniques to study what McKusick has termed the morbid anatomy of the human genome.

References

Adams J. (1814) *A Treatise on the Supposed Hereditary Properties of Diseases.* J. Callow, London.

Auerbach C. (1976) *Mutation Research: Problems, Results and Perspectives.* Chapman and Hall, London.

Auerbach C, Robson JM. (1946) Chemical production of mutations. *Nature* **157**: 302.

Avery OT, MacLeod CM, McCarty M. (1944) Studies on the chemical nature of the substance inducing transformation of pneumococcal types: induction of transformation by a desoxyribonucleic acid fraction isolated from *Pneumococcus* type III. *J. Exp. Med.* **79**: 137–158.

Baglioni C. (1962) The fusion of two peptide chains in hemoglobin Lepore and its interpretation as a genetic deletion. *Proc. Natl. Acad. Sci. USA* **48**: 1880–1886.

Bartsocas CS. (1982) An introduction to ancient Greek genetics and skeletal dysplasias. *Prog. Clin. Biol. Res.* **104:** 3–13.

Bartsocas CS. (1984) Aristotle: the father of genetics. *Philos. Inquiry* **4:** 35–38.

Bateson W. (1894) *Materials for the Study of Variation Treated with Especial Regard to Discontinuity in the Origin of Species.* MacMillan, London.

Bateson W, Saunders ER. (1902) Experimental studies in the physiology of heredity. *Rep. Evol. Comm. R. Soc.* **1:** 1–160.

Bateson W. (1909) *Mendel's Principles of Heredity.* 2nd Edn. (1913) Cambridge University Press, Cambridge.

Bateson W. (1913) *Problems of Genetics.* Yale University Press, New Haven, Connecticut.

Bauhin G. (1596) *Phytopinax.*

Beadle GW. (1945) Biochemical genetics. *Chem. Rev.* **37:** 15–32.

Bell J, Haldane JBS. (1937) The linkage between the genes for colour blindness and haemophilia in man. *Proc. R. Soc. B.* **123:** 119–150.

Benzer S. (1955) Fine structure of a genetic region in bacteriophage. *Proc. Natl. Acad. Sci. USA* **41:** 344–354.

Benzer S. (1961) On the topography of the genetic fine structure. *Proc. Natl. Acad. Sci. USA* **47:** 403–415.

Benzer S, Freese E. (1958) Induction of specific mutations with 5-bromouracil. *Proc. Natl. Acad. Sci. USA* **44:** 112–119.

Boyce RP, Howard-Flanders P. (1964a) Release of ultra violet light-induced thymine dimers from DNA in *E. coli* K12. *Proc. Natl. Acad. Sci. USA* **51:** 293–300.

Boyce RP, Howard-Flanders P. (1964b) Genetic control of DNA breakdown and repair in *E. coli* K-12 treated with mitomycin C or ultraviolet light. *Z. Vererblehre* **95:** 345–350.

Brenner S, Benzer S, Barnett L. (1958) Distribution of proflavin-induced mutations in the genetic fine structure. *Nature* **182:** 983–985.

Brenner S, Barnett L, Crick FHC, Orgel A. (1961) The theory of mutagenesis. *J. Mol. Biol.* **3:** 121–124.

Crick FH, Barnett L, Brenner S, Watts-Tobin RJ. (1961) General nature of the genetic code for proteins. *Nature* **192:** 1227–1232.

Crick FHC. (1961) The genetic code. *Proc. R. Soc. B* **167:** 331–347.

D'Azara F. (1801) *Essais sur l'Histoire Naturelle des Quadrupèdes de la Province du Paraguay,* Parts I and II. Paris.

Darwin C. (1859) *On the Origin of Species by Means of Natural Selection.* John Murray, London.

Darwin C. (1868) *The Variation of Animals and Plants under Domestication,* Vol. II. John Murray, London.

Demerec M. (1931) Behaviour of two mutable genes of *Delphinium ajacis. J. Genet.* **24:** 179–193.

Demerec M. (1937) Frequency of spontaneous mutations in certain stocks of *Drosophila melanogaster. Genetics* **22:** 469–478.

Demerec M. (1941) Unstable genes in *Drosophila. Cold Spring Harb. Symp. Quant. Biol.* **9:** 122–126.

De Vries H. (1901) Die Mutationstheorie. [English translation: *The Mutation Theory,* Vol. I. (1909), Vol II. (1910). Open Court, Chicago].

Donahue RP, Bias WB, Renwick JH, McKusick VA. (1968) Probable assignment of the Duffy blood group locus to chromosome 1 in man. *Proc. Natl. Acad Sci. USA* **61:** 949–955.

Drake JW. (1970) *The Molecular Basis of Mutation.* Holden-Day, San Francisco, California.

Dulbecco R. (1949) Reactivation of ultraviolet-inactivated bacteriophage by visible light. *Nature* **163:** 949–950.

Faber K. (1930) *Nosography. The Evolution of Clinical Medicine in Modern Times.* Paul B. Hoeber, New York.

Fisher RA. (1930) *The Genetical Theory of Natural Selection.* Clarendon Press, Oxford.

Fitch WM. (1967) Evidence suggesting a non-random nature to nucleotide replacements in naturally occurring mutations. *J. Mol. Biol.* **26:** 499–507.

Freese E. (1959) The difference between spontaneous and base analogue induced mutations of phage T4. *Proc. Natl. Acad. Sci. USA* **45:** 622–633.

Friedberg EC. (1985) *DNA Repair*. Freeman, New York.

Garrod AE. (1902) The incidence of alcaptonuria: A study in chemical individuality. *Lancet* **ii:** 1616–1620.

Garrod AE. (1909) *Inborn Errors of Metabolism*. Oxford University Press, Oxford.

Gibson QH. (1948) The reduction of methaemoglobin in red blood cells and studies on the cause of idiopathic methaemoglobinaemia. *Biochem. J.* **42:** 13–22.

Goldschmidt R. (1946) Position effect and the theory of the corpuscular gene. *Experientia* **2:** 250–256.

Haeckel E. (1866) *Generelle Morphologie der Organismen*, 2 vols. G. Reimer, Berlin.

Haldane JBS. (1932) *The Causes of Evolution*. Longmans, Green, London.

Haldane JBS. (1935) The rate of spontaneous mutation of a human gene. *J. Genet.* **31:** 317–326.

Henning U, Yanofsky C. (1962) Amino acid replacements associated with reversion and recombination within the A gene. *Proc. Natl. Acad. Sci. USA* **18:** 1497–1504.

Hershey AD, Chase M. (1952) Independent functions of viral protein and nucleic acid in growth of bacteriophage. *J. Gen. Physiol.* **36:** 39–56.

Ingram VM. (1957) Gene mutations in human haemoglobin: the chemical difference between normal and sickle cell haemoglobin. *Nature* **180:** 326–328.

Jackson DA, Symons RH, Berg P. (1972) Biochemical method for inserting new genetic information into DNA of Simian virus 40: circular SV40 DNA molecules containing lambda phage genes and the galactose operon of *Escherichia coli*. *Proc. Natl. Acad. Sci. USA* **69:** 2904–2909.

Johannsen W. (1909) *Elemente der Exakten Erblichkeitslehre*. Gustav Fischer, Jena.

Kan YW, Dozy AM. (1978a) Polymorphism of DNA sequence adjacent to human β-globin structural gene: relationship to sickle mutation. *Proc. Natl. Acad. Sci. USA* **75:** 5631–5635.

Kan YW, Dozy AM. (1978b) Antenatal diagnosis of sickle-cell anaemia by DNA analysis of amniotic fluid cells. *Lancet* **ii:** 910–912.

Kelner A. (1949) Effect of visible light on the recovery of *Streptomyces griseus* conidia from radiation injury. *Proc. Natl. Acad. Sci. USA* **35:** 73–79.

Kimball RF. (1987) The development of ideas about the effect of DNA repair on the induction of gene mutations and chromosomal aberrations by radiation and by chemicals. *Mutat. Res.* **186:** 1–34.

Knapp E, Schreiber H. (1939) Quantitive Analyse der mutationsauslösenden Wirkung monochromatischen UV-Lichtes in Spermatozoiden von *Sphaerocarpus*. *Naturwissenschaften* 27: 304.

Koch RE. (1971) The influence of neighboring base pairs upon base-pair substitution mutation rates. *Proc. Natl. Acad. Sci. USA* **68:** 773–776.

Kölliker A von. (1864) Über die Darwinische Schöpfungstheorie. *Z. Wiss. Zool.* **XIV:** 174–186.

Korschinsky S. (1901) Heterogenesis und Evolution. *Flora* **89: 240–363.**

Lamarck J.B de. (1809) *Philosophie Zoologique*. Paris.

Maxam AM, Gilbert W. (1977) A new method for sequencing DNA. *Proc. Natl. Acad. Sci. USA* **74:** 560–564.

Meckel JF. (1812) *Handbuch der Pathologischen Anatomie*. Vol. 1. C.H. Reclam, Leipzig.

Mendel G. (1866) Versuche über Pflanzenhybriden. *Verh. Naturf. Ver. Brünn* **4:** 3–44. [English translation, 'Experiments in plant hybridization' in Bateson (1909), pp. 317–361.]

Meselson M, Yuan R. (1968) DNA restriction enzyme from *E. coli*. *Nature* **217:** 1110–1114.

Miescher F. (1871) Über die chemische Zusammensetzung der Eiterzellen. In: Hoppe-Zeyler F. *Medizinisch-Chemische Untersuchungen*. pp. 441–460. August Hirschwald, Berlin.

Mohn G, Würgler FE. (1972) Mutator genes in different species. *Humangenetik* **16:** 49–58.

Mohr J. (1951) Search for linkage between Lutheran blood group and other hereditary characters. *Acta Pathol. Microbiol. Scand.* **28:** 207–210.

Morgan TH. (1912) *The Physical Basis of Heredity*. J.B. Lippincott, Philadelphia, Pennsylvania.

Morgan TH. (1926) *The Theory of the Gene*. Yale University Press, New Haven, Connecticut.

Motulsky AG. (1959) Joseph Adams (1756–1818). *Arch. Intern. Med.* **104:** 490–496.

Muller HJ. (1922) Variation due to change in the individual gene. *American Naturalist* **56:** 32–50.

Muller HJ. (1927) Artificial transmutation of the gene. *Science* **66:** 84–87.

Muller HJ. (1928) The measurement of gene mutation rate in *Drosophila*, its high variability and its dependence upon temperature. *Genetics* **13:** 279–357.

Muller HJ. (1932) Further studies on the nature and causes of gene mutations. *Proc. 6th Int. Congr. Genetics*, Brooklyn Botanic Gardens, USA, Vol. 1, pp. 213–255.

Muller HJ, Mott-Smith LM. (1930) Evidence that natural radioactivity is inadequate to explain the frequency of 'natural' mutations. *Proc. Natl. Acad. Sci. USA* **16:** 277–285.

Olby R. (1985) *Origins of Mendelism*, 2nd Edn, University of Chicago Press, Chicago, Illinois.

Orkin SH, Alter BP, Altay C, Mahoney MJ, Lazarus H, Hobbins JC, Nathan DG. (1978) Application of endonuclease mapping to the analysis and prenatal diagnosis of thalassemias caused by globin gene deletion. *N. Engl. J. Med.* **299:** 166–172.

Otto JC. (1803) An account of an haemorrhagic disposition existing in certain families. *The Medical Repository*, Vol. VI. New York.

Pauling L, Itano HA, Singer SJ, Wells IC. (1949) Sickle cell anemia, a molecular disease. *Science* **110:** 543–548.

Pettijohn D, Hanawalt P. (1964) Evidence for repair-replication of ultraviolet damaged DNA in bacteria. *J. Mol. Biol.* **9:** 395–410.

Rosner F. (1969) Hemophilia in the Talmud and Rabbinic writings. *Ann. Intern. Med.* **70:** 833–837.

Rupert CS, Goodgal SH, Herriott RM. (1958) Photoreactivation *in vitro* of ultraviolet inactivated *Haemophilus influenzae* transforming factor. *J. Gen. Physiol.* **41:** 57–68.

Saiki RK, Scharf S, Faloona F, Mullis KB, Horn GT, Erlich HA, Arnheim N. (1985) Enzymatic amplification of β-globin genomic sequences and restriction site analysis for diagnosis of sickle cell anemia. *Science* **230:** 1350–1354.

Sanger F, Nicklen S, Coulson AR. (1977) DNA sequencing with chain-terminating inhibitors. *Proc. Natl. Acad. Sci.* **74:** 5463–5467.

Setlow RB, Carrier WL. (1964) The disappearance of thymine dimers from DNA: an error-correcting mechanism. *Proc. Natl. Acad. Sci. USA* **51:** 226–231.

Shine J, Seeburg PH, Martial JA, Baxter JD, Goodman HM. (1977) Construction and analysis of recombinant DNA for chorionic somatomammotropin. *Nature* **270:** 494–499.

Southern EM. (1975) Detection of specific sequences among DNA fragments separated by gel electrophoresis. *J. Mol. Biol.* **98:** 503–517.

Speyer JF. (1965) Mutagenic DNA polymerase. *Biochem. Biophys. Res. Commun.* **21:** 6–8.

Streisinger G, Okada Y, Emrich J, Newton J, Tsugita A, Terzaghi E, Inouye M. (1967) Frameshift mutations and the genetic code. *Cold Spring Harb. Symp. Quant. Biol.* **31:** 77–84.

Stubbe H. (1972) *History of Genetics from Prehistoric Times to the Rediscovery of Mendel's Laws.* MIT Press, Cambridge, Massachusetts.

Sturtevant AH. (1913) The linear arrangement of six sex-linked factors in *Drosophila* as shown by their mode of association. *J. Exp. Zool.* **14:** 43–59.

Sutton WS. (1903) The chromosomes in heredity. *Biol. Bull. Mar. Biol. Lab. Woods Hole* **4:** 231–248.

Theophrastus (*c.* 300 BC) *De Causis Plantarum* (lib. 2, cap 3). Teubner Verlag, Leipzig, 1854.

Vogel F, Röhrborn, G. (1965) Mutationsvorgänge bei der Entstehung von Hämoglobinvarianten. *Humangenetik* **1:** 635–650.

Watson JD, Crick FHC. (1953) A structure for deoxyribose nucleic acid. *Nature* **171:** 737–738.

Weinberg W. (1912) Zur Vererbung des Zwergwuchses. *Arch. Rassen Gesellschafts Biol.* **9:** 710–717.

Weismann A (1893) *The Germplasm: A Theory of Heredity.* Walter Scott, London.

Wilson EB. (1911) The sex chromosomes. *Arch. Mikrosk. Anat. Entwicklungsmech.* **77:** 249–271.

An introduction to structure, function expression of human genes

In a single chapter, it is quite unrealistic to attempt a comprehensive introduction to human molecular genetics. In the following sections, we have therefore aimed to provide the basic background necessary for, and relevant to, the study of human gene mutation as well as a contextual framework within which to place the findings of other chapters.

2.1 Gene structure and expression

The coding portion of the human genome, roughly 5% of the total DNA complement, may contain anywhere between 50 000 and 150 000 different gene sequences. Thus the smallest human chromosome, 21, may well contain as many as 2000 genes. It is now known that most genes in higher organisms are not contiguous as was originally thought, but rather are a complex mosaic of coding (exon) and non-coding (intron) sequences. Each individual gene differs not only with respect to its DNA sequence specifying the amino acid sequence of the protein it encodes, but also with respect to its structure. A few human genes are devoid of introns [e.g. thrombomodulin (THBD) which spans 3.7 kb; Shirai *et al.*, 1988], whereas some possess a considerable number, e.g. 52 in the von Willebrand factor (VWF) gene (length 175 kb; Mancuso *et al.*, 1989) and 79 in the dystrophin (DMD) gene (length 2400 kb; Den Dunnen *et al.*, 1992; Roberts *et al.*, 1992). The production of a mature transcript by the removal of introns from the original pre-mRNA molecule followed by the splicing together of the exons is described in some detail in Section 2.2. The accuracy of this process appears to be determined, at least in part, by the virtually invariant GT and AG dinucleotides present at the 5' and 3' exon/intron junctions respectively.

The archetypal gene (Figure 2.1) contains promoter elements upstream (5') of the transcriptional initiation site (or cap site) at +1 which may itself be

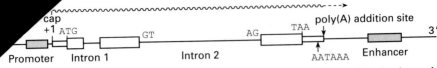

Figure 2.1. Schematic drawing of an archetypal human gene. The horizontal arrow denotes the direction of mRNA transcription. Exons are denoted by open boxes.

some distance upstream of the ATG translational initiation codon. A poly(A) tail is found at the 3′ end following the termination codon (e.g. TAA). The cap site is preceded by a host of upstream (5′) *cis*-acting regulatory elements of defined sequence, from TATAAA and CCAAT motifs which play a role in constitutive gene expression, to enhancers and responsive elements involved in controlling regulation and induction and conferring tissue specificity (reviewed by Maniatis *et al.*, 1987; Mitchell and Tjian, 1989).

Enhancer elements, which may be present either at the 5′ or the 3′ end of a gene and consist of patchworks of *cis*-acting sequences, are capable of activating the transcription of a gene in a tissue-specific fashion independently of their orientation and distance from the correct initiation site (Müller *et al.*, 1988; Wasylyk, 1988). Responsive elements, as the name suggests, are able to confer transcriptional responsiveness to various external trigger stimuli such as hormones and growth factors (e.g. insulin, O'Brien and Granner, 1991; thyroid hormone, Samuels *et al.*, 1988; glucocorticoids, Miesfeld, 1989).

It is now recognized that the primary control of gene expression is usually exerted at the level of transcription. A large number of *cis*-acting DNA sequence motifs have been identified which represent binding sites for DNA-binding proteins (*trans*-acting factors; Johnson and McKnight, 1989) required to confer appropriate regulation on the genes bearing them (reviewed by Latchman, 1990; Freemont *et al.*, 1991; Faisst and Meyer, 1992). The removal of these *cis*-acting elements abolishes the gene's specific pattern of expression whereas their combination with a reporter gene [e.g. chloramphenicol acetyltransferase (CAT); Rosenthal, 1987] confers this pattern of expression upon the heterologous gene *in vitro*. The study of DNA–protein interactions has been enormously facilitated by the use of two techniques: gel retardation analysis (also termed band or mobility shift assays; Revzin, 1989) and DNase I footprinting (Dynan, 1987). The former technique is extremely useful for searching for DNA-binding proteins in crude nuclear extracts, whereas the latter method provides information as to the precise location of the binding site on the DNA sequence under study.

By way of example, a selection of the transcriptional control elements found upstream of the human heat shock protein 70 (HSP70) gene is shown in Figure 2.2. Negative regulation of transcription, by sequence elements known as repressors, is also well documented (Levine and Manley, 1989; Jackson, 1991). Every gene promoter region thus possesses its own unique combination of positive and negative regulatory elements, which serves to dictate its temporal and spatial pattern of expression. These elements permit the binding

20

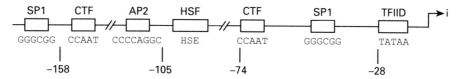

Figure 2.2. Transcriptional control elements in the human heat shock protein 70 (HSP70) gene promoter upstream of the transcriptional initiation site, i. Above the line are shown the DNA binding proteins, below the line the DNA sequence motifs to which they bind. HSE (heat shock element) consensus sequence: CTNGAATNTTCTAGA.

of a specific set of DNA-binding proteins, which are thereby brought into sufficient proximity to allow their interaction both with each other and with the RNA polymerase in order to influence transcription either positively or negatively.

Downstream (3') of the termination codon, other sequences have also been implicated in the termination of transcription and the addition of a poly(A) tail, thought to play a role in determining mRNA stability. These include the polyadenylation motif, AATAAA, 20–30 nucleotides 5' to the site of poly(A) addition and the G/T cluster immediately 3' to the end of the mRNA, which appears to play a crucial role in 3' end formation (Birnstiel *et al.*, 1985). Other less well characterized sequences in the 3' untranslated region may also serve to confer stability or lability upon the mRNA (reviewed by Ross, 1988; Hargrove and Schmidt, 1989).

The regulation of gene expression may occur at any one of a number of different stages in the pathway from gene activation to synthesis of the protein product. This may operate at the level of gene activation, initiation of transcription, or instead occur post-transcriptionally (reviewed by Atwater *et al.*, 1990; Hentze, 1991), e.g. in the rate of addition of the 5' 7-methylguanosine triphosphate cap, the control of mRNA modification, polyadenylation, splicing, transport, stability, translation or post-translational modification (Figure 2.3). Hence there are a considerable number of different levels at which a sequence aberration within the gene may exert its pathological effects. Not surprisingly, the diversity of the mutations found to underlie genetic disease has reflected the complexity of both the structure and the regulation of human genes.

2.2 mRNA splicing and processing

One of the characteristics of eukaryotic genes that distinguishes them from their prokaryotic counterparts is the production of large pre-mRNAs which contain intervening non-coding sequences (introns) that are removed by a highly accurate cleavage/ligation reaction known as splicing before the mRNA is transported to the cytoplasm for translation (reviewed by Green, 1986; Padgett *et al.*, 1986). Splicing not only permits the removal of unwanted

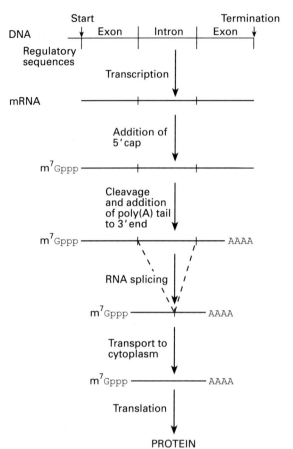

Figure 2.3. Expression pathway of a human gene.

introns from the primary transcript but also allows the generation of different mRNAs from the same gene by alternative splicing, a very economical means of generating biological diversity (Nadal-Ginard *et al.*, 1987). Although few eukaryotic genes are completely devoid of introns, their number may vary from as few as one to as many as 79 in the case of the gene (DMD) encoding the Duchenne muscular dystrophy protein, dystrophin (Den Dunnen *et al.*, 1989; Roberts *et al.*, 1992). Although introns may in some cases be very large, vertebrate exons internal to a gene rarely exceed 800 bp in length (Hawkins 1988).

The splicing of a eukaryotic mRNA appears to occur as a two-stage process. In the case of a simple two-exon gene, the pre-mRNA is first cleaved at the 5′ (donor) splice site to generate two splicing intermediates, an exon-containing RNA species and a lariat RNA species containing the second exon plus intervening intron. Cleavage at the 3′ (acceptor) splice site and ligation of the exons then occurs, resulting in the excision of the intervening intron in the form of a lariat. Clearly, the efficiency of this process is critically dependent on the accuracy of cleavage and rejoining. This accuracy appears to be determined, at least in part, by the virtually invariant GT and AG dinucleotides present at the 5′ and 3′ exon/intron junctions respectively. However, these short sequence motifs obviously cannot be the sole determinants of accurate splicing. Indeed, more extensive consensus sequences spanning the 5′ and 3′ splice junctions have been drawn up by both Breathnach and Chambon (1981) and Mount (1982). The most comprehensive survey to date was reported by Padgett et al. (1986) who scanned some 400 vertebrate genes and derived the following consensus sequences:

5′ (donor) splice site consensus sequence

$$-4 \qquad -3 \quad -2 \quad -1 \quad +1 \quad +2 \quad +3 \quad +4 \quad +5 \quad +6$$

$$C_{29}/A_{34} \ C_{38}/A_{35} \ A_{62} \ G_{77} \ | \ G_{100} \ T_{100} \ A_{60} \ A_{74} \ G_{84} \ T_{50}$$

Exon Intron

3′ (acceptor) splice site consensus sequence

$$-14 \quad -13 \quad -12 \quad -11 \quad -10 \quad -9 \quad -8 \quad -7 \quad -6 \quad -5 \quad -4 \quad -3$$

$$Y_{78} \quad Y_{81} \quad Y_{83} \quad Y_{89} \quad Y_{85} \quad Y_{82} \quad Y_{81} \quad Y_{86} \quad Y_{91} \quad Y_{87} \quad N \quad C_{78}$$

$$-2 \quad -1 \quad +1$$

$$A_{100} \quad G_{100} \ | \ G_{55}$$

Intron Exon

Y = pyrimidine, N = any base, subscript numerals refer to percentage frequency of occurrence.

Some slight difference in these consensus sequences are evident between different vertebrate species but those for human genes appear to be very similar to the above (Ohshima and Gotoh, 1987; Shapiro and Senapathy, 1987). Some variation is nevertheless still apparent; for example, only 5% of donor sites fit the consensus sequence exactly although the majority conform better than other similar sequences in the immediate vicinity (Ohshima and Gotoh, 1987; Shapiro and Senapathy, 1987). At the 3′ splice site, the tract of pyrimidines may well extend much further into the intron than is shown above. According to Ohshima and Gotoh (1987), pyrimidines still comprise more than 70% of bases around position -20. However, not all introns possess a pyrimidine tract (e.g. Shelley and Baralle 1987).

In addition, a further conserved sequence element, the 'branch-point', has been identified in the introns of higher eukaryotes at a site some 18–40 bp upstream of the 3′ splice site (Green, 1986). Although this sequence plays a role in forming a branch with the 5′ terminus of the intron, it appears to exhibit a rather weak consensus sequence ($Y_{81} N Y_{100} T_{87} R_{81} A_{100} Y_{94}$; R = purine; Krainer and Maniatis, 1988). Indeed, branch formation may occur at sequences that differ markedly from this consensus (Padgett et al., 1985;

Ruskin *et al.*, 1985). This notwithstanding, the sequence UACUAAC appears to be the most efficient branch site for mammalian mRNA splicing both *in vitro* and *in vivo* (Zhuang *et al.*, 1989). Whereas both the length and location of the pyrimidine tract may be important determinants of branch-point and acceptor splice site utilization, the 3' acceptor splice site itself appears to possess little specificity and may serve merely as the first AG dinucleotide downstream of the branch-point/pyrimidine tract.

The two stages of the splicing mechanism are illustrated schematically in Figure 2.4. The process is initiated by cleavage at the 5' splice site, generating an exon fragment that contains a 3' hydroxyl group. The 5' phosphorylated terminus of the intron is then esterified with the 2' hydroxyl group of the highly conserved A residue within the branch-point sequence. Cleavage occurs at the 3' splice site followed by joining of the two exons. The intron containing a 3' hydroxyl group is released as a free lariat RNA species.

The above processes occur within the *spliceosome*, a complex assembly of small nuclear ribonucleoprotein particles (snRNPs) composed of a variety of small nuclear ribonucleic acids (snRNAs) and associated proteins (reviewed in detail by Guthrie and Patterson, 1988; Lührmann *et al.*, 1990). The pre-mRNA is folded in such a way that splice sites are optimally aligned for cleavage and ligation. In this, the snRNAs play a vital role; U1 snRNP binds directly to the 5' splice site, a process mediated by base-pairing between the 5' end of the U1 snRNA and its complementary sequence at the mRNA splice

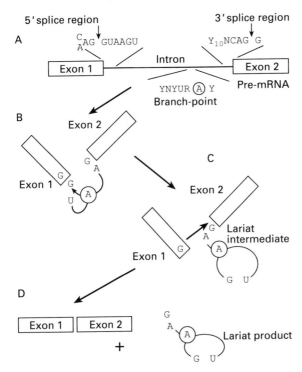

Figure 2.4. Basic model of mRNA splicing in higher eukaryotes. A. Pre-mRNA from archetypal gene with two exons and intervening intron. Consensus sequences of the splice sites and branch region are given. B. The 2' hydroxyl group of the branch-point A nucleotide (circled) attacks the 5' phosphoryl end of the first intron nucleotide. C. The 3' hydroxyl group of the last nucleotide of exon 1 attacks the 5' phosphoryl end of the first nucleotide of exon 2. D. Spliced mRNA plus lariat product.

junction (Figure 2.5; Mount *et al.*, 1983; Krainer and Maniatis, 1985). Although necessary, this sequence complementarity may not be sufficient for recognition of the 5' splice site (Stolow and Berget, 1991). U2 snRNP binds to the branch-point (Nelson and Green, 1989; Wu and Manley, 1989; Zhuang and Weiner, 1989), a process mediated by U2 auxiliary factor (U2AF; Ruskin *et al.*, 1988), whereas the 3' splice site may be recognized by a complex containing the U4, U5 and U6 snRNPs (Gerke and Steitz, 1986; Tazi *et al.*, 1986; Konarska and Sharp, 1987) with the probable additional involvement of U1 snRNP (Goguel *et al.*, 1991; Kuo *et al.*, 1991). U5 snRNA appears to be capable of binding to *exon* sequence at both the 5' and the 3' splice sites (Newman and Norman, 1992). Yet another protein factor is thought to bind to the pyrimidine tract (García-Blanco *et al.*, 1989). The precise RNA–protein interactions involved in spliceosome assembly are still unclear, as is the order in which they occur.

Evolutionary conservation implies an important role for the 5' and 3' consensus sequences in mRNA splicing. It is, however, very unlikely that these sequences are on their own sufficient for unambiguous splice site selection (Nelson and Green, 1988). Since similar sequences can be found within both exons and introns but are not utilized in the splicing reaction, it may be inferred that other factors and/or sequences (e.g. the branch-point) must also play a role in specifying splice site location. Our current understanding of mRNA splicing suggests that the formation of the 5' splice site complex is contingent upon the prior formation of the 3' splice site complex (Robberson *et al.*, 1990; Talerico and Berget, 1990).

2.3 Repetitive sequence elements

A large number of different types of repetitive element are found in the human genome (reviewed by Jelinek and Schmid, 1982; Hardman, 1986; Vogt, 1990). Three main categories are now recognized: (i) a highly repetitive class including sequence families with $> 10^5$ copies per haploid genome, (ii) a middle repetitive sequence class (10^2–10^5 copies) and (iii) a low repetitive class whose members possess between 2 and 100 copies per haploid genome. Coverage of the almost bewildering array of different repetitive elements is beyond the scope of this section. We shall therefore first briefly mention the

Figure 2.5. Complementarity between the 5' end of the U1 snRNA and the 5' splice site consensus sequence (after Lerner *et al.*, 1980; Rogers and Wall, 1980). ψ denotes a pseudouridine nucleoside. Reprinted with permission from *Nature*. © 1990 Macmillan Magazines Limited.

U1 snRNA

5' splice site consensus sequence

different classes of highly repetitive satellite DNA (tandem repeats) which are relevant to the indirect diagnosis of genetic disease by virtue of their high degree of sequence variability. Then we shall consider Alu repeats and LINE elements, the two most abundant and best characterized of the interspersed repetitive sequence families in the human genome. These families of repetitive elements are considered highly relevant to a number of different mechanisms of mutagenesis in human genes (see Sections 7.1.2 and 8.2–8.4).

2.3.1 Tandem repeats

Tandemly repetitive DNA comprises satellite DNA, minisatellite DNA and microsatellite DNA. Satellite DNA comprises the majority of heterochromatin and is clustered in tandem arrays of up to several megabases in length. A number of different families [e.g. simple sequence (5–25 bp repeats), alphoid (171 bp repeat), Sau3A (~68 bp repeat)] have been identified (reviewed by Vogt, 1990). The hypervariable minisatellite sequences (about 10^4 copies/genome) share a core consensus sequence (GGTGGGCAGARG, where R = purine), which is reminiscent of the *Escherichia coli* Chi element known to be a signal for generalized recombination (Jeffreys, 1987). These minisatellites exhibit substantial copy number variability in terms of the number of constituent repeat units, probably due to the processes of unequal recombination and slipped mispairing. The mutation rate for some of these hypervariable loci may be as high as 5.2% (Jeffreys *et al.*, 1988). Microsatellite DNA families are simple sequence repeats, the most common being $(A)_n/(T)_{n'}$ $(CA)_n/(TG)_n$ and $(CT)_n/(AG)_n$ types (Vogt, 1990; Williamson *et al.*, 1991; Beckmann and Weber, 1992). These two different sub-families each account for between 0.2% and 0.5% of the genome respectively. Their high copy number variability and association with a considerable number of different genes has meant that they provide a very valuable source of highly informative markers for indirect diagnosis of human genetic disease.

2.3.2 Alu sequences

The Alu family of short interspersed repeated elements (SINEs) appears to be present in all mammals. Up to 900000 copies are thought to exist in the human genome (some 5% of the total DNA complement), with an average spacing of 4 kb (Hwu *et al.*, 1986). These repeats share a recognizable consensus sequence but the extent of homology to this consensus varies between 72% and 99% (Kariya *et al.*, 1987; Batzer *et al.*, 1990). Human Alu sequences are ~300 bp in length and consist of two related sequences each between 120 and 150 bp long separated by an A-rich region (Figure 2.6). Although their function (if any) is unknown, Ullu and Tschudi (1984) have proposed that Alu sequences may be degenerate forms of 7SL RNA that have been reverse transcribed and integrated into the genome. Several reports of transcription of Alu sequences by RNA polymerase II or III have appeared (reviewed by Kariya *et al.*, 1987). Alu sequences are known to contain an

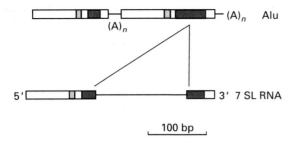

Figure 2.6. Structure of the human Alu repeat element compared with the related 7SL RNA. A 155 bp portion of the 7SL RNA is absent from the Alu sequence as indicated. Poly(A) stretches are denoted by $(A)_n$.

internal RNA polymerase III promoter (Jelinek and Schmid, 1982) and Saffer and Thurston (1989) have shown that they contain a negative regulatory element which represses transcription from a variety of promoters *in vitro*.

Most Alu sequences are flanked by direct repeats (4–19 bp), which are probably created from the target DNA during the process of integration (Kariya *et al.*, 1987). Most of these direct repeats are A + T rich (67%) compared with the rest of the human genome (~ 60%). Alu sequences may thus have a propensity to integrate into A + T-rich regions. Certainly their orientation appears to be influenced by flanking DNA sequence (Daniels and Deininger, 1985). Some spatial clustering of Alu sequences is sometimes also apparent but whether this represents reporting bias, or whether already integrated Alu sequences provide an optimal target site for new integrations, is unclear. However, each integration event is comparatively rare, approximately $1-2/10^4$ years (Batzer *et al.*, 1990).

There appear to be at least four different types of Alu sequence which belong to two distinct subfamilies (Jurka and Smith, 1988; Britten *et al.*, 1988). Some types of Alu sequence are human-specific (Batzer *et al.*, 1990; Batzer and Deininger, 1991). These appear to be derived from a number of different but closely related master copies or 'source genes'. Not all Alu sequences are, however, involved in retrotransposition since (i) the most recently inserted Alu repeats appear to be very highly conserved and (ii) the majority of recent Alu retrotranspositions have been of human-specific family members (Deininger and Slagel, 1988; Britten *et al.*, 1989; Matera *et al.*, 1990a; Batzer and Deininger, 1991). Although the vast majority of human Alu sequences appear to be transcriptionally inert, one of the transpositionally competent human-specific subfamilies is also transcriptionally active (Matera *et al.*, 1990b; Sinnett *et al.*, 1992). This provides evidence in support of the existence of an RNA intermediate required by the retrotransposition hypothesis.

2.3.3 LINE elements

Some 10^5 copies of long interspersed repeat elements (LINEs) are present in the human genome (Hwu *et al.*, 1986) and account for perhaps 2–3% of the total DNA complement (reviewed by Skowronski and Singer, 1986; Weiner *et al.*, 1986; Fanning and Singer, 1987). Human LINE elements vary in size from as little as 60 bp up to 6–7 kb; about 95% represent copies which are truncated at their 5′ ends but they mostly appear to contain the same 3′ sequences as well as a poly(A) tail of variable length. Each individual LINE element differs from the consensus sequence (Scott *et al.*, 1987) by ~13% although many exhibit internal deletions and rearrangements.

A full-length LINE element possesses two open reading frames, ORF1 (1 kb) and ORF2 (4 kb), the latter capable of producing a protein with homology to retroviral reverse transcriptases (Hattori *et al.*, 1986). The structure of a full-length LINE element is shown in Figure 2.7. LINE element transcripts have only been found in undifferentiated teratocarcinoma cells (Skowronski and Singer, 1985; Skowronski *et al.*, 1988) suggesting that they may be expressed early on in mammalian development. A promoter at the 5′ end appears to be responsible for the specific expression of LINE elements in teratocarcinoma cells (Swergold, 1990). However, since transcribed LINE elements differ from the consensus sequence by only ~2% (Scott *et al.*, 1987), it is likely that only a small subset of all LINE elements is capable of transcription. Furthermore, most LINE elements appear to be incapable of producing a translatable mRNA owing to base substitutions, deletions or rearrangements.

The poly(A) tails, the short sequence duplications flanking individual LINE elements and the homology of the putative ORF2 protein with retroviral reverse transcriptases immediately suggested that LINEs might represent processed pseudogene-like copies of reverse transcripts which had been re-integrated into the genome (Hattori *et al.*, 1986). The view that LINEs are a family of retrotransposons received support from the not inconsiderable number of polymorphisms caused by LINE element insertions (reviewed by Weiner *et al.*, 1986), the detection of an RNA-dependent DNA polymerase activity in human teratocarcinoma cells (Deragon *et al.*, 1990) and the demonstration of germline retrotransposition of a LINE element in *Drosophila* (Jensen and Heidmann, 1991). More recently, Mathias *et al.*, (1991) expressed a cloned human ORF2 sequence as a fusion protein in yeast and demonstrated it to have reverse transcriptase activity. Moreover, *in vitro* mutagenesis of a highly conserved sequence motif in the protein abolished its activity. LINE

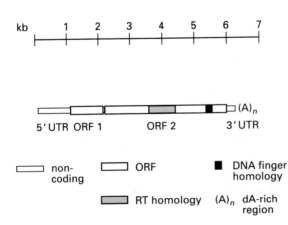

Figure 2.7. Structure of a full-length human LINE element. UTR, untranslated region. ORF, open reading frame. RT, reverse transcriptase.

elements do indeed therefore encode a reverse transcriptase activity which could serve to mediate not only their own retrotransposition but also that of other repetitive elements such as Alu sequences.

The majority of human LINE elements appear to have been generated within the last 30 million years (Scott *et al.*, 1987). As was found for Alu sequences, these repetitive elements have a preference for integrating into A + T-rich DNA. Interestingly, LINE elements also possess short stretches of homology to Alu sequences at their 5' ends. It may therefore be that these two types of repetitive sequence element will sometimes be found to be associated with each other in the genome as a consequence of their similar target site preference and their potential for homologous recombination.

2.4 DNA polymorphisms

The term polymorphism has been defined (Vogel and Motulsky, 1986) as a 'Mendelian trait that exists in the population in at least two phenotypes, neither of which occurs at a frequency of less than 1%'. The majority of recognized DNA polymorphisms are neutral single base-pair changes detected by virtue of the consequent introduction or removal of a restriction enzyme recognition site and are accordingly termed restriction fragment length polymorphisms (RFLPs; reviewed by Cooper and Schmidtke, 1984). They are inherited as simple Mendelian traits since two alleles are generated as a consequence of the presence or absence of each restriction site (Figure 2.8).

The first RFLP reported, detectable with the restriction enzyme Hpa I, was situated 3' to the β-globin gene and was immediately useful in a clinical context since the 13 kb allele occurred in linkage disequilibrium with the β^s allele responsible for sickle cell disease in American Blacks (Kan and Dozy, 1978a, 1978b). As more RFLPs were discovered, it became possible to distinguish allele-specific combinations of RFLPs at the same locus and to use these 'haplotypes' as linked markers to distinguish (albeit indirectly) the different mutations superimposed on them (e.g. in the β-globin gene causing β-thalassaemia; Antonarakis *et al.*, 1985).

RFLPs are not rare, being distributed throughout the genome approximately every 200–300 bp (Cooper *et al.*, 1985). They may be detected using either genes or arbitrary DNA segments as hybridization probes. RFLPs do not, however, appear to occur randomly and some restriction enzymes, most notably MspI and TaqI which contain the hypermutable CpG dinucleotide in their recognition sequences, detect more polymorphic variation than enzymes that do not recognize CpG-containing sequences (Barker *et al.*, 1984; Cooper *et al.*, 1985). DNA sequence polymorphisms which occur outside restriction sites may be detected by a variety of techniques, e.g. oligonucleotide discriminant hybridization, allele-specific polymerase chain reaction (PCR; Section 4.3) amplification and direct DNA sequencing.

RFLPs have revolutionized human gene/disease mapping since they have provided the potential to saturate the entire genome with evenly spaced

(a)

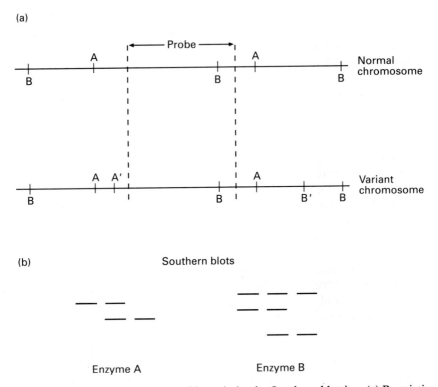

(b)   Southern blots

                    Enzyme A   Enzyme B

Figure 2.8. Detection of polymorphic variation by Southern blotting. (a) Restriction enzyme cleavage sites for enzymes A and B on hypothetical normal and variant chromosomes. The length of DNA corresponding to the cloned hybridization probe is shown. (b) Resulting restriction fragment patterns generated on a Southern blot. Genotypes from left to right: homozygous (absence), heterozygous, homozygous (presence).

markers (Botstein *et al.*, 1980). Already, >2000 DNA polymorphisms have been identified (Stephens *et al.*, 1990; Williamson *et al.*, 1991), many of which have been incorporated into the map of the human genome which currently has a resolution of between 5 and 10 cM (see Section 3.4). Increasingly, genetic mapping is utilizing microsatellites, a new class of highly polymorphic PCR-formatted multiallelic markers which are characterized by variable numbers of short clustered repeat units (see Sections 2.3.1 and 3.4).

2.5 DNA replication and repair

Five different cellular DNA polymerases are now known to exist in eukaryotes: polymerases α, β, δ and ε are involved in replication and repair of the nuclear genome, whilst polymerase γ is thought to be responsible for the replication of the mitochondrial chromosome; their respective properties and roles in

DNA replication and repair are reviewed in detail by Bambara and Jessee (1991), Linn (1991), Wang (1991) and Kornberg and Baker (1992). A brief summary of current knowledge of these polymerases is, however, necessary here to provide the background to studies on misincorporation of bases during DNA synthesis.

DNA polymerase α is a major replicative enzyme in human cells. It possesses an RNA primase activity but may not possess an associated $3' \rightarrow 5'$ exonuclease activity. It binds to large gaps (> 20 nucleotides) in double-stranded DNA but will not bind to nicks; nor will it fill small gaps to completion. It is moderately processive and is thought to incorporate ~ 10 nucleotides per association event. DNA polymerase β is probably involved in repair synthesis although it could play some role in DNA replication. It prefers small gaps as a substrate and fills these to completion but dissociates from the DNA after each nucleotide addition event. It has no associated $3' \rightarrow 5'$ exonuclease activity and is the most error-prone of the five polymerases. DNA polymerase γ is thought to be involved in mitochondrial DNA replication although it is itself nuclear encoded. DNA polymerases δ and ε are both highly processive, although the processivity of polymerase δ is dependent on the presence of its auxiliary protein, proliferating cell nuclear antigen (PCNA). Both enzymes are associated with a proofreading $3' \rightarrow 5'$ exonuclease activity.

It is still largely unclear how each polymerase is involved in DNA replication and repair. A working hypothesis is as follows. Polymerase α synthesizes the primers for both the leading and lagging strands and may also be responsible for replication of the lagging strand. Based on its possession of a $3' \rightarrow 5'$ exonuclease activity and its high processivity, polymerase δ has been proposed as being involved in synthesis of the leading DNA strand. Polymerase ε may play a role either in lagging strand synthesis or in repair.

The fidelity of DNA synthesis has recently been reviewed by Kunkel and Bebenek (1988), Echols and Goodman (1991) and Kunkel (1992). This topic is addressed briefly here, but the interested reader is referred to these review articles for further details. The exceptional fidelity of eukaryotic DNA replication (error frequencies typically between 10^{-9} and 10^{-11} per base-pair replicated) owes much to the *accurate selection* of correct deoxyribonucleoside 5'-triphosphates (dNTPs) during polymerization and to the combination of *proofreading* (exonucleolytic removal of incorrectly inserted bases from the nascent chain prior to continued DNA synthesis) and *mismatch repair* (post-replicative excision of incorrectly inserted bases; see Modrich, 1987). However, misincorporation does occur and it is important to consider the relative contribution of each of these processes to the overall error frequency.

The different DNA polymerases exhibit very different yet very characteristic frequencies of base misincorporation/frameshift mutagenesis. The accuracy of base selection *in vitro* has been assessed by measuring the fidelity of DNA synthesis by mammalian DNA polymerases with or without their associated proofreading exonuclease activities. As regards frameshift mutations, polymerase β generates errors ten-fold more frequently (one in 10^3) than polymerase α (one in 10^4) which generates errors thirty-fold more frequently than polymerase γ (one in 3×10^5; Kunkel, 1986). The relative accuracies associated with each polymerase are very similar with respect to base substitutions (Kunkel, 1985b), with polymerase δ being perhaps even more accurate (one in 10^6) than polymerase γ (Kunkel et al., 1987). Recent data suggest that polymerase ε may be still more accurate than polymerase δ (Thomas et al., 1991). Characteristic differences in error frequencies must be due in part to intrinsic differences in the accuracy of base insertion by the various polymerases. Indeed, 'hotspots' for mutation, when reported, tend to be polymerase-specific (Kunkel, 1985a; Lai and Beattie, 1988), although they are also very sensitive to the local DNA sequence context (Kunkel, 1986).

Misincorporation frequencies are probably determined by a number of different parameters (including the type of polymerase and the local sequence context) as evidenced by the following findings using purified DNA polymerases *in vitro*:

(i) Mutational spectra associated with different DNA polymerases can differ quite considerably (e.g. Kunkel and Alexander, 1986; Lai and Beattie, 1988).

(ii) The same mispair may be generated by the same DNA polymerase at dramatically different frequencies at different sites (e.g. Kunkel and Alexander, 1986; Lai and Beattie, 1988).

(iii) Different mispairs may be generated at very different frequencies at the same site by the same DNA polymerase (e.g. Grosse et al., 1983).

(iv) The relative frequencies of symmetrical mispairs (e.g. C:A and A:C) are dependent on which nucleotide was present in the template and which was the incoming triphosphate (e.g. Kunkel and Alexander, 1986).

Misinsertions may arise through local dNTP pool imbalances, with the DNA polymerase tending toward misincorporation of the excess dinucleotide(s) (Kunz, 1982; Meuth, 1989; Kunz and Kohalmi, 1991; Mathews and Ji, 1992). Consistent with this postulate, increased levels of the next correct nucleotide are associated with an increased probability of extending mismatched primer termini (Mendelman et al., 1990) and a reduced probability of $3'$ to $5'$ proofreading due to enhanced polymerization ('the next nucleotide effect'; Kunkel, 1988).

The potential consequences of the initial misinsertion of a base are two-fold, as can be seen from Figure 2.9. The incorrect base may be permanently incorporated, leading to repair of the correct base on the opposite strand and resulting in a single base-pair substitution. Alternatively, the misinsertion may prompt a realignment, leading eventually to the deletion of a base. The latter proposal is supported by the observation that minus-one base errors at non-run positions occur at high frequency, that most frameshift errors at non-run sites represent losses of template purines that had template pyrimidines as their nearest $5'$ neighbours (Kunkel, 1985a, 1985b) and that increasing the rate of misincorporation through dNTP pool imbalance increased the frequency of frameshifts (Bebenek and Kunkel, 1990).

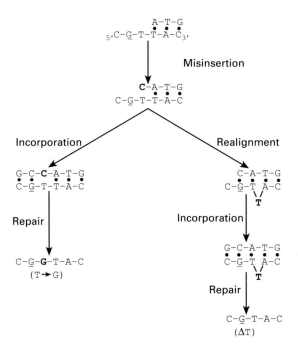

Figure 2.9. Pathways for single base errors during DNA replication as a result of a misinsertion event. Modified from Kunkel (1990) with permission from the American Chemical Society. © 1990 American Chemical Society.

An alternative pathway of mutagenesis is through an initial misalignment event. The role of misalignment at DNA replication in the generation of misincorporation and frameshift errors has been reviewed by Kunkel (1990) and Ripley (1990). The possible pathways for the introduction of single base errors during DNA replication by misalignment at the replication fork are shown in Figure 2.10. In the example given, incorporation of the misaligned base would result in a 1 bp deletion (misalignment-mediated misincorporation), whereas if the misalignment was only transient and the DNA strands realigned after the misincorporation of the first base (dislocation mutagenesis), a single base-pair substitution would be generated. Evidence that misalignment-mediated misincorporation does indeed occur *in vitro* comes from the observation that frameshift errors occur preferentially at runs of identical bases and that the rate at which they occur is proportional to the length of the run (Kunkel, 1985a, 1986). Similarly, the model of dislocation mutagenesis is supported by the high frequency of single base-pair substitutions within runs (Kunkel, 1985a), the kinetic analysis of misinsertion (Boosalis *et al.*, 1989) and the value of the model in predicting the nature and frequency of nucleotide substitutions observed *in vitro* (Kunkel and Soni, 1988).

It remains to be established whether or not all four proposed mechanisms of mutagenesis discussed above operate *in vivo* and, if they do, what their relative importance is for the generation of spontaneous mutations. It must be remembered that, *in vivo*, a number of accessory proteins will be present at DNA replication, which should in principle serve to increase accuracy. More-

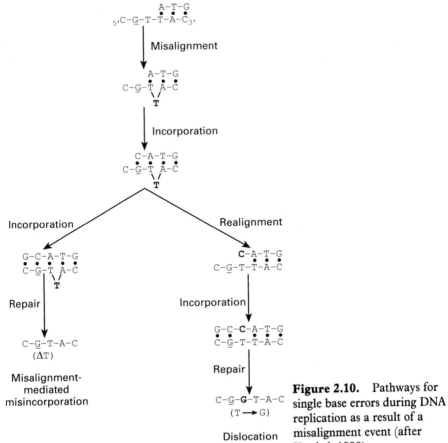

Figure 2.10. Pathways for single base errors during DNA replication as a result of a misalignment event (after Kunkel, 1990).

over, editing mechanisms such as exonucleolytic proofreading and mismatch repair will be employed; these will also presumably exhibit their own characteristic mutational spectra.

Exonucleolytic proofreading is the process by which nucleotides misincorporated by the DNA polymerase during replication are removed (reviewed by Kunkel, 1988). Thus proofreading can be visualized as a process of competition between the extension of the nascent chain by the polymerase from the mispaired base and exonucleolytic excision. *In vitro*, extension from a mispair appears to be rather more difficult than from a correctly paired base, a fact which may lead to its removal. However, in the presence of high local concentrations of the correct following dNTP, the misincorporation frequency rises dramatically. DNA polymerases which lack an associated $3' \rightarrow 5'$ exonuclease are those which catalyse extension from mismatches most readily. This notwithstanding, the efficiency of the proofreading process depends not merely on the polymerase involved but also on the nature of the mispair and the influence of the surrounding DNA sequence.

It thus appears that the accuracy of purified DNA polymerases *in vitro* is insufficient to account for the comparatively low rate of spontaneous mutation observed *in vivo*. Human cells are probably heavily reliant on post-replicative repair processes to achieve the necessary degree of accuracy.

2.6 The mitochondrial genome

Every human cell contains hundreds of mitochondria and each mitochondrion is thought to contain between two and ten mitochondrial DNAs. The entire DNA sequence of the double-stranded circular 16 569 bp mitochondrial genome was determined by Anderson *et al.*, (1981). A map of the human mitochondrial genome is shown in Figure 2.11. For a concise up-to-date review of the structure and function of the mitochondrial genome, the reader is referred to Shoffner and Wallace (1990); only the basic organizational principles will be summarized here.

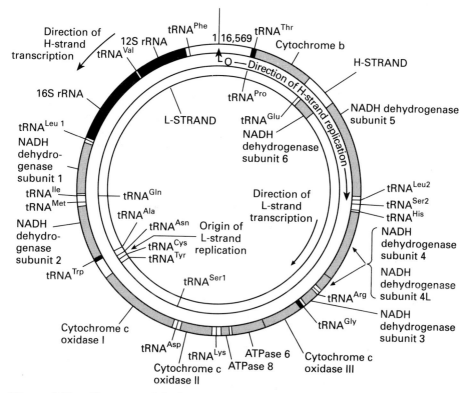

Figure 2.11. Gene map of the human mitochondrial genome (courtesy of DC Wallace).

The two DNA strands of the mitochondrial genome differ markedly in their G and C contents and are distinguished by the letters H (heavy) and L (light) for the guanine-rich and cytosine-rich strands respectively. Mitochondrial DNA replication initiates within a 1123 bp region known as the displacement loop (D loop) with the two strands being replicated in an asynchronous fashion. Transcription of the H and L strands is also initiated from the D loop by an ATP-dependent RNA polymerase, is under the control of two closely linked promoters and proceeds in opposite directions. The mitochondrial genome encodes 13 polypeptides which are all subunits of the multiple polypeptide enzyme complexes of the oxidative phosphorylation pathway. These comprise NADH dehydrogenases 1, 2, 3, 4, 4L, 5 and 6, cytochrome *c* oxidases I, II and III, ATP synthases 6 and 8 and cytochrome *b*. In addition, the mitochondrial genome encodes 22 tRNAs (including two each for Ser and Leu) and two rRNAs (12S and 16S); the tRNAs are removed from the transcribed H and L strands by RNase P. The polypeptide-encoding mRNAs are translated within the mitochondrion using the mitochondrial-encoded rRNAs and tRNAs. The H strand encodes 12 of the oxidative phosphorylation subunits, the two rRNAs and 14 tRNAs, whilst the L strand encodes the remaining subunit and eight tRNAs.

Human (and indeed other mammal) mitochondrial DNAs possess a much simpler genetic code than that employed by the nuclear genome: only 22 tRNAs are required to interpret the mitochondrial code. Moreover, several differences in the codes are apparent: in the mitochondrial genome, TGA and ATA encode Trp and Met respectively, whereas AGA and AGG signify termination codons.

A sizable number of different disorders have now been recognized as being of mitochondrial origin (reviewed by Shoffner and Wallace, 1990; Wallace *et al.*, 1991). Mitochondrial disorders, arising as a direct consequence of a defect in the mitochondrial genome, are maternally inherited; paternal mitochondrial DNA is not transmitted to the progeny. During both mitosis and meiosis, mitochondria are distributed at random to daughter cells. In patients who possess mixed populations of mutant and wild-type mitochondrial DNAs (heteroplasmy), the relative proportions of each may change in a stochastic fashion. This 'replicative drift' may result in some cell lineages becoming homoplasmic for a given mitochondrial DNA species. One consequence of this phenomenon is a threshold effect whereby the cell phenotype is not altered significantly until the mutant mitochondrial DNA exceeds a certain proportion within the cell.

The rate of nucleotide substitution in human mitochondrial DNA has been known for some time to be significantly higher (6–17 times) than that observed in the nuclear genome (Brown *et al.*, 1982; Miyata *et al.*, 1982; Wallace *et al.*, 1987), presumably because mitochondrial DNA must undergo many more rounds of DNA replication than chromosomal DNA. One consequence of this is that the mitochondrially encoded subunits of the oxidative phosphorylation enzyme complexes evolve at a much higher rate than their nuclear-encoded counterparts (reviewed by Shoffner and Wallace, 1990).

Single base-pair substitutions in 13 mitochondrial genes have already been implicated in the aetiology of a range of disorders (summarized briefly in Table 2.1). Further discussion of these lesions is presented in Section 6.9 and mitochondrial gene deletions are covered in Section 7.3.

2.7 DNA methylation and the CpG dinucleotide

5-Methylcytosine (5mC) is the most common form of DNA modification in eukaryotic genomes. Soon after DNA synthesis is complete, it is introduced by a DNA methyltransferase using S-adenosylmethionine as methyl donor (reviewed by Adams, 1990). In humans, between 70 and 90% of 5mC occurs in CpG dinucleotides, the majority of which appear to be methylated (reviewed by Cooper, 1983). Spatially, the distribution of CpG also appears to be non-random in the human genome; about 1% of the genome consists of stretches very rich in CpG, which together account for roughly 15% of all CpG dinucleotides (Cooper *et al.*, 1983). In contrast to most of the scattered CpG dinucleotides, these 'CpG islands' represent unmethylated domains and comprise ~ 50% of all non-methylated CpGs in the genome (Bird *et al.*, 1985). CpG islands occur, on average, every 100 kb in the murine genome (Brown

Table 2.1. Mitochondrial genes in which single base-pair substitutions have been implicated in disease pathology (data from Wallace *et al.*, 1991)

Gene symbol	Gene product	Disease state
MTND1	NADH dehydrogenase 1	Leber's optic neuropathy
MTND2	NADH dehydrogenase 2	Leber's optic neuropathy
MTND4	NADH dehydrogenase 4	Leber's optic neuropathy
MTND5	NADH dehydrogenase 5	Leber's optic neuropathy
MTCYB	Cytochrome *b*	Leber's optic neuropathy
MTATP6	ATP synthase 6	Neurogenic muscle weakness, ataxia and retinitis pigmentosa (NARP)
MTTL1	tRNA Leu1	Mitochondrial encephalomyopathy, lactic acidosis and stroke-like episodes (MELAS) syndrome
MTTL1	tRNA Leu1	Maternal myopathy and cardio-myopathy (MMC)
MTTT	tRNA Thr	Lethal infantile mitochondrial myopathy (LIMM)
MTTI	tRNA Ile	Fatal infantile cardiomyopathy plus MELAS-associated cardio-myopathy (FICP)
MTTK	tRNA Lys	Myoclonic epilepsy and ragged-red fibre disease (MERFF)
MTTS1	tRNA Ser1	Chronic intestinal pseudo-obstruction with myopathy and ophthalmoplegia (CIPO)
MTTG	tRNA Gly	CIPO
MTTL2	tRNA Leu	CIPO

and Bird, 1986) and often correspond to gene coding regions both in the mouse (Lindsay and Bird, 1987) and in humans (Gardiner *et al.*, 1990; Larsen *et al.*, 1992). Not all vertebrate genes, however, possess these unmethylated CpG islands (Bird, 1986; Gardiner-Garden and Frommer, 1987) and many are partially or even heavily methylated (reviewed by Cooper, 1983).

The target of DNA methylation, the CpG dinucleotide, is dramatically under-represented in vertebrate genomes, occurring at between 20 and 25% of the frequency predicted from observed mononucleotide frequencies (cf. 37% expected within gene coding regions). It has become clear that this 'CpG suppression' and the level of DNA methylation are intimately related. This is thought to be due to the propensity of cytosine, methylated at the 5 position, to undergo deamination to form thymine (Coulondre *et al.*, 1978; Duncan and Miller, 1980). Deamination of 5mC probably does not occur during the enzymatic replication of the methylation pattern, which appears to be a high fidelity process (Smith *et al.*, 1992). Indeed, 5mC deamination probably occurs with the same frequency as the deamination of cytosine to uracil. However, whereas uracil DNA glycosylase activity in eukaryotic cells is able to recognize and excise uracil, thymine, being a 'normal' DNA base, is thought to be less readily detectable and hence removable by cellular repair mechanisms. If this is true, the long-term consequences of the presence of DNA methylation in human genes would be the gradual loss of CpG dinucleotides and, with them, any functional characteristics that they might bestow on the region in question. This would, however, only hold if methylation were present in the germline as well as in somatic tissues.

This model is supported by various pieces of evidence. At the level of the genome, the extent of CpG suppression (and consequent CpA + TpG elevation) appears to be related to the overall level of DNA methylation (Bird, 1980; Nussinov, 1981; Beutler *et al.*, 1989). However, this correlation is far from perfect (Schorderet and Gartler, 1992) implying that other factors, including perhaps the optimization of translation efficiency, may play a role in determining CpG distribution. At the level of the gene, $C \rightarrow T$ transitions and the corresponding $G \rightarrow A$ transitions on the complementary DNA strand occur at high frequency within methylated gene regions (e.g. Selker and Stevens, 1985; Savatier *et al.*, 1985). Furthermore, a high rate of polymorphism is detected by restriction enzymes that contain CpG in their recognition sequences (Barker *et al.*, 1984; Cooper and Schmidtke, 1984). Finally, some 35% of single base-pair substitutions within gene coding regions causing human genetic disease were shown to occur within CpG dinucleotides (Cooper and Youssoufian, 1988); over 90% of these mutations were $C \rightarrow T$ or $G \rightarrow A$ transitions, which thus occurred within coding regions at a frequency 42-fold higher than that predicted from random mutation. These findings strongly support the concept that methylation-mediated deamination of 5mC is an important influence on the mutation (and hence the frequency and distribution) of the CpG dinucleotide in the human genome.

DNA methylation patterns exhibited by genes in somatic cells are often tissue specific and these patterns are inherited clonally in a semi-conservative fashion (reviewed by Razin, 1984 and Taylor 1984). Maintenance of the somatic DNA methylation pattern is achieved by virtue of the methyltransferase being capable of recognizing asymmetrically methylated CpG dinucleotides and converting the symmetrically placed cytosines on the daughter strand to 5mC, thus restoring symmetry and reproducing the parental pattern of DNA methylation. [It should be noted that 5mC may also be present in small amounts in CpC and CpT (Woodcock et al., 1987).] Although this enzymatic process appears to possess high fidelity (Smith et al., 1992), there is some evidence to suggest that partially methylated sites (sites only methylated in a specific proportion of cells) may under some circumstances be stably maintained in mammalian tissues/cell lines (Turker et al., 1989). Both demethylation and de novo methylation of specific sites have been reported (Trasler et al., 1990; reviewed by Doerfler et al., 1990), suggesting that the control of DNA methylation pattern formation could be rather complex. The efficiency of de novo methylation (which initially creates hemimethylated DNA in which only one DNA strand is modified) is considerably lower than maintenance methylation (Hare and Taylor, 1988; Pfeifer et al., 1990); patterns of hemimethylated DNA have sometimes been observed to be stable over several cell generations (Saluz et al., 1986; Toth et al., 1989). Demethylation during differentiation, simply the replacement of 5mC by cytosine, appears to occur (at least in some cases) by an active and enzymatic mechanism rather than merely by a passive failure to methylate the hemimethylated site (Razin et al., 1986) since methylation patterns are sometimes rapidly lost in the absence of DNA replication.

Some variation in the methylation status of homologous sites on different alleles is apparent; this variation is tissue specific and the pattern is reproducible after transmission through the germline (Silva and White, 1988). This phenomenon has been reviewed in the context of genomic imprinting by Monk (1988) and is discussed further in Section 12.5. By contrast, methylation patterns of many genes are altered during early embryonic development in a cell-type specific manner (reviewed by Cedar and Razin, 1990; Ghazi et al., 1992). As far as bulk genomic DNA is concerned, murine oocyte DNA is relatively undermethylated and sperm is heavily methylated, whereas the methylation status of the dividing embryo is intermediate (Monk et al., 1987). Demethylation then occurs at the blastocyst stage and is followed by de novo methylation, which eventually establishes the adult tissue-specific patterns (Monk et al., 1987).

The means by which CpG islands are protected from germline DNA methylation are unknown but some DNA sequences still appear able to avoid de novo methylation (Kolsto et al., 1986). Since CpG island methylation commonly occurs in genes present on the inactive X chromosome in women (reviewed by Cedar and Razin 1990), it has been proposed that one role for DNA methylation might be in the selective silencing of gene transcription. A detailed discussion of the possible role(s) of DNA methylation in the formation of active/inactive chromatin and in transcriptional regulation is beyond the remit of this section. However, where DNA methylation does inhibit transcription, it appears to do so either by interfering directly with the interaction between transcription factors and their binding sites and/or indirectly by promoter inactivation through the binding of methylated CpG-specific binding proteins (see Antequera *et al.*, 1989; Meehan *et al.*, 1989; Jost *et al.*, 1991; Levine *et al.*, 1991). In the latter case, repression appears to be dependent on both CpG dinucleotide density and the strength of the natural gene promoter (Boyes and Bird, 1991, 1992). Methylation may exert its effects on protein binding by inducing local distortions in the structure of duplex DNA (Hodges-García and Hagerman, 1992). The interested reader is referred to recent reviews on this subject for further information (Adams, 1990; Lewis and Bird, 1991; Bird, 1992).

Active roles for DNA methylation have been postulated in DNA replication and repair as well as in transcriptional regulation (Adams, 1990). Whatever the actual function(s) of DNA methylation, this modification is clearly important since the mutational inactivation of the murine DNA methyltransferase gene causes abnormal development and embryonic lethality (Li *et al.*, 1992). More indirectly, its legacy of deamination-type mutations represents a significant contribution to the incidence of human genetic disease.

2.8 Genes, mutations and disease

Point mutations and deletions are without doubt the most frequently encountered gene lesions in the human genome. The remainder comprise a mixed assortment of insertions, duplications, inversions and complex rearrangements (Cooper and Schmidtke, 1991). As we shall see, characterized mutations have been found to occur not only in coding sequences but also in promoter regions, in splice junctions, within introns and in polyadenylation sites. Indeed, they may interfere with any stage in the pathway of expression from gene to protein product.

From the considerable number of human gene mutations now known, it is possible to attempt to construct a basic classificatory system by reference to the nature and position of the lesion and the stage in the expression pathway with which it interferes. Such a classificatory scheme is presented in Table 2.2. In this table, mutations are first divided on the basis of whether they result in the reduced synthesis of a gene product (a) or the synthesis of a structurally/ functionally abnormal gene product (b). Mutations are then secondarily divided into four categories: promoter function, gene structure, RNA processing and translation. Clearly, this scheme is incomplete and, since its category boundaries are somewhat arbitrarily defined, some gene lesions could be placed into more than one category. For example, missense mutations with drastic effects on protein structure and stability, or which serve to activate an exonic cryptic splice site, could also fall into both categories. Similarly, a missense mutation close to an intron–exon splice junction could affect mRNA splicing efficiency as well as protein structure.

The scheme as presented does, however, serve as a guide to the mutations considered in detail in Chapters 6–11. It will be seen that effects of mutations

Table 2.2. A classification of types of mutation found to cause human single gene defects through either reduced synthesis of a normal protein or synthesis of an abnormal protein

(a) *Reduced synthesis of a normal gene product*	
Defect in:	
Promoter function	Binding of positive regulatory protein reduced or abolished
	Binding of negative regulatory protein increased
Gene structure	Deletions (frameshift)
	Insertions, duplications, inversions (frameshift)
RNA processing	Cap site mutations causing failure to initiate transcription
	Splice junction mutations resulting in exon skipping and/or cryptic splice site utilization
	Activation of cryptic splice sites
	Polyadenylation/cleavage signal mutations
Translation	Initiation and termination codon mutations
	Nonsense mutations
(b) *Synthesis of a structurally or functionally abnormal gene product*	
Gene structure defect resulting in:	
Altered function	Missense mutations
Shortened gene product	Deletions (in-frame)
Fusion genes	Deletions involving two linked genes
Elongated gene product	Insertions, duplications (in-frame)
	Termination codon mutations

Defects in post-translational processing affecting the structure or function of the protein are not included.

on protein structure and function have been deliberately omitted. The effects of specific amino acid substitutions on protein structure are the subject of two recent reviews (Pakula and Sauer, 1989; Alber, 1989). Such mutations are of course very important in disease pathogenesis since they may serve to disrupt post-translational modification or processing, render the protein product unstable, impair its proper assembly or secretion or alter its substrate–cofactor–receptor affinity. Our remit is such, however, that these mechanisms cannot be considered within the confines of this volume but will instead be addressed in future titles in this series.

References

Adams RLP. (1990) DNA methylation. The effect of minor bases on DNA-protein interactions. *Biochem. J.* **265**: 309–320.

Alber T. (1989) Mutational effects on protein stability. *Ann. Rev. Biochem.* **58**: 765–798.

Anderson S, Bankier AT, Barrell BG, de Bruijn MHL, Coulson AR, Drouin J, Eperon IC, Nierlich DP, Roe BA, Sanger F, Schreier PH, Smith AJH, Staden R, Young IG. (1981) Sequence and organization of the human mitochondrial genome. *Nature* **290**: 457–465.

Antequera F, Macleod D, Bird AP. (1989) Specific protection of methylated CpGs in mammalian nuclei. *Cell* **58**: 509–517.

Antonarakis SE, Kazazian HH, Orkin SH. (1985) DNA polymorphism and molecular pathology of the human globin gene clusters. *Hum. Genet.* **69**: 1–14.

Atwater JA, Wisdom R, Verma IM. (1990) Regulated mRNA stability. *Ann. Rev. Genet.* **24:** 519–541.

Bambara RA, Jessee CB. (1991) Properties of DNA polymerases δ and ε and their roles in eukaryotic DNA replication. *Biochim. Biophys. Acta* **1088:** 11–24.

Barker D, Schäfer M, White R. (1984) Restriction sites containing CpG show a higher frequency of polymorphism in human DNA. *Cell* **36:** 131–138.

Batzer MA, Deininger PL. (1991) A human-specific subfamily of Alu sequences. *Genomics* **9:** 481–487.

Batzer MA, Kilroy GE, Richard PE, Shaikh TH, Desselle TD, Hoppens CL, Deininger PL. (1990) Structure and variability of recently inserted Alu family members. *Nucleic Acids Res.* **18:** 6793–6798.

Bebenek K, Kunkel TA. (1990) Frameshift errors initiated by nucleotide misincorporation. *Proc. Natl. Acad. Sci. USA* **87:** 4946–4950.

Beckmann JS, Weber JL. (1992) Survey of human and rat microsatellites. *Genomics* **12:** 627–631.

Beutler E, Gelbart T, Han J, Koziol JA, Beutler B. (1989) Evolution of the genome and the genetic code: selection at the dinucleotide level by methylation and polyribonucleotide cleavage. *Proc. Natl. Acad. Sci. USA* **86:** 192–196.

Bird AP. (1980) DNA methylation and the frequency of CpG in animal DNA. *Nucleic Acids Res.* **8:** 1499–1504.

Bird AP. (1986) CpG-rich islands and the function of DNA methylation. *Nature* **321:** 209–213.

Bird A. (1992) The essentials of DNA methylation. *Cell* **70:** 5–8.

Bird A, Taggart M, Frommer M, Miller OJ, Macleod D. (1985) A fraction of the mouse genome that is derived from islands of nonmethylated CpG-rich DNA. *Cell* **40:** 91–99.

Birnstiel ML, Busslinger M, Strub K. (1985) Transcription termination and 3′ processing: the end is in sight. *Cell* **41:** 349–359.

Boosalis MS, Mosbaugh DW, Hamatake R, Sugino A, Kunkel TA, Goodman MF. (1989) Kinetic analysis of base substitution mutagenesis by transient misalignment of DNA and by miscoding. *J. Biol. Chem.* **264:** 11360–11366.

Botstein D, White RL, Skolnick M, Davis RW. (1980) Construction of a genetic linkage map in man using restriction fragment length polymorphisms. *Am. J. Hum. Genet.* **32:** 314–331.

Boyes J, Bird A. (1991) DNA methylation inhibits transcription indirectly via a methyl-CpG binding protein. *Cell* **64:** 1123–1134.

Boyes J, Bird A. (1992) Repression of genes by DNA methylation depends on CpG density and promoter strength: evidence for involvement of a methyl-CpG binding protein. *EMBO J.* **11:** 327–333.

Breathnach R, Chambon P. (1981) Organization and expression of eukaryotic split genes coding for proteins. *Ann. Rev. Biochem.* **50:** 349–383.

Britten RJ, Baron WF, Stout DB, Davidson EH. (1988) Sources and evolution of human Alu repeated sequences. *Proc. Natl. Acad. Sci. USA* **85:** 4770–4774.

Britten RJ, Stout DB, Davidson EH. (1989) The current source of human Alu retroposons is a conserved gene shared with Old World monkey. *Proc. Natl. Acad. Sci. USA* **86:** 3718–3722.

Brown WM, Prager EM, Wang A, Wilson AC. (1982) Mitochondrial DNA sequences in primates: tempo and mode of evolution. *J. Mol. Evol.* **18:** 225–239.

Brown WRA, Bird AP. (1986) Long-range restriction site mapping of mammalian genomic DNA. *Nature* **322:** 477–481.

Cedar H, Razin A. (1990) DNA methylation and development. *Biochim. Biophys. Acta* **1049:** 1–8.

Cooper DN. (1983) Eukaryotic DNA methylation. *Hum. Genet.* **64:** 315–333.

Cooper DN, Schmidtke J. (1984) DNA restriction fragment length polymorphisms and heterozyosity in the human genome. *Hum. Genet.* **66:** 1–16.

Cooper DN, Schmidtke J. (1991) Diagnosis of human genetic disease using recombinant DNA. Third edition. *Hum. Genet.* **87:** 519–560.

Cooper DN, Taggart MH, Bird AP. (1983) Unmethylated domains in vertebrate DNA. *Nucleic Acids Res.* **11:** 647–658.

Cooper DN, Smith BA, Cooke HJ, Niemann S, Schmidtke J. (1985) An estimate of unique DNA sequence heterozygosity in the human genome. *Hum. Genet.* **69:** 201–205.

Cooper DN, Youssoufian H. (1988) The CpG dinucleotide and human genetic disease. *Hum. Genet.* **78:** 151–155.

Coulondre J, Miller JH, Farabaugh PJ, Gilbert W. (1978) Molecular basis of base substitution hotspots in *Escherichia coli. Nature* **274:** 775–780.

Daniels GR, Deininger PL. (1985) Integration site preferences of the Alu family and similar repetitive DNA sequences. *Nucleic Acids Res.* **13:** 8939–8954.

Deininger PL, Slagel VK. (1988) Recently amplified Alu family members share a common parental Alu sequence. *Mol. Cell. Biol.* **8:** 4566–4569.

Den Dunnen JT, Grootscholten PM, Bakker E, Blonden LAJ, Ginjaar HB, Wapenaar MC, van Paassen MC, van Broeckhoven C, Pearson PL, van Ommen GJB. (1989) Topography of the Duchenne muscular dystrophy (DMD) gene: FIGE and cDNA analysis of 194 cases reveals 115 deletions and 13 duplications. *Am. J. Hum. Genet.* **45:** 835–847.

Den Dunnen JT, Grootscholten PM, Dauwerse JG, Walker AP, Monaco AP, Butler R, Anand R, Coffey AJ, Bentley DR, Steensma HY, van Ommen GJB. (1992) Reconstruction of the 2.4 Mb human DMD gene by homologous YAC recombination. *Hum. Mol. Genet.* **1:** 19–28.

Deragon J-M, Sinnett D, Labuda D. (1990) Reverse transcriptase activity from human embryonal carcinoma cells NTera2D1. *EMBO J.* **9:** 3363–3368.

Doerfler W, Toth M, Kochanek S, Achten S, Freisem-Rabien U, Behn-Krappa A, Orend G. (1990) Eukaryotic DNA methylation: facts and problems. *FEBS Lett* **268:** 329–333.

Duncan BK, Miller JH. (1980) Mutagenic deamination of cytosine residues in DNA. *Nature* **287:** 560–561.

Dynan WS. (1987) DNase I footprinting as an assay for mammalian gene regulatory proteins. pp. 75-87. In *Genetic Engineering. Principles and Methods.* Vol. 9 (ed. JK Setlow). Plenum Press, New York.

Echols H, Goodman MF. (1991) Fidelity mechanisms in DNA replication. *Ann. Rev. Biochem.* **60:** 477–511.

Faisst S, Meyer S. (1992) Compilation of vertebrate-encoded transcription factors. *Nucleic Acids Res.* **20:** 3–26.

Fanning TG, Singer MF. (1987) LINE-1: a mammalian transposable element. *Biochim. Biophys. Acta* **910:** 203–212.

Freemont PS, Lane AN, Sanderson MR. (1991) Structural aspects of protein–DNA recognition. *Biochem. J.* **278:** 1–23.

García-Blanco MA, Jamison SF, Sharp PA. (1989) Identification and purification of a 62 000-dalton protein that binds specifically to the polypyrimidine tract of introns. *Genes Dev.* **3:** 1874–1886.

Gardiner K, Horisberger M, Kraus J, Tantravahi U, Korenberg J, Rao V, Reddy S, Patterson D. (1990) Analysis of human chromosome 21: correlation of physical and cytogenetic maps; gene and CpG island distributions. *EMBO J.* **9:** 25–34.

Gardiner-Garden M, Frommer M. (1987) CpG islands in vertebrate genomes. *J. Mol. Biol.* **196:** 261–282.

Gerke V, Steitz JA. (1986) A protein associated with small nuclear ribonucleoprotein particles recognizes the 3′ splice site of premessenger RNA. *Cell* **47:** 973–984.

Ghazi H, Gonzales FA, Jones PA. (1992) Methylation of CpG island-containing genes in human sperm, fetal and adult tissues. *Gene* **114:** 203–210.

Goguel V, Liao X, Rymond BC, Rosbash M. (1991) U1 snRNP can influence 3′-splice site selection as well as 5′-splice site selection. *Genes Dev.* **5:** 1430–1438.

Green MR. (1986) Pre-mRNA splicing. *Ann. Rev. Genet.* **20:** 671–708.

Grosse F, Krauss G, Knill-Jones JW, Ferscht AR. (1983) Accuracy of DNA polymerase α in copying natural DNA. *EMBO J.* **2:** 1515–1519.

Guthrie C, Patterson B. (1988) Spliceosomal snRNAs. *Ann. Rev. Genet.* **22:** 387–419.

Hardman N. (1986) Structure and function of repetitive DNA in eukaryotes. *Biochem. J.* **234:** 1–11.

Hare JT, Taylor JH. (1988) Hemi-methylation dictates strand selection in repair of G/T and A/ C mismatches in SV40. *Gene* **74:** 159-161.

Hargrove JL, Schmidt FH. (1989) The role of mRNA and protein stability in gene expression. *FASEB J.* **3:** 2360-2370.

Hattori M, Kuhara S, Takenaka O, Sakaki Y. (1986) L1 family of repetitive DNA sequences in primates may be derived from a sequence encoding a reverse-transcriptase-related protein. *Nature* **321:** 625-628.

Hawkins JD. (1988) A survey on intron and exon lengths. *Nucleic Acids Res.* **16:** 9893-9908.

Hentze MW. (1991) Determinants and regulation of cytoplasmic mRNA stability in eukaryotic cells. *Biochim. Biophys. Acta* **1090:** 281-292.

Hodges-Garcia Y, Hagerman PJ. (1992) Cytosine methylation can induce local distortions in the structure of duplex DNA. *Biochemistry* **31:** 7595-7599.

Hwu HR, Roberts JW, Davidson EH, Britten RJ. (1986) Insertion and/or deletion of many repeated DNA sequences in human and higher ape evolution. *Proc. Natl. Acad. Sci. USA* **83:** 3875-3879.

Jackson ME. (1991) Negative regulation of eukaryotic transcription. *J. Cell Sci.* **100:** 1-7.

Jeffreys A. (1987) Highly variable minisatellites and DNA fingerprints. *Biochem. Soc. Trans.* **15:** 309-317.

Jeffreys AJ, Royle NJ, Wilson V, Wong Z. (1988) Spontaneous mutation rates to new length alleles at tandem-repetitive hypervariable loci in human DNA. *Nature* **332:** 278-281.

Jelinek WR, Schmid CW. (1982) Repetitive sequences in eukaryotic DNA and their expression. *Ann. Rev. Biochem.* **51:** 813-844.

Jensen S, Heidmann T. (1991) An indicator gene for detection of germline retrotransposition in transgenic *Drosophila* demonstrates RNA-mediated transposition of the LINE 1 element. *EMBO J.* **10:** 1927-1937.

Johnson PF, McKnight SL. (1989) Eukaryotic transcriptional regulatory proteins. *Ann. Rev. Biochem.* **58:** 799-839.

Jost J-P, Saluz H-P, Pawlak A. (1991) Estradiol down regulates the binding activity of an avian vitellogenin gene repressor (MDBP-2) and triggers a gradual demethylation of the mCpG pair of its DNA binding site. *Nucleic Acids Res.* **19:** 5771-5775.

Jurka J, Smith T. (1988) A fundamental division in the Alu family of repeated sequences. *Proc. Natl. Acad. Sci. USA* **85:** 4775-4778.

Kan YW, Dozy AM. (1978a) Polymorphism of DNA sequence adjacent to the human β-globin structural gene: relationship to sickle mutation. *Proc. Natl. Acad. Sci. USA* **75:** 5631-5635.

Kan YW, Dozy AM. (1978b) Antenatal diagnosis of of sickle-cell anemia by DNA analysis of amniotic fluid cells. *Lancet* **ii:** 910-912.

Kariya Y, Kato K, Hayashizaki Y, Himeno S, Tarui S, Matsubara K. (1987) Revision of consensus sequence of human Alu repeats — a review. *Gene* **53:** 1-10.

Kolsto AB, Kallias G, Giguere V, Isobe KI, Prydz H, Grosveld F. (1986) The maintenance of methylation-free islands in transgenic mice. *Nucleic Acids Res.* **14:** 9667-9677.

Konarska MM, Sharp PA. (1987) Interactions between small ribonucleoprotein particles in the formation of spliceosomes. *Cell* **49:** 763-774.

Kornberg A, Baker TA. (1992) *DNA Replication*, 2nd Ed. W.H. Freeman, New York.

Krainer AR, Maniatis T. (1985) Multiple factors including the small nuclear ribonucleoproteins U1 and U2 are necessary for pre-mRNA splicing *in vitro*. *Cell* **42:** 725-736.

Krainer AR, Maniatis T. (1988) RNA splicing. In: *Transcription and Splicing* (eds BD Hames, DM Glover). IRL Press, Oxford, pp. 131-206.

Kunkel TA. (1985a) The mutational specificity of DNA polymerase β during *in vitro* DNA synthesis. *J. Biol. Chem.* **260:** 5787-5796.

Kunkel TA. (1985b) The mutational specificity of DNA polymerases α and γ during *in vitro* DNA synthesis. *J. Biol. Chem.* **260:** 12866-12874.

Kunkel TA. (1986) Frameshift mutagenesis by eucaryotic DNA polymerases *in vitro*. *J. Biol. Chem.* **261:** 13581-13587.

Kunkel TA. (1988) Exonucleolytic proofreading. *Cell* **53:** 837-840.

Kunkel TA. (1990) Misalignment-mediated DNA synthesis errors. *Biochemistry* **29:** 8003-8011.

Kunkel TA. (1992) DNA replication fidelity. *J. Biol. Chem.* **267:** 18251–18254.

Kunkel TA, Alexander PS. (1986) The base substitution fidelity of eucaryotic DNA polymerases. *J. Biol. Chem.* **261:** 160–166.

Kunkel TA, Bebenek K. (1988) Recent studies of the fidelity of DNA synthesis. *Biochim. Biophys. Acta* **951:** 1–15.

Kunkel TA, Soni A. (1988) Mutagenesis by transient misalignment. *J. Biol. Chem.* **263:** 14784–14789.

Kunkel TA, Sabatino RD, Bambara RA. (1987) Exonucleolytic proofreading by calf thymus DNA polymerase ∂. *Proc. Natl. Acad. Sci. USA* **84:** 4865–4869.

Kunz BA. (1982) Genetic effects of deoxyribonucleotide pool imbalances. *Environ. Mutagen.* **4:** 695–725.

Kunz BA, Kohalmi SE. (1991) Modulation of mutagenesis by deoxyribonucleotide levels. *Ann. Rev. Genet.* **25:** 339–359.

Kuo H-C, Nasim FH, Grabowski PJ. (1991) Control of alternative splicing by the differential binding of U1 small nuclear ribonuclearprotein particle. *Science* **251:** 1045–1050.

Lai M-D, Beattie KL. (1988) Influence of DNA sequence on the nature of mispairing during DNA synthesis. *Biochemistry* **27:** 1722–1728.

Larsen F, Gundersen G, Lopez R, Prydz H. (1992) CpG islands as gene markers in the human genome. *Genomics* **13:** 1095–1107.

Latchman DS. (1990) Eukaryotic transcription factors. *Biochem. J.* **270:** 281–289.

Lerner MR, Boyle JA, Mount SM, Wolin SL, Steitz JA. (1980) Are snRNPs involved in splicing? *Nature* **283:** 220–224.

Levine M, Manley JL. (1989) Transcriptional repression of eukaryotic promoters. *Cell* **59:** 405–408.

Levine A, Cantoni GL, Razin A. (1991) Inhibition of promoter activity by methylation: possible involvement of protein mediators. *Proc. Natl. Acad. Sci. USA* **88:** 6515–6518.

Lewis J, Bird A. (1991) DNA methylation and chromatin structure. *FEBS Letts.* **285:** 155–159.

Li E, Bestor TH, Jaenisch R. (1992) Targeted mutation of the DNA methyltransferase gene results in embryonic lethality. *Cell* **69:** 915–926.

Lindsay S, Bird AP. (1987) Use of restriction enzymes to select potential gene sequences in mammalian DNA. *Nature* **327:** 336–338.

Linn S. (1991) How many pols does it take to replicate nuclear DNA? *Cell* **66:** 185–187.

Lührmann R, Kastner B, Bach M. (1990) Structure of spliceosomal snRNPs and their role in pre-mRNA splicing. *Biochim. Biophys. Acta* **1087:** 265–292.

Mancuso DJ, Tuley EA, Westfield LA, Worrall NK, Shelton-Inloes BB, Sorace JM, Alevy YG, Sadler JE. (1989) Structure of the gene for human von Willebrand factor. *J. Biol. Chem.* **264:** 19514–19527.

Maniatis T, Goodbourn S, Fischer JA. (1987) Regulation of inducible and tissue-specific gene expression. *Science* **236:** 1237–1244.

Matera AG, Hellmann U, Hintz MF, Schmid CW. (1990a) Recently transposed Alu repeats result from multiple source genes. *Nucleic Acids Res.* **18:** 6019–6023.

Matera AG, Hellmann U, Schmid CW. (1990b) A transpositionally and transcriptionally competent Alu subfamily. *Mol. Cell. Biol.* **10:** 5424–5432.

Mathews CK, Ji J. (1992) DNA precursor asymmetries, replication fidelity and variable genome evolution. *Bioessays* **14:** 295–301.

Mathias SL, Scott AF, Kazazian HH, Boeke JD, Gabriel A. (1991) Reverse transcriptase encoded by a human transposable element. *Science* **254:** 1808–1810.

Meehan RR, Lewis JD, McKay S, Kleiner EL, Bird AP. (1989) Identification of a mammalian protein that binds specifically to DNA containing methylated CpGs. *Cell* **58:** 499–507.

Mendelman LV, Petruska J, Goodman MF. (1990) Base mispair extension kinetics. *J. Biol. Chem.* **265:** 2338–2346.

Meuth M. (1989) The molecular basis of mutations induced by deoxyribonucleoside triphosphate pool imbalances in mammalian cells. *Exp. Cell Res.* **181:** 305–316.

Miesfeld RL. (1989) The structure and function of steroid receptor proteins. *CRC Crit. Rev.*

Biochem. **24**: 101–117.

Mitchell PJ, Tjian R. (1989) Transcriptional regulation in mammalian cells by sequence-specific DNA binding proteins. *Science* **245**: 371–378.

Miyata T, Hayashida H, Kikuno R, Hasegawa M, Kobayashi M, Koike K. (1982) Molecular clock of silent substitution: at least six-fold preponderance of silent changes in mitochondrial genes over those in nuclear genes. *J. Mol. Evol.* **19**: 28–35.

Modrich P. (1987) DNA mismatch correction. *Ann. Rev. Biochem.* **56**: 435–466.

Monk M. (1988) Genomic imprinting. *Genes Dev.* **2**: 921–925.

Monk M, Boubelik M, Lehnert S. (1987) Temporal and regional changes in DNA methylation in the embryonic, extraembryonic and germ cell lineages during mouse embryo development. *Development* **99**: 371–382.

Mount SM. (1982) A catalogue of splice junction sequences. *Nucleic Acids Res.* **10**: 459–472.

Mount SM, Pettersson I, Hinterberger M, Karmas A, Steitz JA. (1983) The U1 small nuclear RNA-protein complex selectively binds a 5′ splice site *in vitro*. *Cell* **33**: 509–518.

Müller MM, Gerster T, Schaffner W. (1988) Enhancer sequences and the regulation of gene transcription. *Eur. J. Biochem.* **176**: 485–495.

Nadal-Ginard B, Gallego ME, Andreadis A. (1987) Alternative splicing: mechanistic and biological implications of generating multiple proteins from a single gene. In: *Genetic Engineering. Principles and Methods*, Vol. 9 (ed. JK Setlow). Plenum Press, New York.

Nelson KK, Green MR. (1988) Splice site selection and ribonucleoprotein complex assembly during *in vitro* pre-mRNA splicing. *Genes Dev.* **2**: 319–329.

Nelson KK, Green MR. (1989) Mammalian U2 snRNP has a sequence-specific RNA-binding activity. *Genes Dev.* **3**: 1562–1571.

Newman AJ, Norman C. (1992) U5 snRNA interacts with exon sequences at 5′ and 3′ splice sites. *Cell* **68**: 743–754.

Nussinov R. (1981) Eukaryotic dinucleotide preference rules and their implications for degenerate codon usage. *J. Mol. Biol.* **149**: 125–131.

O'Brien RM, Granner DK. (1991) Regulation of gene expression by insulin. *Biochem. J.* **278**: 609–619.

Ohshima Y, Gotoh Y. (1987) Signals for the selection of a splice site in pre-mRNA: computer analysis of splice junction sequences and like sequences. *J. Mol. Biol.* **195**: 247–259.

Padgett RA, Konarska MM, Aebi M, Hornig H, Weissmann C, Sharp PA. (1985) Non-consensus branch-site sequences in the *in vitro* splicing of transcripts of mutant rabbit β-globin genes. *Proc. Natl. Acad. Sci. USA* **82**: 8349–8353.

Padgett RA, Grabowski PJ, Konarska MM, Seiler S, Sharp PA. (1986) Splicing of messenger RNA precursors. *Ann. Rev. Biochem.* **55**: 1119–1150.

Pakula AA, Sauer RT. (1989) Genetic analysis of protein stability and function. *Ann. Rev. Genet.* **23**: 289–310.

Pfeifer GP, Steigerwald SD, Hansen RS, Gartler SM, Riggs AD. (1990) Polymerase chain reaction-aided genomic sequencing of an X chromosome-linked CpG island: methylation patterns suggest clonal inheritance, CpG site autonomy and an explanation of activity state stability. *Proc. Natl. Acad. Sci. USA* **87**: 8252–8256.

Razin A. (1984) DNA methylation patterns: formation and biological functions. In: *DNA Methylation: Biochemistry and Biological Significance* (eds A Razin, H Cedar, AD Riggs). Springer-Verlag, New York.

Razin A, Szyf M, Kafri T, Roll M, Giloh H, Scarpa S, Carotti D, Cantoni GL. (1986) Replacement of 5-methylcytosine by cytosine: a possible mechanism for transient DNA demethylation during differentiation. *Proc. Natl. Acad. Sci. USA* **83**: 2827–2831.

Revzin A. (1989) Gel electrophoresis assays for DNA–protein interactions. *Biotechniques* **7**: 346–355.

Ripley LS. (1990) Frameshift mutation: determinants of specificity. *Ann. Rev. Genet.* **24**: 189–213.

Robberson BL, Cote GJ, Berget SM. (1990) Exon definition may facilitate splice site selection in RNAs with multiple exons. *Mol. Cell. Biol.* **10**: 84–94.

Roberts RG, Coffey AJ, Bobrow M, Bentley DR. (1992) Determination of the exon structure of the distal portion of the dystrophin gene by vectorette PCR. *Genomics* **13**: 942–950.

Rogers J, Wall R. (1980) A mechanism for RNA splicing. *Proc. Natl. Acad. Sci. USA* **77**: 1877–1879.

Rosenthal N. (1987) Identification of regulatory elements of cloned genes with functional assays. *Methods Enzymol.* **152**: 704–720.

Ross J. (1988) Messenger RNA turnover in eukaryotic cells. *Mol. Biol. Med.* **5**: 1–14.

Ruskin B, Greene JM, Green MR. (1985) Cryptic branch point activation allows accurate *in vitro* splicing of human β-globin intron mutants. *Cell* **41**: 833–844.

Ruskin B, Zamore PD, Green MR. (1988) A factor, U2AF, is required for U2 snRNP binding and splicing complex assembly. *Cell* **52**: 207–219.

Saffer JD, Thurston SJ. (1989) A negative regulatory element with properties similar to those of enhancers is contained within an Alu sequence. *Mol. Cell. Biol.* **9**: 355–364.

Saluz HP, Jiricny J, Jost JP. (1986) Genomic sequencing reveals a positive correlation between the kinetics of strand-specific DNA demethylation of the overlapping estradiol/glucocorticoid-receptor binding sites and the rate of avian vitellogenin mRNA synthesis. *Proc. Natl. Acad. Sci. USA* **83**: 7167–7171.

Samuels HH, Forman BM, Horowitz ZD, Ye Z-S. (1988) Regulation of gene expression by thyroid hormone. *J. Clin. Invest.* **81**: 957–967.

Savatier P, Trabuchet G, Fauré C, Cheblouré Y, Gouy M, Verdier G, Nigon VM. (1985) Evolution of the primate β-globin gene region: high rate of variation in CpG dinucleotides and in short repeated sequences between man and chimpanzee. *J. Mol. Biol.* **182**: 21–29.

Schorderet DF, Gartler SM. (1992) Analysis of CpG suppression in methylated and nonmethylated species. *Proc. Natl. Acad. Sci. USA* **89**: 957–961.

Scott AF, Schmeckpeper BJ, Abdelrazik M, Comey CT, O'Hara B, Rossiter JP, Cooley T, Heath P, Smith KD, Margolet L. (1987) Origin of the human L1 elements: proposed progenitor genes deduced from a consensus DNA sequence. *Genomics* **1**: 113–125.

Selker EV, Stevens JN. (1985) DNA methylation at asymmetric sites is associated with numerous transition mutations. *Proc. Natl. Acad. Sci. USA* **82**: 8114–8118.

Shapiro MB, Senapathy P. (1987) RNA splice junctions of different classes of eukaryotes: sequence statistics and functional implications in gene expression. *Nucleic Acids Res.* **15**: 7155–7174.

Shelley CS, Baralle FE. (1987) Deletion analysis of a unique 3′ splice site indicates that alternating guanine and thymine residues represent an efficient splicing signal. *Nucleic Acids Res.* **15**: 3787–3799.

Shirai T, Shiojiri S, Ito H, Yamamoto S, Kusumoto H, Deyashika Y, Maruyama I, Suzuki K. (1988) Gene structure of human thrombomodulin, a cofactor for thrombin-catalysed activation of protein C. *J. Biochem.* **103**: 281–285.

Shoffner JM, Wallace DC. (1990) Oxidative phosphorylation diseases. Disorders of two genomes. *Adv. Hum. Genet.* **19**: 267–330.

Silva AJ, White R. (1988) Inheritance of allelic blueprints for methylation patterns. *Cell* **54**: 145–152.

Sinnett D, Richer C, Deragon J-M, Labuda D. (1992) Alu RNA transcripts in human embryonal carcinoma cells. *J. Mol. Biol.* **226**: 689–706.

Skowronski J, Singer MF. (1985) Expression of a cytoplasmic LINE-1 transcript is regulated in a human teratocarcinoma cell line. *Proc. Natl. Acad. Sci. USA* **82**: 6050–6054.

Skowronski J, Singer MF. (1986) The abundant LINE-1 family of repeated DNA sequences in mammals: genes and pseudogenes. *Cold Spring Harb. Symp. Quant. Biol.* **51**: 457–464.

Skowronski J, Fanning TG, Singer MF. (1988) Unit-length LINE-1 transcripts in human teratocarcinoma cells. *Mol. Cell. Biol.* **8**: 1385–1397.

Smith SS, Kaplan BE, Sowers LC, Newman EM. (1992) Mechanism of human methyl-directed DNA methyltransferase and the fidelity of cytosine methylation. *Proc. Natl. Acad. Sci. USA* **89**: 4744–4748.

Stephens JC, Cavanaugh ML, Gradie MI, Mador ML, Kidd KK. (1990) Mapping the human genome: current status. *Science* **250:** 237–244.

Stolow DT, Berget SM. (1991) Identification of nuclear proteins that specifically bind to RNAs containing 5′ splice sites. *Proc. Natl. Acad. Sci. USA* **88:** 320–324.

Swergold GD. (1990) Identification, characterization and cell specificity of a human LINE-1 promoter. *Mol. Cell. Biol.* **10:** 6718–6729.

Talerico M, Berget SM. (1990) Effect of 5′ splice site mutations on splicing of the preceding intron. *Mol. Cell. Biol.* **10:** 6299–6305.

Taylor JH. (1984) *DNA Methylation and Cellular Differentiation.* Springer, Vienna.

Tazi J, Alibert C, Temsamani J, Reveillaud I, Cathala G, Brunel C, Jeanteur P. (1986) A protein that specifically recognizes the 3′ splice site of mammalian pre-mRNA introns is associated with a small nuclear ribonuclearprotein. *Cell* **47:** 755–766.

Thomas DC, Roberts JD, Sabatino RD, Myers TW, Tan C-K, Downey KM, So AG, Bambara RA, Kunkel TA. (1991) Fidelity of mammalian DNA replication and replicative DNA polymerases. *Biochemistry* **30:** 11751–11759.

Toth M, Lichtenberg U, Doerfler W. (1989) Genomic sequencing reveals a 5-methylcytosine-free domain in active promoters and the spreading of preimposed methylation patterns. *Proc. Natl. Acad. Sci. USA* **86:** 3728–3732.

Trasler JM, Hake LE, Johnson PA, Alcivar AA, Millette CF, Hecht NB. (1990) DNA methylation and demethylation events during meiotic prophase in the mouse testis. *Mol. Cell. Biol.* **10:** 1828–1834.

Turker MS, Swisshelm K, Smith AC, Martin GM. (1989) A partial methylation profile for a CpG site is stably maintained in mammalian tissues and cultured cell lines. *J. Biol. Chem.* **264:** 11632–11636.

Ullu E, Tschudi C. (1984) Alu sequences are processed 7SL RNA genes. *Nature* **312:** 171–172.

Vogel F, Motulsky AG. (1986) *Human Genetics — Problems and Approaches,* 2nd Edn. Springer, Berlin.

Vogt P. (1990) Potential genetic functions of tandem repeated DNA sequence blocks in the human genome are based on a highly conserved 'chromatin folding code'. *Hum. Genet.* **84:** 301–336.

Wallace DC, Ye JH, Neckelman SN, Singh G, Webster KA, Greenberg BD. (1987) Sequence analysis of cDNAs for the human and bovine ATP synthase β subunit: mitochondrial DNA genes sustain seventeen times more mutations. *Curr. Genet.* **12:** 81–90.

Wallace DC, Lott MT, Torroni A, Shoffner JM. (1991) The human mitochondrial DNA. *Cytogenet. Cell Genet.* **58:** 1103–1123.

Wang T S-F. (1991) Eukaryotic DNA polymerases. *Ann. Rev. Biochem.* **60:** 513–552.

Wasylyk B. (1988) Enhancers and transcription factors in the control of gene expression. *Biochim. Biophys. Acta* **951:** 17–35.

Weiner AM, Deininger PL, Efstratiadis A. (1986) Nonviral retroposons: genes, pseudogenes and transposable elements generated by the reverse flow of genetic information. *Ann. Rev. Biochem.* **55:** 631–661.

Williamson R, Bowcock A, Kidd K, Pearson P, Schmidtke J, Ceverha P, Chipperfield M, Cooper DN, Coutelle C, Hewitt J, Klinger K, Langley K, Beckmann J, Tolley M, Maidak B. (1991) Report of the DNA Committee and catalogues of cloned and mapped genes, markers formatted for PCR and DNA polymorphisms. *Cytogenet. Cell Genet.* **58:** 1190–1832.

Woodcock DM, Crowther PJ, Diver WP. (1987) The majority of methylated deoxycytidines in human DNA are not in the CpG dinucleotide. *Biochem. Biophys. Res. Commun.* **145:** 888–894.

Wu J, Manley JL. (1989) Mammalian pre-mRNA branch site selection by U2 snRNP involves base pairing. *Genes Dev.* **3:** 1553–1561.

Zhuang Y, Weiner AM. (1989) A compensatory base change in human U2 snRNA can suppress a branch site mutation. *Genes Dev.* **3:** 1545–1552.

Zhuang Y, Goldstein AM, Weiner AM. (1989) UACUAAC is the preferred branch site for mammalian mRNA splicing. *Proc. Natl. Acad. Sci. USA* **86:** 2752–2756.

Human genetic disease, its analysis and diagnosis: an overview

3.1 The problem in its perspective

The majority of people living in societies with a high individual life expectancy will sooner or later suffer from a disease in which genetic lesions have played a major causative role. Over 4000 different Mendelian disorders or traits have been described in which genetic factors are directly involved (McKusick, 1990). It is estimated that one in 30 children is born with a genetic handicap as defined by an inborn error of metabolism, a congenital malformation, or mental and physical retardation (Harper, 1984; Baird *et al.*, 1988). About 0.7% of all newborns have a chromosome abnormality (Jacobs *et al.*, 1974) while around 1% are carriers of a genetic disease caused by a single gene mutation (approximately 0.5–1% autosomal dominant, 0.2% autosomal recessive, and 0.1% sex-linked; Baird *et al.*, 1988; Lenz, 1990). The remainder of congenital disease states are not associated with a chromosome aberration and do not follow any clear Mendelian pattern of inheritance. It is nevertheless probable that, in many of these conditions, genetic factors play an important role. These diseases have been variously called polygenic or multifactorial although it is not usually known how many genetic loci are involved or how they interact with environmental factors.

Some Mendelian disorders are not immediately apparent at birth but manifest themselves during childhood (e.g. Duchenne muscular dystrophy), adolescence (various kinds of hypogonadism), or even much later in life (e.g. Huntington disease, polycystic kidney disease, Alzheimer disease). The same is true for many types of multifactorial disease which can either be present at birth (the majority of common malformations such as congenital heart disease, spina bifida, hip joint dislocation), or become apparent later in life (e.g. diabetes mellitus, epilepsy, psychotic disorders). Many types of malignant tumour disease probably also fall into this category, although a number of tumour-predisposing conditions are inherited in clear Mendelian fashion

(Harper, 1984). Recombinant DNA technology has made an important contribution to our understanding of the role of genetic factors in the aetiology of spontaneous, multifactorial and Mendelian tumour diseases (reviewed by Caskey, 1987; Antonarakis, 1989).

If all disorders are considered in which genetic factors play at least a partial role, almost everyone in developed countries will at one point or another during their lifetime be affected by such a disease. Most of these conditions are serious enough to affect quite drastically the course of life of the patient and that of members of their immediate family. Usually, therapeutic measures are either not available or are likely to be of only limited utility; chronic illness and a shortened life expectancy tend to be the rule. Thus, although most genetic diseases are individually infrequent, together they constitute a huge health problem with which our societies (and their economies) have to cope. It is obvious that the application of diagnostic testing and the management of genetically based or co-influenced disorders is an important issue at the level of both the individual and society.

Recombinant DNA technology has made possible the study of genetic disease at the level of the primary lesion (whether in chromosomal or mito-chondrial DNA) and the *in vitro* expression of both normal and mutant genetic information at the mRNA and protein levels. Undoubtedly, the most immediate practical spin-off from recombinant DNA technology in medical genetics has been in the sphere of improved disease diagnosis, where advances have been very dramatic (Cooper and Schmidtke, 1991; Appendix 1). Indeed, molecular genetics is now an indispensable tool of modern pathology. In combination with no less impressively advanced techniques in protein biochemistry, cell biology and immunology, the foundations have now been laid upon which to build a thorough understanding of the processes of disease pathogenesis. Such an understanding will potentiate the correction of inherited gene defects through the introduction of novel therapies.

Disease diagnosis is an essential basis for causal therapy, and pre-symptomatic diagnosis is in many instances a prerequisite for successful treatment or prevention. The ability to detect presymptomatically a disease which is at present not amenable to therapy may, however, present serious ethical problems. If screening of the general population is envisaged, whether for treatment or for genetic counselling purposes, the problems are further multiplied (Fost, 1992; Holtzman, 1992). Knowledge of the disease susceptibility of an individual may be misused in terms of employment opportunities or access to health and life insurance (Billings et al., 1992). Finally, the relative simplicity of the methodology involved and the low cost incurred in prenatal diagnosis may well divert both interest and resources away from curative and social measures. We believe that, in this context, the focus of research attention should be directed toward the analysis of the molecular basis of inherited disease and its cure by substitution or direct somatic gene therapy (Miller, 1992; Roemer and Friedmann, 1992). Disease diagnosis, important as it is, should not be an end in itself.

3.2 The diagnostic setting

The diagnostic setting in medical genetics is basically of two distinct kinds: (i) confirmation/exclusion and (ii) prediction. In the first, a disease may already be suspected in an individual through clinical observation. A DNA test is then employed to confirm or exclude the diagnosis. Ultimate confirmation will, however, only be obtained once the pathological lesion has been detected in the patient. If this is not possible, indirect methods of genotype analysis (see Chapter 5) can provide a very powerful diagnostic tool either on their own or in combination with independent phenotypic tests. The classic example of the use of associated genetic traits is HLA-typing for suspected ankylosing spondylitis: due to the strong association of this disease with the HLA-B27 allele, the *posterior* probability of B27-positive individuals carrying the disease is above 90% even if the *prior* probability after clinical examination was only 50% (Khan and Khan, 1982).

The greater the clinical heterogeneity manifested by a disease, the greater will be the differential diagnostic uncertainty, and the more often will objective confirmation be sought. Myopathies, thrombotic disorders, and disturbances of sexual differentiation are examples of rather frequent conditions in which the correct diagnosis would also greatly affect management, prognosis and reproductive counselling. Of enormous importance, in the latter context, is the ability to distinguish between heritable and non-heritable types of one and the same clinical entity ('phenocopies').

Locus heterogeneity must be considered in a number of disease states. For example, osteogenesis imperfecta types 1 and 2 can both be caused by mutation in either the collagen $\alpha 1(I)$ (COL1A1) or $\alpha 2(I)$ (COL1A2) genes. Molecular genetic analysis in the form of RFLP tracking has permitted the confirmation of disease locus heterogeneity in a number of other conditions. Thus two genetically distinct forms of elliptocytosis, neurofibromatosis, polycystic kidney disease and Waardenburg syndrome have been identified. The chromosomal localization of at least one locus for each distinct disease type has been determined; evidence for the second locus has come either from the establishment of linkage to a locus unlinked to the first or from the absence of co-segregation with the first locus in some families. Three distinct forms of Charcot–Marie–Tooth disease (chromosomes 1, 17 and X) and two forms of tuberous sclerosis (chromosomes 9 and 16) are now recognized, and at least seven different genes are thought to be involved in retinitis pigmentosa [chromosomes 1, 3, 6, 8 and X (three loci)]. Linkage studies can of course also provide evidence for locus homogeneity. Thus the clinically variable conditions Huntington disease and Friedreich ataxia have shown no sign of locus heterogeneity and probably result from the malfunction of a single gene in each case.

Allelic heterogeneity can give rise to considerable phenotypic and clinical heterogeneity. Thus distinct lesions in the COL1A1 gene are responsible for a variety of different conditions, namely osteogenesis imperfecta types I–IV and Ehlers–Danlos syndrome type VIIA. Similarly, mutations in the COL2A1 gene have been found in patients with Stickler syndrome, spondyloepiphyseal dysplasia and osteoarthritis. Allelic heterogeneity can be enormous in some disorders: phenylketonuria (PKU) with around 75 different allelic variants of the phenylalanine hydroxylase (PAH) gene, cystic fibrosis (CF) with over 230 different mutations in the cystic fibrosis transmembrane regulator (CFTR) gene and haemophilia B with over 270 independent point mutations in the factor IX (F9) gene identified to date are three of the more dramatic examples. In PKU, a disease of variable severity, a close correlation often exists between clinical phenotype and PAH genotype, inasmuch as the clinical course is directly related to PAH rest activity; this, in turn, depends on the location and type of the molecular lesion involved (Okano *et al.*, 1991). In CF, genotype–phenotype correlations are far more difficult to establish: clinical heterogeneity cannot simply be attributed to the large number of disease-causing alleles, and hence to the huge number of different compound heterozygotes, since differences in the clinical course of the disease also exist among patients with identical CFTR genotypes (Kerem *et al.*, 1990). It is likely that both environmental factors and the 'genetic background' of the individual, perhaps including genes closely linked to CFTR, play a major role in determining the CF phenotype. By contrast, in haemophilia B, the bleeding severity manifested by patients is usually predictable from the nature of the underlying mutational lesion, although it may still occasionally vary between individuals bearing the same mutation. Lesions in the factor IX gene are very variable in type and location. Known mutations occur in the regions encoding the signal peptide (4), propeptide (5), Gla region (32), EGF1 (22) and EGF2 (19) domains, the activation peptide (29) and catalytic region (126) of the factor IX protein, the promoter (11), and within donor (15), acceptor (11) or cryptic splice sites (4) (Giannelli *et al.*, 1992).

The second diagnostic setting, 'predictive diagnosis', is not altogether novel: high blood pressure, obesity, serum cholesterol levels, family history, behavioural traits and many other features have long been recognized as risk factors and hence predictors of future disease in otherwise apparently healthy individuals. However, the application of recombinant DNA methodology has greatly increased the power and scope of predictive (and preventive) medicine (see Section 5.5). In the absence of possibilities for therapeutic intervention, such advances can be expected to generate all kinds of ethical problems in their wake. Indeed, for many disorders (e.g. Huntington disease, polycystic kidney disease, Alzheimer disease), predictive tests are, or soon will be, available which confer little or no direct therapeutic benefit upon the patient. However, immediate therapy is not the only goal of molecular diagnostic medicine. At-risk individuals who opt for predictive testing for a disease for which no cure currently exists usually emphasize two main reasons: to be able to readjust their lives to the unavoidable prospect of a shortened period of health and/or to be able to plan their social and reproductive lives accordingly. However, counsellees may find themselves trapped in a complicated network of psychological and social pressures to undergo such testing.

3.3 Prenatal diagnosis of genetic disease

3.3.1 Ethical considerations

Another area in which DNA-based techniques are being used at an increasing rate is the prenatal diagnosis of genetic disease (reviewed by Boehm, 1987; Antonarakis, 1989). Although widely employed, prenatal diagnosis also remains an area for ethical concern since, in the absence of therapy, a positive result usually leads to abortion and thus the termination of a human life. In only a very few countries (e.g. Republic of Ireland) is this procedure forbidden by law, but countries with less stringent regulations still differ quite considerably with respect to legally acceptable grounds for termination as well as in the practicalities of the process. Quite apart from the legal situation, parents and doctors are often caught in an unresolvable dilemma, having to decide in whose interest (the family, the mother, the unborn child?) the course of action is being taken. Those who participate in the decision-making process usually agree that, the less 'severe' a disorder appears to them, the more difficult it is to resolve this question. This is of course not a problem introduced by the advent of DNA technology; it had already been encountered when, for example, prenatal cytogenetic analysis revealed a sex chromosome anomaly in a fetus. Nevertheless, both the extent and the severity of the problem are bound to increase markedly since, with the ever-increasing number of diseases amenable to prenatal diagnosis, the proportion of 'less severe' disorders will increase correspondingly. On the other hand, it must be said that prenatal diagnosis of severe genetic disease has been, and will remain, an important tool for those who feel able to participate fully in the decision-making process. Those interested in further discussion of the complex ethical, social and legal issues involved in prenatal diagnosis are referred to reviews by Crawfurd (1983) and Powledge and Fletcher (1979).

3.3.2 Practical approaches

Once analytical techniques had become sufficiently refined to allow 'same-day' diagnosis by direct detection of pathological gene lesions, the attention of those involved in prenatal diagnosis turned to the question of how to obtain fetal material in the necessary quantities at the earliest possible stage in pregnancy. An overview of current possibilities in this field will now be attempted, concentrating on what are seen as the most important of recent advances.

Exclusion diagnosis of X-linked recessive conditions (e.g. Duchenne muscular dystrophy, haemophilia) may be achieved, albeit crudely, by fetal sexing employing polymerase chain reaction (PCR) amplification of DNA repeat sequences which are specific to the human Y chromosome (Kogan et al., 1987). An unsuccessful attempt to carry out PCR-based fetal sexing by the non-invasive approach of examining fetal cells in the maternal circulation was first reported by Adinolfi et al. (1989). These authors concluded that the ratio of fetal to maternal cells in the circulation must be less than 1:70000. Subsequently, Lo *et al.* (1989) increased the detection limit to one fetal cell per 10^7 maternal cells using nested primers and two rounds of PCR amplification (a total of 60 cycles). Nineteen pregnancies of between 9 and 41 weeks' gestation were examined and correct prenatal sex determination was achieved in all cases. These authors, however, emphasized the potential problem of false positive results, which might arise either through the use of too many PCR cycles or if stringent measures were not taken to avoid contamination. A further potential problem of autosomal sequences being homologous to the Y chromosome repeat sequence employed as the PCR target (Nakagome *et al.*, 1990) may be avoided by use of a Y-specific repeat sequence (Holzgreve *et al.*, 1990). A great improvement in this technique has recently been reported by Mueller *et al.*, (1990) who successfully purified fetal trophoblast cells (yield 10–1000 cells) from maternal peripheral blood using murine monoclonal antibodies against human syncytiotrophoblast and non-villus cytotrophoblast cells. Fetal sexing by PCR amplification of Y-specific repeat sequences was confirmed later in pregnancy by the karyotyping of chorionic villus samples.

Sexing of the conceptus before implantation would in principle, by permitting the selection of healthy embryos, avoid the necessity to terminate affected pregnancies. This was first achieved (again by PCR amplification of Y-specific repeat sequences) by analysis of a single cell taken from a 6–10 cell stage embryo 3 days after *in vitro* fertilization (Handyside *et al.*, 1989). This technique has now been successfully used to allow couples known to be at risk of transmitting the X-linked disorders adrenoleukodystrophy and fragile-X linked mental retardation syndrome to give birth to normal offspring (Handyside *et al.*, 1990).

Ideally, a methodologically uniform antenatal diagnostic strategy applicable to a wide range of human genetic diseases would require *in vitro* analysis before implantation. This would involve either direct detection of the genetic lesion responsible for the condition or the indirect tracking of the lesion using linked RFLPs (see Section 5.2) rather than fetal sexing, which is appropriate only for sex-linked disorders. Coutelle *et al.*, (1989) indirectly analysed the genotypes of single human oocytes using RFLPs closely linked to the genes for cystic fibrosis (CF) and Duchenne muscular dystrophy. Monk and Holding (1990) reported the PCR amplification of a segment of the β-globin (HBB) gene directly from unfertilized human oocytes and first polar bodies isolated from them. The success of this approach demonstrated the feasibility of carrying out preconception diagnosis of sickle cell disease and illustrated the potential for circumvention of the ethical–legal difficulties arising from the analysis of early human embryos. Individual sperms can also be analysed in the same way (Li *et al.*, 1988; Liu *et al.*, 1992).

Preconception diagnosis of CF has now been successfully performed (Strom *et al.*, 1990). First polar bodies were removed before fertilization from oocytes obtained under ultrasound guidance. Direct analysis of the common δF508 CFTR gene deletion causing CF has already been accomplished by PCR. In women heterozygous for a genetic disease, the polar body will (in the absence of recombination) be homozygous for the gene not contained in the oocyte from which it was removed. If crossing over has occurred, however, the polar body will be heterozygous and it will not be possible to determine the genotype of the oocyte in this way. This technique was applied to a couple who were known to be heterozygous carriers of CF and an oocyte, found to be abnormal in its polar body, was fertilized. Homozygosity for the δF508 deletion was confirmed by biopsy and PCR analysis at the six-cell stage. The affected pre-embryo was then frozen at the blastocyst stage. Further applications of this technology are to be found in Verlinsky *et al.* (1992). It is not unreasonable to suppose that, before too long, such techniques will begin to enter the realms of routine analysis for a wide range of human inherited disorders.

3.4 Progress in gene cloning and mapping the human genome

DNA-based strategies of disease analysis, gene cloning, and mapping the human genome are clearly interdependent processes (reviewed by Smith and Hood, 1987). One of our strongest motives in attempting to understand the structure and function of the human genome is the expectation that new advances, both practical and conceptual, will find applications in the field of diagnostic medicine. Conversely, the study of the molecular basis of inherited disease is expected to provide fundamental insights into the 'normal' function of the genome and the interaction of its component elements.

The data collated in Appendix 1 illustrate how disease analysis and genome mapping have developed in scale over the last few years. These data have been taken from the DNA Committee reports of the proceedings of the Human Gene Mapping Workshops, held every 2 years (Kidd *et al.*, 1989; Williamson *et al.*, 1991) as well as from our own database (Cooper and Schmidtke, 1991). Over the last 8 years, the number of cloned and chromosomally mapped DNA markers has approximately doubled every 2 years and has thus increased almost 30-fold during this period (Figure 3.1). Over 2000 different protein coding genes have been cloned from the human genome (Schmidtke and Cooper, 1992), a figure which probably represents between 1 and 2% of the total. At present, in excess of 600 genetic markers are PCR-formatted and the vast majority of these are polymorphic. Although the 'classical' genetic polymorphisms are usually made up of two (and occasionally more) alleles per locus, a new class of multi-allelic, and thus highly informative, DNA polymorphisms has now been identified (Beckmann, 1988); these are characterized by variable numbers of short clustered repeat units ('microsatellites'), with sequence motifs of one to five nucleotides and heterozygosities of at least 70% (Williamson *et al.*, 1991; see Section 2.3.1). The availability of microsatellite markers is greatly facilitating genetic mapping and may soon permit genes to be rapidly and regionally localized in the human genome without any prior idea of their chromosomal position.

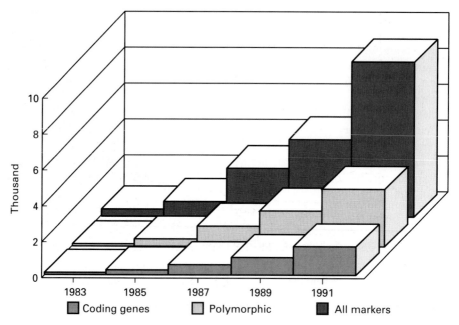

Figure 3.1. Progress made in the cloning of different types of DNA marker from the human genome.

The average spacing of chromosomally assigned DNA polymorphisms known to date is already less than 1 million base-pairs on the human genetic map, corresponding to an average genetic distance of less than 1 cM. However, whereas some chromosome regions are extremely well mapped genetically, most are mapped only at the 5–10 cM level. Currently, the 'mapping community' is attempting to establish a linear order of 'reference markers' for each chromosome with inter-marker distances of between 1 and 5 cM. The most recent genetic linkage map of the human genome consists of 1416 loci including 279 genes or expressed sequences and 339 microsatellite markers; it spans ~92% of the length of the autosomes and ~95% of the length of the X chromosome (NIH/CEPH Collaborative Mapping Group, 1992). Physical maps are also being constructed: highly detailed maps of chromosomes 21q and Y are now available which consist of continuous arrays of overlapping genomic clones derived from human yeast artificial chromosome libraries (Foote *et al.*, 1992; Chumakov *et al.*, 1992). The future integration of the cytogenetic, genetic and physical maps of the human genome into a single highly informative, multi-level map should greatly facilitate the mapping of disease loci of hitherto unknown location and will potentiate the eventual determination of the DNA sequence of each and every human chromosome.

Figure 3.2 illustrates some of the information derived from Appendix 1. It presents on an annual basis the cumulative number of genetic diseases amenable to direct or indirect methods of molecular genetic analysis. There is

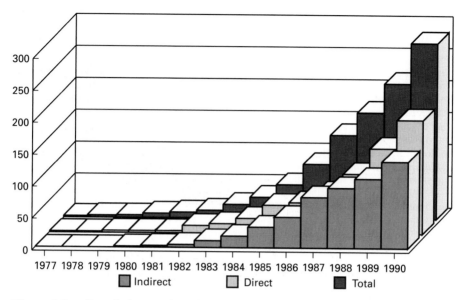

Figure 3.2. Cumulative number of inherited human diseases amenable to DNA-based diagnosis.

no reason to doubt that our ability both to diagnose and to study the aetiology of human genetic disease will continue to grow at the same pace for the foreseeable future.

References

Adinolfi M, Camporese C, Carr T. (1989) Gene amplification to detect fetal nucleated cells in pregnant women. *Lancet* **ii:** 328–329.

Antonarakis SE. (1989) Diagnosis of genetic disorders at the DNA level. *N. Engl. J. Med.* **320:** 153–163.

Baird PA, Anderson TW, Newcombe HB, Lowry RB. (1988) Genetic disorders in children and young adults: a population study. *Am. J. Hum. Genet.* **42:** 677–693.

Beckmann JS. (1988) Oligonucleotide polymorphisms: a new tool for genomic genetics. *Biotechnology* **6:** 1061–1064.

Billings PR, Kohn MA, Cuevas M de, Beckwith J, Alper JS, Natowicz MR. (1992) Discrimination as a consequence of genetic testing. *Am. J. Hum. Genet.* **50:** 476–482.

Boehm CD. (1987) Prenatal diagnosis and carrier detection by DNA analysis. In: *Molecular Genetics in Medicine* (eds B Childs, NA Holtzman, HH Kazazian, DL Valle). Elsevier, New York.

Caskey CT. (1987) Disease diagnosis by recombinant DNA methods. *Science* **236:** 1223–1229.

Chumakov I, Rigault P, Guillou S, Ougen P, Billaut A, Guasconi G, Gervy P, LeGall I, Soularue P, Grinas L, Bougueleret L, Bellanné-Chantelot C, Lacroix B, Barillot E, Gesnouin P, Pook S, Vaysseix G, Frelat G, Schmitz A, Sambucy J-L, Bosch A, Estivill X, Weissenbach J, Vignal A, Riethman H, Cox D, Patterson D, Gardiner K, Hattori M, Sakaki Y, Ichikawa H, Ohki M, Le Paslier D, Heilig R, Antonarakis S, Cohen D. (1992) Continuum of overlapping clones spanning the entire human chromosome 21q. *Nature* **359:** 380–387.

Cooper DN, Schmidtke J. (1991) Diagnosis of human genetic disease using recombinant DNA. Third edition. *Hum. Genet.* **87:** 519–560.

Coutelle C, Williams C, Handyside A. (1989) Genetic analysis of DNA from single human oocytes: a model for pre-implantation diagnosis of cystic fibrosis. *Br. Med. J.* **299:** 22–24.

Crawfurd M. d'A. (1983) Ethical and legal aspects of early prenatal diagnosis. *Br. Med. Bull.* **39:** 310–314.

Foote S, Vollrath D, Hilton A, Page DC. (1992) The human Y chromosome: overlapping DNA clones spanning the euchromatic region. *Science* **258:** 60–66.

Fost N. (1992) Ethical implications of screening asymptomatic individuals. *FASEB J.* **6:** 2813–2817.

Giannelli F, Green PM, High KA, Sommer S, Lillicrap DP, Ludwig M, Olek K, Reitsma PH, Goossens M, Yoshioka A, Brownlee GG. (1992) Haemophilia B: database of point mutations and short additions and deletions — third edition. *Nucleic Acids Res.* **20:** 2027–2063.

Handyside AH, Pattinson JK, Penketh RJA, Delhanty JDA, Winston RML, Tuddenham EGD. (1989) Biopsy of human preimplantation embryos and sexing by DNA amplification. *Lancet* **i:** 347–349.

Handyside AH, Kontogianni EH, Hardy K, Winston RML. (1990) Pregnancies from biopsied human preimplantation embryos sexed by Y-specific DNA amplification. *Nature* **344:** 768–770.

Harper PS. (1984) *Practical Genetic Counselling*, 2nd Edn. John Wright, Bristol.

Holtzman NA. (1992) The diffusion of new genetic tests for predicting disease. *FASEB J.* **6:** 2806–2812.

Holzgreve W, Gaenshirt-Ahlert D, Bwschyk M, Horst J, Miny P, Gal A, Pohlschmidt M. (1990) Detection of fetal DNA in maternal blood by PCR. *Lancet* **335:** 1220.

Jacobs PA, Melville M, Ratcliffe S, Keay AJ, Syme J. (1974) A cytogenetic survey of 11,680 newborn infants. *Ann. Hum. Genet.* **37:** 359–376.

Kerem E, Corey M, Kerem B-S, Rommens J, Markiewicz D, Levison H, Tsui L-C, Durie P. (1990) The relationship between genotype and phenotype in cystic fibrosis — analysis of the most common mutation. (δF508). *N. Engl. J. Med.* **323:** 1517–1522.

Khan MA, Khan MK. (1982) Diagnostic value of HLA-B27 testing in ankylosing spondylitis and Reiter's syndrome. *Ann. Intern Med.* **96:** 70–76.

Kidd KK, Bowcock AM, Schmidtke J, Track RK, Ricciuti F, Hutchings G, Bale A, Pearson P, Willard HF. (1989) Report of the DNA Committee and catalogues of cloned and mapped genes and DNA polymorphisms. *Cytogenet. Cell Genet.* **51:** 622–947.

Kogan SC, Doherty M, Gitschier J. (1987) An improved method for prenatal diagnosis of genetic diseases by analysis of amplified DNA sequences. *N. Engl. J. Med.* **317:** 985–990.

Lenz W. (1990) On the frequency of congenital and inherited disorders. In: *Congenital Malformations and Genetic Disease in Society and Family Today* (eds I Nippert, W. Tünte). Kohlhammer, Stuttgart.

Li H, Gyllensten UB, Cui X, Saiki RK, Erlich HA, Arnheim NA. (1988) Amplification and analysis of DNA sequences in single human sperm and diploid cells. *Nature* **335:** 414–417.

Liu J, Lissens W, Devroey P, Van Steirteghem A, Liebaers I. (1992) Efficiency and accuracy of polymerase chain reaction assay for cystic fibrosis allele δF508 in single cell. *Lancet* **339:** 1190–1192.

Lo Y-M, Patel P, Wainscoat JS, Sampietro M, Gillmer MDG, Fleming KA. (1989) Prenatal sex determination by DNA amplification from maternal peripheral blood. *Lancet* **ii:** 1363–1365.

McKusick VA. (1990) *Mendelian Inheritance in Man*, 9th Edn. Johns Hopkins University Press, Baltimore, Maryland.

Miller AD. (1992) Human gene therapy comes of age. *Nature* **357:** 455–460.

Monk M, Holding C. (1990) Amplification of a β-haemoglobin sequence in individual human oocytes and polar bodies. *Lancet* **335:** 985–988.

Mueller UW, Hawes CS, Wright AE, Petropoulos A, DeBoni E, Firgaira FA, Morley

AA, Turner DR, Jones WR. (1990) Isolation of fetal trophoblast cells from peripheral blood of pregnant women. *Lancet* **336:** 197–200.

Nakagome Y, Nagafuchi S, Nakahori Y. (1990) Prenatal sex determination. *Lancet* **335:** 291.

NIH/CEPH Collaborative Mapping Group. (1992) A comprehensive genetic linkage map of the human genome. *Science* **258:** 67–86.

Okano Y, Eisensmith RC, Güttler F, Lichter-Konecki U, Konecki DS, Trefz FK, Dasovich M, Wang T, Henriksen K, Lou H, Woo SLC. (1991) Molecular basis of phenotypic heterogeneity in phenylketonuria. *N. Engl. J. Med.* **324:** 1232–1238.

Powledge TM, Fletcher J. (1979) Guidelines for the ethical, social and legal issues in prenatal diagnosis. *N. Engl. J. Med.* **300:** 168–172.

Roemer K, Friedmann T. (1992) Concepts and strategies for human gene therapy. *Eur. J. Biochem.* **208:** 211–225.

Schmidtke J, Cooper DN. (1992) A comprehensive list of cloned human DNA sequences — 1991 update. *Nucleic Acids Res.* **20** (Suppl.): 2181–2198.

Smith L, Hood L. (1987) Mapping and sequencing the human genome: how to proceed. *Biotechnology* **5:** 933–939.

Strom CM, Verlinsky Y, Milagera S, Evsikov S, Cieslak J, Lifchez A, Valle J, Moise J, Ginsberg N, Appelbaum M. (1990) Preconception genetic diagnosis of cystic fibrosis. *Lancet* **336:** 306–307.

Verlinsky V, Rechitsky S, Evsikov S, White M, Cieslak J, Lifchez A, Valle J, Moise J, Strom CM. (1992) Preconception and preimplantation diagnosis for cystic fibrosis. *Prenat. Diagn.* **12:** 103–110.

Williamson R, Bowcock A, Kidd K, Pearson P, Schmidtke J, Ceverha P, Chipperfield M, Cooper DN, Coutelle C, Hewitt J, Klinger K, Langley K, Weber J, Beckman J, Tolley M, Maidak B. (1991) Report of the DNA Committee and catalogues of cloned and mapped genes, markers formatted for PCR and DNA polymorphisms. *Cytogenet. Cell Genet.* **58:** 1190–1832.

The methodology of mutation detection

4.1 Southern and Northern blotting

With the discovery of restriction enzymes, site-specific endonucleases that cleave large DNA fragments at defined sites, and with the development of techniques to mass-produce these fragments (DNA cloning), the way was open to analyse the fine structure of human genes and to begin to characterize the genetic lesions underlying inherited disease. The technique of Southern blotting (Southern, 1975) represented a very important milestone on the road to developing the capability to analyse and diagnose human genetic disease directly. Total genomic DNA, isolated from an easily accessible tissue such as blood lymphocytes, is cleaved with a restriction enzyme and transferred from the agarose gel upon which it has been size-fractionated to a porous membrane which serves as a solid support; it may then be challenged with a radiolabelled probe (usually a cloned gene or DNA segment) to reveal the structure of the homologous region of DNA in the genome of both patients and controls (Figure 4.1).

It is a tribute to the power of this technique that it has not been entirely superseded by PCR-based technology. Indeed, Southern blotting may often be used in parallel to PCR/direct sequencing analysis to exclude the deletion or partial deletion of an allele of a given disease gene. Further, the first hint of a gross alteration or rearrangement of a gene will often come from the application of this method and indeed it is this technique to which the majority of known gross gene deletions, insertions and duplications (Cooper and Schmidtke, 1991) owe their detection. Adaptation of the basic technique to include very large DNA fragments by employing pulsed-field gel electrophoresis (Smith et al., 1988a) has permitted the analysis of chromosome deletion syndromes and translocations associated with both genetic and somatic disease at the same time as potentiating the physical mapping of complex gene loci on the chromosome. Further adaptations have extended the use of the technique from agarose to acrylamide (Martinson and Clegg, 1990) suitable for the analysis of very small (< 100 bp) DNA fragments.

Northern blotting, based upon the same principle but adapted for use on RNA (Alwine et al., 1977), is also an important means of studying the pheno-

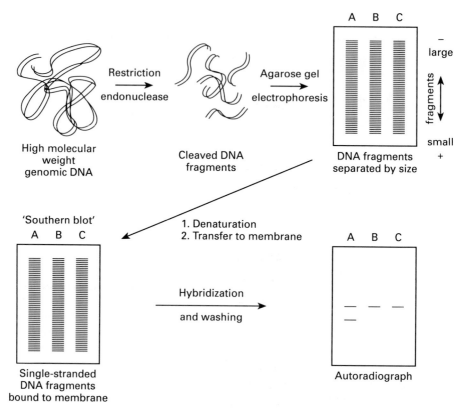

Figure 4.1 The technique of Southern blotting. Shown on the blot are restriction digests from a patient (A) with a given disorder and two controls (B and C). After autoradiography, a novel DNA fragment from the locus of interest, which is not present in the controls, may be noted in the patient.

typic *sequelae* (whether qualitative or quantitative) of a given disease lesion at the RNA level. It may be used as a check for the presence or absence of the mRNA species under study, to examine its stability or to measure the length of the mRNA transcript in order, for example, to seek evidence for exon skipping or cryptic splice site utilization. The accurate and reliable quantitation of increases or decreases in the steady state level of an mRNA species in a given condition is also very important and this is often very difficult to attain by PCR-based means.

4.2 The polymerase chain reaction

In 1985, Saiki *et al.* described an elegant new method which, by circumventing the need to clone specific DNA fragments, has revolutionized the practice of molecular diagnostics. This technique involves the primer-mediated enzymatic *in vitro* amplification of specific target sequences in genomic DNA by repeated

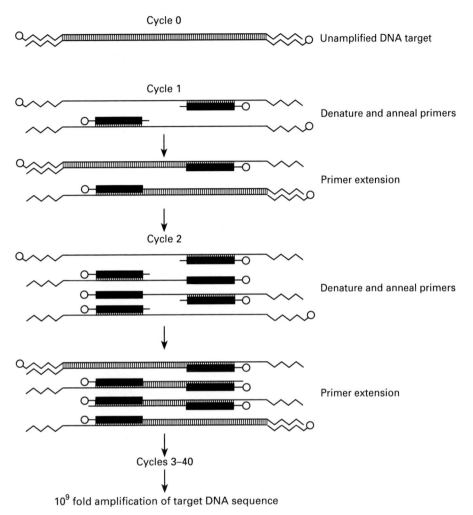

Figure 4.2. The technique of PCR amplification.

cycles of (i) heat denaturation of the double-stranded template, (ii) primer annealing and (iii) extension of the annealed primers with DNA polymerase (Figure 4.2). Target specificity is determined by the choice of short (~ 20 bp) oligonucleotide primers which are designed to hybridize to opposite DNA strands flanking the sequence to be amplified, with their $3'$ ends facing inwards. Successive cycles of amplification result in a continuous doubling of, and exponential increase in, the sequence copy number as newly synthesized copies become available for primer binding. This extremely versatile technique is now well known as the polymerase chain reaction (PCR) and is typically capable of amplifying a single copy DNA sequence from the human genome approximately 10^9-fold (corresponding to 30 cycles of complete PCR) in a few hours. The method, however, only became widely established with the introduction of the thermostable Taq DNA polymerase (Kogan *et al.*, 1987) thus avoiding the necessity of adding thermolabile Klenow polymerase after each denaturation step. This has allowed automation of the procedure with its important advantages of sensitivity, speed and convenience. DNA fragments of up to 6 kb have been successfully amplified (Ponce and Micol, 1992).

Taq DNA polymerase is error prone, with a basic nucleotide misincorporation frequency of about one in 9000 bases polymerized (Tindall and Kunkel, 1988) but under appropriate conditions fidelity may be increased to about one error per 10^6 bases (Eckert and Kunkel, 1990). For most purposes, however, the error rate may be neglected if sufficient initial template DNA is used (Krawczak *et al.*, 1989).

'Same-day' genetic diagnosis has therefore now become a reality. The theory and practice of PCR have been well reviewed elsewhere (Saiki *et al.*, 1988; Vosberg, 1989; Williams, 1989; Bloch, 1991). Use of the PCR technique in gene analysis has provided welcome alternatives to the laborious cloning and sequencing of disease alleles required in the past. In the majority of cases reported to date, DNA diagnosis has been retrospective in the sense that direct sequencing of the PCR-amplified disease allele(s) was employed to analyse the gene sequence of an individual already known to be suffering from a given disorder. However, antenatal diagnostic procedures have now also fully incorporated PCR technology (Reiss and Cooper, 1990). Determination of the gene lesion may be accomplished by subjecting PCR-amplified DNA to restriction enzyme cleavage, oligonucleotide discrimination hybridization, mismatch analysis etc (reviewed by Vosberg, 1989). Indeed, virtually all modern methods for the detection and localization of gene lesions in complex genes are now PCR based. Techniques currently available for mutational screening and analysis are briefly reviewed in the following section.

4.3 PCR-based methods of mutation detection and analysis

The introduction of PCR has made possible the detection and characterization of a wide variety of different gene lesions underlying human genetic disease (Reiss and Cooper, 1990). Most genetic diseases exhibit considerable allelic heterogeneity, meaning that a considerable number of different mutations are likely to occur within the sequence of the gene responsible for the disease in question. The major constraint on our ability to detect mutations in cases where the gene responsible is already known has often been the great size and complexity of the gene under study. For example, the Duchenne muscular dystrophy (DMD) gene contains 79 exons spanning approximately 2400 kb of genomic DNA. The considerable variation in gene size and structure together with the variety of mutational lesions underlying genetic disease argue for the development of techniques capable of simultaneously screening such gene loci for both gross and subtle alterations in structure. The availability of a battery of different screening techniques permits the appropriate selection of a mutation screening method to suit the particular characteristics of the gene under study. Once a specific lesion has been detected, other PCR-based procedures may be utilized to detect rapidly the presence of that lesion in other patients with the same condition or in relatives of the original patient.

Methods for screening genes for mutations are many and varied and a selection of the most important are described below. Examples of the use of each technique are given and different methods are compared wherever possible. All have advantages and disadvantages, e.g. a requirement for hetero-duplex analysis, an RNA probe or specialist apparatus, the use of toxic chemicals or radioactivity, relative complexity, ease of use, efficiency of mutation detection, etc. The eventual choice of a method will usually be determined by a combination of the characteristics of the particular experimental system under study and personal preference. The interested reader is referred to several recent reviews which have attempted to keep pace with the increasingly rapid progress in this area (Cotton, 1989; Forrest and Cotton, 1990; Rossiter and Caskey, 1990).

4.3.1 Deletion screening

For the purpose of screening for deletions, as in cases where gene deletions are by far the most common cause of the disease under analysis (e.g. Duchenne muscular dystrophy, steroid sulphatase deficiency), a simple PCR-based approach often suffices, particularly if the gene is not too complex or if the deletions tend to cluster in 'hotspots'. Such an approach is exemplified by Chamberlain *et al.* (1988) who simultaneously PCR-amplified and analysed six DNA fragments from the DMD gene of muscular dystrophy patients in what has become known as 'multiplex PCR'. Figure 4.3 illustrates this strategy. Six DNA fragments from the dystrophin (DMD) gene from eight patients with Duchenne muscular dystrophy were PCR amplified. These fragments, derived from putative deletion 'hotspots' in the DMD gene, were subjected to agarose

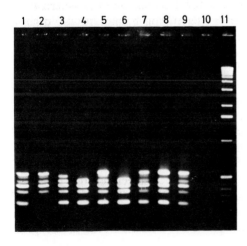

Figure 4.3. Multiplex DNA amplification of six fragments of the Duchenne muscular dystrophy (DMD) gene derived from putative deletion hotspots (from Hentemann *et al.*, 1990; reproduced by permission of Springer Verlag). Lane 1, positive control (normal healthy male); Lanes 2-8, patient DNA samples (deletions are present in lanes 2, 3, 4, 6 and 8); Lane 10, negative control (no DNA); Lane 11, size marker.

gel electrophoresis; several deletions were detected by virtue of their associated absent fragments (Hentemann *et al.*, 1990). It should be noted that the multiplex approach is sometimes impossible because the amplification of different exons may (i) require very different reaction conditions, (ii) lead to the generation of similarly sized PCR products or (iii) be abolished by interference between the oligonucleotide primer pairs used.

Accurate dosage determination, so necessary for the reliable detection of heterozygous carriers of gene deletions, may now be performed using a combination of PCR and high-performance liquid chromatography described by Asakawa *et al.* (1992); these authors applied their method to deletions in the F9 and DMD genes.

4.3.2 Use of mRNA/cDNA as analytical material

RNA may also be used as a substrate for analysis. Harbath and Vosberg (1988) first described a method to prime specifically the reverse transcription of a myosin cDNA. The principle is illustrated in Figure 4.4. The use of PCR-amplified cDNA as analytical material permitted Grompe *et al.* (1989) among others to detect gene lesions responsible for ornithine transcarbamylase deficiency. Gene-specific oligonucleotide primers have also been used in the successful PCR amplification of cDNAs derived from rare mRNA transcripts (Frohman *et al.*, 1988).

In principle, cDNA analysis would be of enormous benefit in diagnostic medicine because it would obviate the need to examine many exons individually, at the same time as providing the means to detect splicing defects. However, in practice, the barrier to the early exploitation of this strategy has been that the expressing tissues for many tissue-specific disease genes [e.g. liver for the factor VIII (F8) gene and muscle for the DMD gene] have been accessible only through biopsy, which is usually undesirable and may not be feasible.

Several recent reports (Chelly *et al.*, 1988, 1989; Sarkar and Sommer, 1989) have demonstrated the existence of extremely low background levels of

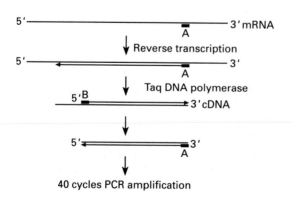

Figure 4.4. PCR amplification of reverse transcripts using primer oligonucleotides A and B.

correctly spliced mRNA transcripts of tissue-specific genes in a number of supposedly 'non-expressing' cell types. Berg *et al.* (1990) detected F8 mRNA transcripts in preparations of lymphocyte total RNA at a level of one mRNA molecule per 500–1000 cells. These ectopic transcripts could be PCR amplified after reverse transcription and used directly for DNA sequence analysis. The diagnostic potential of this basal rate of ectopic transcription in a non-expressing yet readily accessible tissue was then demonstrated by the detection of an already known CGA→TGA transition at codon Arg 427 of the F8 gene by direct sequencing of an ectopic transcript, spanning exons 8 and 9, derived from the lymphocytes of a haemophilia A patient (Berg *et al.*, 1990). The general utility of this method was then illustrated by the detection and characterization of a DMD gene deletion causing Becker muscular dystrophy in pathological ectopic mRNA transcripts isolated from the peripheral lymphocytes of both a patient and a heterozygous carrier (Schlösser *et al.*, 1990).

This approach was greatly improved and refined by Naylor *et al.* (1991) who screened cDNAs corresponding to the essential coding region of the F8 gene (and derived from ectopic gene transcripts) from haemophilia A patients with the chemical mismatch cleavage method of mutation detection (see Section 4.3.3). These authors thereby successfully located the positions of two novel point mutations in the F8 gene. An increasing number of other reports of the use of ectopic transcript analysis facilitating the identification of lesions within tissue-specific genes causing human genetic disease have appeared (e.g. Roberts *et al.*, 1990, 1991; Chalkley and Harris, 1991; Chan and Cole, 1991; Knebelman *et al.*, 1991; Rosenzweig *et al.*, 1991).

Perhaps the major caveat has been that splicing patterns exhibited by normal and ectopic transcripts might not be exactly identical. Although by no means trivial, this potential problem now appears to be less serious in practical terms than was at first thought. Correctly spliced ectopic transcripts have been detected in all cases so far reported in which cDNAs have been sequenced across intron–exon junctions. Further, Chelly *et al.* (1991), in a study of Duchenne/Becker muscular dystrophy patients, have shown that processed dystrophin (DMD) mRNA transcripts from both expressing and non-expressing cell types are indistinguishable. Finally, alternative splicing of exon 12 of the cystic fibrosis transmembrane regulator (CFTR) gene, found in the nasal epithelium of normal individuals, can be observed to the same extent in ectopic transcripts derived from blood lymphocytes (Slomski *et al.*, 1992).

Ectopic transcript analysis also promises to be an invaluable tool for the characterization of defects of mRNA splicing. Berg *et al.* (1992) reported a heterozygous silent AAG→AAA transition at Lys 176 in the liver-expressed antithrombin III (AT3) gene in a patient with recurrent venous thrombosis. This lesion occurred at the conserved −1 position in the exon 3a donor splice site. Ectopic transcript analysis of lymphocyte mRNA demonstrated the presence of an abnormally sized AT3 mRNA specific to the patient which was shown by cDNA sequencing to lack exon 3a. Oligonucleotide discriminant hybridization then demonstrated the absence of any detectable transcript of normal length derived from the disease allele. Similar ectopic transcript analyses of donor splice site mutations in the parathyroid hormone (PTH) gene causing hypoparathyroidism (Parkinson and Thakker, 1992) and the phenyl-alanine hydroxylase (PAH) gene causing phenylketonuria (Ramus *et al.*, 1992) have also been reported.

In principle, therefore, ectopic transcription and chemical mismatch cleavage (Section 4.3.3.) would seem to represent an almost ideal diagnostic tool because the analytical material is easily obtained, the same method may be applied to the analysis of any large and complex gene and most, if not all, mutations, including those affecting splicing, can be detected. It remains to be seen, however, whether this technique can be transferred successfully to the routine laboratory. In this context, mass-production of cDNA fragments by PCR could give rise to difficulties with contamination of reaction mixtures by the products of previous reactions.

4.3.3 Chemical mismatch cleavage

The chemical mismatch cleavage technique (Cotton *et al.*, 1988) is one of the most important techniques for detecting single base-pair changes in human genes. It serves to detect mismatched bases in hybrid duplexes formed between wild-type and mutant DNAs and has been successfully applied diagnostically to the detection of single base-pair substitutions in the factor IX (F9) gene causing haemophilia B using genomic DNA from the patients (Montandon *et al.*, 1989). Briefly, the principle involved (Figure 4.5) is as follows. Each PCR product derived from the patient's mutant gene is denatured and reannealed in a 10:1 ratio to radiolabelled homologous sequences derived from normal liver mRNA. Mutations in the target strands give rise to mispaired C or T residues in the heterodimers formed which are then specifically modified by hydroxyl-amine (for C mismatches) and osmium tetroxide (for C and T mismatches). The sites of these mismatches are then cleaved by treatment with piperidine and reaction products detected by autoradiography after polyacrylamide gel electrophoresis (Figure 4.5). The relative sizes of the reaction products provide some indication of the location of the lesion within a given DNA fragment. In principle, chemical mismatch cleavage detects all types and classes of mutation. However, since mismatched G and A bases cannot be detected directly, but only indirectly via C and T mismatches, both sense and antisense probes must be used. Matched bases adjacent to mismatched or unmatched bases can also be reactive with hydroxylamine or osmium tetroxide by trans-mission of the distortion, thereby indirectly indicating the presence of insertions and deletions.

Chemical mismatch cleavage has been successfully used in mutation screening in a number of inherited disease states, including Tay–Sachs disease (Akli *et al.*, 1991) and β-thalassaemia (Dianzani *et al.*, 1991). Schwartz *et al.* (1992) have demonstrated the practical utility of this technique in antenatal diagnosis, performing a prenatal exclusion analysis of haemophilia A in the family of a sporadic case (Figure 4.6). The causative lesion in the factor VIII (F8) gene was an Arg 795 → Term substitution (CGA → TGA) in exon 14.

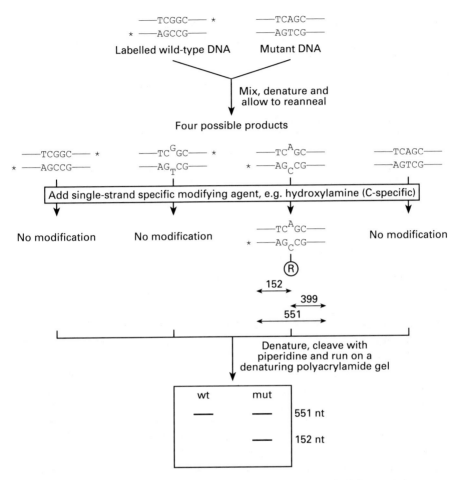

Figure 4.5. Principle of the chemical mismatch cleavage method for mutation detection as applied to the factor IX (F9) gene (after Montandon *et al.*, 1989; reproduced by permission of Oxford University Press). Asterisks denote the presence of ^{32}P at the termini of the end-labelled DNA strands. The expected sizes of the heteroduplex cleavage products generated by hydroxylamine are given in nucleotides (nt). Only the uncleaved 551 nt and cleaved 152 nt bands are visualized; the other strand is not labelled. R denotes modification of mismatched cytosine.

Chemical mismatch cleavage clearly demonstrated the carrier status of the mother and daughter but excluded carriership in the fetus. Grompe *et al.* (1989) have also reported successful carrier detection analyses in ornithine transcarbamylase deficiency, using chemical mismatch cleavage.

In common with most mutation screening methods, chemical mismatch cleavage may not be capable of detecting all point mutations; Theophilus *et al.* (1989) reported that not all patient samples yielded specific cleavage bands, probably due to the influence of the local DNA sequence context. These authors also experienced technical difficulties with osmium tetroxide, which

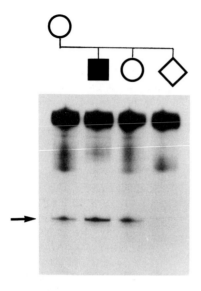

Figure 4.6. Chemical mismatch cleavage of heteroduplexes between the sense control strand and the antisense mutant strand of a fragment containing the portion of exon 14 of the factor VIII (F8) gene around codon 795. The band diagnostic of the Arg 795 → Term mutation is arrowed.

resulted in a high level of background cleavage. Perhaps the main disadvantage of the method is that it is rather labour intensive and time consuming.

4.3.4 Denaturing gradient gel electrophoresis

Mismatches within heteroduplexes as a result of mutation may also be detected by denaturing gradient gel electrophoresis (DGGE; Fischer and Lerman, 1983; Myers et al., 1985d). The basic principle is simply that DNA duplexes migrate through a gradient of denaturant until they reach a position where the strands melt. At this point, no further migration occurs. The melting behaviour of a double-stranded DNA molecule is a function of the base composition of its constituent sequences or melting domains. When such a sequence is altered (e.g. as is the case with mutant/wild-type DNA heteroduplexes), so is its melting behaviour and rate of electrophoretic migration (reviewed by Lerman et al., 1986; Myers et al., 1988). An example of the use of this powerful technique to detect mutational lesions in a hypothetical gene fragment is given in Figure 4.7.

Simplified versions of the original technique have been reported by Noll and Collins (1987), Cariello et al. (1988) and Attree et al. (1989). A multiplex PCR-DGGE approach to detecting mutations in the β-globin gene causing β-thalassaemia has been reported by Ghanem et al. (1992). However, DGGE on its own is relatively insensitive to mutations in the late (highest temperature) melting domains. To overcome this problem, most techniques have now incorporated a 'GC-clamp' (e.g. Myers et al., 1985a, 1985c; Sheffield et al., 1989; Kogan and Gitschier, 1990) which serves to stabilize the duplex and permits the detection of differences in the melting profile of the remainder of

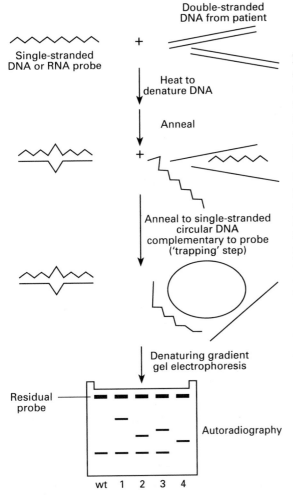

Single-stranded DNA or RNA probe

Double-stranded DNA from patient

Heat to denature DNA

Anneal

Anneal to single-stranded circular DNA complementary to probe ('trapping' step)

Denaturing gradient gel electrophoresis

Residual probe

Autoradiography

wt 1 2 3 4

Figure 4.7. The use of denaturing gradient gel electrophoresis (DGGE) in the detection of single base-pair substitutions (from Myers *et al.*, 1988; reproduced by permission of Oxford University Press). A labelled single-stranded nucleic acid probe is mixed with a double-stranded DNA from the patient (cloned or PCR-amplified), denatured, reannealed and subjected to DGGE. In the 'trapping' step, an excess of single-stranded circular DNA complementary to the probe is added to the mixture to bind any residual probe. Mismatches resulting from mutations in the region of interest give rise to fragments with reduced mobility under denaturing conditions. In the example given, wt denotes a wild-type control; individuals 1–3 are heterozygous and individual 4 is homozygous for non-identical mutations.

the fragment. With a GC-clamp, DGGE may be able to detect 90% or more of single base-pair substitutions (Myers *et al.*, 1985a; Theophilus *et al.*, 1989; Traystman *et al.*, 1990). Although DGGE may thus be the most efficient available mutation screening method, its distinct disadvantage for occasional users must be the requirement for specialist equipment. Also, since no cleavage occurs at the site of mismatch, initial localization of the mutation is fairly imprecise. Thus although DGGE can identify the approximate location of a mutation, it cannot reveal its nature or exact position. This must be done by DNA sequencing.

A variation of DGGE, termed temperature gradient gel electrophoresis, has also been described (Rosenbaum and Riesner, 1987; Riesner *et al.*, 1989) which differs only in that temperature is employed as the denaturing agent.

The mismatch analysis of PCR-amplified DNA has generally assumed the absence of artificially introduced base substitutions in a significant proportion of the amplification product. However, this approach differs from the direct sequencing of PCR-amplified DNA in that non-specific substitutions will render a molecule useless in analysis. Reiss *et al.* (1990) have shown that a number of different parameters, including initial template copy number and the number of replication cycles employed, must influence the 'signal-to-noise' ratio but that fragment length can be chosen so as to optimize signal detection.

4.3.5 Heteroduplex analysis

Heteroduplex scanning can also be accomplished by enzymatic means, mismatches in RNA:DNA hybrids (Jones *et al.*, 1985; Myers *et al.*, 1985b) or RNA:RNA hybrids (Forrester *et al.*, 1987; Gibbs and Caskey, 1987) being detectable by RNase A cleavage of the single-stranded region. Labelled wild-type mRNA or single-stranded DNA is hybridized to mutant mRNA and analysed by electrophoresis after RNase A treatment. RNA:DNA mismatch cleavage is pictorially represented in Figure 4.8. This method may, however, be

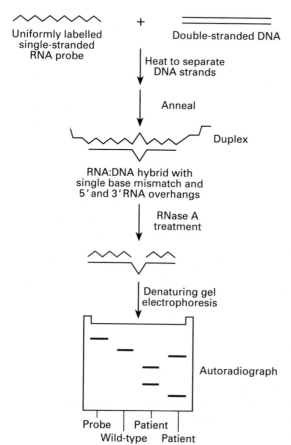

Figure 4.8. RNase cleavage analysis of RNA:DNA hybrids (modified from Myers *et al.*, 1988; reproduced by permission of Oxford University Press). The RNA probe may be synthesized *in vitro* under the control of an SP6 promoter. The labelled RNA is mixed with double-stranded test DNA from the patient, heated, reannealed and treated with RNase A. The RNase removes the 5′ and 3′ overhangs and cleaves at any mismatch. Denaturing gel electrophoresis separates RNA fragments according to size: any mutations will be detected by the loss of the wild-type band and the appearance of two smaller bands.

able to detect only 50% of point mutations (Myers *et al.*, 1985b; Gibbs and Caskey, 1987; Theophilus *et al.*, 1989), although the additional use of S1 nuclease (Atweh *et al.*, 1988) is claimed to increase the frequency of detection somewhat.

Other heteroduplex methods of mutation screening are also available. One such method is that of Smith *et al.* (1988b), which relies on the differential melting of RNA:RNA heteroduplexes in solution on exposure to differing concentrations of formamide. RNA is produced using the SP6 expression system and the method appears to be capable of detecting mutations in the highest melting domain of the duplex. Latham and Smith (1989) have applied this method to RNA:DNA heteroduplexes and reportedly achieved detection of all possible mismatches. The use of RNase A in combination with RNA probes derived from cDNA templates to scan coding regions ('exon scanning'; Kaufman *et al.*, 1990) appears to be successful in terms of detecting point mutations and deletions but not insertions.

White *et al.* (1992) have reported a method which is in principle very similar to SSCP (see Section 4.3.6) but, since it employs heteroduplexes between wild-type and mutant alleles, does not rely on secondary structure formation. It reportedly detects single base-pair substitutions which cannot be detected by SSCP and, as the same PCR product may be made for use in both techniques, the two methods may be used in parallel to complement each other.

Novack *et al.* (1986) have reported the detection of mismatched G and T bases through specific binding to, and modification by, carbodiimide. Since homoduplexes do not react with carbodiimide, gel electrophoresis under non-denaturing conditions is sufficient to detect mismatches in heteroduplexes by virtue of a mobility shift. As with DGGE, because no cleavage occurs at the site of mismatch, information on the precise location of the mutation is limited.

Finally, Lu and Hsu (1992) have reported a mismatch repair enzyme cleavage (MREC) assay for the rapid identification of point mutations. MREC employs the *E. coli* mismatch repair protein MutY, which is capable of nicking the mispaired DNA strand at A:G or A:C mismatches; the reaction products may then be resolved by DGGE. This method promises to be extremely sensitive in comparison with other available methods, including PCR/direct sequencing; it can reportedly detect specific cleavage products even when mutant cells comprise only 1% of the total. Other mismatch repair enzymes could in principle be recruited to detect different types of mismatch.

4.3.6 Single-strand conformation polymorphism analysis

Single base-pair substitutions may also be detected by a novel technique known as single-strand conformation polymorphism (SSCP) analysis, which relies on the electrophoretic mobility of a single-stranded DNA molecule being a function not only of its size but also of its nucleotide sequence (Orita *et al.*, 1989a, 1989b; reviewed by Hayashi, 1991). Both parameters determine the folding structure(s) of the single-stranded molecule, whose mobility is in turn likely to be dependent on its size, shape and surface charge density as well as the ambient temperature and ionic strength. The majority of single base-pair substitutions can be detected by this method, whose utility lies in its relative simplicity. DNA fragments, radiolabelled during PCR amplification (either by primers or deoxynucleotides), are run on polyacrylamide gels under non-denaturing conditions with single-base changes being detectable by a mobility shift (Figure 4.9). The radiolabelling may be omitted if asymmetric PCR (Section 4.3.7) is used for the production of single strands. SSCP variants can thus be visualized by ethidium bromide staining after polyacrylamide gel electrophoresis. Usually, PCR-amplified fragments of <400 bp are employed. The probability of detection of a given lesion is optimized if a number of different running temperatures (±5% glycerol) are used (reviewed by Hayashi, 1991).

SSCP has certainly acquitted itself well in prospective searches for mutations, namely those detecting single base-pair substitutions in the human genes encoding NRAS, KRAS and HRAS (Orita *et al.*, 1989a), hexosaminidase-α (HEXA; Ainsworth *et al.*, 1991), the neurofibromatosis protein (NF1; Cawthon *et al.*, 1990), lipoprotein lipase (LPL; Hata *et al.*, 1990), phenylalanine hydroxylase (PAH; Labrune *et al.*, 1991), factor IX (F9; Demers *et al.*, 1990), ornithine δ-aminotransferase (OAT; Michaud *et al.*, 1992) and cystic fibrosis transmembrane conductance regulator (CFTR; Dean *et al.*, 1990) among others. Since a mobility shift provides little or no positional information on the mutation detected, confirmatory DNA sequencing is always required.

Four retrospective studies (i.e. on known mutations) of a total of 46 single base-pair substitutions have between them reported a 98% detection efficiency for SSCP although optimization of running conditions was found to be necessary in some cases (O'Rahilly *et al.*, 1991; Michaud *et al.*, 1992; Plieth *et al.*, 1992; Sarkar *et al.*, 1992a). Moreover, Plieth *et al.* (1992) showed that band patterns characteristic of each CFTR gene mutation were reproducible under identical experimental conditions. Hayashi (1991) has claimed that, by using

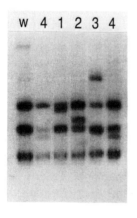

Figure 4.9. Single-strand conformation polymorphism (SSCP) analysis of single base-pair substitutions in the cystic fibrosis transmembrane regulator (CFTR) genes of patients with cystic fibrosis (gel photograph courtesy of Dr J. Reiss; analysis performed as described by Plieth *et al.*, 1992). w, wild-type (healthy control). 1, individual heterozygous for G551D (GGT → GAT); 2, individual heterozygous for 1717-1G → A; 3, Individual heterozygous for G542X (GGA → TGA); 4, Individuals heterozygous for R553X (CGA → TGA).

gels with 5–10% glycerol, 97% of mutations in 100–300 nucleotide strands resulted in a mobility shift, although this high detection efficiency drops to 67% for strands of 300–450 nucleotides. Similar efficiencies of mutation detection for fragments in these size ranges have been reported by Sarkar *et al.* (1992a). It is likely that the efficiency of mutation detection by SSCP is probably not determined simply by the nature of the single base-pair substitutions involved but rather may be a complex function of the local DNA sequence environment which serves to influence secondary structure formation in single-stranded molecules. The major advantage of SSCP is its simplicity. In addition, since mutations are detected by virtue of a mobility shift rather than by the absence of a signal, PCR failure does not lead to false positive results. One caveat should, however, be mentioned: the occasional occurrence of additional bands which may correspond to different stable conformations ('conformers') of the same sequence and whose presence may be sensitive to the temperature employed.

One variation on this theme has been described by Keen *et al.* (1991): the detection of mutations in DNA heteroduplexes on Hydrolink gels under non-denaturing conditions. This technique has been used successfully to detect an 18 bp deletion in the PAX3 gene causing type 1 Waardenburg syndrome (Tassabehji *et al.*, 1992). Another variation, termed RNA conformation polymorphism analysis (rSSCP), has been described by Danenberg *et al.* (1992) and Sarkar *et al.* (1992a): RNA is used instead of DNA, the RNA being generated in this case by T7 RNA polymerase transcription from a PCR-amplified DNA template fragment. Sense and antisense RNA strands yielded different conformational patterns. The rSSCP method has been claimed to be more efficient than SSCP in a prospective study (70% versus 35% detection efficiency; Sarkar *et al.*, 1992a) and successful in a number of cases where conventional SSCP had failed. Finally, another method, termed dideoxy fingerprinting, has been reported to be successful in detecting single base changes (Sarkar *et al.*, 1992b). As the name suggests, this technique combines dideoxy sequencing with SSCP. It was reportedly 100% successful in detecting a total of 84 different lesions in the factor IX (F9) gene causing haemophilia B.

4.3.7 DNA sequencing

DNA sequencing is both a screening method in its own right (albeit a laborious one) and a final check as to the precise nature and position of the lesion detected. PCR-amplified DNA may be sequenced directly, in either single-stranded or double-stranded form, or may be cloned into phage M13. The latter technique may generate clearer sequencing patterns but is more time consuming and is sensitive to artefactual errors introduced during PCR amplification, reverse transcription or the cloning process itself. An example of PCR/direct sequencing of a double-stranded DNA fragment to reveal a disease lesion is shown in Figure 4.10. A variation of normal PCR ('asymmetric' PCR) can also be employed to generate single-stranded DNA for sequencing (Gyllensten and Erlich, 1988) and the quality of DNA sequencing

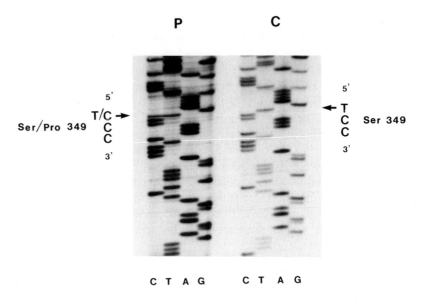

Figure 4.10. PCR/direct sequencing of exon 4 of the human antithrombin III (AT3) gene in a patient with recurrent venous thrombosis (from Grundy *et al.*, 1992; reproduced by permission of Springer Verlag). A TCC → CCC transition converting Ser349 to Pro can be seen in the patient (P) but not in the healthy control (C).

appears to be much improved by the use of single-stranded DNA as template. The enormous variety of techniques now available for direct sequencing of PCR-amplified material is reviewed by Gyllensten (1989), Rossiter and Caskey (1990) and Bloch (1991). Two methods particularly commend themselves for use on grounds of either simplicity or quality of results: Meltzer *et al.* (1990); Thein and Hinton (1991).

4.3.8 Rapid screening for known mutations

Once the position of a mutation is known, the problem reduces to being able to detect its presence quickly, simply and reliably. PCR/direct sequencing may often be the method of choice (e.g. if a once-only experiment is anticipated) but there are a number of alternatives of use in screening large numbers of patients for mutations.

Restriction enzyme cleavage or allele-specific oligonucleotide discriminant hybridization (e.g. Connor *et al.*, 1983) performed on PCR-amplified DNA samples are two options. Alternatively, allele-specific oligonucleotides (ASOs; e.g. Gibbs *et al.*, 1989; Newton *et al.*, 1989) can be used to discriminate between alleles during the PCR amplification itself ('competitive oligonucleotide priming'). When hybridized under appropriately chosen conditions, these oligonucleotides anneal to and amplify their complementary target sequences only if they are perfectly matched. With adequate controls, the presence or absence of PCR products can then be used to determine the identity of the alleles. These techniques are particularly useful for diseases such as sickle cell anaemia where one mutation accounts for all (or a majority of) cases. This has been achieved for both sickle cell anaemia (Wu *et al.*, 1989) and $\alpha 1$ antitrypsin deficiency (Newton *et al.*, 1989), being termed ASPCR (allele-specific PCR) or ARMS (amplification refractory mutation system) respectively. This method may be adapted for mutation detection by a restriction enzyme by modifying the primers employed to incorporate a specific restriction site. An interesting variation of this system is the allele-specific DNA ligase-mediated gene detection technique described by Landegren *et al.* (1988) and Wu and Wallace (1989). Additional variations on these themes have now become so numerous as to be impossible to cover in full here. The interested reader is referred to reviews by Vosberg (1989) and Cotton (1989).

All the above approaches may of course be applied to closely linked restriction fragment length polymorphisms (RFLPs), assuming that sufficient flanking DNA sequence is known to allow PCR formatting. The PCR-based indirect tracking of human genetic disease states has been reviewed by Reiss and Cooper (1990). If diagnosis rather than mutation characterization is the ultimate aim, this approach may be preferable to a more labour-intensive mutation screening and analysis programme.

The testing for the presence of specific alleles is very useful for diseases such as sickle cell anaemia where only one mutation is involved, or cystic fibrosis where one mutation clearly predominates. However, for disorders such as haemophilia B or Lesch–Nyhan syndrome, which manifest considerable allelic heterogeneity, the PCR amplification and oligonucleotide hybridization of every patient sample can be a very laborious process. One approach has been the technique known as single nucleotide primer extension (SNuPE), first employed by Kuppuswamy *et al.* (1991) in the detection of point mutations in haemophilia B and cystic fibrosis. Briefly, an oligonucleotide primer that ends at the base immediately preceding the site of mutation is annealed to gel-purified PCR-amplified sample DNA. Two extension reactions are then performed, with radiolabelled wild-type and mutant dNTPs respectively. The primer is extended by one nucleotide only if the appropriate template sequence is present; products can be detected by electrophoresis and autoradiography. SNuPE has recently been modified for multiplex PCR and for use on pooled patient samples (Krook *et al.*, 1992).

An alternative strategy is to attach the wild-type and mutation-specific oligonucleotides to a solid support and to hybridize the PCR-amplified sample DNAs to the membrane — the 'reverse dot blot' (Saiki *et al.*, 1989; Zhang *et al.*, 1991). This method can thus be used to screen for a whole series of mutations simultaneously as exemplified for cystic fibrosis (Serre *et al.*, 1991; Chehab and Wall, 1992). This may also be achieved by a one-step process using the ligase chain reaction described in Section 4.4.

4.4 The ligase chain reaction

PCR is not the only means to amplify specific DNA sequences for mutation detection and analysis. Barany (1991a) reported the application of a new technique, known as the ligase chain reaction (LCR), to the diagnosis of sickle cell anaemia. LCR can achieve both amplification and detection as a one-step process by employing two pairs of adjacent oligonucleotides, complementary to each target strand, which bind specifically and exclusively to the DNA sequences immediately flanking the site of the gene lesion (Barany, 1991b). Although LCR is to some extent a synthesis of existing methodologies [owing much to the oligonucleotide ligation assay of Landegren *et al.* (1988) and the ligase amplification reaction of Wu and Wallace (1989) and Barringer *et al.* (1990)], it nevertheless represents a considerable technical advance by virtue of its utilization of a thermostable DNA ligase. The thermostable DNA ligase can covalently link the adjacent oligonucleotides only when the nucleotides at the ligation junction are perfectly base-paired (the 'ligase detection reaction' or LDR) whereas negligible ligation occurs in the presence of a mismatch (the signal from correctly paired ligation products is 50–500-fold higher than that

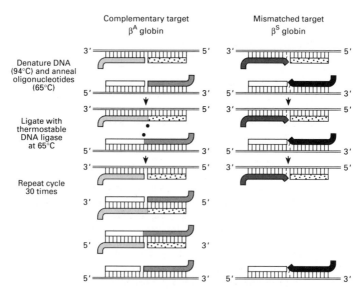

Figure 4.11. The ligase detection reaction (LDR)/ligase chain reaction (LCR) as applied to the diagnosis of sickle cell anaemia (after Barany, 1991a). The DNA is denatured (94°C, 1 min) and two pairs of adjacent oligonucleotides are annealed to the target DNA sequence containing the disease lesion at a temperature (65°C, 4 min) near to their melting temperature, T_m. The thermostable DNA ligase (●) covalently joins only those oligonucleotides which match the target sequences perfectly. Products from the LDR become targets for subsequent rounds of LCR, leading to an exponential increase in copy number. Oligonucleotides containing a mismatch at the junction due to the mutation do not ligate efficiently and thus do not result in an amplified DNA product.

from mismatched products). The products of this very specific reaction can then be exponentially amplified in a ligase chain reaction (LCR) by thermal cycling just as in PCR (see Figure 4.11). Barany (1991a) has claimed that LCR was capable of faithfully detecting the sickle cell allele with as few as 200 target molecules as starting material.

The most important property of LCR is the avoidance of target-independent ligation. This is accomplished by means of: (i) the thermostable ligase, (ii) the addition of carrier DNA, (iii) the use of single base $3'$ overhangs on the discriminating oligonucleotides, (iv) $5'$ phosphorylation on the adjacent (ligating) oligonucleotides only, (v) the presence of non-complementary tails on the outside oligonucleotides and (vi) the use of cycling conditions at or near the oligonucleotide T_m. LCR is quite compatible with PCR; indeed, a combination of PCR and LCR promises to yield the next generation of diagnostic text procedures. In principle, multiplexed LCR probes could be employed to screen either large numbers of patients simultaneously for different types of known gene lesion underlying a given disease, or for non-allelic mutations at different loci. LCR thus represents an important new method for allele-specific amplification on account of its one-step nature and its high signal-to-noise ratio.

References

Ainsworth PJ, Surh LC, Coulter-Mackie MB. (1991) Diagnostic single strand conformational polymorphism (SSCP): a simplified non-radioisotopic method as applied to a Tay–Sachs B1 variant. *Nucleic Acids Res.* **19**: 405–406.

Akli S, Chelly J, Lacorte J-M, Poenaru L, Kahn A. (1991) Seven novel Tay–Sachs mutations detected by chemical mismatch cleavage of PCR-amplified cDNA fragments. *Genomics* **11**: 124–134.

Alwine JC, Kemp DJ, Stark GR. (1977) Method for detection of specific RNAs in gels by transfer to diazobenzyloxymethyl-paper and hybridization with DNA probes. *Proc. Natl. Acad. Sci. USA* **74**: 5350–5354.

Asakawa J, Satoh C, Yamasaki Y, Chen S-H. (1992) Accurate and rapid detection of heterozygous carriers of a deletion by combined polymerase chain reaction and high-performance liquid chromatography. *Proc. Natl. Acad. Sci. USA* **89**: 9126–9130.

Attree O, Vidaud D, Vidaud M, Amselem S, Lavergne J-M, Goossens M. (1989) Mutations in the catalytic domain of human coagulation factor IX: rapid characterization by direct genomic sequencing of DNA fragments displaying an altered melting behaviour. *Genomics* **4**: 266–272.

Atweh GF, Baserga SJ, Brickner HE. (1988) Detecting small mutations in expressed genes by a combination of S1 nuclease and RNase A. *Nucleic Acids Res.* **16**: 8709.

Barany F. (1991a) Genetic disease detection and DNA amplification using cloned thermostable ligase. *Proc. Natl. Acad. Sci. USA* **88**: 189–193.

Barany F. (1991b) The ligase chain reaction (LCR) in a PCR world. *PCR Meth. Appl.* **1**: 5–16.

Barringer KJ, Orgel L, Wahl G, Gingeras TR. (1990) Blunt-end and single-strand ligations by *Escherichia coli* ligase: influence on an *in vitro* amplification scheme. *Gene* **89**: 117–122.

Berg L-P, Wieland K, Millar DS, Schlösser M, Wagner M, Kakkar VV, Reiss J, Cooper DN. (1990) Detection of a novel point mutation causing haemophilia A by PCR/direct sequencing of ectopically-transcribed factor VIII mRNA. *Hum. Genet.* **85**: 655–658.

Berg L-P, Grundy CB, Thomas F, Millar DS, Green PJ, Slomski R, Reiss J, Kakkar VV, Cooper DN. (1992) *De novo* splice site mutation in the antithrombin III (AT3) gene causing recurrent venous thrombosis: demonstration of exon skipping by ectopic transcript analysis. *Genomics* **13**: 1359–1361.

Bloch W. (1991) A biochemical perspective of the polymerase chain reaction. *Biochemistry* **30:** 2735–2747.

Cariello NF, Scott JK, Kat AG, Thilly WG, Keohavong P. (1988) Resolution of a missense mutant in human genomic DNA by denaturing gradient gel electrophoresis and direct sequencing using *in vitro* DNA amplification: HPRT Munich. *Am. J. Hum. Genet.* **42:** 726–734.

Cawthon RM, Weiss R, Xu G, Viskochil D, Culver M, Stevens J, Robertson M, Dunn D, Gesteland R, O'Connell P, White R. (1990) A major segment of the neurofibromatosis type 1 gene: cDNA sequence, genomic structure and point mutations. *Cell* **62:** 193–201.

Chalkley G, Harris A. (1991) Lymphocyte mRNA as a resource for detection of mutations and polymorphisms in the CF gene. *J. Med. Genet.* **28:** 777–780.

Chamberlain JS, Gibbs RA, Ranier JE, Nguyen PN, Caskey CT. (1988) Deletion screening of the Duchenne muscular dystrophy locus via multiplex DNA amplification. *Nucleic Acids Res.* **16:** 11141–11156.

Chan D, Cole WG. (1991) Low basal transcription of genes for tissue-specific collagens by fibroblasts and lymphoblastoid cells. *J. Biol. Chem.* **266:** 12487–12494.

Chehab FF, Wall J. (1992) Detection of multiple cystic fibrosis mutations by reverse dot blot hybridization: a technology for carrier screening. *Hum. Genet.* **89:** 163–168.

Chelly J, Kaplan J-C, Maire P, Gautron S, Kahn A. (1988) Transcription of the dystrophin gene in human muscle and non-muscle tissues. *Nature* **333:** 858–860.

Chelly J, Concordet J-P, Kaplan J-C, Kahn A. (1989) Illegitimate transcription: transcription of any gene in any cell type. *Proc. Natl. Acad. Sci. USA* **86:** 2617–2621.

Chelly J, Gilgenkrantz H, Hugnot J, Hamard G, Lambert M, Recan D, Akli S, Cometto M, Kahn A, Kaplan J-C. (1991) Illegitimate transcrition: application to the analysis of truncated transcripts of the dystrophin gene in nonmuscle cultured cells from Duchenne and Becker patients. *J. Clin. Invest.* **88:** 1161–1166.

Connor BJ, Reyes AA, Morin C, Hakura K, Teplitz RL, Wallace RB. (1983) Detection of sickle cell β S-globin allele by hybridization with synthetic oligonucleotides. *Proc. Natl. Acad. Sci. USA* **80:** 278–282.

Cooper DN, Schmidtke J. (1991) Diagnosis of genetic disease using recombinant DNA. Third edition. *Hum. Genet.* **87:** 519–560.

Cotton RGH. (1989) Detection of single base changes in nucleic acids. *Biochem. J.* **263:** 1–10.

Cotton RGH, Rodrigues NR, Campbell RD. (1988) Reactivity of cytosine and thymine in single base-pair mismatches with hydroxylamine and osmium tetroxide and its application to the study of mutations. *Proc. Natl. Acad. Sci. USA* **85:** 4397–4401.

Danenberg PV, Horikoshi T, Volkenandt M, Danenberg K, Lenz H-J, Shea LCC, Dicker AP, Simoneau A, Jones PA, Bertino JR. (1992) Detection of point mutations in human DNA by analysis of RNA conformation polymorphism(s). *Nucleic Acids Res.* **20:** 573–579.

Dean M, White MB, Amos J, Gerrard B, Stewart C, Khaw K-T, Leppert M. (1990) Multiple mutations in highly conserved residues are found in mildly affected cystic fibrosis patients. *Cell* **61:** 863–870.

Demers DB, Odelberg SJ, Fisher LM. (1990) Identification of a factor IX point mutation using SSCP analysis and direct sequencing. *Nucleic Acids Res.* **18:** 5575.

Dianzani I, Camaschella C, Saglio G, Forrest SM, Ramus S, Cotton RGH. (1991) Simultaneous screening for β-thalassemia mutations by chemical cleavage of mismatch. *Genomics* **11:** 48–53.

Eckert KA, Kunkel TA. (1990) High fidelity DNA synthesis by the *Thermus aquaticus* DNA polymerase. *Nucleic Acids Res.* **18:** 3739–3744.

Fischer SG, Lerman LS. (1983) DNA fragments differing by single base-pair substitutions are separated in denaturing gradient gels: correspondence with melting theory. *Proc. Natl. Acad. Sci. USA* **80:** 1579–1584.

Forrest S, Cotton RGH. (1990) Methods of detection of single base substitutions in clinical genetic practice. *Mol. Biol. Med.* **7:** 451–459.

Forrester K, Almoguera C, Han K, Grizzle WE, Perucho M. (1987) Detection of high incidence of K-Ras oncogenes during human colon tumorigenesis. *Nature* **327:** 298–303.

Frohman MA, Dush MK, Martin GR. (1988) Rapid production of full—length cDNAs from rare transcripts: amplification using a single gene-specific oligonucleotide primer. *Proc. Natl. Acad. Sci. USA* **85**: 8998–9002.

Ghanem N, Girodon E, Vidaud M, Martin J, Fanen P, Plassa F, Goossens M. (1992) A comprehensive scanning method for rapid detection of β-globin gene mutations and polymorphisms. *Hum. Mutation* **1**: 229–239.

Gibbs RA, Caskey CT. (1987) Identification and localization of mutations at the Lesch–Nyhan locus by ribonuclease A cleavage. *Science* **236**: 303–305.

Gibbs RA, Nguyen PN, Caskey CT. (1989) Detection of single DNA base differences by competitive oligonucleotide priming. *Nucleic Acids Res.* **17**: 2437–2448.

Grompe M, Muzny M, Caskey CT. (1989) Scanning detection of mutations in human ornithine transcarbamoylase by chemical mismatch cleavage. *Proc. Natl. Acad. Sci. USA* **86**: 5888–5892.

Grundy CB, Holding S, Millar DS, Kakkar VV, Cooper DN. (1992) A novel missense mutation in the antithrombin III gene (Ser349 → Pro) causing recurrent venous thrombosis. *Hum. Genet.* **88**: 707–708.

Gyllensten UB. (1989) PCR and DNA sequencing. *Biotechniques* **7**: 700–708.

Gyllensten UB, Erlich HA. (1988) Generation of single-stranded DNA by the polymerase chain reaction and its application to direct sequencing of the HLA-DQ locus. *Proc. Natl. Acad. Sci. USA* **85**: 7652–7656.

Harbath P, Vosberg HP. (1988) Enzymatic amplification of myosin heavy chain mRNA sequences *in vitro*. *DNA* **7**: 297–306.

Hata A, Robertson M, Emi M, Lalouel J-M. (1990) Direct detection and automated sequencing of individual alleles after electrophoretic strand separation: identification of a common nonsense mutation in exon 9 of the human lipoprotein lipase gene. *Nucleic Acids Res.* **18**: 5407–5411.

Hayashi K. (1991) PCR-SSCP: a simple and sensitive method for detection of mutations in the genomic DNA. *PCR Methods Appl.* **1**: 34–38.

Hentemann M, Reiss J, Wagner M, Cooper DN. (1990) Rapid detection of deletions in the Duchenne muscular dystrophy gene by PCR amplification of deletion-prone exon sequences. *Hum. Genet.* **84**: 228–232.

Jones FS, Grimberg JI, Fischer SG, Ford JP. (1985) Detection of sickle-cell mutation by electrophoresis of partial RNA:DNA hybrids following solution hybridization. *Gene* **39**: 77–83.

Kaufman DL, Ramesh V, McClatchey AI, Menkes JH, Tobin AJ. (1990) Detection of point mutations associated with genetic diseases by an exon scanning technique. *Genomics* **8**: 656–663.

Keen J, Lester D, Inglehearn C, Curtis A, Bhattacharya S. (1991) Rapid detection of single base mismatches as heteroduplexes on Hydrolink gels. *Trends Genet.* **7**: 5.

Knebelman B, Boussin L, Guerrier D, Legeai L, Kahn A, Josso N, Picard J-Y. (1991) Anti-Müllerian hormone Bruxelles: a nonsense mutation associated with the persistent Müllerian duct syndrome. *Proc. Natl. Acad. Sci. USA* **88**: 3767–3771.

Kogan S, Gitschier J. (1990) Mutations and a polymorphism in the factor VIII gene discovered by denaturing gradient gel electrophoresis. *Proc. Natl. Acad. Sci. USA* **87**: 2092–2096.

Kogan SC, Doherty M, Gitschier J. (1987) An improved method for prenatal diagnosis of genetic diseases by analysis of amplified DNA sequences. *N. Engl. J. Med.* **317**: 985–990.

Krawczak M, Reiss J, Schmidtke J, Rösler U. (1989) Polymerase chain reaction: replication errors and reliability of gene diagnosis. *Nucleic Acids Res.* **17**: 2197–2201.

Krook A, Stratton IM, O'Rahilly S. (1992) Rapid and simultaneous detection of multiple mutations by pooled and multiplex single nucleotide primer extension: application to the study of insulin-responsive glucose transporter and insulin receptor mutations in non-insulin-dependent diabetes. *Hum. Mol. Genet.* **1**: 391–395.

Kuppuswamy MN, Hoffmann JW, Kasper CK, Spitzer SG, Groce SL, Bajaj SP. (1991) Single nucleotide primer extension to detect genetic diseases: experimental application to hemophilia B and cystic fibrosis genes. *Proc. Natl. Acad. Sci. USA* **88**: 1143–1147.

Labrune P, Melle D, Rey F, Berthelon M, Caillaud C, Rey J, Munnich A, Lyonnet S. (1991) Single-strand conformation polymorphism for detection of mutations and base substitutions in phenylketonuria. *Am. J. Hum. Genet.* **48:** 1115–1120.

Landegren U, Kaiser R, Sanders J, Hood L. (1988) A ligase-mediated gene detection technique. *Science* **241:** 1077–1080.

Latham T, Smith FI. (1989). Detection of single-base mutations in DNA molecules using the solution melting method. *DNA* **8:** 223–231.

Lerman LS, Silverstein K, Grinfeld E. (1986) Searching for gene defects by denaturing gradient gel electrophoresis. *Cold Spring Harb. Symp. Quant. Biol.* **51:** 285–297.

Lu A-L, Hsu I-C. (1992) Detection of single DNA base mutations with mismatch repair enzymes. *Genomics* **14:** 249–255.

Martinson JJ, Clegg JB. (1990) Alkaline transfer of small restriction fragments from polyacrylamide gels. *Nucleic Acids Res.* **18:** 1307.

Meltzer SJ, Mane SM, Wood PK, Johnson L, Needleman SW. (1990) Sequencing products of the polymerase chain reaction directly without purification. *Biotechniques* **8:** 142–148.

Michaud J, Brody LC, Steel G, Fontaine G, Martin LS, Valle D, Mitchell G. (1992) Strand-separating conformational polymorphism analysis: efficacy of detection of point mutations in the human ornithine δ-aminotransferase gene. *Genomics* **13:** 389–394.

Montandon AJ, Green PM, Giannelli F, Bentley DR. (1989) Direct detection of point mutations by mismatch analysis: application to haemophilia B. *Nucleic Acids Res.* **17:** 3347–3357.

Myers RM, Fischer SG, Lerman LS, Maniatis T. (1985a) Nearly all single-base substitutions in DNA fragments joined to a GC-clamp can be detected by denaturing gradient gel electrophoresis. *Nucleic Acids Res.* **13:** 3131–3145.

Myers RM, Larin Z, Maniatis T. (1985b) Detection of single base substitutions by ribonuclease cleavage at mismatches in RNA:DNA duplexes. *Science* **230:** 1242–1246.

Myers RM, Fischer SG, Maniatis T, Lerman LS. (1985c) Modification of the melting properties of duplex DNA by attachment of a GC-rich DNA sequence as determined by denaturing gradient gel electrophoresis. *Nucleic Acids Res.* **13:** 3111–3129.

Myers RM, Lumelsky N, Lerman LS, Maniatis T. (1985d) Detection of single base substitutions in total genomic DNA. *Nature* **313:** 495–498.

Myers RM, Sheffield VC, Cox DR. (1988) Detection of single-base changes in DNA: ribonuclease cleavage and denaturing gradient gel electrophoresis. In: *Genome Analysis: A Practical Approach* (ed. KE Davies). IRL Press, Oxford.

Naylor JA, Green PM, Montandon AJ, Rizza CR, Giannelli F. (1991) Detection of three novel mutations in two haemophilia A patients by rapid screening of whole essential region of factor VIII gene. *Lancet* **337:** 635–639.

Newton CR, Graham A, Heptinstall LE, Powell SJ, Summers C, Kalsheker N, Smith JC, Markham AF. (1989) Analysis of any point mutation in DNA: the amplification refractory mutation system. *Nucleic Acids Res.* **17:** 2503–2516.

Noll WW, Collins M. (1987) Detection of human DNA polymorphisms with a simplified denaturing gradient gel electrophoresis technique. *Proc. Natl. Acad. Sci. USA* **84:** 3339–3343.

Novack DF, Casna NJ, Fischer SG, Ford JP. (1986) Detection of single base-pair mismatches in DNA by chemical modification followed by electrophoresis in 15% polyacrylamide gel. *Proc. Natl. Acad. Sci. USA* **83:** 586–590.

O'Rahilly S, Choi WH, Patel P, Turner RC, Flier JS, Moller DE. (1991) Detection of mutations in insulin-receptor gene in NIDDM patients by analysis of single-stranded conformation polymorphisms. *Diabetes* **40:** 777–782.

Orita M, Suzuki Y, Sekiya T, Hayashi K. (1989a) Rapid and sensitive detection of point mutations and DNA polymorphisms using the polymerase chain reaction. *Genomics* **5:** 874–879.

Orita M, Iwahana H, Kanazawa H, Hayashi K, Sekiya T. (1989b) Detection of polymorphisms of human DNA by gel electrophoresis as single-strand conformation polymorphisms. *Proc. Natl. Acad. Sci. USA* **86:** 2766–2770.

Parkinson DB, Thakker RV. (1992) A donor splice site mutation in the parathyroid hormone gene is associated with autosomal recessive hypoparathyroidism. *Nature Genetics* **1:** 149–152.

Plieth J, Rininsland F, Schlösser M, Cooper DN, Reiss J. (1992) Single-strand conformation polymorphism (SSCP) analysis of exon 11 of the CFTR gene reliably detects more than one third of non-δF508 mutations in German cystic fibrosis patients. *Hum. Genet.* **88**: 283–287.

Ponce MR, Micol JL. (1992) PCR amplification of long DNA fragments. *Nucleic Acids Res.* **20**: 623.

Ramus SJ, Forrest SM, Cotton RGH. (1992) Illegitimate transcription of phenylalanine hydroxylase for detection of mutations in patients with phenylketonuria. *Hum. Mutation* **1**: 154–158.

Reiss J, Cooper DN. (1990) Application of the polymerase chain reaction to the diagnosis of human genetic disease. *Hum. Genet.* **85**: 1–8.

Reiss J, Krawczak M, Schlösser M, Wagner M, Cooper DN. (1990) The effect of replication errors on the mismatch analysis of PCR-amplified DNA. *Nucleic Acids Res.* **18**: 973–978.

Riesner D, Steger G, Zimmat R, Owens RA, Wagenhöfer M, Hillen W, Vollbach S, Henco K. (1989) Temperature gradient gel electrophoresis of nucleic acids: analysis of conformational transitions, sequence variations and protein–nucleic acid interactions. *Electrophoresis* **10**: 377–389.

Roberts RG, Bentley DR, Barby TFM, Manners E, Bobrow M. (1990) Direct diagnosis of carriers of Duchenne and Becker muscular dystrophy by amplification of lymphocyte RNA. *Lancet* **336**: 1523–1526.

Roberts RG, Barby TFM, Manners E, Bobrow M, Bentley DR. (1991) Direct detection of dystrophin gene rearrangements by analysis of dystrophin mRNA in peripheral blood lymphocytes. *Am. J. Hum. Genet.* **49**: 298–310.

Rosenbaum V, Riesner D. (1987) Temperature-gradient gel electrophoresis: thermodynamic analysis of nucleic acids and proteins in purified form and in cellular extracts. *Biophys. Chem.* **26**: 235–246.

Rosenzweig A, Watkins H, Hwang D-S, Miri M, McKenna W, Traill TA, Seidman JG, Seidman CE. (1991) Preclinical diagnosis of familial hypertrophic cardiomyopathy by genetic analysis of blood lymphocytes. *N. Engl. J. Med.* **325**: 1753–1760.

Rossiter BJF, Caskey CT. (1990) Molecular scanning methods of mutation detection. *J. Biol. Chem.* **265**: 12753–12756.

Saiki RD, Scharf S, Faloona F, Mullis KB, Horn GT, Erlich HA, Arnheim N. (1985) Enzymatic amplification of β-globin genomic sequences and restriction site analysis for diagnosis of sickle-cell anemia. *Science* **230**: 1350–1354.

Saiki RK, Gyllensten UB, Erlich HA. (1988) The polymerase chain reaction. In: *Genome Analysis: a Practical Approach* (ed. KE Davies). IRL Press, Oxford.

Saiki RK, Walsh PS, Levenson CH, Erlich HA. (1989) Genetic analysis of amplified DNA with immobilized sequence-specific oligonucleotide probes. *Proc. Natl. Acad. Sci. USA* **86**: 6230–6234.

Sarkar G, Sommer SS. (1989) Access to a messenger RNA sequence or its protein product is not limited by tissue or species specificity. *Science* **244**: 331–334.

Sarkar G, Yoon H-S, Sommer SS. (1992a) Screening for mutations by RNA single-strand conformation polymorphism (rSSCP): comparison with DNA-SSCP. *Nucleic Acids Res.* **20**: 871–878.

Sarkar G, Yoon H-S, Sommer SS. (1992b) Dideoxy fingerprinting (ddF): a rapid and efficient screen for the presence of mutations. *Genomics* **13**: 441–443.

Schlösser M, Slomski R, Wagner M, Reiss J, Berg L-P, Kakkar VV, Cooper DN. (1990) Characterization of pathological dystrophin transcripts from the lymphocytes of a muscular dystrophy carrier. *Mol. Biol. Med.* **7**: 519–523.

Schwartz M, Cooper DN, Millar DS, Kakkar VV, Scheibel E. (1992) Prenatal exclusion of haemophilia A and carrier testing by direct detection of a disease lesion. *Prenat. Diagn.* **12**: 861–866.

Serre JL, Taillandier A, Mornet E, Simo-Boué B, Boué J, Boué A. (1991) Nearly 80% of cystic fibrosis heterozygotes and 64% of couples at risk may be detected through a unique screening of four mutations by ASO reverse dot blot. *Genomics* **11**: 1149–1151.

Sheffield VC, Cox DR, Lerman LS, Myers RM. (1989) Attachment of a 40 base-pair G + C-rich sequence (GC-clamp) to genomic DNA fragments by the polymerase chain reaction results in improved detection of single-base changes. *Proc. Natl. Acad. Sci. USA* **86:** 232–236.

Slomski R, Schlösser M, Berg L-P, Wagner M, Kakkar VV, Cooper DN, Reiss J. (1992) Omission of exon 12 in CFTR gene transcripts. *Hum. Genet.* **89:** 615–619.

Smith CL, Klco SR, Cantor CR. (1988a) Pulsed-field gel electrophoresis and the technology of large DNA molecules. In: *Genome Analysis: A Practical Approach* (ed. K Davies). IRL Press, Oxford, pp 41–72.

Smith FI, Latham TE, Ferrier JA, Palese P. (1988b) Novel method of detecting single base substitutions in RNA molecules by differential melting behavior in solution. *Genomics* **3:** 217–223.

Southern EM. (1975) Detection of specific sequences among DNA fragments separated by gel electrophoresis. *J. Mol. Biol.* **98:** 503–517.

Tassabehji M, Read AP, Newton VE, Harris R, Balling R, Gruss P, Strachan T. (1992) Waardenburg's syndrome patients have mutations in the human homologue of the *Pax-3* paired box gene. *Nature* **355:** 635–636.

Thein SL, Hinton J. (1991) A simple and rapid method of direct sequencing using Dynabeads. *Br. J. Haematol.* **79:** 113–115.

Theophilus BDM, Latham T, Grabowski GA, Smith FI. (1989) Comparison of RNase A, a chemical cleavage and GC-clamped denaturing gradient gel electrophoresis for the detection of mutations in exon 9 of the human acid β-glucosidase gene. *Nucleic Acids Res.* **17:** 7707–7722.

Tindall KR, Kunkel TA. (1988) Fidelity of DNA synthesis by the *Thermus aquaticus* DNA polymerase. *Biochemistry* **27:** 6008–6013.

Traystman MD, Higuchi M, Kasper CK, Antonarakis SE, Kazazian HH. (1990) Use of denaturing gradient gel electrophoresis to detect point mutations in the factor VIII gene. *Genomics* **6:** 293–301.

Vosberg HP. (1989) The polymerase chain reaction: an improved method for the analysis of nucleic acids. *Hum. Genet.* **83:** 1–15.

White MB, Carvalho M, Derse D, O'Brien SJ, Dean M. (1992) Detecting single base substitutions as heteroduplex polymorphisms. *Genomics* **12:** 301–306.

Williams JF. (1989) Optimization strategies for the polymerase chain reaction. *Biotechniques* **7:** 762–768.

Wu DY, Wallace RB. (1989) The ligation amplification reaction (LAR)-amplification of specific DNA sequences using sequential rounds of template-dependent ligation. *Genomics* **4:** 560–569.

Wu DY, Ugozzoli L, Pal BK, Wallace RB. (1989) Allele-specific enzymatic amplification of β-globin genomic DNA for diagnosis of sickle cell anaemia. *Proc. Natl. Acad. Sci. USA* **86:** 2757–2760.

Zhang Y, Coyne MY, Will SG, Levenson CH, Kawasaki ES. (1991) Single-base mutational analysis of cancer and genetic diseases using membrane bound modified oligonucleotides. *Nucleic Acids Res.* **19:** 3929–3933.

Indirect analysis of human genetic disease

5.1 The principles of linkage analysis

Genes are organized in chromosomes and hence do not always obey Mendel's law of independent segregation. Any two genes located on the same chromosome ought in principle to be transmitted together from one generation to the next, implying that polymorphic loci in the vicinity of a mutated gene could serve as markers for the presence of a given gene lesion. The pathway of the mutation through families or populations may thus be traced by studying the segregation of marker alleles instead of the disease alleles. In reality, however, alleles at distinct loci may well be separated and turn up in different germ cells, even if they were originally situated on one and the same parental chromosome. During the prolonged prophase of the first meiotic division, homologous chromosomes line up close to one another and exchange pieces of DNA in a process of breakage and reunion called 'crossing-over' (Figure 5.1). With respect to any pair of loci on homologous chromosomes, germ cells — or the chromosomes they contain — may be divided into two groups, called 'recombinants' and 'non-recombinants'. In recombinants, the genetic material at one locus is of a different chromosomal origin than that at the other. Since there are precisely two alternative sources of DNA (i.e. homologous parental chromosomes), a chromosome must undergo an uneven number of crossing-overs between non-sister chromatids in order to become a recombinant. An even number of crossing-overs (including zero) yields a non-recombinant. For a recombination event to be detected as such, the DNA must of course be polymorphic at both loci because otherwise the different chromosomal origins could not be distinguished.

The observed proportion of recombinants with respect to any two loci, say A and B, is termed their 'recombination fraction', usually denoted by the Greek letter theta (θ). We now want to show that there is a particular relationship between θ and both the number and frequency of crossing-overs. If exactly one crossing-over takes place between A and B in a given meiosis, which thus involves half of the chromatids, then the average number of germ cells containing a recombinant chromosome is obviously two. Now, if an additional crossing-over affects the region between A and B, the same non-

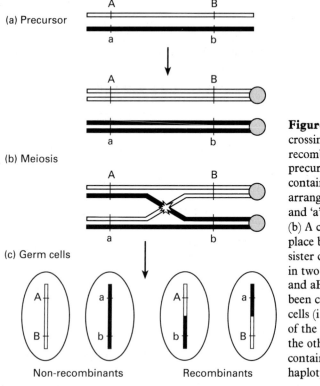

(a) Precursor

(b) Meiosis

(c) Germ cells

Non-recombinants   Recombinants

Figure 5.1. The process of crossing-over and recombination. (a) The precursor of a germ cell contains alleles 'A' and 'B' arranged in one haplotype, and 'a' and 'b' in the other. (b) A cross-over event takes place between two of the non-sister chromatids and results in two novel haplotypes, Ab and aB. (c) After meiosis has been completed, two germ cells (i.e. one half) contain one of the new haplotypes whereas the other two germ cells contain the original haplotypes.

sister chromatids as before will be involved with probability 0.25, converting the former two recombinants into two non-recombinants and resulting in a total of zero recombinants. With probability 0.25, however, the remaining two chromatids take part in the crossing-over and are converted from non-recombinants into recombinants, resulting in a total of four recombinants. Finally, one recombinant and one non-recombinant with respect to the first crossing-over will be involved with probability 0.5. Although this would alter the recombination status of both chromatids, the total number of recombinants (i.e. two) remains unchanged. Thus, the mean number of recombinants is again

$$0 \times 0.25 + 2 \times 0.5 + 4 \times 0.25 = 2$$

Applying similar arguments, it is easily shown that, in the case of at least one crossing-over taking place between two loci, half the germ cells will *on average* be recombinants and half will be non-recombinants, irrespective of the actual number of crossing-overs. Thus, the recombination fraction equals exactly half the probability of *at least* one crossing-over taking place, and is therefore directly related to the physical distance between the two loci. The closer the loci are, the smaller the recombination fraction, with a value of zero attained when both loci coincide. The upper limit of θ is 0.5, corresponding theoretically to the recombination fraction between loci located on non-homologous chromosomes. It is thus clear that the study of recombination fractions represents a useful means to analyse and localize new genes and/or markers. Strictly speaking, two loci on the same chromosome should always be termed 'linked' but it has become common practice to use this expression only when the recombination fraction between them is considerably smaller than 0.5.

Major goals for the characterization of markers for a mutation of unknown chromosomal location are (i) to prove that the marker and mutated gene are linked and (ii) to estimate θ. Both questions are easily answered for organisms that can be studied in controlled breeding experiments: if parental genotypes are selected accordingly, then the proportion of offspring stemming from recombinant germ cells can be determined directly by counting. In humans, however, such 'linkage studies' are rather more difficult and potential recombinants must be identified by examination of inheritance patterns in large and informative pedigrees (see White and Caskey, 1988). Informativity, as already mentioned above, means that a sufficient degree of polymorphism/ heterozygosity must be present at the loci under study. Evidence in favour of or against a recombination fraction of say θ_1 is expressed by the quantity $z(\theta_1)$, termed the 'lod score'. This statistical measure, introduced by Morton (1955), is defined as the decadic logarithm of the likelihood ratio, i.e.

$$z(\theta_1) = \log_{10}[L(\text{data}:\theta_1)/L(\text{data}:\theta = 0.5)] \qquad (1)$$

Here, $L(\text{data}:\theta_1)$ denotes the likelihood of the observed genotype and/or phenotype data, assuming that θ_1 is in fact the true value of θ; $L(\text{data}:\theta = 0.5)$ is the likelihood assuming that θ equals 0.5, i.e. that the two loci are unlinked. An example of a lod score calculation is presented in Figure 5.2.

Any positive value of $z(\theta_1)$, which implies that the numerator of the likelihood ratio is larger than the denominator, argues in favour of linkage: a lod score exceeding three is usually regarded as sufficient evidence for linkage. If $z(\theta_1)$ is < -2, meaning that the observed data are at least 100 times less likely assuming θ_1 instead of $\theta = 0.5$, then recombination fractions even smaller than θ_1 are excluded from being the true value. Finally, θ is estimated by that recombination fraction, θ_{max}, which yields the maximum lod score, i.e. the maximum likelihood. The greater the number of informative families studied, the more reliable and convincing are the results generated from linkage studies. Since crossing-overs in different meioses can be assumed to be statistically independent of each other, the overall likelihood of data from different families equals the product of the family-wise likelihoods. This allows the overall lod score to be calculated as the sum of the lod scores obtained in separate families. It should be realized that the likelihood ratio, and hence the lod score, is *not* a posterior probability of linkage. Claiming that a lod score of three between any two loci would be equivalent to linkage between them being 1000 times more likely than localization on different chromosomes would be a serious misinterpretation. Approaches to the computation of posterior probabilities, which of course depend on appropriate prior probabilities, are described in detail by Ott (1985).

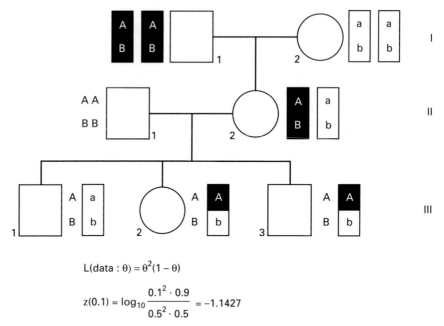

$$L(data : \theta) = \theta^2(1 - \theta)$$

$$z(0.1) = \log_{10} \frac{0.1^2 \cdot 0.9}{0.5^2 \cdot 0.5} = -1.1427$$

Figure 5.2. Lod score calculation for two autosomal loci. The maternally derived chromosome of individual III.1 is a non-recombinant, whereas individuals III.2 and III.3 have inherited recombinants (the grandpaternal and grandmaternal origins of the chromosomal material are indicated by black and white respectively). Other meioses are not informative. The likelihood of the data assuming a recombination fraction of θ is therefore $\theta^2(1 - \theta)$, and the lod score for $\theta_1 = 0.1$ is -1.1427.

The recombination fraction is not necessarily equal for meioses in different sexes, an extreme disparity being observed for the fruit fly *Drosophila melanogaster*, where males do not exhibit any recombination. Rao *et al.* (1978) demonstrated that the sex difference is in fact the major cause of heterogeneity of θ in humans. Estimates of the ratio of the female to male recombination fraction vary between different chromosomal regions, with an average of 1.8 for all 22 autosomes combined (Donis-Keller *et al.*, 1987). It may therefore be advisable to perform linkage analyses on two distinct parameters θ_m and θ_f, allowing for different recombination fractions in males and females. Although the lod score is then a function of two variables instead of one, i.e. $z = z(\theta_m, \theta_f)$, the basic principles described for the one-parameter case still apply.

If three loci, A, B and C, are located on the same chromosome, with A and C flanking B, any recombination between A and C is due to one of two mutually exclusive events:

(i) recombination between A and B but not between B and C
(ii) recombination between B and C but not between A and B.

If recombination in adjacent chromosomal regions is assumed to be statistically independent, then it follows that

$$\theta_{AC} = \theta_{AB}(1 - \theta_{BC}) + \theta_{BC}(1 - \theta_{AB}) = \theta_{AB} + \theta_{BC} - 2\theta_{AB}\theta_{BC} \qquad (2)$$

Thus, the recombination fraction θ, although directly related to physical distance, cannot be regarded as a simple linear function along a particular chromosome. This property appears to detract from the utility of θ as a means of establishing genetic maps, since distances along a linear map should normally be expected to be capable of summation when moving from one landmark to the next. Indeed, in the context of gene mapping, θ is often replaced by another quantity, d, called the 'genetic distance' between loci, which is computed from θ by specific 'mapping functions'. The simplest mapping function is that originally introduced by Haldane (1919), defined as

$$d = d(\theta) = -0.5 \ln(1 - 2\theta) \qquad (3)$$

To commemorate the work of the great American geneticist T.H. Morgan, genetic distance is measured in units of Morgans (Haldane, 1919), the more commonly used measure being its fraction, the centiMorgan (cM). For example, $\theta = 0.3$ corresponds to a genetic distance of $d(0.3) = 0.458$, or 45.8 cM when formula 3 is applied. For recombination fractions smaller than 0.2, θ and $d(\theta)$ are approximately equal so that the two expressions are sometimes used synonymously for closely linked loci.

Recombination is a phenomenon which, by definition, affects *pairs* of genetic loci; any set of corresponding observations can be divided into two distinct classes, namely recombinants (coded as '1') and non-recombinants ('0'). If, however, three loci, A, B, and C, are considered simultaneously, the number of such classes is four. When coded with respect to locus A, the possible outcomes of a meiotic crossing-over are

B	C	
1	1	recombination of A and both B and C
1	0	recombination of A and B, but not of A and C
0	1	recombination of A and C, but not of A and B
0	0	recombination of neither pair of loci

If the expected frequencies of these classes are denoted by r_1 to r_4, in the above order, then the following relationships between pairwise recombination frequencies and frequencies of three-point recombination classes hold:

$$\theta_{AB} = r_1 + r_2$$

$$\theta_{AC} = r_1 + r_3$$

$$\theta_{BC} = r_2 + r_3 \qquad (4)$$

This system of equations can be solved for the r_i values, and, since $r_1 + r_2 + r_3 + r_4 = 1$, it follows that

$$r_1 = (\theta_{AB} + \theta_{AC} - \theta_{BC})/2$$
$$r_2 = (\theta_{AB} + \theta_{BC} - \theta_{AC})/2$$
$$r_3 = (\theta_{AC} + \theta_{BC} - \theta_{AB})/2$$
$$r_4 = 1 - (\theta_{AB} + \theta_{AC} + \theta_{BC})/2 \tag{5}$$

Since, in reality, frequencies of three-point recombination classes can never be smaller than zero, it follows from equations 5 that pairwise recombination fractions for three loci must always fulfil the 'triangular' inequalities: the sum of any two θ values is at least as large as the third remaining θ value. This condition is automatically fulfilled when θ values are estimated from three-point recombination data, but not necessarily in a combination of independent two-point analyses. Therefore, confining the analysis to only pairwise considerations may sometimes yield inconsistent and thus inaccurate results.

The higher accuracy bound up with 'multipoint analyses' attains special importance when a novel locus is mapped within an existing framework of markers. Let us assume, for example, that θ_{AB} is known to equal 0.1, and that the study of 100 fully informative meioses reveals the following number of observations of three-point classes: $n_1 = 15$, $n_2 = 1$, $n_3 = 10$, and $n_4 = 74$. Two-point analyses would yield estimates of $\theta_{AC} = (n_1 + n_3)/100 = 0.25$ and $\theta_{BC} = (n_2 + n_3)/100 = 0.11$. However, since $\theta_{AC} > \theta_{AB} + \theta_{BC}$ in this case, these two-point estimates will not be very reliable. On the other hand, the log-likelihood of the data allowing for three-point data is proportional to

$$L = n_1 \log(r_1) + n_2 \log(r_2) + n_3 \log(r_3) + n_4 \log(r_4) \tag{6}$$

Applying formulae 5, L is maximized by $\theta_{AC} = 0.201$ and $\theta_{BC} = 0.113$. These estimates are more likely to fit the true recombination fractions because the triangular inequalities are now fulfilled.

The relative benefits from multipoint linkage analysis were studied by Lathrop et al. (1984, 1985) who concluded that three-point linkage analysis may be up to twice as accurate as two-point analysis, measured by means of the variances of recombination frequency estimates. The same authors also suggested that empirical evidence provided for a particular genetic map could be measured by a quantity called the 'location score' or 'loc score'. For the definition of this multipoint equivalent of the lod score, the localizations of all but one locus are assumed to be known. Since the genetic distances involved can be transformed into recombination fractions by mapping functions, the multipoint likelihoods $L(\text{data}:d_1)$ can be computed for various distances, d_1, between the locus of interest and an arbitrarily defined origin of the map. Now, the loc score is defined as

$$\text{loc}(d_1) = 2 \ln[L(\text{data}:d_1)/L(\text{data}:d_1 = \text{infinity})] \tag{7}$$

where $d_1 =$ infinity means adoption of a d_1 value large enough to imply no linkage. (Note that the natural instead of the decadic logarithm is employed in formula 7). Loc scores resulting from a variety of localizations of C in the above example are presented in Figure 5.3. These loc scores were calculated using Haldane's mapping function (formula 3), fixing the origin of the map at locus A. The resulting curve indicates that the most likely position of C is approximately 24 cM distant from A, with A and C flanking B.

Adopting Haldane's mapping function, however, appears to be somewhat inappropriate here, since use of this function implies that crossing-overs in non-overlapping chromosomal intervals must be statistically independent. However, the probability of simultaneous recombination between both A and B, and B and C equals

$$r_2 = (0.1 + 0.113 - 0.201)/2 = 0.006$$

which is smaller than

$$\theta_{AB}\theta_{BC} = 0.10 \times 0.113 = 0.0113$$

as expected under the assumption of independence. Double recombination thus appears to occur less frequently than expected in our example, i.e. there is 'interference' with recombination. Interference, which is a common phenomenon in the genetic material of all species, is usually measured by the coefficient of coincidence, c (Ott, 1985), being the ratio of observed vs. expected frequency of double recombination. A c value of unity would correspond to

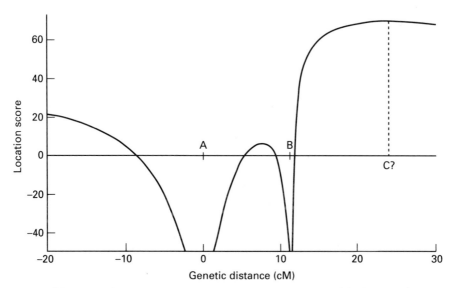

Figure 5.3. Location score curve. Location scores are presented for locus C from the example given in the text. The genetic distance held fixed between loci A and B corresponds to a recombination fraction of 0.1.

independence, but in our (artificial) example c equals $0.006/0.0113 = 0.53$. Lathrop *et al.* (1984, 1985) nevertheless demonstrated that an assumption of null interference may be satisfactory for most linkage analyses in humans. This was claimed to be due to (i) the limited relevance of realistic interference levels for the construction of genetic maps, and (ii) the impracticability of detecting and estimating interference with sufficient accuracy. However, Morton (1988) pointed out that multipoint mapping degenerates to multiple pairwise mapping when interference is neglected: for any assumed gene order, the multipoint likelihood would equal the product of the two-point likelihoods over adjacent intervals, and no additional information would in fact be conveyed by a multipoint approach.

It should be noted in this context that, although linkage data are obviously analysed more accurately in multipoint than in pairwise studies, some peculiarities may at least in part outweigh this advantage: incorporation of results from pairwise into multipoint analyses or vice versa is hardly feasible since likelihood ratios are calculated on the basis of different statistical hypotheses. Mapping of novel loci using previously analysed material would always require redundant re-analysis of the complete set of raw data. Furthermore, when these data are not available, they are rendered fairly useless for multipoint analyses; sufficient information would be recovered from lod scores only by multiple pairwise studies. These shortcomings caused Morton (1988) to challenge rightly the claimed superiority of multipoint over multiple pairwise studies whenever interference is assumed to be lacking.

Linkage data, as they occur in reality, are only rarely as easily analysed as in the example of Figure 5.2, and can be of virtually unlimited complexity. Therefore, appropriate computer programs have been developed for linkage analysis, among which are LIPED (Ott, 1976), LINKAGE (Lathrop and Lalouel, 1984) and, more recently, GRONPED (Meerman, 1991), to name only a few. Although different in handling and computing efficiency, these and other programs work according to similar principles.

When studying the localization of one or more mutated genes, phenotypes rather than genotypes form the basis of any formal analysis, so that the accuracy of linkage studies will depend critically on the assumptions made about the phenotypic expression and segregation of the loci studied, and the ascertainment and classification of the families involved. Among possible pitfalls leading to erroneous results are:

(i)   Incomplete penetrance and variable expressivity
(ii) Biased ascertainment or selection of families
(iii) Segregation distortion (e.g. due to antenatal selection)
(iv) Genetic or non-genetic sources of heterogeneity (e.g. phenocopies)
(v)   Phenotype modification by other genes (e.g. epistasis)

Preconditions for reliable results to be obtained in linkage analyses are thus accurately specified genetic models and careful sampling of family data. Underlying genetic models and relevant parameters are usually determined in segregation studies, which should precede a linkage analysis whenever the mode of inheritance, the number of loci involved in an inherited condition or the influence of non-genetic factors is unclear at the outset. These considerations acquire especial importance in cases where the genotype–phenotype relationship is as complex as, for example, in most psychiatric disorders. A detailed review of these problems and of approaches to their solution is given by Risch (1990).

5.2 Linkage analysis using RFLPs

A variety of markers of different types have been employed successfully in linkage studies. Before the advent of recombinant DNA technology, these markers were mainly scored by:

(i) antigenic properties of erythrocytes (ABO, MNS, Kell, Duffy etc), leukocytes (HLA) and serum (e.g. lipoproteins)
(ii) charge differences in electrophoresis (e.g. acid phosphatase, adenosine deaminase, transferrin)
(iii) sensitivity to enzyme inhibitors (e.g. cholinesterase)
(iv) secretory properties (Renwick, 1969).

After the discovery that DNA in almost all species contains an abundance of polymorphisms characterized by variations in the length of restriction fragments, Botstein *et al.* (1980) outlined the potential utility of these restriction fragment length polymorphisms (RFLPs) in linkage studies. These authors estimated that about 150 RFLPs, spread out over the human genome at 20 cM intervals, would be sufficient to map a gene responsible for a given trait without direct access to its DNA sequence. However, even if all RFLPs exhibit a moderate degree of polymorphism, a large number of individuals may still be required in order to attain this goal. Thus, for gene mapping on the basis of phenotype data alone, the above estimates apply merely to frequent mutations or to the establishment of marker maps and appear to be over-optimistic for rare conditions. Furthermore, Edwards (1987) pointed out that the probability of erroneous assignment due to chance increases when several loci are tested simultaneously. If n RFLPs are considered, the threshold for the lod score must be increased by $\log_{10}(n)$ in order to maintain the reliability of defined linkages to a given gene. Therefore, the number of observations necessary for a precise localization within an existing map is much larger than for the study of a single pair of loci. However, if sufficient evidence for the molecular pathology of a particular trait is already provided by its phenotypic consequences, selecting markers within or close to a few 'candidate' genes may be more efficient than testing a random collection of evenly spaced RFLPs. Exclusion of close linkage, and therefore of the involvement of a given gene, is feasible on the basis of testing many fewer individuals than would be required for positive proof of linkage (Edwards, 1987). Finally, linkage analyses should be further facilitated by markers with extremely high degrees of polymorphism, 'variable number tandem repeat' (VNTR) markers (Jeffreys *et al.* 1985; Nakamura *et al.* 1987). These loci consist of multiple repeats of single core motifs, where the number of repeats, and therefore the length of resulting restriction fragments, varies enormously between individuals. The high degree of heterozygosity and informativity expected from this allelic diversity allows recombinants to be detected very efficiently.

A paradigm of successful 'tracking' and mapping of a gene mutation using RFLPs is provided by the search for the molecular defect(s) underlying cystic fibrosis (CF), a recessive multi-system disease affecting exocrine gland function leading to pulmonary obstruction and pancreatic insufficiency. CF is very common in Caucasian populations, with approximately one in 2000 newborns affected. In 1985, the gene locus for CF was mapped to the long arm of chromosome 7 using RFLPs detected by anonymous DNA probes DOCRI-917 (D7S15) (Knowlton *et al.*, 1985), pJ3.11 (D7S8) (Wainwright *et al.*, 1985) and one located at the MET oncogene (White *et al.*, 1985a). These linkage results were then confirmed in various studies, with impressive lod scores such as $z(0.004) = 91.0$ for CF and MET, and $z(0.003) = 71.3$ for CF and pJ3.11 (Beaudet *et al.*, 1986). Further markers, more closely linked to CF, were detected and mapped (e.g. by Estivill *et al.*, 1987) and the candidate region for the putative CF locus was reduced stepwise to a few hundred kilobases (Iannuzzi *et al.*, 1989). Finally, researchers from the USA and Canada (Kerem *et al.*, 1989; Riordan *et al.*, 1989) were able to demonstrate that most cases of CF were due to a 3 bp deletion in the newly isolated 'cystic fibrosis trans-membrane conductance regulator' (CFTR) gene.

5.3 Risk analysis

Once the linkage between a marker and a disease gene has been established, and when the recombination fraction θ between them is known with sufficient accuracy, the marker can be employed in diagnostic testing. To determine whether an individual carries one or more mutant alleles, and if phenotypic information regarding carriership is lacking, chromosomes carrying the mutation(s) must be identified in other family members, preferably including the parents. If the marker allele characterizing a mutant chromosome is also present in the proband, he may also have inherited the mutation. However, if marker and disease gene do not coincide, i.e. if $\theta > 0$, the identification of mutants by marker alleles generates probabilistic results.

In Figure 5.4, the case is presented of a boy who suffers from a severe X-linked recessive condition. His mother is a proven, albeit asymptomatic, heterozygous carrier of the mutant allele, and heterozygous for a closely linked marker. Two marker genotypes are possible for any prospective son. If the son does not share the marker allele with his affected brother, then he will be unaffected unless a recombination has taken place in the germ cell from which either one or the other stems. Thus, the risk of being a carrier is $r(\theta) = 2\theta(1 - \theta)$ and if, for example, $\theta = 0.01$ then $r(0.01) = 0.018$. If, on the other hand, both sons have the same marker genotype, the carrier risk is $r(\theta) = \theta^2 + (1 - \theta)^2$. In the example presented here, the risk either increases or

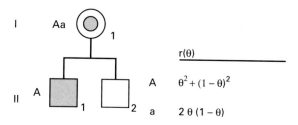

Figure 5.4. Risk analysis for an X-linked recessive condition. Individual II.1 is affected, individual I.1 is heterozygous for both the disease-causing mutation and a linked marker. $r(\theta)$ is the carrier risk of a prospective son II.2, depending on θ and the marker genotype.

$$r(\theta)$$

A	$\theta^2 + (1-\theta)^2$
a	$2\theta(1-\theta)$

decreases the closer the marker is linked to the disease gene. This finding may be intuitively apparent but fails to hold in general (Krawczak, 1987).

The efficiency and accuracy of risk assessment can be improved in several ways:

(i) If, in the example presented in Figure 5.4, two markers *flanking* the disease gene both yield discordant results between the two sons, then two independent recombinations would be a prerequisite for the proband to be affected. With θ values of 0.01 each, the risk would thus reduce to approximately $0.02^2 = 0.0004$.

(ii) Phenotypic markers associated with inherited diseases can provide further information regarding carrier status. For example, serum creatine kinase levels are raised in carriers of mutations causing Duchenne muscular dystrophy, and several microvillar enzymes exhibit aberrant activities in pregnancies affected by cystic fibrosis.

(iii) In some instances, mutations occur predominantly on chromosomes carrying specific marker alleles or haplotypes, thus exhibiting 'allelic association' or 'linkage disequilibrium' to a particular disease locus. Allelic association can help to identify mutated chromosomes in families that are otherwise only partially informative for linkage analysis. This phenomenon was, for example, helpful in the molecular genetic diagnosis of cystic fibrosis before the underlying molecular defect was detected. In the German population, 85% of CF mutations were shown to be located on haplotypes comprising allele 2 of marker KM19 (D7S23) and allele 1 of marker XV2c (D7S23) (Estivill *et al.*, 1987; Krawczak *et al.*, 1988). An example of a risk analysis applying these two markers is given in Figure 5.5; the affected child was not available for testing. In this family, which would otherwise have been completely uninformative for prenatal diagnosis, the risk of carrying both mutations could be reduced from its prior value of 0.25 to 0.0009 for child II.2.

5.4 Positional cloning

Although linkage analysis is primarily a method for genetic mapping (White *et al.*, 1985b), it also serves to potentiate the physical isolation of genes in the immediate vicinity of a well mapped region. Although a detailed description of

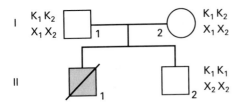

Figure 5.5. Risk analysis for cystic fibrosis. Individual II.1 was not available for testing. K_1, K_2: alleles of marker KM19; X_1, X_2: alleles of marker XV2c.

the methodology of physical mapping is beyond the scope of this volume, it is pertinent to present a brief overview of the progress made in the last few years in what is now referred to as 'positional cloning'. This strategy has been successfully implemented in cases where initially nothing was known about the structure and function of the protein product of the disease gene but where the approximate position of the gene on the chromosomal map was known (reviewed by Orkin, 1986). Unless a microscopically visible chromosomal deletion or rearrangement is known to be associated with a given disease, positional information must be obtained from genetic linkage data. The strategy then employed usually begins with constructing an overlapping set of recombinant DNA clones encompassing large stretches of chromosomal DNA [cosmids or yeast artificial chromosome vectors (YACs; Elvin *et al.*, 1990)]. The establishment of map order is often aided by using pulsed-field gel electrophoresis of genomic DNA (Smith *et al.*, 1988) or new genetic linkage or linkage disequilibrium data with polymorphic loci pulled *en route*. Homing onto a candidate gene is sometimes facilitated by gene-specific landmarks such as CpG islands (Bird, 1987; see Section 2.7), by identifying a sequence that shows evolutionary conservation ('zoo-blot') or by the direct isolation of transcribed genes from a specific chromosome region (reviewed by Hochgeschwender and Brennan, 1991). Ultimate proof that a candidate gene is the disease gene itself is obtained only, however, if a mutation is found to be both specifically associated with that disease and contained within the confines of that gene.

A selection of some important disease genes isolated by positional cloning is presented in Table 5.1. From inspection of the time intervals between mapping (by any method) and cloning a given gene, it is apparent that this interval is becoming ever shorter.

5.5 DNA polymorphism and disease associations

Many diseases are ill-defined with respect to their mode of inheritance, and a considerable proportion may prove to have a multifactorial basis (Vogel and Motulsky, 1986). Undoubtedly, many Mendelian traits remain to be recognized, having been obscured so far by their rarity or by other factors such as late onset or variable penetrance. For others, the terms predisposition, susceptibility or penetrance serve perhaps only to cloak our ignorance in acceptable garb rather than to illuminate our thinking. This notwithstanding, such diseases may still be amenable to the same analytical techniques that have

Table 5.1. Disease genes isolated by positional cloning

Disease	OMIM number	Year mapped	Year isolated
Agammaglobulinaemia	300300	1952	1993
Gonadal dysgenesis	306100	1956	1991
Adrenoleukodystrophy	300100	1964	1993
Wilms' tumour	194070	1979	1990
Myotonic dystrophy	160900	1982	1992
Muscular dystrophy, Duchenne and Becker	310200	1982	1987
Mental retardation, fragile X-linked	309530	1983	1991
Retinoblastoma	180200	1983	1987
Aniridia	106210	1983	1991
Huntington disease	143100	1983	1993
Alport syndrome	301050	1984	1990
Choroideremia	303100	1985	1990
Cystic fibrosis	219700	1985	1989
Granulomatous disease, chronic	306400	1985	1987
Norrie disease	310600	1985	1992
Kallmann syndrome	308700	1986	1991
Neurofibromatosis, type 1	162200	1987	1990
Polyposis, adenomatous (APC gene)	175100	1987	1991
Lowe oculocerebrorenal syndrome	309000	1987	1992
Colorectal cancer (DCC gene)	114500	1988	1990
Waardenburg syndrome	193500	1989	1992
Hyperthermia, malignant	145600	1990	1990
Marfan syndrome	154700	1990	1991

been applied to the study and diagnosis of single gene defects (Cooper and Clayton, 1988; Humphries, 1988; Sobell *et al.*, 1992).

For many complex diseases, the question initially reduces to defining the extent of the genetic basis and preferably identifying a genetic marker. One approach that is frequently used in such preliminary studies is to test for association between particular alleles of a polymorphism and the disease phenotype. This has proved very successful in the HLA-associated diseases and also with red blood cell surface antigens. The use of DNA polymorphisms in this context has greatly extended the scope of such studies but has also greatly increased the complexities of interpretation. Usually a candidate gene for the disease in question is selected and a nearby RFLP is used as a tool to compare patients and controls ('population association' or 'case-referent' studies). Positive associations can be pursued by demonstrating an increased risk to relatives of the proband ('family association' studies). In this section, we shall attempt to explore the potential utility of this approach as well as its problems and pitfalls; examples of its practical application will then be drawn from studies of atherosclerosis and ischaemic heart disease.

The possible mechanisms by which DNA polymorphisms arise and are maintained in human populations are clearly important in the interpretation of association data. According to the neutralist hypothesis, RFLPs in general should have no effect on phenotype and hence no direct effect on disease susceptibility (but see counter examples discussed in Section 10.7). Ferns *et al.*

(1986) have succinctly summed up the rationale behind studies of possible RFLP associations in the context of hyperlipidaemia and atherosclerosis. Such variants are 'simply markers for different alleles which may or may not be in linkage disequilibrium with gene variants that may predispose to hyperlipidaemia'. Further, 'firm proof of the association can only come from family studies or from the demonstration of a phenotypic difference associated with the allele'.

The relationship between an RFLP and a disease susceptibility should be interpreted in terms of linkage disequilibrium. Linkage disequilibrium is said to be present when certain alleles at one locus occur with certain alleles of another locus on the same chromosome at frequencies greater than can be attributed to chance alone. For our purposes, it can be considered to be due to a mutation in a gene a number of generations ago. This mutant gene has then increased in frequency within the population, affected individuals of succeeding generations inheriting not only the mutant gene but also the particular alleles of neighbouring RFLPs. Gradually, the relationship between the marker alleles and mutant gene will decay due to recombination: the greater the probability of recombination, the greater the rate of decay. In a random-mating equilibrium population with no selection, the expected linkage disequilibrium is zero. Since in practice these conditions are rarely if ever fulfilled, some degree of linkage disequilibrium may be expected to be a normal occurrence over relatively short distances.

This model imposes strict limits on the nature of diseases that can be studied in this way. The first requirement is that the rate of mutation of the disease gene must be low. If it were not, other sources of mutant genes would become available to the population and these would in all probability be surrounded by different alleles at the marker loci. Hence, a significant association would never arise. Secondly, for there to be a significant prevalence of the disease, the mutant gene must be, or have been, capable of an increase in frequency within the population. This is unlikely to occur if the mutant gene is even neutral to reproductive fitness. It certainly cannot have reduced this fitness. The increase in frequency of a neutral haplotype is, however, extremely slow (Cooper and Clayton, 1988). Thirdly, the populations to be studied must be to some extent inbred, since a significant proportion of the population must be derived from the ancestral individual who first carried the disease gene. The greater the frequency of the disease gene, the greater the time that must have elapsed since this ancestor, and the greater the coefficient of inbreeding for the population. In practice, these requirements are interrelated, although in a fairly complex fashion.

Proof of the existence of linkage disequilibrium is usually based on the comparison of the frequencies of marker allelotypes in disease and control populations. One aspect of the difficulty in assessing the significance of such associations is the considerable number of studies being carried out. At the 5% level of significance, 5% of reports will be spurious and reports of no association will generally neither be submitted nor accepted for publication. This problem could be reduced if authors adopted a policy of declaring the numbers of markers they have tested and, more controversially, the number they intended to test on the same data set. The P value for a 'significant' result should be reduced by a factor equal to this number.

Marker–disease associations from different populations are extremely difficult to interpret. This is the case not only because RFLP allele frequencies can differ between populations, but also because minor biases in sampling can produce gross errors in estimates of the allele frequencies. As with blood group studies (Mourant *et al.*, 1978), allele frequencies can be expected to vary dramatically between areas and even between districts of the same city. Hence, if the disease and normal population samples are not very closely matched geographically and socially, significant differences in allele frequencies, which have no relation to the disease state, can be expected to be observed. Most of the disease association studies quoted below define their subject retrospectively; under these circumstances, it is virtually impossible for investigators to ensure such matching. A specific example of this is the comparison of myocardial infarct survivors from a public hospital with controls selected from private health clinics. In this case, socioeconomic stratification is almost guaranteed. Pooling data can obscure a true association, due, for example, to differing linkage phase between populations. Conversely, it is virtually impossible to disprove a spurious association by looking at a new population. This effect may be compounded by the effect of selective reporting and publishing referred to above.

Atherosclerosis is a major cause of morbidity and mortality in the western world and, since it is known to cluster in families, it is not surprising that RFLPs have been used in attempts to identify a genetic component to this disease. A number of environmental factors are known to predispose to it, including diet and smoking. Further, a heterogeneous group of biochemical abnormalities, characterized by increased blood lipids and hence termed hyperlipidaemias, have been shown to be major risk factors for the development of atherosclerosis (Goldstein and Brown, 1989).

At first sight, it might appear that ischaemic heart disease is an improbable candidate for the RFLP association approach. This disease must be assumed to reduce reproductive fitness, despite its relatively late onset. Even a small reduction in fitness would provide significant selection against those genetic elements predisposing to it. If the prevalence of these genetic elements is maintained by new mutation, no disease association will be found. There is, however, another argument. The genetic elements that, given current western lifestyle, predispose to ischaemic heart disease, may in other cultures be neutral or perhaps even beneficial. Thus, the spread of the predisposing genotype in the population could have occurred in a period with a considerably different sociocultural environment.

The risk of ischaemic heart disease is directly related to the amount of serum cholesterol and the levels of low density and very low density lipoproteins (LDL and VLDL) and may be inversely related to the level of high density lipoprotein (HDL). These lipoproteins are composed of different amounts of the apolipoproteins, broadly classed as A, B, C, D and E. HDL (high A1 and A2, low CI, CII, CIII, D and E) and LDL (high B, low CI and CII) are essential for the normal transport of cholesterol and triglycerides, and their component apolipoproteins probably play an important role in determining lipoprotein conformation, receptor binding and metabolism. Some of the rarer forms of hyperlipoproteinaemia have been shown to be associated with altered levels of specific apolipoproteins [reviewed by Zannis and Breslow (1985), Li et al. (1988) and Breslow (1989)].

The genetic mechanism of the commoner subtypes of hyperlipidaemia remains unclear. Associations with atherosclerosis have nevertheless been sought with RFLPs identified by the cloned apolipoprotein genes. The apolipoprotein genes for which cloned copies are available fall naturally into groups, depending on their chromosomal location. These are the APO1–C3–A4 gene cluster on the long arm of chromosome 11, the APOC2–E–C1 cluster on chromosome 19, APOA2 on chromosome 1 and APOD on chromosome 3. APOB, structurally unrelated to the other apolipoprotein genes, is located on chromosome 2. Studies of the RFLPs in and around these genes that compare frequencies between disease and control groups have been reviewed by Hegele and Breslow (1987), Cooper and Clayton (1988) and Lusis (1988).

Each study must be considered not only in terms of the particular RFLP employed but also with reference to definitions of normal and disease states. There are a number of possible classifications of disease state: the various hyperlipoproteinaemias (including hypertriglyceridaemia), myocardial infarct survivors and angiographically-proven atherosclerosis. Similarly, normals can be taken either to be a randomly selected group from the general population ('random') or a group in which the disease has been actively excluded ('control'). In few studies has there been any indication of attempts to match the normal and disease groups with respect to any parameters other than race, age and sex.

Rees et al., (1985) claimed a very high incidence (relative incidence 57) of the rarer (S2) allele in a study of the SstI polymorphic site in the APOC3 gene between hypertriglyceridaemics (Types IV and V) and controls in Caucasians from the English population. This association did not, however, extend to Type IIb (Rees et al., 1983) or to type III (Vella et al., 1985) hyperlipidaemia. A dramatic difference in S2 allele frequency was also noted between survivors of myocardial infarction, regarded as end-stage atherosclerosis, and a control sample (Ferns et al. 1985). This putative disease association would, however, appear to be population-specific since no differences in S2 allele frequency were found between normolipidaemic and hyperlipidaemic individuals from Scottish (Morris and Price, 1985; Ferns et al., 1986; Price et al., 1986), Norwegian (Kessling et al., 1986), Chinese, African and Indian/Asian populations (Rees, et al., 1985; Law et al., 1986). Similarly, no difference was observed in S2 allele frequency between Japanese myocardial infarct survivors and healthy controls (Onuki *et al.*, 1986; Satoh *et al.*, 1987).

The deviation of the relative incidence of the S2 allele in the English population (confirmed by Shoulders *et al.*, 1986) and in Caucasians from Canada and the USA (Deeb *et al.*, 1986; Hayden *et al.*, 1987) is highly significant, but the validity of the conclusions drawn must nevertheless be doubted. The reported result of no rare allele heterozygotes out of 52 normolipidaemic individuals (Rees *et al.*, 1985) is so much at variance with the results of other groups on similar populations that it is hard to escape the conclusion that some bias must have been operating. Most probably, this was a random effect based on socioeconomic stratification. Since this bias was also operating in the selection of hypertriglyceridaemics in this study, the results are probably invalid. Socioeconomic and geographical differences in RFLP frequencies are certainly not unexpected and may well be complicating factors in other studies.

In an attempt to confirm postulated disease–marker associations, additional RFLPs around the APOA1–C3–A4 gene cluster have been recruited to allow more informative haplotype analysis to be carried out (reviewed by Shoulders and Baralle, 1986). Although a PstI RFLP showed no association with myocardial infarct survival or hyperlipidaemia (Kessling *et al.*, 1985; Ferns and Galton, 1986a; Hayden *et al.*, 1987), an association with HDL levels and premature coronary artery vessel disease was claimed by Ordovas *et al.*, (1986) and Anderson *et al.*, (1986). The rare allele of an EcoRI RFLP was reported to be found more frequently in patients with clinical symptoms of coronary heart disease, namely myocardial infarction and angina pectoris (Buraczynska *et al.*, 1986). XmnI (Kessling *et al.*, 1985; Hayden *et al.*, 1987) and MspI (Ferns and Galton, 1986a) RFLPs in this gene complex reportedly showed only weak associations with hyperlipidaemia and myocardial infarct survival, respectively. A specific SstI/MspI haplotype (S1–M2) at the APOA1/C3 locus was significantly increased in Japanese hypertriglyceridaemic individuals although this haplotype differed from that associated with disease in Caucasians (Anderson *et al.*, 1986; Rees *et al.*, 1986; Stocks *et al.*, 1987). Similarly, the S1–M2 haplotype at the APOA1/C3 locus was found to be significantly increased in Japanese myocardial infarction survivors compared with healthy controls (Satoh *et al.*, 1987). A specific XmnI/SstI haplotype (X2–S2) was also found to be associated with hyperlipidaemia, although this association did not reach a level of statistical significance when each RFLP was considered separately (Hayden *et al.*, 1987).

Homozygosity for an MspI RFLP allele within an Alu sequence 3' to the human APOA2 gene was reported to be associated with a 20% increase in serum apo A2 levels (Scott *et al.*, 1985). However, since only eight homozygotes were examined, the authors' claim that homozygosity for the RFLP marker might provide 'protection' against atherosclerosis was somewhat premature. An MspI RFLP allele at the APOA2 locus was reported to be associated with lower HDL levels and high triglyceride levels (Deeb *et al.*, 1986), the former association being significant at the 1% level. An XbaI RFLP allele in the APOB gene was reported to be associated with a 36% higher triglyceride level in clinically normal male Caucasians (Deeb *et al.*, 1986; Law *et al.*, 1986), and was claimed to increase the risk of atherosclerosis. However, this was not found in a study of myocardial infarct survivors (Ferns and Galton, 1986b). Interestingly, other workers have found this allele to be associated primarily with the level of serum cholesterol (Talmud and Humphries, 1986). Hegele *et al.* (1986) have reported that the frequencies of the XbaI RFLP alleles, and two additional RFLP alleles (EcoRI and MspI) around the APOB gene, were significantly increased in survivors of myocardial infarction. However, no significant difference in the XbaI RFLP allele frequency has been found between survivors of myocardial infarction and healthy controls in the Japanese population (Aburatani *et al.*, 1987). Deeb *et al.* (1986) reported two RFLPs, TaqI and PvuII, around the APOB gene that were associated with an elevated level of cholesterol and a lower level of HDL respectively. The three APOB RFLPs reported by Hegele *et al.* (1986) were not associated with variation of levels of lipid, lipoprotein or apolipoprotein and could, if the association is confirmed in other populations, indicate the existence of a further independent risk factor for myocardial infarction.

Some authors, through careless use of language, have done nothing to reduce confusion that might arise in interpreting their results and conclusions. Claims that the presence of RFLPs 'might provide protection against', or 'increase risk of' atherosclerosis are misleading and likely to lead to the confusion of *a posteriori* risk assessment from empirical data with direct causation.

Clearly, allelotype associations are difficult indicators of disease to use. Although the RFLP frequency or linkage phase of the markers used may be established in one population, both may differ dramatically between populations. Indeed, one of the features often apparent in studies performed to date is the variation of allele frequencies of all RFLPs in the normal groups (Cooper and Clayton, 1988). Pooling of data from different samples will thus result in a loss of information on account of the differing phase relationships of the alleles. It is clear that careful selection of the normal population sample is of paramount importance in such work. Methodological sources of error have also been apparent in many studies: sample sizes of the control and disease groups screened have often been rather low (usually less than 50 individuals). In addition, the sex ratio within these groups is often severely skewed in favour of males. No formal test of heterogeneity has been or indeed can be attempted since some of these studies have re-used control and/or disease groups partially or completely.

The delineation of a continuous variable such as plasma lipid concentration into 'normolipidaemia' and 'hyperlipidaemia' is perhaps inherently flawed due to the arbitrarily defined cut-off points. An alternative approach would be to determine the average allele 'effect' on phenotypic variation associated with each RFLP. This strategy has been employed in polymorphism studies at the APOE locus (Utermann *et al.*, 1984; Sing and Davignon 1985; Davignon *et al.*, 1986; Zannis, 1986). This approach does not, however, obviate the need for careful matching of disease and control populations.

The ultimate goal of RFLP association studies should be the demonstration that a given phenotypic difference may be attributed to the presence of a specific disease allele. Marker–disease associations should be regarded only as a means to this end and should, by themselves, be interpreted with extreme caution. The results of such analyses may, however, be regarded as an indication that classical segregation studies should be performed on affected families with the assumption of a single major locus that predisposes to the disease. An increasing number of linkage studies have now been successfully performed in families with hypercholesterolaemia, hyperlipaemia and other forms of chronic heart disease (reviewed by Cooper and Schmidtke, 1991; see Appendix 1).

5.6 X-chromosome inactivation analysis

One source of phenotypic heterogeneity in female carriers of X-linked recessive disorders is X-inactivation. Early on in female embryogenesis, one of the two X chromosomes in every cell is inactivated and this inactivation event is both random and clonal: the pattern of X chromosome inactivation in each progenitor cell is transmitted to daughter cells. Each and every cell in a female carrier of an X-linked recessive disorder therefore bears the disease allele on either the active or the inactive X chromosome. Populations of cells with the mutant gene on the active X chromosome are functionally equivalent to cells from an affected male, whereas cells with the mutant gene on the inactive X chromosome will be normal. Carrier females are thus effectively mosaics of cells with either mutant or wild-type characteristics. The ratio of active maternal to active paternal X chromosomes exhibits a normal distribution in a sample of females around a mean ratio of 50:50. It is now known that alterations in the transcriptional status of X-chromosomal genes are associated with changes in DNA methylation (reviewed by Lyon, 1988) so that the active and inactive X chromosomes may be readily distinguished by their methylation status. Indeed, X-inactivation may be a special case of genomic imprinting (Section 12.5).

X-linked agammaglobulinaemia (XLA) is a recessive disorder characterized by recurrent infection due to a deficiency of immunoglobulins and a lack of B cells. If it was supposed that the normal function of the underlying gene was to promote the maturation of pre-B cells to B lymphocytes, then in XLA carrier females, pre-B lymphocytes in which the mutant X chromosome has been inactivated would be able to mature successfully. However, those pre-B lymphocytes in which the wild-type allele had been inactivated would not. A clonal selection process during development might thus operate to ensure that the X chromosomes bearing the disease allele in mature B lymphocytes would always be inactivated.

Fearon et al. (1987) devised an elegant strategy to prove the correctness of the above hypothesis. Using two constitutively active X-chromosomal genes [hypoxanthine phosphoribosyltransferase (HPRT) and phosphoglycerokinase (PGK)] as probes, maternal and paternal alles were distinguished by RFLP tracking whereas discrimination between the active and inactive X chromosomes was achieved by using methylation-sensitive restriction enzymes (e.g. HpaII,

HhaI). The basic underlying principle is that analysis of a polyclonal cell population with HpaII should affect maternal and paternal alleles equally since both would have had the same chance of being inactivated. If on the other hand the cell population had arisen from a single progenitor cell, then the maternal X chromosome would be either active or inactive in all cells and this non-randomness would be apparent in HpaII cleavage of either the maternal or the paternal allele, but not both. Fearon *et al.* (1987) found that X-inactivation patterns were non-random in granulocytes and T and B lymphocytes of non-carrier women but, in XLA carriers, one of the two X chromosomes was preferentially active in B cells but not in other cell types. This finding not only supports the hypothesis that XLA is a defect of B-cell development and that clonal selection operates in carrier females, but also provides the means to directly identify such women in families with the disease. This is particularly important in XLA, where the gene has not yet been isolated and where 45–50% of known patients are sporadic cases.

X-inactivation analysis commends itself for use in other X-linked recessive conditions which interfere with the normal development of particular cell lineages. So far it has also been successfully applied to carrier detection analysis in colorectal carcinoma, severe combined immunodeficiency and Wiscott–Aldrich syndrome.

References

Aburatani H, Murase T, Takaku F, Itoh H, Matsumoto A, Itakura H. (1987) Apolipoprotein B-gene polymorphism and myocardial infarction. *N. Engl. J. Med.* **317:** 52.

Anderson RA, Benda TJ, Wallace RB, Eliason SL, Lee J, Burns TL. (1986) Prevalence and associations of apolipoprotein A1-linked DNA polymorphisms: results from a population study. *Genet. Epidemiol.* **3:** 385–397.

Beaudet A, Bowcock A, Buchwald M, Cavalli-Sforza L, Farrall M, King MC, Klinger K, Lalouel JM, Lathrop G, Naylor S, Ott J, Tsui LC, Wainwright B, Watkins P, White R, Williamson R. (1986) Linkage of cystic fibrosis to two tightly linked DNA markers: joint report from a collaborative study. *Am. J. Hum. Genet.* **39:** 681–693.

Bird AP. (1987) CpG islands as gene markers in the vertebrate nucleus. *Trends Genet.* **3:** 342–347.

Botstein D, White RL, Skolnick M, Davis RW. (1980) Construction of a genetic linkage map in man using restriction fragment length polymorphisms. *Am. J. Hum. Genet.* **32:** 314–331.

Breslow JL. (1989) Genetic basis of lipoprotein disorders. *J. Clin. Invest.* **84:** 373–380.

Buraczynska M, Hanzlik J, Grzywa M. (1986) Apo A-1 related DNA polymorphism in humans with coronary heart disease. *Hum. Genet.* **74:** 165–167.

Cooper DN, Clayton JF. (1988) DNA polymorphism and the study of disease associations. *Hum. Genet.* **78:** 299–312.

Cooper DN, Schmidtke J. (1991) Diagnosis of genetic disease using recombinant DNA. Third edition. *Hum. Genet.* **87:** 519–560.

Davignon J, Sing CF, Lussier-Cacan S, Nestruk AC, Bouthillier D. (1986) Importance of apolipoprotein E polymorphism in determining plasma lipid levels and atherosclerosis. In: *Atherosclerosis VII.* (eds NH Fidge, PJ Nestel). Elsevier, Amsterdam, pp. 171–175.

Deeb S, Failor A, Brown BG, Brunzell JD, Albers JJ, Motulsky AG. (1986) Molecular genetics of apolipoproteins and coronary heart disease. *Cold Spring Harb. Symp. Quant. Biol.* **51:** 403–409.

Donis-Keller H, Green P, Helms C, Cartinhour S, Weiffenbach B, Stephens K, Keith TP, Bowden DW, Smith DR, Lander ES, Botstein D, Akots G, Rediker KS, Gravius T, Brown VA, Rising MB, Parker C, Powers JA, Watt DE, Kauffman ER, Bricker A, Phipps P, Muller-Kahle H, Fulton TR, Ng S, Schumm JW, Braman JC, Knowlton RG, Barker DF, Crooks SM, Lincoln SE, Daly MJ, Abrahamson J. (1987) A genetic linkage map of the human genome. *Cell* **51**: 319–337.

Edwards JH. (1987) Exclusion mapping. *J. Med. Genet.* **24**: 539–543.

Elvin P, Slynn G, Black D, Graham A, Butler R, Riley J, Anand R, Markham AF. (1990) Isolation of cDNA clones using yeast artificial chromosome probes. *Nucleic Acids Res.* **18**: 3913–3917.

Estivill X, Farrall M, Scambler PJ, Bell GM, Hawley KM, Lench NJ, Bates GP, Kruyer HC, Frederick PA, Stanier P, Watson EK, Williamson R, Wainwright B. (1987) A candidate for the cystic fibrosis locus isolated by selection for methylation-free islands. *Nature* **326**: 840–845.

Fearon ER, Winkelstein JA, Civin CI, Pardoll DM, Vogelstein B. (1987) Carrier detection in X-linked agammaglobulinemia by analysis of X-chromosome inactivation. *N. Engl. J. Med.* **316**: 427–431.

Ferns GAA, Galton DJ. (1986a) Haplotypes of the human apoprotein AI–CIII–AIV gene cluster in coronary atherosclerosis. *Hum. Genet.* **73**: 245–249.

Ferns GAA, Galton DJ. (1986b) Frequency of XbaI polymorphism in myocardial infarct survivors. *Lancet* **ii**: 572.

Ferns GAA, Ritchie C, Stocks J, Galton DJ. (1985) Genetic polymorphisms of apolipoprotein C-III and insulin in survivors of myocardial infarction. *Lancet* **ii**: 300–303.

Ferns GAA, Stocks J, Galton DJ. (1986) C-III DNA restriction fragment length polymorphism and myocardial infarction. *Lancet* **i**: 94.

Goldstein JL, Brown MS. (1989) Familial hypercholesterolemia. In: *The Metabolic Basis of Inherited Disease*, 6th Edn, (eds CR Scriver, AL Beaudet, WS Sly, D Valle). McGraw-Hill, New York, pp. 1215–1250.

Haldane JBS. (1919) The combination of linkage values and the calculation of distances between the loci of linked factors. *J. Genet.* **8**: 299–309.

Hayden MR, Kirk H, Clark C, Frohlich J, Rabkins S, McLeod R, Hewitt J. (1987) DNA polymorphisms in and around the apo AI-CIII genes and genetic hyperlipidaemias. *Am. J. Hum. Genet.* **40**: 421–430.

Hegele RA, Breslow JL. (1987) Apolipoprotein genetic variation in the assessment of atherosclerosis susceptibility. *Genet. Epidemiol.* **4**: 163–184.

Hegele RA, Huang L-S, Herbert PN, Blum CB, Buring JE, Hennekens CH, Breslow JL. (1986) Apolipoprotein B-gene DNA polymorphisms associated with myocardial infarction. *N. Engl. J. Med.* **315**: 1509–1515.

Hochgeschwender U, Brennan MB. (1991) Identifying genes within the genome: new ways for finding the needle in a haystack. *Bioessays* **13**: 139–144.

Humphries SE. (1988) DNA polymorphisms of the apolipoprotein genes — their use in the investigation of the genetic component of hyperlipidaemia and atherosclerosis. *Atherosclerosis* **72**: 89–108.

Iannuzzi MC, Dean M, Drumm ML, Hidaka N, Cole JL, Perry A, Stewart C, Gerrard B, Collins FS. (1989) Isolation of additional polymorphic clones from the cystic fibrosis region, using chromosome jumping from D7S8. *Am. J. Hum. Genet.* **44**: 695–703.

Jeffreys AJ, Wilson V, Thein SL. (1985) Hypervariable 'minisatellite' regions in human DNA. *Nature* **314**: 67–73.

Kerem BS, Rommens JM, Buchanan JA, Markiewicz D, Cox TK, Chakravarti A, Buchwald M, Tsui LC. (1989) Identification of the cystic fibrosis gene: genetic analysis. *Science* **245**: 1073–1080.

Kessling AM, Horsthemke B, Humphries SE. (1985) A study of DNA polymorphisms around the human apolipoprotein A1 gene in hyperlipidaemic and normal individuals. *Clin. Genet.* **28**: 296–306.

Kessling AM, Berg K, Mockleby E, Humphries SE. (1986) DNA polymorphisms around the apo AI gene in normal and hyperlipidaemic individuals selected for a twin study. *Clin. Genet.* **29:** 485–490.

Knowlton RG, Cohen-Haguenauer O, Nguyen VC, Frzal J, Brown V, Barker D, Braman JC, Schumm JW, Tsui LC, Buchwald M, Donis-Keller H. (1985) A polymorphic DNA marker linked to cystic fibrosis is located on chromosome 7. *Nature* **318:** 380–382.

Krawczak M. (1987) Genetic risk and recombination fraction — an example of non-monotonic dependency. *Hum. Genet.* **75:** 189–190.

Krawczak M, Konecki DS, Schmidtke J, Dück M, Engel W, Nützenadel W, Trefz FK. (1988) Allelic association of the cystic fibrosis locus and two DNA markers, XV2c and KM19, in 55 German families. *Hum. Genet.* **80:** 78–80.

Lathrop GM, Lalouel JM. (1984) Easy calculations of lod scores and genetic risks on small computers. *Am. J. Hum. Genet.* **36:** 460–465.

Lathrop GM, Lalouel JM, Julier C, Ott J. (1984) Strategies for multilocus linkage analysis in humans. *Proc. Natl. Acad. Sci. USA* **81:** 3443–3446.

Lathrop GM, Lalouel JM, Julier C, Ott J. (1985) Multilocus linkage analysis in humans: detection of linkage and estimation of recombination. *Am. J. Hum. Genet.* **37:** 482–498.

Law A, Powell LM, Brunt H, Knott TJ, Altman DG, Rajput J, Wallis SC, Pease RJ, Priestley LM, Scott J, Miller GJ, Miller NE. (1986) Common DNA polymorphism within coding sequence of apolipoprotein B gene associated with altered lipid levels. *Lancet* **i:** 1301–1303.

Li W-H, Tanimura M, Luo C-C, Datta S, Chan L. (1988) Apolipoprotein multigene family: biosynthesis, structure, structure-function relationships and evolution. *J. Lipid Res.* **29:** 245–271.

Lusis AJ. (1988) Genetic factors affecting blood lipoproteins: the candidate gene approach. *J. Lipid Res.* **29:** 397–429.

Lyon MF. (1988) X-chromosome inactivation and the location and expression of X-linked genes. *Am. J. Hum. Genet.* **42:** 8–16.

Meerman G te. (1991) *A Logic Programming Approach to Pedigree Analysis.* Thesis Publishers, Amsterdam.

Morris SW, Price WH. (1985) DNA sequence polymorphisms in the apolipoprotein A-1/C-III gene cluster. *Lancet* **ii:** 1127–1128.

Morton NE. (1955) Sequential test for the detection of linkage. *Am. J. Hum. Genet.* **7:** 266–318.

Morton NE. (1988) Multipoint mapping and the emperor's clothes. *Ann. Hum. Genet.* **52:** 309–318.

Mourant AE, Kopec AC, Domaniewska-Sobczak K. (1978) *Blood Groups and Diseases.* Oxford University Press, Oxford.

Nakamura Y, Leppert M, O'Connell P, Wolff R, Holm T, Culver M, Martin C, Fujimoto E, Hoff M, Kumlin E, White R. (1987) Variable number of tandem repeat (VNTR) markers for human gene mapping. *Science* **235:** 1616–1622.

Onuki M, Iwamura Y, Humphries SE, Satoh J, Hattori N, Yamakawa K, Yamanouchi Y, Okafuji T, Hamaguchi H. (1986) Apolipoprotein AI–CIII gene polymorphisms in a Japanese population. *Jpn. J. Hum. Genet.* **31:** 337–343.

Ordovas JM, Schaefer EJ, Salem D, Ward RH, Glueck CJ, Vergani C, Wilson PWF, Karathanasis SK. (1986) Apolipoprotein A-1 gene polymorphism associated with premature coronary artery disease and familial hypoalphalipoproteinemia. *N. Engl. J. Med.* **314:** 671–677.

Orkin SH. (1986) Reverse genetics and human disease. *Cell* **47:** 845–850.

Ott J. (1976) A computer program for linkage analysis of general human pedigrees. *Am. J. Hum. Genet.* **28:** 528–529.

Ott J. (1985) *Analysis of Human Genetic Linkage.* Johns Hopkins University Press, Baltimore, Maryland.

Price WH, Morris SW, Burgon R, Donald PM, Kitchin AH. (1986) Apolipoprotein CIII polymorphism and coronary heart disease. *Lancet* **ii:** 1041.

Rao DC, Keats BJB, Morton NE, Yee S, Lew R. (1978) Variability of human linkage data. *Am. J. Hum. Genet.* **30:** 516–529

Rees A, Stocks J, Shoulders CC, Galton DJ, Baralle FE. (1983) DNA polymorphism adjacent to human apoprotein A-1 gene: relation to hypertriglyceridaemia. *Lancet* **i:** 444–446.

Rees A, Stocks J, Sharpe CR, Vella MA, Shoulders CC, Katz J, Jowett NI, Baralle FE, Galton DJ. (1985) Deoxyribonucleic acid polymorphism in the apolipoprotein A-1 C-III gene cluster association with hypertriglyceridaemia. *J. Clin. Invest.* **76:** 1090–1095.

Rees A, Stocks J, Paul H, Ohuchi Y, Galton D. (1986) Haplotypes identified by DNA polymorphisms at the apolipoprotein A-1 and CIII loci and hypertriglyceridaemia. *Hum. Genet.* **72:** 168–171.

Renwick JH. (1969) Progress in mapping human autosomes. *Br. Med. Bull.* **25:** 65–73

Riordan JR, Rommens JM, Kerem BS, Alon N, Rozmahel R, Grzelczak Z, Zielenski J, Lok S, Plavsic N, Chou JL, Drumm ML, Iannuzzi ML, Collins FS, Tsui LC. (1989) Identification of the cystic fibrosis gene: cloning and characterization of complementary DNA. *Science* **245:** 1066–1073.

Risch N. (1990) Genetic linkage and complex diseases, with special reference to psychiatric disorders. *Genet. Epidemiol.* **7:** 3–16.

Satoh J, Hattori N, Onuki M, Yamakawa K, Fujiwara H, Amamiya H, Nagaoka H, Sakuma T, Yamanouchi Y, Okafuji T, Iwamura Y, Tsuchiya S, Fukutomi H, Ohsuga T, Hamaguchi H. (1987) Apolipoprotein AI-CIII gene polymorphisms in Japanese myocardial infarction survivors. *Jpn. J. Hum. Genet.* **32:** 15–20.

Scott J, Knott TJ, Priestley LM, Robertson ME, Mann DV, Kostner G, Miller GJ, Miller NE. (1985) High-density lipoprotein composition is altered by a common DNA polymorphism adjacent to apoprotein AII gene in man. *Lancet* **i:** 771–773.

Shoulders CC, Baralle FE. (1986) Genetic polymorphism in the Apo A1–CIII complex. *Methods Enzymol.* **128:** 727–745.

Shoulders CC, Ball MJ, Mann JI, Baralle FE. (1986) Genetic marker in apolipoprotein AI/CIII gene complex associated with hypercholesterolaemia. *Lancet* **ii:** 1286.

Sing CF, Davignon J. (1985) Role of the apolipoprotein E polymorphism in determining normal plasma lipid and lipoprotein variation. *Am. J. Hum. Genet.* **37:** 268–285.

Smith CL, Klco SR, Cantor CR. (1988) Pulsed-field gel electrophoresis and the technology of large DNA molecules. In *Genome Analysis: A Practical Approach.* (ed. KE Davies). IRL Press, Oxford, pp. 41–72.

Sobell JL, Heston LL, Sommer SS. (1992) Delineation of genetic predisposition to multifactorial disease: a general approach on the threshold of feasibility. *Genomics* **12:** 1–6.

Stocks J, Paul H, Galton D. (1987) Haplotypes identified by DNA restriction fragment length polymorphisms in the AI–CIII–AIV gene region and hypertriglyceridemia. *Am. J. Hum. Genet.* **41:** 106–118.

Talmud P, Humphries S. (1986) DNA polymorphisms and the apolipoprotein B gene. *Lancet* **ii:** 104.

Utermann G, Kindermann I, Kaffarnik H, Steinmetz A. (1984) Apolipoprotein E phenotypes and hyperlipidaemia. *Hum. Genet.* **65:** 232–237.

Vella M, Kessling A, Jowett N, Rees A, Stocks J, Wallis S, Galton DJ. (1985) DNA polymorphisms flanking the apo A-1 and insulin genes and type III hyperlipidaemia. *Hum. Genet.* **69:** 275–276.

Vogel F, Motulsky AG. (1986) *Human Genetics*, 2nd Edn. Springer, Berlin.

Wainwright BJ, Scambler PJ, Schmidtke J, Watson EA, Law HY, Farrall M, Cooke HJ, Eiberg H, Williamson R. (1985) Localization of cystic fibrosis locus to human chromosome 7cen-q22. *Nature* **318:** 384–385.

White R, Caskey CT. (1988) The human as an experimental system in molecular genetics. *Science* **240:** 1483–1488.

White R, Woodward S, Leppert M, O'Connell P, Nakamura Y, Hoff M, Herbst J, Lalouel JM, Dean M, Vande-Woude G. (1985a) A closely linked genetic marker for cystic fibrosis. *Nature* **318:** 382–384.

White R, Leppert M, Bishop DT, Barker D, Berkowitz J, Brown C, Callahan P, Holm T, Jerominski L. (1985b) Construction of linkage maps with DNA markers for human chromosomes. *Nature* **313:** 101–105.

Zannis VI. (1986) Genetic polymorphism in human apolipoprotein E. *Methods Enzymol.* **128:** 823–851.

Zannis VI, Breslow JL. (1985) Genetic mutations affecting human lipoprotein metabolism. *Adv. Hum. Genet.* **14:** 125–215.

6

Single base-pair substitutions

6.1 Introduction

One of the most important properties of genetic material is its capacity to organize its own faithful replication within the cell. If, however, no errors were ever made during the process of DNA replication, the evolution of complex genomes would scarcely have been possible. Although *in vivo* studies of eukaryotic DNA replication have indicated that this process is extremely accurate, errors do nevertheless occur at a frequency of between 10^{-9} to 10^{-11} per incorporated nucleotide (Drake, 1970; Nalbantoglu *et al.*, 1983; Thacker, 1985). This is much lower than the 10^{-3} to 10^{-6} error frequency observed *in vitro*, and the disparity is thought to be a result of the efficiency of *in vivo* proofreading and error correction mechanisms (Roberts and Kunkel, 1986; Kunkel and Bebenek, 1988).

Mutation rates calculated for specific human genetic diseases also vary widely (Vogel and Motulsky, 1986; see also Chapter 13). Intuitively, we may surmise that, at least for dominant and sex-linked recessive conditions, differences in incidence and prevalence are a reflection of underlying differences in the relative mutability of certain genes in the germline. The challenge now facing us is to be able to relate observed differences in the incidence and prevalence of genetic disease to the structure of the mutant genes responsible and to the function of the proteins that they encode. A major step towards this aim would be the development of the ability to make predictions regarding the probable frequency and location of lesions within any given gene by reference to the DNA sequence and genomic architecture of that gene.

With the advent of recombinant DNA and the introduction of new analytical techniques, rapid progress has been made in the characterization of gene mutations causing human inherited disease (reviewed by Cooper and Schmidtke, 1991). For most conditions, a substantial proportion of the underlying lesions is now thought to consist of point mutations together with a smaller number of deletions, the remainder being made up of insertions, inversions and complex rearrangements. Considerable variation nevertheless exists in the relative proportions of the different types of mutation found for different gene loci. This variation may reflect individual characteristics of the genes, such as length, number of splice junctions and the degree of DNA methylation or sequence repetitivity.

The discovery in phage T4 of mutational 'hotspots' (Benzer, 1961) indicated that the frequency of mutational lesions may be strongly influenced by the local DNA sequence environment. Moreover, this and other early work also provided the first clear evidence for the existence of endogenous mechanisms of mutation as distinct from the hitherto better characterized exogenous causes such as radiation or chemical mutagens (see Chapter 1). Nowadays, the study of gene mutation is considered important not only for what it can teach us of the basic cellular mechanisms underlying mutagenesis, but also because explanatory models can be constructed whose predictive value may be empirically tested.

Mutation of human genes may arise either as a consequence of endogenous error-prone processes, such as DNA replication and repair, or as a result of exposure to exogenous factors, e.g. chemical mutagens or ionizing/UV irradiation (reviewed by Auerbach, 1976). Most studies to date have concentrated on the latter category of induced mutations to the detriment of the former. This is for the simple reason that induced mutations are usually many orders of magnitude more frequent than their spontaneous *in vivo* counterparts. However, induced mutations probably arise by different mechanisms

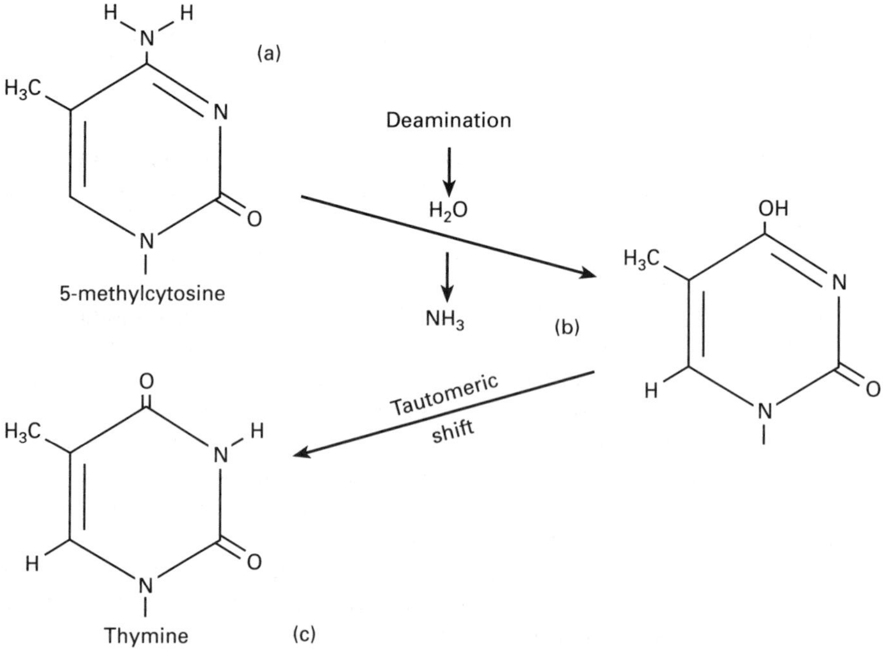

Figure 6.1. Spontaneous deamination of 5-methylcytosine. In aqueous solution, a spontaneous hydrophilic attack at C-4 of 5-methylcytosine (a) results in a replacement of the amino by a hydroxyl group. The intermediate *enol*-type product (b) undergoes a tautomeric transition into the more stable *keto*-type product, thymine (c).

from 'spontaneous' mutations and may not provide a viable or realistic model for the study of *in vivo* mutation. Moreover, most mutation studies have been carried out in bacteria or viruses on account of their relative ease of culture and analysis. In consequence, relatively little is known of the nature of spontaneous mutation in higher eukaryotes. In humans, despite numerous studies of the potential genetic consequences of exposure to known *in vitro* mutagens (ionizing radiation, alkylating agents, cytostatic drugs etc), not a single agent has been identified as causing the increased incidence of a genetic disorder (Rüdiger, 1991).

By contrast, considerable evidence for endogenous mechanisms of mutagenesis has begun to accumulate. Thus, nucleotide substitutions are thought to result either from chemical (e.g. deamination of 5-methylcytosine, Coulondre *et al.*, 1978; depurination, Loeb and Preston, 1986), physical (e.g. DNA slippage, Kunkel and Soni, 1988) or enzymatic (e.g. post-replicative mismatch repair or exonucleolytic proofreading, Modrich, 1987; Loeb and Kunkel, 1982) mechanisms. Since the efficiency of all these processes is known to be sequence-dependent, it is hardly surprising that the distribution of point mutations is non-random, thereby giving rise to hotspots and possibly coldspots of base substitution in eukaryotic genomes. These mechanisms will now be explored in more detail and the relative contribution of each to the observed spectrum of human gene mutation assessed.

6.2 Methylation-mediated deamination of 5-methylcytosine

6.2.1 CpG distribution in the vertebrate genome and its origins

5-Methylcytosine (5mC) has been known for some time to be hypermutable in prokaryotes (Coulondre *et al.*, 1978). This is thought to be due to the increased mutability of 5mC by deamination to thymine (Duncan and Miller, 1980; Figure 6.1) together with a less-than-perfect repair mechanism for resulting G:T mismatches (Kramer *et al.*, 1984; Lu *et al.*, 1984; Jones *et al.* 1987a; Shenoy *et al.*, 1987; Zell and Fritz 1987). [The interested reader should, however, note the discussion below (Section 6.4.4) of the possible role of DNA methyltransferase in promoting 5mC deamination.] In eukaryotic genomes, 5mC occurs predominantly in CpG dinucleotides, the majority of which appear to be methylated (Section 2.7). One consequence of the hypermutability of 5mC is therefore the paucity of CpG in the genomes of many eukaryotes (Josse *et al.* 1961; Setlow, 1976; see Section 2.7), the heavily methylated vertebrate genomes exhibiting the most extreme 'CpG suppression' (Bird, 1980). (The extent of CpG suppression is measured by comparison of the observed CpG frequency with its random expectation, i.e. the product of the mononucleotide frequencies for C and G.)

Spatially, the distribution of CpG is also non-random: about 1% of vertebrate genomes consist of a fraction that is rich in CpG and which accounts for about 15% of all CpG dinucleotides (reviewed by Bird, 1986; see Section 2.7). In contrast to most of the scattered CpG dinucleotides, these

'CpG islands' represent unmethylated domains and in many cases appear to coincide with transcribed regions.

The question of the origin of CpG islands in vertebrate genomes is associated with the question of whether or not they perform a precise function or whether they have arisen merely as a consequence of the absence of methylation. Cooper and Gerber-Huber (1985) reviewed the arguments for the functional importance of at least some CpG dinucleotides within coding regions and their consequent conservation by selection. It is nevertheless clear that DNA regions that remain unmethylated either by active (physical removal; Razin *et al.*, 1986) or passive (protein binding; Bird, 1986) processes or by the presence/absence of methylase-instructional sequences (Bolden *et al.*, 1986) will not lose CpG dinucleotides through methylation-mediated deamination and will thus retain their 'island character'. Since the 5′ regions of genes are often unmethylated in the germline (Bird, 1986), these sequences can perhaps be regarded as the 'last remnants of the long tracts of non-methylated DNA' (Bird, 1987) that once made up the bulk of ancestral non-vertebrate genomes. In other words, it may be unnecessary to invoke mechanisms to account for the existence of CpG islands other than the absence of methylation and hence 5mC deamination.

6.2.2 The mutability of CpG dinucleotides

At the level of the gene, a high level of $C \rightarrow T$ transitions was first reported by Vogel and Röhrborn (1965) in a study of the mutations responsible for haemoglobin variants in humans. Further studies (Vogel and Kopun, 1977) confirmed the existence of this phenomenon. Many sequence comparison studies in eukaryotes (reviewed in Section 2.7) have now shown that the CpG dinucleotide is specifically associated with a high frequency of $C \rightarrow T$ and $G \rightarrow A$ transitions. ($G \rightarrow A$ transitions arise as a result of a $5mC \rightarrow T$ transition on the antisense DNA strand, followed by miscorrection of $G \rightarrow A$ on the sense strand.) This observation would predict the progressive loss of CpG residues over evolutionary time as a direct consequence of their methylation in the germline.

Comparable conclusions may also be drawn at the clinical level: of a total of 880 base changes reported to cause human genetic disease (Appendix 2), 38% were found to involve a CpG dinucleotide, and 86.5% (32.8% of the total) of these were either $C \rightarrow T$ or $G \rightarrow A$ transitions. These data are consistent with conclusions drawn from the much smaller mutation sample reported by Cooper and Youssoufian (1988). As will be described in detail in Section 6.5, the *relative rate* (m_d) at which CpG mutates to either TpG or CpA can be shown to be 7.4 times higher than the *base mutation rate* (m_b). [Note: This ratio is arrived at by dividing the average of the two relative mutabilities ($CG \rightarrow TG$ and $CG \rightarrow CA$) from Table 6.6 by three times the average of all other relative dinucleotide mutabilities.]

In the following sections (6.2.3–6.2.6), we shall determine whether or not this clinically derived (relative) CpG mutation rate is compatible with both evolutionary data and the 5mC deamination rate as measured by *in vitro* studies. This approach extends our earlier study on 5mC mutation rates (Cooper and Krawczak, 1989), which has been substantially revised, and compares our original conclusions to those subsequently obtained by others.

6.2.3 CpG mutation in the β-globin gene cluster

Is the ratio $m_d/m_b = 7.4$, derived from clinical data, consistent with estimates of the CpG mutation rate derived from the comparison of evolutionarily related sequences? The globin genes represent a good model system for such a comparison since their DNA sequences and evolutionary history have both been well studied. To quantify the likelihood of evolutionary change, however, we must make an assumption as to the actual value of m_b. Based on an analysis of 58 genes, Bulmer *et al.* (1991) estimated the neutral base substitution rate for primates to be 2.2×10^{-9} per nucleotide per year. Since we shall first compare human and chimpanzee ψ β1-pseudogene sequences (GenBank, latest release) with respect to mutation at CpG dinucleotides, we regard this figure as an appropriate estimate of m_b. The ψ β1-pseudogenes were chosen for comparison because (i) they are known to be heavily methylated (Mavilio *et al.*, 1983) and (ii) their analysis is not complicated by the action of selection.

Let us define P as the probability that a single CpG mutates to either TpG or CpA and becomes fixed as a mutation in the time since the divergence of man and chimpanzee, i.e. 7 million years (Sibley and Ahlquist, 1984). Since, in 20 CpG sites of the ψ β1-pseudogene, 2 C→T or G→A transitions were found in both species, the estimate of P is 0.1 for both species. The time until such a mutation occurs can be assumed to follow an exponential distribution with density function

$$m_d^{-1}\exp(-m_d t)$$

and, thus, we have

$$P = 1 - \exp(-m_d t)$$

where $t = 7 \times 10^6$ years. Rearranging this equality yields

$$m_d = -\ln(1-P)/t = 1.51 \times 10^{-8} \text{ year}^{-1}$$

which is 6.9 times higher than m_b.

A similar analysis of the human and chimpanzee β-globin (HBB) structural gene sequences yielded five out of a possible total 37 CG→TG or CG→CA transitions in humans, and seven out of a possible total of 37 in chimpanzees. From this, P is estimated as

$$P_H = 0.1351 \quad \text{and} \quad P_C = 0.1892$$

where P_H and P_C denote probabilities for humans and chimpanzees, respectively. After transformation, the estimates of m_d are

Human: $\qquad m_d = 2.07 \times 10^{-8} \text{ year}^{-1} \qquad$ i.e. $9.4 \times m_b$

Chimpanzee: $\qquad m_d = 3.00 \times 10^{-8} \text{ year}^{-1} \qquad$ i.e. $13.6 \times m_b$

Thus, at least for humans, the m_d/m_b ratio is compatible with the clinical findings.

Comparison of the ψ β-globin gene regions in humans and rhesus macaques (Miyamoto *et al.*, 1988) yielded 16 of a possible 28 (human) and 17 of a possible 31 (macaque) CG→TG or CG→CA transitions. These two species are thought to have diverged about 50 million years ago (Young, 1973). If P is redefined accordingly, we have

$$P_H = 0.5714 \quad \text{and} \quad P_M = 0.5484$$

Transformation yields the following estimates for m_d:

Human: $\qquad m_d = 1.69 \times 10^{-8}$ year^{-1} $\qquad$ i.e. $\qquad 7.7 \times m_b$

Macaque: $\qquad m_d = 1.59 \times 10^{-8}$ year^{-1} $\qquad$ i.e. $\qquad 7.2 \times m_b$

These two m_d/m_b ratios are also very close to our former estimate.

Only three pairs of sequences have been examined here, and so any conclusion must remain tentative. Further data are thus required to substantiate these findings. However, the derivation of similar results from both clinical data and evolutionary sequence comparison studies argues strongly for the accuracy of the two estimates:

$$m_b = 2.2 \times 10^{-9} \text{ year}^{-1} \quad \text{and} \quad m_d = 7.4 m_b = 1.63 \times 10^{-8} \text{ year}^{-1}$$

The absence of any significant difference derived from the comparison of gene sequences on the one hand and pseudogene sequences on the other strongly suggests that the action of selection has had a negligible effect on the transition rate at CpG dinucleotides in primate β-globin genes. This constancy in CpG deamination rate thus provides strong support for the neutralist view of gene evolution. Further, the successful use of evolutionary comparisons of DNA sequences to derive consistent values of m_d demonstrates the feasibility of using the CpG mutation rate as a molecular clock, at least over relatively short periods of evolutionary time. Rate constancy, however, would also both assume and require the temporal stability of the methylation pattern. The validity of this assumption remains to be verified by more extensive sequence comparison studies, by analysis of the methylation patterns exhibited by homologous genes in different species, and by the stability or otherwise of transgene methylation patterns tracked down the generations (reviewed by Monk, 1988). Clearly, the use of such a molecular clock over long periods of evolutionary time is fraught with dangers, not the least being possible differences in the efficiency of repair mechanisms and the degree of selection (Britten, 1986; Li and Tanimura, 1987). The existence of a relatively fast moving molecular clock might nevertheless be potentially useful for the study of gene divergence in human populations.

Point mutations do not normally arise merely through a time-dependent process; many spontaneous base-pair substitutions and frameshift mutations are replication dependent (reviewed by Vogel *et al.*, 1976). The frequent occurrence of transitions within CpG dinucleotides does not, however, arise from mispairing or misincorporation of bases during replication, but is instead caused by the spontaneous deamination of 5mC. Indeed, no particular preponderance of G:T mispairs or C→T and G→A transitions has been found to be associated with a DNA polymerase activity in human cells (Kunkel and Alexander, 1986). Further, our finding that the CpG mutation rate, as measured from clinical data, is in broad agreement with that derived from evolutionary sequence comparisons provides strong support for the time-dependent nature of CpG deamination and for its independence from such factors as DNA replication, number of meiotic divisions or generation time.

6.2.4 The emergence of CpG suppression

It is clearly a hazardous undertaking to extrapolate too far from the apparent constancy of the CpG mutation rate over the relatively short time period of primate evolution. We may nevertheless attempt to estimate the length of time it would take to create a CpG deficiency of the magnitude that is observed today [frequency (CpG) = 20% of expected] in total vertebrate genomic DNA, using the estimates of m_d and m_b derived above. Again, we need not consider selection here, since its conservative influence is unlikely to affect non-coding regions, which make up the bulk of the genome. We have thus adopted a simple neutralist model in which the loss of CpG dinucleotides has occurred merely through a passive time-dependent process. For ease of modelling, we assume that all mutation rates involved have remained constant over this time period. This is a big assumption, since the rate of 5mC deamination may be determined by many different factors. Moreover, the relative efficiency of G:T mismatch repair processes is likely to have been influenced by variation in the level of 5mC and its consequent deamination.

Let $x(t)$ denote the frequency of either guanine or cytosine and let $y(t)$ denote the frequency of CpG dinucleotides at time t. The behaviour of these functions can be described by the following system of differential equations:

$$x' = -(m_d + 2m_b/3)y - m_b(x - y) + m_b(1 - x)/3$$

$$y' = -(2m_d + 4m_b/3 + m_b^2)y + 2m_b(x - y)/3 + m_b^2(1 - 2x + y)/9 \qquad (1)$$

System 1 can be interpreted as follows: cytosine, for example, is lost with probability $m_d + 2m_b/3$ if it occurs in a CpG dinucleotide, and with probability m_b from any other CpN dinucleotide. By contrast, C residues arise from other nucleotides with probability $m_b/3$. CpG dinucleotides are lost with probability $2m_d + 4m_b/3 + m_b^2$, whereas one out of three possible mutation events creates a CpG, if C is in the first or G is in the second position. The frequency of such dinucleotides is $2(x - y)$. Finally, two simultaneous mutations would give rise to a CpG from any of the remaining dinucleotides, the total frequency of which is $1 - 2x + y$. It should be noted that the same arguments apply to G residues if NpG instead of CpN dinucleotides are considered.

If we rearrange System 1 and drop out terms with factor m_b^2, the system is simplified to

$$x' = -4m_b x/3 + (m_b/3 - m_d)y + m_b/3$$

$$y' = 2m_b x/3 - 2(m_d + m_b)y \qquad (2)$$

To solve these differential equations, we have to make assumptions about the initial values $x(0)$ and $y(0)$, which cannot be determined exactly. However, since CpG islands are almost completely unmethylated, we consider that these regions are likely to reflect the overall constitution of DNA before cytosine methylation and consequent deamination occurred. Since CpG islands exhibit neither mononucleotide nor dinucleotide suppression (Gardiner-Garden and Frommer, 1987), we also consider it reasonable to assume a more or less random composition of the ancestral genome, i.e. $x(0) = 1/4$, and $y(0) = x^2(0) = 1/16$. Using these figures, System 2 is solved by the functions

$$x(t) = \exp(s_1 t - 3.99) + \exp(s_2 t - 3.69) + 0.2066$$

$$y(t) = \exp(s_1 t - 7.11) + \exp(s_2 t - 2.93) + 0.0082 \qquad (3)$$

where $s_1 = -3.62 \times 10^{-9}$ and $s_2 = -3.63 \times 10^{-8}$.

Functions x and y are depicted in Figure 6.2, showing that the CpG frequency decreases relatively quickly within approximately 100 Myr and remains almost constant thereafter. Within 100 Myr, the frequency of C or G nucleotides decreases from 25 to 22%, and then also decreases slowly. Nevertheless, if we take $t_0 = 450$ Myr, the time thought to have elapsed since the evolution of the first vertebrates and their heavily methylated genomes, this yields

$$x(t_0) = 0.2102 \qquad \text{and} \qquad y(t_0) = 0.0084 = 0.18 x^2(t_0)$$

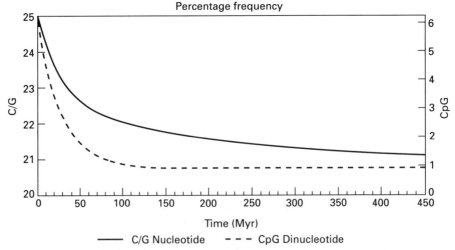

Figure 6.2. Time-dependent frequencies of C/G mononucleotides (solid line) and CpG dinucleotides (dashed line) in vertebrate genomes. The presented data are theoretical expectations based on an evolutionary model described in the text.

These values are very close to the mononucleotide and dinucleotide frequencies that are actually observed in the human genome (0.210 and 0.010 respectively; Setlow, 1976), suggesting that 450 Myr can indeed be regarded as a valid approximation of the time required to create the CpG suppression now observed in vertebrate genomes. The heavily methylated genome, characteristic of the vertebrate-type pattern of methylation, is thought to have emerged about this time from an ancestral echinoderm-type pattern exhibiting much lower levels of cytosine methylation and hence minimal CpG suppression (Bird, 1980). Although expected mononucleotide and dinucleotide frequencies may be within the limits of chance variation for any time period longer than 100 Myr, our estimate of the CpG mutation rate is most consistent with a permanent (and still ongoing) decay of CpG dinucleotides from vertebrate genomes over evolutionary time.

An analysis similar to that described above has been performed by Sved and Bird (1990). Although the model presented by these authors appears to be slightly more general (each dinucleotide other than CpG was considered separately, and different rates of transitions and transversions were allowed for), most of their findings are compatible with our own. Sved and Bird assumed that the observed CpG suppression (20% expected) represents an equililibrium state and demonstrated that, to create this suppression, m_d must be 18 times higher than any other nucleotide substitution rate. In our notation, the latter rate is $m_b/3$, and therefore our ratio of mutation rates is 22 (3×7.4), based upon both clinical and evolutionary data. However, whereas the equilibrium frequency of CpG is approximately 0.01 for both models, the C (or G) frequency of 0.23 at equilibrium predicted by Sved and Bird's study appears to be too high in view of its present value. Finally, the authors estimated the time necessary to attain equilibrium to be 25 Myr. This figure was, however, arrived at by comparison of only two DNA sequences (human α1- and ψ α1-globin) and was also based on a poor assumption: since the pseudogene exhibits a CpG content of 20% of that of the functional gene, this was held as sufficient evidence for equilibrium. The authors themselves, however, demonstrated that the dinucleotide distribution within the pseudogene sequence was more likely to represent a transient rather than an equilibrium state.

6.2.5 The measurement of deamination rates in vitro

Various attempts have been made to measure the deamination rate of 5mC *in vitro*. Wang *et al.* (1982) demonstrated that 5mC in single-stranded bacteriophage M13 DNA underwent alkali- or heat-induced deamination at rates 1.5–3 times faster than those at which cytosine becomes deaminated to form uracil. A later study, using the same substrate, permits the estimation of the deamination rate of 5mC at physiological temperature and pH: from observations at 70°C, the deamination rate was extrapolated to be 9.5×10^{-10} s^{-1} at 37°C, pH 7.4 (Ehrlich *et al.*, 1986). Double-stranded DNA, however, appeared to be less prone to deamination: At 70°C, deamination of 5mC in double-stranded DNA occurred at 3.6% of the rate exhibited by single-stranded DNA (Ehrlich *et al.*, 1986). This was in agreement with the findings of Lindahl and Nyberg (1974), who found deamination of cytosine in native *E. coli* DNA to be < 1% of that for single-stranded DNA and suggested that the duplex structure of DNA might confer some protection against deamination. Using a more sensitive genetic assay based on the reversion of mutations in the lacZα gene of phage M13, Frederico *et al.* (1990) measured the cytosine deamination rate in double-stranded DNA as 7×10^{-13} s^{-1} ($= 2.21 \times 10^{-5}$ year^{-1}) at 37°C and pH 7.4. This figure was found to be 140 times smaller than that observed for single-stranded DNA under the same experimental conditions.

Deamination of cytosine to uracil in mammalian cells is corrected at high efficiency by uracil–DNA glycosylase (Lindahl, 1982). Thymine, the product of 5mC deamination, cannot be removed by this enzyme. There is now, however, good evidence for a specific repair mechanism that restores G:C base pairs lost through 5mC deamination: Brown and Jiricny (1987) have measured the efficiency of correction of mismatched G:T base pairs in African green monkey cells. Mispairs were repaired in 98% of cases and correction in favour of guanine was observed in 90% of them. In 8% of cases, mispairs were corrected in favour of T, thus allowing the C→T transition to be fixed. If we modify the estimate of Frederico *et al.* (1990) accordingly and define

$$c_d = 0.08 \times 2.21 \times 10^{-5} \text{ year}^{-1} = 1.77 \times 10^{-6} \text{ year}^{-1}$$

then this value may be regarded as an alternative estimate of the mutation rate of 5mC to thymine. If it were assumed that all C residues located within CpG dinucleotides were methylated, c_d should equal m_d. In practice, c_d is 100 times larger than m_d. The possible reasons for this disparity are explored in Section 6.2.6.

6.2.6 The disparity between in vitro and clinically observed 5mC mutation rates

If it is true that the rate of 5mC→T mutation is increased when DNA is single stranded (Adams *et al.*, 1987), the tight packing of double-stranded DNA with nucleosomal proteins in chromatin might well confer some protection against 5mC deamination. We should then have greatly overestimated the true cellular rate of deamination of 5mC. Furthermore, according to Adams and Eason (1984), G + C rich regions exhibit a much reduced frequency of deamination. These authors have contended that deamination events are less prevalent in these regions because of their inherent high stability (Adams *et al.*, 1987). G + C poor (i.e. A + T rich) regions, on the other hand, are less stable and thereby liable to become transiently denatured. Since deamination occurs much more readily in single-stranded DNA *in vitro*, the argument goes that this will also be true *in vivo* for the less stable G + C-poor DNA regions. The validity of this idea is, however, contentious. Although it is consistent with available data, Gardiner-Garden and Frommer (1987) have shown that, whereas a high G + C content is generally necessary to prevent CpG depletion, it is probably not sufficient.

It may be possible that the value used for the proportion of G:T mismatches that are repaired correctly (Brown and Jiricny, 1987) is too low and may not reflect the true *in vivo* situation. The efficiency of G:T mismatch repair is nevertheless consistently high, considerably higher than for other mismatches, at least in SV40 constructs introduced into simian cells (Brown and Jiricny, 1988). However, correction mechanisms probably act with optimal efficiency when their substrate, mismatched DNA, is packed into normal chromatin. This may be a result of the structure of the bound DNA itself, the availability of putative auxiliary repair proteins, the transient absence of 5mC or the presence of 'nicks' on the nascent DNA strand during replication. Hare and Taylor (1985) presented evidence for 5mC directing strand discrimination in the mammalian G:T mismatch-repair system and claimed a repair efficiency of 100%. Although Brown and Jiricny (1987) claim that correction in favour of guanine occurs irrespective of methylation, this runs contrary to the findings of Hare and Taylor (1985), who reported that both cytosine methylation, and DNA nicks introduced by the discontinuous nature of DNA replication, provided strong cues for correct strand selection. Thus, in normal chromatin, it appears likely that an intrinsic bias in favour of T→C repair coupled with cues from methylation status and DNA nicks all act synergistically to optimize the efficiency of the G:T mismatch-repair process. The repair process appears to be mediated by a DNA glycosylase which effects the excision of the mismatched thymine and its replacement with a cytosine (Wiebauer and Jiricny, 1989, 1990).

The experiments of Hare and Taylor (1985) and Brown and Jiricny (1987) were well designed and executed, but their substrates for mismatch-repair correction were nevertheless only naked SV40 DNA molecules. In the absence of further reports on the eukaryotic G:T mismatch repair system *in vivo*, it is difficult to speculate further as to its likely efficiency. Ehrlich *et al.* (1986) report that 5mC is about 4.5 times more prone to deamination to thymine than cytosine is to uracil, suggesting that the uracil–DNA glycosylase correction mechanism is at least twice as efficient as the G:T mismatch repair system. This speculative assertion awaits experimental verification but is perhaps consistent with a more recent evolutionary origin for the G:T mismatch repair system. Brown and Jiricny (1988) suggest that G:T mismatches may be subject to repair by two distinct repair pathways, one specific for G:T mismatches and their correction to G:C pairs and a second that may be common to all mispairs. This distinction remains to be validated, but one may nevertheless speculate that the emergence of heavily methylated genomes may have predated, and thereby created the need for, a G:T mismatch-specific repair system. It would be most interesting to ascertain whether or not G:T-specific repair activity is present in cells from organisms that exhibit minimal cytosine methylation (e.g. *Drosophila*) or vertebrate cell lines that possess abnormally low levels of methylation (Lindsay *et al.*, 1989).

Regarding the disparity between the *in vitro* and clinically observed CpG mutation rates, a further contributory factor may be the ameliorating effects of selection. For many genes, selection pressure on mutations is expected to be intense. Indirect evidence for this assertion comes from the comparison of CpG frequencies between coding and non-coding regions. In the absence of selection, the CpG frequency in coding sequences (37% expected; Nussinov 1981a, 1981b) would be expected to be comparable to the 20–25% expected value exhibited by non-coding sequences (Josse *et al.*, 1961; Setlow, 1976) which comprise the bulk of the genome. Indeed, it is likely that many of those CpG dinucleotides that remain are either (i) of some functional significance (at DNA, RNA or protein levels) since selection has acted at some time so as to retain them, or (ii) relatively immune to deamination because of the lack of cytosine methylation. This line of argument could be held to imply that a higher proportion of mutations in CpG dinucleotides within a gene coding sequence will be deleterious (and therefore undetectable) as compared with other dinucleotides less subject to mutational removal. This question is discussed further in Section 6.2.7.

6.2.7 The CpG dinucleotide and human genetic disease

CpG has been known for some time to be a 'hotspot' for mutation in verte-brate genomes (see Section 2.7), its mutation rate being 8.5 times higher than that of the average dinucleotide (Table 6.6). Thus, a high frequency of poly-morphism is detected in the human genome by restriction enzymes containing CpG in their recognition sequences (Barker *et al.*, 1984; Cooper and Schmidtke, 1984). CpG has also been found to be a hotspot for mutation in a wide range of different human genes, including those encoding albumin (ALB; Brennan *et al.*, 1990), α- and β-globin (HBA, HBB; Perutz, 1990), glucose-6-phosphate dehydrogenase (G6PD; Vulliamy *et al.*, 1988), C1 inhibitor (C1I; Skriver *et al.*, 1989), phenylalanine hydroxylase (PAH; Abadie *et al.*, 1989), antithrombin III (AT3; Perry and Carrell, 1989), protein C (PROC; Reitsma *et al.*, 1993), factor VIII (F8; Youssoufian *et al.*, 1988; Tuddenham *et al.*, 1991) and factor IX (F9; Giannelli *et al.*, 1992). Indeed, one may take advantage of CpG hypermutability to optimize diagnostic screening procedures, e.g. by employing a 'directed-search' strategy for detecting point mutations in the F8 gene causing haemophilia A (Pattinson *et al.*, 1990).

The calculated proportion of human gene mutations compatible with a model of methylation-mediated deamination (CG → TG, CA) is, however, very much an average figure and provides no information on values for individual genes. When these values are recalculated on a gene-specific basis (for genes with more than 10 mutations reported in Appendix 2), considerable variation becomes apparent. The frequency of CG → TG and CG → CA mutations may be < 20% [CFTR (18%), COL1A1 (15%), GBA (12%), HBB (8%), HPRT (5%)] or > 50% [ADA (71%), APOE (60%), HEXA (55%), VWF (68%)]. In the assumed absence of a detection bias, we may surmise that this variation is due either to differences in (i) germline DNA methylation and/or (ii) relative intragenic CpG frequency [itself dependent on (i)].

The distribution of CpG mutations within a gene may also be strikingly non-random. Thus, for example, in the protein C (PROC) gene, nine of 12 single base-pair substitutions in exon 7 occur in CpG dinucleotides, whereas none of the 13 point mutations reported in exons 5 and 6 are in CpG dinucleotides (Reitsma et al., 1993). In this gene, CpG suppression, as measured by the ratio of GpC:CpG, is at a minimum for the region around exons 4-6 (Reitsma et al., 1993). This relatively high CpG frequency is both indicative of a lower level of cytosine methylation in the germline and consistent with the absence of methylation-mediated deamination events.

One possible source of error in estimating the actual contribution of CpG hypermutability to the incidence of human genetic disease should be mentioned. If, contrary to current received opinion, a sizable proportion of total 5mC were to be found in dinucleotides other than CpG (see Woodcock et al., 1987; 1988), this would reduce the apparent contribution of CpG mutation to the incidence of human genetic disease.

CpG hypermutability in inherited disease implies that the CpG sites in question are methylated in the germline and thereby rendered prone to 5mC deamination. However, on its own, CpG hypermutability still represents very indirect evidence for CpG methylation. That 5mC deamination is itself directly responsible for these mutational events is evidenced by the fact that several cytosine residues known to have undergone a germline mutation in the low density lipoprotein receptor (LDLR; hypercholesterolaemia) and p53 (TP53; various types of tumour) genes are indeed methylated in this tissue (Rideout et al., 1990). As yet, however, this is the only study to have attempted to correlate directly CpG hypermutability with DNA methylation for specific CpG dinucleotides; more such studies on other genes are urgently needed.

Differences in mutation frequency at specific CpG sites within the factor VIII (F8) gene have been noted between ethnic groups (Pattinson et al., 1990); a disproportionate number of mutations were found to have occurred in individuals of Indo-Pakistani origin as compared with European Caucasians. However, a direct demonstration that these differences in mutability are due to population-specific differences in the methylation status of particular CpG sites must await further studies on the methylation of the F8 gene in the germlines of these ethnic groups. By contrast, the pattern of germline CpG mutation in the factor IX (F9) gene appears to be indistinguishable between Asians, mostly of Korean origin, and Caucasians (Bottema et al., 1990). This argues both for an endogenous origin for these mutations and, indirectly, for the absence of population-specific methylation patterns. Analysis of patterns of DNA methylation exhibited by a variety of other DNA sequences is consistent with the absence of frequent differences in methylation between individuals from different ethnic backgrounds (Behn-Krappa et al., 1991).

A random sample of CpG transitions in the F9 gene causing haemophilia B were considered by Green et al. (1990): 82% occurred at nine sites that corresponded to functionally critical and evolutionarily conserved amino acid residues, whereas the remaining 18% of transitions occurred at 11 poorly conserved sites. This disproportionately high number of CpG mutations at conserved residues was explained in terms of selection retaining CpG dinucleotides at these locations despite the attendant high risk of deleterious mutation (see discussion of this point in Section 6.5.2). Green *et al.* (1990) concluded that consideration of the ratio of CpG to non-CpG mutation might thus lead to overestimation of the intrinsic mutability of the CpG dinucleotide. However, our demonstration that similar values for the relative mutability of CpG may be derived from both clinical (Section 6.2.2) and evolutionary (Section 6.2.3) studies argues strongly against the validity of this postulate. Further, Koeberl *et al.* (1990) have shown that *all* factor IX missense mutations, not merely those which occur in CpG dinucleotides, tend to be located in evolutionarily conserved residues. The puzzle is therefore not so much why CpG dinucleotides are retained at functionally important sites, but rather why these sites are methylated, since it is their modification that is ultimately responsible for their hypermutability.

6.3 Single base-pair substitutions causing human genetic disease

6.3.1 The point mutation database

Appendix 2 lists single base-pair substitutions (used here synonymously with the term point mutation) that cause human genetic disease and that have been located and characterized in as unbiased a fashion as possible. These data were collected for analysis since it was considered probable that this would provide valuable information on both the nature and frequency of spontaneous point mutations in man.

The database includes reports of disease-causing single base-pair substitutions (up until May 1992) that were characterized by DNA sequencing. A preliminary version of this list has been published previously (Cooper and Krawczak, 1990). Each entry consists of the name of the disease, the McKusick symbol for the disease gene (McKusick, 1990), the base-pair change responsible for the disease phenotype, the resulting amino acid substitution at a specified codon and the literature reference under the name of the first author. Nucleotides outside the altered codon (denoted by a lower case letter) are given when the mutation occurs in the first or third position in the codon. This information is provided to allow the assessment of the potential influence of neighbouring bases on the relative likelihood of a specific mutational change. Mutations that occur within CpG dinucleotides and that are consistent with the process of methylation-mediated deamination (i.e. either $C \to T$ or $G \to A$) are marked with a *. Several omissions have been made in the interest of obtaining an unbiased sample of point mutations causing human genetic disease:

(i)   In the case of single base-pair substitutions that have been reported independently more than once, the first example only has been logged. This is because of the difficulty in determining whether these mutations are identical-by-descent or whether they are truly recurrent (see Section 6.7). Adoption of this policy may, however, result in the underestimation of the actual proportion of independent point mutations that occur in the hypermutable CpG dinucleotide.

(ii) Examples of point mutations in the factor IX (F9) gene causing haemophilia B are not included, in order to provide an independent test for the predictive power of any models generated (see Section 6.6.2).

(iii) Point mutations in the mitochondrial genome (see Sections 2.6 and 6.9) resulting in diseases such as the mitochondrial myopathies are not included. Since mitochondrial DNA is replicated by its own DNA polymerase, evolves at a much faster rate than nuclear DNA and is not detectably methylated (Groot and Kroon, 1979; Castora *et al.*, 1980), its mutational spectrum is unlikely to be comparable to that exhibited by the nuclear genome.

(iv) Point mutations in oncogenes are not included because tumorigenesis occurs in somatic cells and may be caused by the action of environmental mutagens. In addition, it is usually difficult to determine whether or not the mutation detected is itself a cause or a consequence of the transformed phenotype. This is not to say that mechanisms of mutagenesis are entirely different; e.g. CpG mutations, in the *gsp* oncogene, consistent with methylation-mediated deamination, have been shown to be a cause of pituitary tumours (Landis *et al.*, 1989). The possible relevance of methylation-mediated deamination of 5mC to carcinogenesis has been reviewed by Loeb (1989), Ehrlich *et al.* (1990) and Jones *et al.* (1992).

(v)   Point mutations within intron/exon splice junctions and cryptic splice sites are not included. Such mutations are not uncommon but consideration of mutations occurring within a consensus sequence common to all genes would be expected to bias any analysis of mutation at the dinucleotide level. This particular type of lesion is covered separately in Chapter 9.

With missense mutations, one is frequently faced with the decision as to whether or not the single base-pair change detected is indeed the pathological lesion causing the disease. Although the absence of any other lesion in the coding region is good evidence that a given base change is causative, some doubt usually still remains. Evidence for causality in such cases comes from one or more of the following sources: (i) occurrence of the mutation in a region of known structure or function, (ii) occurrence of the lesion in an evolutionarily conserved residue, (iii) the previous independent occurrence of the mutation in an unrelated patient, (iv) the failure to observe such a mutation in a large sample of normal controls, (v) the novel appearance and subsequent co-segregation of the gene lesion and disease phenotype through a family pedigree, (vi) the demonstration that an *in vitro*-produced mutant protein possesses the same biochemical properties and characteristics as its *in vivo* counterpart, and (vii) the reversal of the pathological phenotype in the patient/ cultured cells by replacement of the mutant gene/protein with its wild-type counterpart. Most of the missense mutations listed in Appendix 2 will have some but not all of these pieces of evidence to support their authenticity.

The total of 880 point mutations listed in Appendix 2 are summarized in Table 6.1; those occurring in CpG dinucleotides account for 334 of them (38.0% of the total). However, if only CG→TG and CG→CA mutations (i.e. consistent with methylation-mediated deamination, Table 6.1b) are considered, this figure falls to 289 (32.8%) which approximates almost exactly to the proportions noted previously by Cooper and Youssoufian (1988) and Cooper and Krawczak (1990), respectively, on the basis of much smaller samples of human gene mutations. Of the 289 CpG mutations, 61 (21.1%) affected X-linked genes, whereas 228 (78.9%) were reported from genes located on autosomes. Similar proportions apply to the remaining 591 mutations, of which 133 (22.5%) occurred on the X chromosome.

Among the 880 point mutations listed, we have observed transversion and transition frequencies of 275 (31.3%) and 605 (68.7%) respectively. There is therefore a highly significant excess of transitions compared with the expected frequency (33%) ($\chi^2 = 496.482$; 1 d.f.; $P < 10^{-5}$). The noted proportions are similar to those first reported by Vogel et al. (1976) and Vogel and Kopun (1977) for globin genes, and by Li et al. (1984) for a collection of pseudogene sequences. Most but not all of the excess of transitions over expectation can be attributed to the hypermutability of the CpG dinucleotide; when CpG mutation data are removed (289 mutations = 47.8% of all transitions) from the

Table 6.1. Number of point mutations (N) consistent with methylation-mediated deamination of 5-methylcytosine (b) and all other types (a)

(a) Point mutations causing human genetic disease other than CG→TG or CG→CA

Initial nucleotide	Nucleotide resulting from single base-pair change				Total
	T	C	A	G	
T	—	72	20	29	121
C	66	—	35	31	132
A	17	13	—	67	97
G	84	46	111	—	241
Total	167	131	166	127	591

(b) Point mutations in CG dinucleotides consistent with methylation-mediated deamination of 5-methylcytosine

Mutation	N
CG→TG	147
CG→CA	142

analysis, the excess of transitions is still significant ($\chi^2 = 107.817$; 1 d.f.; $P < 10^{-5}$).

6.3.2 Codon choices and the CpG dinucleotide

To some extent, the redundancy of the genetic code has provided the vertebrates with the potential for ameliorating the detrimental effects of cytosine methylation through appropriate codon usage. Table 6.2a illustrates the codon 'choices' exhibited by the genes of human and six other vertebrates for the amino acids serine, proline, threonine and alanine, one of whose codons in each case contains a CpG dinucleotide. For all codon choices, considerable avoidance of the codon containing a CpG dinucleotide is exhibited. However, despite the redundancy of the genetic code, complete avoidance of CG-containing codons within the coding sequences is not seen. It is nevertheless difficult to distinguish the possible selective pressures of mutation avoidance from those resulting from mere structural constraints at the DNA/RNA level (Cooper and Gerber-Huber, 1985).

Avoidance of CG-containing codons is also seen with arginine (Table 6.2b) at least for codons CGA and CGT. It was anticipated that avoidance would be at its highest for CGA, since deamination of 5mC in this codon could give rise to a TGA termination codon and selection against the use of CGA might be expected to be correspondingly high. However, contrary to this prediction, CGA occurs more frequently than CGT, although less frequently than CGC and CGG. As a control, we also examined 3670 bp of DNA encoding 18S rRNA, 5S rRNA, U1 snRNA and U4a snRNA genes and eight tRNA genes. Because the expression of these genes does not result in a protein product, no especial avoidance of CGA was to be expected since a C→T transition giving rise to TGA would be no more deleterious than such a transition in any other codon. Consistent with this postulate, a total of 63 CGA trinucleotides (1.76%) were found in all 'reading frames', exactly the proportion predicted from mononucleotide frequencies. We have $f(C) = 0.278$, $f(G) = 0.294$, $f(A) = 0.215$ and therefore

$$f(C) \, f(G) \, f(A) = 0.0172$$

i.e. the expected proportion is 1.72%. However, the finding that RNA-encoding genes exhibit neither CpG nor CGA avoidance is merely suggestive of selection at the level of codon usage and does not prove it. This finding might equally well be an indirect consequence of the uniform absence of cytosine methylation in these sequences in the germline (as for example in rRNA genes; Cooper et al., 1983).

Nevertheless, when the frequency of C→T and G→A mutations in each of the four CpG-containing arginine codons were compared after taking into account the differential usage of these codons in human genes, substitutions affecting CGA codons appear to be significantly over-represented, whereas those affecting CGC codons are under-represented. This result may reflect our

Table 6.2. Codon choices for amino acids encoded by CpG-containing codons

(a) Codon choices (% occurrence) for serine, proline, threonine and alanine

Amino acid	Codon	Humans	Average of seven vertebrates
Serine	TCA	0.96	0.85
	TCC	1.76	1.77
	TCG	0.40	0.41
	TCT	1.32	1.29
	AGC	1.86	1.80
	AGT	0.97	0.88
Proline	CCA	1.49	1.36
	CCC	2.01	1.89
	CCG	0.66	0.62
	CCT	1.58	1.52
Threonine	ACA	1.42	1.35
	ACC	2.28	2.21
	ACG	0.66	0.66
	ACT	1.26	1.21
Alanine	GCA	1.43	0.40
	GCC	2.95	2.93
	GCG	0.71	0.72
	GCT	2.94	2.04

(b) Codon choices for arginine

Codon	Humans	Average of seven vertebrates	Number of CG→TG, CA[†]	χ^2[‡]
CGA	0.55	0.54	63	32.318§
CGC	1.12	1.17	50	7.089§
CGG	1.05	0.97	51	3.619
CGT	0.46	0.51	28	0.002
AGA	0.99	1.01		
AGG	1.08	1.06		

Data from Wada et al. (1991)*. *These authors screened 833 083 codons in 1985 genes for humans; for six other vertebrates (hamster, mouse, rat, bovine, rabbit, chicken), 965 630 codons in 2554 genes were screened. †Number of corresponding substitutions in database of Appendix 2. ‡Expected substitution frequencies were assumed to be proportional to codon usage in humans; codons CGA and CGC, marked §, yielded a χ^2 value > 6.24, which is the appropriate limit of significance allowing for multiple testing ($P < 0.05$).

expectation that CGA→TGA transitions resulting in termination codons have a higher chance of coming to clinical attention (demonstrated in Section 6.5.3), or may instead indicate an imbalance consistent with the findings of Bains and Bains (1987) who reported differences in the mutability of CpG dinucleotides with different flanking nucleotides.

The hypothesis of different CpG mutabilities associated with different flanking mononucleotides can be best tested by the analysis of CG→TG mutations occurring at position 1 within a codon. This is because, under the null hypothesis of no influence, the frequency distribution for 5' flanking bases should equal the overall distribution of nucleotides at position 3 of human gene codons. Variable likelihoods of clinical detection do not play a role here since the underlying amino acid substitution is independent of the 5' flanking nucleotide. A total of 117 base substitutions from Appendix 2 fulfilled the above conditions. However, when compared with the position 3 base frequencies calculated from tabulated codon usage (Wada *et al.*, 1991), no significant preponderance of any 5' flanking base could be detected ($\chi^2 = 5.19$, 3 d.f., n.s.).

6.4 Single base-pair mutagenesis: mechanisms and models

For non-CpG mutations, marked differences in the frequency of different single base-pair substitutions also occur and in theory may have arisen through the influence of one or more different factors. Thus, the non-randomness of the initial mutation event, the non-randomness of the DNA sequences under study, differences in the relative efficiency with which certain mutations are repaired, differences in phenotypic effect (and hence selection), or a bias in the clinical detection of such variants, may all in principle play a role in determining the observed mutational spectrum. Whereas all these factors could conceivably contribute to the observed non-randomness of point mutation, their individual contributions have neither been determined nor even properly estimated.

We shall thus extend our analysis of human gene mutation beyond the CpG dinucleotide to the remaining approximately 62% of point mutations that occur within other doublets. It will be demonstrated that these mutations are also distributed non-randomly with respect to DNA sequence and we shall explore several possible mechanisms that may be responsible for this phenomenon.

6.4.1 DNA polymerase fidelity and the relative frequencies of single base-pair substitutions

DNA replication occurs as a result of an accurate yet error-prone multistep process (see Section 2.5). The final accuracy is clearly dependent upon (i) the initial fidelity of the replicative step and (ii) the efficiency of subsequent error correction mechanisms (Loeb and Kunkel, 1982). Since DNA polymerases are involved in replication, recombination and repair processes, their base incorporation fidelity is probably a critical factor in determining mutation rates in the cell. We have tested the hypothesis that non-random base misincorporation during DNA replication is a major contributory factor in producing the observed spectrum of mutations causing human genetic disease. To this end, the observed base substitution frequencies from Table 6.1 were compared with the measured *in vitro* base substitution error rates exhibited by vertebrate DNA polymerases α, β and δ (Kunkel and Alexander, 1986; Thomas *et al.*, 1991), i.e. the major polymerases required for the replication and repair of vertebrate chromosomal (nuclear) DNA. Error rates were determined using a bacterial complementation assay to detect mutations in lacZ α/M13mp2 constructs synthesized *in vitro* (Kunkel, 1985a, 1985b). Although approximate, the resulting values may nevertheless be considered as possessing some validity relative to each other. The rates applying to different single base-pair substitution errors are given in Table 6.3, together with the corresponding observed frequencies from Table 6.1. A Spearman rank correlation test indicated a significant correlation between these two sets of values for polymerase β ($r = 0.782$, $P = 2.63 \times 10^{-3}$), but not for polymerase α or polymerase δ. However, it should be noted that the base substitution error rate of polymerase δ is approximately one order of magnitude smaller than that of polymerase β. This may have obscured any existing correlation between polymerase δ fidelity and point mutation frequencies.

In comparing the specific base substitution error rates of vertebrate polymerases α, β and δ with the frequencies of the different transitions and transversions causing human genetic disease, we have effectively excluded any consideration of the efficacy of the different proofreading (e.g. Bialek *et al.*, 1989) and post-replicative mismatch-repair (Modrich, 1987) mechanisms. This is because the purified polymerase preparations used *in vitro* lack the $3' \rightarrow 5'$ exonuclease activities thought to be responsible for proofreading *in vivo*. The highly significant result obtained for DNA polymerase β is thus consistent

Table 6.3. Comparison of base substitution error rates associated with mammalian polymerases α, β ($\times 10^{-5}$) and δ ($\times 10^{-6}$) with the observed frequencies of single base-pair (non-CpG) substitutions causing human genetic disease

Base-pair substitution	Human pol α*	Rat pol β*	Calf pol δ†	Number of mutations
T→C	21.7	47.6	3.6	72
T→A	5.6	6.7	20.8	20
T→G	3.0	7.1	<3.6	29
C→T	33.3	111.1	25.6	66
C→A	17.5	<10.3	11.1	35
C→G	<5.0	<12.1	<9.1	31
A→T	13.3	4.6	7.4	17
A→C	<3.9	<9.1	<6.3	13
A→G	2.6	47.6	5.5	67
G→T	29.4	28.6	29.4	84
G→C	38.5	9.1	4.3	46
G→A	16.1	29.4	15.9	111
Spearman r	0.448	0.782	0.203	
P	n.s.	2.63×10^{-3}	n.s.	

*Data from Kunkel and Alexander (1986); these data are not dissimilar to the mispairing frequencies associated with *Drosophila* polymerase α (Mendelman *et al.*, 1989). †Data from Thomas *et al.* (1991). r, Spearman rank correlation coefficient between corresponding error rates and numbers of point mutations; n.s., not significant.

with the postulate that a substantial proportion of the point mutations causing human genetic disease detected to date are caused by misincorporation of bases during DNA replication. Further, it suggests that if cellular DNA proof-reading and mismatch repair mechanisms have attempted to compensate for the initial non-random distribution of mutations causing human genetic disease by correcting high-frequency mutations with increased efficiency, they have not been so successful as to have obscured the original association.

Although, in prokaryotes, transition mismatches (G:T and A:C) are reportedly repaired more efficiently than transversion mismatches (G:A and C:T) (Jones et al., 1987b), the analogous repair mechanisms and proofreading activities in eukaryotes are relatively uncharacterized and in some cases undoubtedly still remain to be identified. Some evidence, however, is beginning to emerge for differential repair of mispaired bases by the sequence-dependent proofreading activities of eukaryotic DNA polymerases (Petruska and Good-man, 1985; Reyland et al., 1988). Moreover, Brown and Jiricny (1988) have reported efficient repair of G:T mismatches but with a bias in favour of $T \to C$ correction over $G \to A$. Since repair enzymes are known to act on unstable regions of DNA, it may be that they are less efficient in excising errors in $G + C$-rich regions of duplex DNA (Bessman and Reha-Krantz, 1977; Petruska and Goodman, 1985); this would contribute still further to the non-random-ness of point mutations.

6.4.2 A slipped mispairing model for single base-pair mutagenesis

An alternative model, put forward by Kunkel (1985a), seeks to explain nucleo-tide misincorporation through transient misalignment of the primer template caused by looping out of a template base (Figure 6.3). Immediate realignment leads to incorporation of a single mispair. 'Misalignment' or 'dislocation' mutagenesis (see Section 2.5), as it has become known, is thought to be mediated by repetitive DNA sequences in the vicinity. In principle, it provides an explanation for many point mutations not predicted by base mispairing hypotheses (e.g. Topal and Fresco, 1976), which instead invoked base analogues and tautomers of the naturally occurring nucleotides.

If misincorporation mediated by one base-pair slippage were to play an important role in the generation of the point mutation spectrum (Appendix 2), a substantial proportion of mutations should exhibit identity of the newly introduced base to one of the bases flanking the mutation site. This was actually observed for 137 (identical to 5' base) and 148 (identical to 3' base) of the point mutations not readily explicable by a process of methylation-mediated deamination. Nevertheless, when the expected number of mutations exhibiting nearest-neighbour identity was calculated, assuming that all three possible base changes at a given site are equally likely, no significant difference between observed and expected values was noted. (Expected numbers were 145.0 mutations with identity to the 5' flanking nucleotide and 139.8 identical to the 3' nucleotide.) Thus, identity to at least one neighbouring base does not occur at higher frequency than might be expected from random mutation. It is

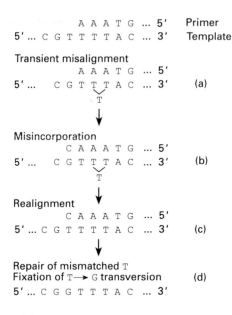

```
              A A A T G ... 5'    Primer
5' ... C G T T T T A C ... 3'    Template

Transient misalignment
              A A A T G ... 5'
5' ...    C G T T T A C ... 3'    (a)
                    V
                  . T

                    ↓

Misincorporation
            C A A A T G ... 5'
5' ...    C G T T T A C ... 3'    (b)
                  V
                  T

                    ↓

Realignment
            C A A A T G ... 5'
5' ... C G T T T T A C ... 3'    (c)

                    ↓

Repair of mismatched T
Fixation of T→ G transversion    (d)
5' ... C G G T T T A C ... 3'
```

Figure 6.3. A model of misalignment mutagenesis. During replication synthesis, the template strand slips back one base (a), resulting in a misincorporation of cytosine at the 3' end of the run of adenine residues (b). After realignment of both primer and template strand (c), the C-T mismatch is corrected in favour of C, thereby fixing the T→G transversion (d).

concluded that one-base slippage does not appear to be an important mechanism of template-mediated mutagenesis in human genes.

It cannot, however, be immediately excluded that misincorporation of single bases might result from slippage events involving repeat regions larger than just one nucleotide. In order to test this hypothesis, the sequence context of 219 point mutations observed in one of the following 17 genes was examined: AT3, CFTR, DMD, F10, F11, F7, F8, G6PD, HBB, HPRT, INS, INSR, OAT, OTC, PAH, PROC and VWF. Mutations explicable by methylation-mediated deamination were excluded. In each case, DNA sequence comprising 10 bp either side of the point mutation was aligned with itself so that the newly introduced base matched with one base of the original sequence. The maximum distance allowed between the mutation site and the position at which the new base matched (i.e. the extent of slippage) varied from 3 to 7 bp. Next, a window of size 3–7 bp was moved along the overlap and the number of matching bases was scored for each position of the window. Finally, the distribution of the maximum number of matches obtained for all possible alignments and all possible positions of the window was compared with its random expectation. Expected frequencies of maximum matches were determined from the entire cDNA sequences of the genes involved, assuming that each possible base change was equally likely. However, no comparison yielded a significant result. This implies that the extent of self-homology exhibited by sequences in the neighbourhood of the base changes analysed was not significantly different from expectation. It may therefore be concluded that direct repeat-mediated slippage is of no more relevance to the generation of point mutations in human genes than one base-pair slippage.

Table 6.4. Hotspots for single base-pair substitutions in human genes not explicable by methylation-mediated deamination

Gene	Codon	Surrounding DNA sequence
AT3	384	TGAAGCAGCTgCAAGTACCGCTG
AT3	402	CAGGGTGACTTtCAAGGCCAACA
CFTR	549	AATCACACTGagtGGAGGTCAAC
F8	473	AAGCAGACCAtaTAACATCTACC
F8	1680	TTTTGACATTTaTGATGAGGATG
F8	1922	CCATGCAATCaaTGGCTACATAA
F9*	291	TATTTGCATTgCTGACAAGGAAT
HBB	−1	AACAGACACCatGGTGCACCTGA
HBB	121	CTTTGGCAAAgAATTCACCCCAC
HPRT	50	ACGTCTTGCTcgAGATGTGATGA
HPRT	131	GAATGTCTTGAttGTGGAAGATA
HPRT	203	GGATTTGAATcaTGTTTGTGTCA
INS	24	GGAACGAGGCTtcTTCTACACAC
PALB	58	GCTGCATGGGCtCACAACTGAGG
PROC	105	CAACGGCGGCTgcACGCATTACT
RHO	23	GGTACGCAGCCcCTTCGAGTACC
RHO	347	CCAGGTGGCCcccGGCCTAAGACC
SPTA	28	CCAGGAGAGGcgTCAGGAAGTGT

Exact locations of recurring single base-pair substitutions are indicated by lower-case letters (lower-case letters within a given DNA sequence denote sites affected by at least two independent mutations). The numbered codon is underlined. Although mutations occur within CpG dinucleotides in three cases, the mutations quoted are not C→T or G→A transitions and are therefore not explicable by methylation-mediated deamination. *The F9 mutation is not included in Appendix 2; several examples of the G→A transition resulting in an Ala 291→Thr substitution are known and these have been shown to be recurrent mutations by RFLP haplotyping (Green *et al.*, 1992).

6.4.3 Non-CpG point mutation hotspots

Among the point mutations listed in Appendix 2 not readily explicable by methylation-mediated deamination, a total of 18 codons in 11 different genes were identified as potential 'hotspots' for single base-pair substitutions (Table 6.4). These residues are characterized either by a single base being affected by at least two non-identical substitutions, or by mutations affecting two or three nucleotides within that codon.

Using the approach described above (Section 6.4.2), no trinucleotide or tetranucleotide sequence was found to be significantly over-represented in the vicinity of the mutation hotspots of Table 6.4 (data not shown). Nevertheless, some of the sequence information in Table 6.4 appears to provide mechanistic explanations for the observed mutations. For example, one of the two mutations affecting the guanine residue within codon 384 of the AT3 gene was G→T. This transversion creates a 6 bp inverted repeat (GCTTCA) of the flanking sequence motif TGAAGC. The misincorporation of T could thus be

131

explained as a template-mediated event facilitated by 'hairpin loop' formation. The second mutation affecting the same site resulted in a $G \rightarrow A$ transition. For this event, two neighbouring AGC repeats could have played a role, involving three-base slippage, in mediating the observed base change. A similar model, involving a four-base slippage of the CAAT motif, could explain the misincorporation of guanine residues at positions 1 and 2 in codon 1922 of the F8 gene. However, although a powerful computer and a little imagination might well prove successful in deriving credible mechanisms to explain all the 'hotspots' listed in Table 6.4, a unified theory appears to be lacking.

6.4.4 Other mechanisms responsible for single base-pair substitutions

Several other explanations for base misincorporation may be considered. The first involves the proposed requirement for balanced dNTP pools to maintain the accuracy of replication. An excess of any one dNTP can lead to increased misincorporation of that nucleotide (Kunkel *et al.*, 1981; Phear *et al.*, 1987; reviewed by Meuth, 1989; Mathews and Ji, 1992; see Section 2.5). Using cultured mammalian cells, Kresnak and Davidson (1992) have shown that a high concentration of thymine resulted in $G/C \rightarrow A/T$ transitions which occurred preferentially at the 3' guanine residue of a run of two or more guanines. Guanine residues flanked on the 3' side by other guanine residues were markedly less mutable, indicating that thymine induces mutations in a sequence-specific manner.

Enzymatic and chemical causes of mutation may sometimes be difficult to disentangle. Thus depurination results from cleavage of the *N*-glycosylic bond that connects the purine to the deoxyribose sugar; the base is removed but the phosphodiester backbone is left intact (Loeb, 1985). Apurinic sites may occur spontaneously by hydrolysis of the *N*-glycosylic bond, result from exposure to chemical agents that form bulky adducts on DNA or from the action of DNA glycosylase in the enzymatic repair of damaged DNA (Loeb and Preston, 1986). Depurination occurs spontaneously at a rate of 3×10^{-11} events/base/s under physiological conditions (Lindahl and Nyberg, 1972), a figure similar to that noted for the deamination of 5mC *in vitro* (Ehrlich *et al.*, 1986). The rate of depurination of single-stranded DNA is about four times greater than that of double-stranded DNA (Loeb and Preston, 1986). Although depurination occurs some 100 times faster than depyrimidation, the relative order of rates of *N*-glycosylic bond cleavage is $dG > dA > dC > dT$ (Loeb and Preston, 1986). Since DNA polymerases misincorporate bases opposite abasic sites (Shearman and Loeb, 1979; Kunkel *et al.*, 1983) during replication, this could be an important cause of spontaneous mutation. Deoxyadenosine has been found to be the most frequently misincorporated base with both prokaryotic and eukaryotic DNA polymerases (Sagher and Strauss, 1983; Schaaper *et al.*, 1983; Kunkel, 1984; Takeshita *et al.*, 1987). One consequence expected from this so-called 'A-rule' would be an increased frequency of transversions at sites of depurination. Among point mutations causing human inherited disease, however, transversions have been shown to be seriously under-represented, even when $C \to T$ and $G \to A$ transitions explicable by methylation-mediated deamination of cytosine are disregarded (Table 6.1). Thus, depurination and consequent incorporation of deoxyadenosine residues at abasic sites can be excluded from playing an important role in the formation of disease-associated single base-pair substitutions in humans.

The spectrum of mutations induced in cultured mammalian cells by ultraviolet light is highly non-random; mutations occur almost exclusively in dipyrimidine sequences (Drobetsky et al., 1987). $G \to A$ and $C \to T$ transitions predominate in human cells (Keohavong et al., 1991; Seetharam et al., 1991). This finding is consistent with the bias of DNA polymerases toward the insertion of an adenine residue opposite UV-induced lesions.

A further chemical mutation mechanism is through damage by oxygen free radicals (Hsie et al., 1986; Richter et al., 1988). A major product of oxidative DNA damage is 8-hydroxyguanine. Cheng et al. (1992) have shown that, in Escherichia coli, 8-hydroxyguanine was associated with $G \to T$ or $A \to C$ transversions depending on whether the analogue served as a template or a substrate during DNA replication. Since neither type of substitution is over-represented in our spectrum of human gene mutations, we may infer that oxidative damage is not a major mechanism of spontaneous mutation in man. Other types of endogenous oxidative damage of cytidine have been noted in calf thymus DNA (Wagner et al., 1992).

Nitrite (NO_2^-) has long been known as a mutagen under acid conditions. The physiological messenger, nitric oxide (NO), may also be mutagenic in the presence of oxygen. Nguyen et al. (1992) demonstrated the formation of xanthine and hypoxanthine in NO-treated human cells through the deamination of guanine and adenine. Guanine appears to be the most reactive base followed by cytosine and adenine. Nitric oxide may thus be responsible for a proportion of 5-methylcytosine residues deaminated to thymine.

The suggestion that CpG deamination may perhaps result from endogenous enzymatic activity has been mooted by Steinberg and Gorman (1992). These authors found that some 70% of their (independent) mouse lymphoma cell mutants possessed a specific $CGG \to TGG$ substitution converting Arg 334 to Trp in the gene encoding protein kinase regulatory subunit. In 5% of these mutants, a second mutation ($CGT \to TGT$) was found converting Arg 332 to Cys. The co-occurrence of these two mutations at such a high frequency is very hard to explain on the basis of two independent yet spatially localized spontaneous methylation-mediated deamination events, and argues instead for some type of enzymatic mechanism. Such a mechanism could involve a deaminase, as has been postulated before to account for the high frequency of CpG transitions in duplicated genomic sequences of Neurospora crassa (Cambareri et al., 1989), although no such activity has yet been purified. This observation is most intriguing but requires further work for its findings to be substantiated. Its relevance to human gene mutation is doubtful since (i) it does not alter the fact that CpG is a hotspot for mutation, (ii) there are no known examples, including CpG dinucleotides, of pathological base changes in humans that occur with such a high proportional frequency, and (iii) although a very few isolated examples of double mutation have been reported as causes of human genetic disease [e.g. Mullan *et al.*, 1992; β-amyloid (APP) gene; Alzheimer disease], these do not involve CpG dinucleotides. Multiple spontaneous mutation of the adenosine phosphoribosyltransferase (APRT) gene of a human carcinoma cell line has been reported (Harwood *et al.*, 1991). In this case, however, no preference for mutation in CpG sites was apparent and the cause was put down to error-prone DNA synthesis.

Shen *et al.* (1992b) have recently reported evidence to show that DNA methyltransferase is capable of inducing $C \rightarrow T$ transitions directly. Moreover, the mutation frequency was found to be very sensitive to the concentration of the methyl donor, S-adenosylmethionine. Shen *et al.* (1992b) have proposed that deamination may occur enzymatically via the formation of a covalent complex between the methyltransferase and the C-6 position of cytosine; this would labilize the C-4 amino group and allow deamination of the dihydropyrimidine intermediate, resulting in a $C \rightarrow T$ transition.

One alternative to an endogenous deaminase could be the mispairing of 5mC with A which, if the latter base were to be stably incorporated, would increase the frequency of $G \rightarrow A$ transitions. However, no evidence for such a mechanism has been found from studies of a eukaryotic DNA polymerase α *in vitro* (Shen *et al.*, 1992a).

Evidence has been put forward by Woodcock *et al.* (1987) for the presence of cytosine methylation at dinucleotides other than CpG. These authors have further suggested (Woodcock *et al.*, 1988) that maintenance methylases might recognize and methylate the trinucleotide C(A/T)G in addition to the dinucleotide CpG, thus raising the possibility of methylation-mediated deamination in C(A/T)G sequences. In the point mutation sample presented in Appendix 2, 20 substitutions were noted at CAG triplets, 13 of which (65%) were CAG $\rightarrow$ TAG. However, as with CGA $\rightarrow$ TGA transitions, this excess may be at least partly due to a bias favouring the clinical detection of newly introduced termination codons. Furthermore, contrary to the situation observed for CG-containing codons, CAG and CTG codons (Gln and Leu) occur more frequently in human genes than do the alternative codons for these amino acids (Maruyama *et al.*, 1986; Ohno, 1988). There would therefore appear at present to be no compelling evidence for the high-frequency occurrence of methylation-mediated deamination mutations at sites other than CpG. The observation that a eukaryotic DNA methylase methylates CA and CT dinucleotides at a 50-fold lower rate than CG *in vitro* (Hubrich-Kuhner *et al.*, 1989) is not inconsistent with this finding.

A variety of DNA sequence motifs are known to play an important role in the breakage and rejoining of DNA, and these sequence elements could therefore represent potential determinants of single base-pair mutagenesis. To identify sequence motifs specifically associated with point mutations, we again screened a region of ± 10 bp around the 219 base substitution sites described in Section 6.4.2. This time, we searched for triplets and quadruplets which may have occurred at significantly increased frequencies by comparison with the total cDNA sequence of the genes involved. Since either 64 or 256 comparisons of observed and expected frequencies had to be performed, thresholds for χ^2 analyses ($P = 0.05$, 1 d.f.) were 11.28 and 13.87 respectively. This limit was exceeded for only one trinucleotide: CTT, the topoisomerase I cleavage site consensus sequence described by Bullock *et al.* (1985). CTT was actually observed 36 times in the vicinity of a point mutation, whereas the expected frequency was 20 ($\chi^2 = 14.086$). By contrast, two tetranucleotides were significantly over-represented at the screened positions. TCGA (Taq I restriction site) was observed 17 times (7 expected, $\chi^2 = 14.757$), while TGGA was observed 25 times (11.7 expected, $\chi^2 = 15.972$). Interestingly, the latter motif fits perfectly with the deletion hotspot consensus sequence drawn up previously for human genes (Krawczak and Cooper, 1991; see Chapter 7) which, in turn, resembles the putative arrest site for DNA polymerase α. Thus, the arrest or pausing of the polymerase at the replication fork may dispose the replication complex to misincorporation of nucleotides as well as deletions.

6.5 A nearest-neighbour analysis of single base-pair substitutions

6.5.1 The nearest-neighbour pattern of point mutations

Methylation-mediated deamination as the primary cause of point mutation is characterized by increased rates of CG → TG and CG → CA transitions. We shall now determine in more detail the relative likelihoods of other point mutations, depending upon which dinucleotide is affected. To try to discern patterns of mutation at the dinucleotide level, each point mutation can be regarded as occurring within two distinct dinucleotides, depending on whether one considers the 5' or the 3' neighbouring base. The nearest-neighbour frequencies observed for the point mutations listed in Appendix 2 are given in Table 6.5.

In Table 6.5, considerable differences are apparent with respect to the nearest-neighbour frequencies of the point mutations listed in Appendix 2. For example, guanine residues are clearly over-represented as 3' flanking nucleotides when thymine is mutated, and mutated guanines are themselves most often flanked by another guanine residue on their 5' side. These few examples illustrate that observed relative rates of base substitutions are undoubtedly influenced by nucleotides flanking the mutation site. As already discussed in detail in Section 6.4, this finding is explicable in terms of a number of different factors responsible for the non-randomness either of the initial mutation event or of the mutation repair process. However, a further contributory factor may be differences in the phenotypic consequences of specific point mutations and thus in the likelihood of their coming to clinical attention.

6.5.2 A bias in clinical detection?

In-depth studies of the phenotypic effect of large numbers of different missense mutations in a specific gene are few. One such study is that reported

Table 6.5. Nearest-neighbour frequencies on the 3'(a) and 5'(b) sides of point mutations causing human genetic disease

(a)

Mutated base	3' neighbouring base				Total
	T	C	A	G	
T	19	26	12	64	121
C	31	36	49	163 (16)	279 (132)
A	40	21	26	10	97
G	92 (63)	82 (54)	93 (57)	116 (67)	383 (241)
	182 (153)	165 (137)	180 (144)	353 (157)	880 (591)

(b)

5' neighbouring base	Mutated base				Total
	T	C	A	G	
T	20	65 (28)	21	72	178 (141)
C	47	96 (39)	31	171 (29)	345 (146)
A	34	53 (32)	15	40	142 (121)
G	20	65 (33)	30	100	215 (183)
	121	279 (132)	97	383 (241)	880 (591)

Values in parentheses denote observed nearest-neighbour frequencies when CG → TG (a) and CG → CA (b) transitions are excluded.

by Bottema *et al.* (1991) for missense mutations in the factor IX (F9) gene causing haemophilia B. These authors showed that mutations at 'generic' residues (amino acid residues conserved in other mammalian species and in three related serine proteases) would invariably cause disease. Mutations at factor IX-specific residues (residues conserved in other mammalian species but not in three related serine proteases) were some six-fold less likely to cause disease, whereas mutations at non-conserved residues were 33-fold less likely to result in a haemophilia B phenotype. Bottema *et al.* (1991) estimated that 40% of all possible missense changes would cause haemophilia B, implying that the remaining 60% of residues serve merely as 'spacers' to maintain the relative position of critical amino acid residues and do not fulfil any specific function. Thus detectable mutations, identified by virtue of their effect on protein structure and function and subsequently on clinical phenotype, appear to be a subset of a rather larger number of mutations, many of which will have no clinical effect, at least in the case of haemophilia B. It may not, however, be possible to extrapolate from this finding in haemophilia B (in which < 5% normal factor IX activity must be present to generate a clinically abnormal phenotype) to other genetic disorders.

Intuitively, it would seem reasonable to suppose that the phenotypic consequences of a given point mutation would be determined ultimately by the magnitude of the amino acid exchange as assessed by the resulting structural perturbation of the protein in question. In further analyses, we therefore wish to take into account the possibility that certain base-pair changes giving rise to specific amino acid substitutions may come to clinical attention more readily, depending on the severity of the resulting phenotype.

Several methods have been reported for assessing the relative net effect of a specific amino acid exchange. Designed as a means to make evolutionary comparisons between amino acid sequences of proteins, these methods were originally used to demonstrate that homologous proteins had evolved in such a way as to minimize the conformational effects of their amino acid replacements (Epstein, 1967; Grantham, 1974). Perhaps the best comparative measure of amino acid relatedness available is that devised by Grantham (1974), who combined the three interdependent properties of composition, polarity and molecular volume to assign each amino acid pair a mean *chemical difference* ('D value'). For the sake of simplicity, we shall subdivide the range of D values into 11 equal-sized intervals, 0–20, 20–40, ..., 200–220, and use the class variable instead of the original D in our analysis.

Clearly, the phenotypic consequences of a given mutation must depend not only on the nature of the amino acid substitution, but also on the location of that substitution within the protein. Mutational effects on protein stability have recently been well reviewed (Alber, 1989; Pakula and Sauer, 1989). In general, and with the exception of charged residues, most amino acids that make critical interactions (e.g. disulphide bonds, hydrophobic forces, hydrogen bonds etc) are rigid or buried within the protein structure, and their mutational substitution will be profoundly destabilizing. Our knowledge of the complex relationship between protein structure and function must, however, be greatly expanded before we are in a position to be able to incorporate such data into statistical models. Therefore, we shall make the simplifying assumption that the probability of clinical detection of a specific amino acid substitution depends exclusively on the corresponding chemical difference.

6.5.3 Relative dinucleotide mutabilities

To account formally for the nearest-neighbour dependence of point mutations, we shall now introduce a novel parameter, the *relative dinucleotide mutability*, rdm. This quantity will be proportional to the rate at which a particular dinucleotide is affected by point mutation at one of its two bases. Thus, rdm is a function of dinucleotides. In principle, rdm is calculated in a similar fashion to our previously published approach (Cooper and Krawczak, 1990). However, the analysis will be substantially refined here by allowing properly for codon usage in human genes, for the redundancy of the genetic code, and for the impact that differences in the type of amino acid substitution may have on the likelihood of detection of point mutations.

Let δ and δ' denote two dinucleotides which differ at exactly one position. Then we define

$$\mathrm{rdm}(\delta \to \delta') = O(\delta \to \delta')/E(\delta \to \delta')$$

where O is the observed frequency of $\delta \to \delta'$ among the point mutations listed in Appendix 2, and E is a real number proportional to the expected frequency, assuming that all dinucleotide mutations are equally likely. Since E depends on the overall frequency of dinucleotides within coding regions, we have to restrict our analysis to dinucleotides which start at positions 1 and 2 within a codon. This is because dinucleotide frequencies can be computed directly from tabulated codon usage (Wada et $al.$, 1991) only for these positions. Although dinucleotides overlapping neighbouring codons will thus be systematically excluded, this is very unlikely to bias our estimates of dinucleotide mutabilities.

Each mutation of δ affects one of the four triplets δN or $N\delta$ (N denoting any base), respectively, depending on whether δ is located at position 1 or 2. Therefore, except for a constant factor, we have

$$E(\delta \to \delta') = \Sigma_N f(\delta N)\, C(\delta N \to \delta' N) + \Sigma_N f(N\delta)\, C(N\delta \to N\delta')$$

where summation is over all four nucleotides, $f(.)$ is the triplet frequency, and $C(\delta N \to \delta' N)$ and $C(N\delta \to N\delta')$ respectively denote the probability of clinical detection of the particular codon substitution.

Relative dinucleotide mutabilities are estimated in a recursive manner, with C values being adjusted at the end of each computational loop: dinucleotide mutabilities estimated in that loop are transformed into $triplet$ $mutabilities$, rtm, as will be described in Section 6.6.1. Then, for a given class of chemical difference, say G, the corresponding C value is calculated as

$$C = O(G)/\Sigma_{t \to t'} f(t)\, \mathrm{rtm}(t \to t')$$

where $O(G)$ is the observed frequency of class G among the point mutations listed in Appendix 2, and summation is over all triplet mutations $t \to t'$ resulting in a chemical difference that falls into class G.

This recursive algorithm is in fact a so-called 'EM algorithm' and yields maximum likelihood estimates of both the rdm and C values. Table 6.6 summarizes the results of the analysis in the form of rdm values standardized by $\mathrm{rdm}(TT \to CT)$. The latter transition appears to be the least likely mutational event, apart from $CA \to CT$ transversions, which were observed twice but only at overlapping positions. [Thus, the estimate of $\mathrm{rdm}(CA \to CT) = 0.0$ should be regarded as tentative.] Also included in Table 6.6 are the sums of the rdm values for each nucleotide δ, yielding a single quantity $\mathrm{rdm}(\delta)$ in each line. This figure is reminiscent of the relative dinucleotide mutability as described before (Cooper and Krawczak, 1990) and, for the sake of consistency, $\mathrm{rdm}(\delta)$ is also standardized by $\mathrm{rdm}(TA)$ here.

In the process of estimating relative dinucleotide mutabilities, we have also determined the relative likelihoods of clinical detection of amino acid substitutions, depending on their corresponding chemical difference. These figures, i.e. the C values mentioned above, are depicted in Figure 6.4 in a standardized

Table 6.6. Relative dinucleotide mutabilities rdm($\delta \rightarrow \delta'$) and rdm($\delta$)

δ	Newly introduced 5' base				Newly introduced 3' base				
	T	C	A	G	T	C	A	G	rdm(δ)
TT	—	1.00	0.07	0.39	—	0.63	0.08	0.45	0.74
CT	1.18	—	0.16	0.17	—	2.06	0.07	0.29	1.11
AT	0.37	0.06	—	2.28	—	1.66	0.34	0.21	1.39
GT	1.84	0.67	4.27	—	—	0.48	0.22	0.28	2.20
TC	—	0.59	0.52	0.20	1.38	—	0.34	0.42	0.98
CC	1.09	—	0.32	0.15	3.77	—	1.23	0.32	1.95
AC	0.09	0.17	—	0.92	1.86	—	0.44	0.52	1.13
GC	0.57	0.75	2.99	—	1.44	—	0.41	0.13	1.78
TA	—	0.99	0.23	0.08	0.25	0.12	—	1.87	1.00
CA	1.14	—	0.29	0.45	0.00	0.44	—	1.32	1.03
AA	0.14	0.20	—	0.85	0.04	0.24	—	0.98	0.69
GA	0.40	0.60	3.31	—	0.36	0.04	—	0.67	1.52
TG	—	1.85	0.17	0.36	0.63	0.40	1.51	—	1.39
CG	13.27	—	0.64	0.45	1.76	1.03	23.01	—	11.36
AG	0.03	0.18	—	0.20	0.18	0.32	0.93	—	0.52
GG	0.60	0.45	4.18	—	1.20	0.43	2.42	—	2.62

δ, Original dinucleotide; rdm(δ), sum of values in each row, standardized so that rdm(TA) = 1.00.

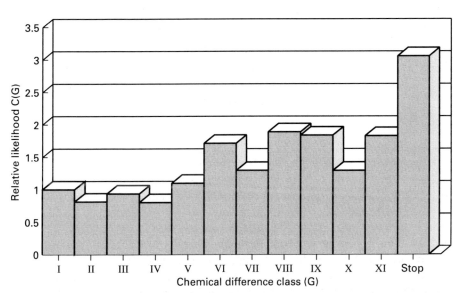

Figure 6.4. Relative likelihood of clinical detection of an amino acid exchange. The relative likelihoods, C(G), are given depending on the corresponding class (G) of chemical difference. Classes are defined in intervals of size 20, i.e. I: 0–20, II: 20–40 etc. Class 'Stop' refers to the creation of termination codons.

form: all C values were divided by C(0 to 20). As is evident from Figure 6.4, the likelihood of clinical detection increases with chemical difference and is highest for point mutations resulting in termination codons. For the latter, the likelihood of detection is approximately three times as high as for base substitutions which change the corresponding amino acid only slightly (chemical difference < 20). However, the variation of relative mutability estimates resulting from the consideration of variable likelihoods of clinical detection is negligible, with one important exception: if all amino acid substitutions are regarded as being equally likely to come to clinical attention, the algorithm described above yields rdm(CG → TG) = 20.52 and rdm(CG → CA) = 18.82 (i.e. the relative ranking of CG → TG and CG → CA is reversed). This discrepancy can be explained easily by the fact that CGA → TGA transitions result in termination codons whereas CG → CA transitions do not. Thus the higher the likelihood of detection is assumed to be for termination codons, the smaller rdm(CG → TG) needs to be to explain a given number of mutations of this type.

6.5.4 The strand difference in base substitution rates

A noteworthy feature of Table 6.6 is that it reveals some asymmetry, suggesting a strand difference for single base-pair substitutions. For example, rdm(CT → CC) = 2.06 while rdm(AG → GG) = 0.20, i.e. the relative likelihoods differ by one order of magnitude. Since the latter transition is complementary to the former one, these two figures should in fact coincide if point mutagenesis were acting similarly on both DNA strands. A search of the data presented in Appendix 2, restricted to dinucleotides starting at positions 1 or 2, yielded 10 pairs of substitutions, complementary to each other, which exhibit a similar feature. These are listed in Table 6.7, together with their expected frequencies assuming both equal rdm values and a constant number of

Table 6.7. A strand difference in point mutagenesis

Subst.	Obs.	Exp.	Compl. Subst.	Obs.	Exp.	χ^2
TC–TT	14	26.25	GA–AA	56	43.75	9.187
CT–CC	22	9.10	AG–GG	4	16.90	28.116*
CC–TC	20	30.91	GG–GA	36	25.09	8.641
CC–AC	6	14.69	GG–GT	25	16.31	9.771
CG–CT	12	7.96	CG–AG	5	9.04	3.873
CG–CA	79	53.12	CG–TG	152	177.88	16.159*
AC–AT	14	24.83	GT–AT	47	36.17	7.925
GT–TT	27	15.12	AC–AA	9	20.88	16.145*
GC–CC	13	7.97	GC–GG	2	7.03	6.782
GC–GT	10	17.69	GC–AC	51	43.31	4.685

Subst., substitution; Compl., complementary; Obs., observed; Exp., expected frequency of a substitution assuming that the rdm value equals that of the complementary substitution. The sum of observed values was held fixed within a row. The appropriate threshold for χ^2 analysis was 10.75 (48 comparisons, $P = 0.05$). Significant strand differences are marked with an asterisk.

observations for each pair, and making allowance for the genetic code and variable likelihoods of detection.

A strand difference in mutation rates has already been described by Wu and Maeda (1987). By comparison of non-functional sequences near the β-globin genes of six primate species, these authors demonstrated that purine to pyrimidine (R→Y) transversions occurred approximately 1.5 times more frequently than their pyrimidine to purine counterparts (Y→R). Complementary transitions were, however, found to occur at equal frequencies. These findings are compatible with the data from Appendix 2: R→Y was observed 1.4 times more frequently than Y→R, and both T→C and A→G transitions account for approximately 12% of the mutations in Table 6.1a. A slightly different result was obtained for G→A transitions, which are 1.7 times more frequent than C→T transitions. Nevertheless, the rdm values of Table 6.6 reveal that strand differences in mutation rates depend on the nucleotides flanking the site of mutation. For example, whereas CT→CC is 10 times more likely than AG→GG, TA is almost twice as likely to mutate to TG than to CA.

The most interesting finding in Table 6.7 is probably the disparity between the relative frequencies of CG→TG and CG→CA transitions, i.e. those point mutations explicable by methylation-mediated deamination. This observation strongly suggests that, at least within gene coding regions, the two strands are differentially methylated and/or differentially repaired. *De novo* methylation (see Section 2.7) appears to exhibit some DNA sequence specificity, at least *in vitro*, and can thus generate sequence-specific (and by implication strand-specific) sites of hemimethylated DNA (Bolden *et al.*, 1986). Furthermore, hemimethylated DNA (only one strand methylated) has sometimes been observed to be stable over several cell generations (Saluz *et al.*, 1986; Toth *et al.*, 1989), implying that maintenance methylation can be delayed even after DNA replication is complete. The frequent occurrence of hemimethylated DNA could in principle account for the strand difference in CpG mutability since methylation-mediated deamination events would tend to occur more frequently on the methylated DNA strand. Although Hare and Taylor (1985) suggested that, in eukaryotes, either DNA methylation or single strand breaks could provide cues for strand discrimination in mismatch repair, evidence for strand specificity has until recently been lacking. Holmes *et al.* (1990) have now demonstrated, at least *in vitro*, the existence of a strand-specific correction process in human and *Drosophila* cells whose efficiency is dependent on the nature of the mispair. Such differential repair could also in principle help to account for the observed strand differences in mutation frequency.

6.6 Towards a predictive model (MUTPRED)

6.6.1 The relative mutability of amino acid sequences

We shall now present a mathematical model that attempts (i) to predict tentatively both the location and relative frequency of point mutations within a given gene sequence and (ii) to relate a derived 'mutability quotient' for that gene to the clinically observed prevalence of the deficiency of the gene product. To this end, we shall first compute a value proportional to the probability that a single nucleotide b_2 mutates to b_2', depending on its sequence context $b_1b_2b_3$. At the dinucleotide level, such an event is equivalent to both $b_1b_2 \rightarrow b_1b_2'$ and $b_2b_3 \rightarrow b_2'b_3$, so that the sought-after likelihood should take a value between the corresponding rdm values. Further, if we assume that the relevance for mutation is the same for the 5' and 3' bases, respectively, then a good estimate of the relative likelihood is

$$[\text{rdm}(b_1b_2 \rightarrow b_1b_2') + \text{rdm}(b_2b_3 \rightarrow b_2'b_3)]/2$$

i.e. the average of the two relative dinucleotide mutabilities. Since we shall use these values only relative to each other, we need not worry about a constant factor which would transform the average of the two rdm values into a real mutation rate. Nevertheless, our definition allows us to calculate the relative likelihood of any given base substitution depending on the nucleotides flanking the mutation site.

Now, let us consider a triplet encoding amino acid A. If we adopt the average of the flanking rdm values as the likelihood of a given base change within this triplet, we can also compute the *relative likelihood of an amino acid change*, ram(A), for that particular codon. Since multiple mutations are unlikely, ram(A) should approximate to the sum of likelihoods for those base changes which alter the encoded amino acid. Thus, any ratio ram(A)/ram(B) represents an estimate of how much more likely it is for amino acid A than for amino acid B to be changed by point mutation, taking into account the actual DNA sequences encoding both residues.

The calculations described above were introduced into a computer program (MUTPRED) that uses the relative dinucleotide mutabilities of Table 6.6 and the gene coding sequence of interest (GenBank, latest release) as input. From these data, a mutability profile of the protein can be derived by plotting the ram values against the corresponding amino acid sequence. Regions prone to amino acid substitutions caused by point mutations can be recognized in such a plot by a concentration of higher peaks (see Figure 6.5). Additionally, the program calculates the sum of all ram values, the mutability quotient. This figure can be taken as a measure of the overall mutability of the amino acid sequence, even although it lacks any stochastic meaning. However, we shall demonstrate in Section 6.6.3 that the mutability quotient correlates well with the prevalence of inherited disease caused by point mutations within the corresponding gene.

6.6.2 Application of MUTPRED to point mutations causing haemophilia B

The finding that dinucleotides differ with respect to their likelihood of mutation as a consequence of errors in a basic cellular mechanism (DNA replication) argues strongly for the general applicability of derived dinucleotide mutability values beyond the narrow confines of our sample of point mutations.

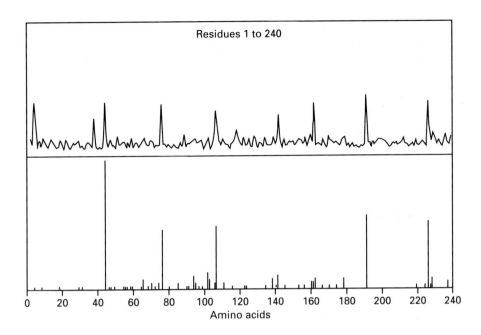

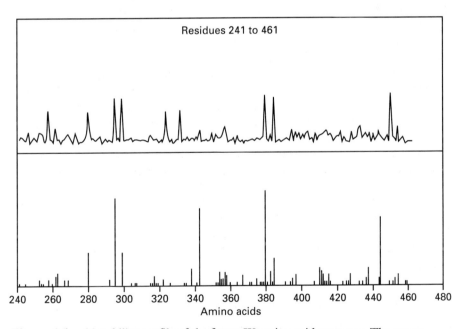

Figure 6.5. Mutability profile of the factor IX amino acid sequence. The upper sections represent the mutability profile, i.e. the plot of the relative mutabilities of single amino acid residues. The lower sections depict the observed distribution of amino acid substitutions. The height of each bar is proportional to the number of mutations found.

MUTPRED may be tested empirically by directly comparing the predicted spectrum of mutations for a given gene (mutation data for which were not included in Appendix 2 or in subsequent calculations) with the observed mutational spectrum. The factor IX (F9) gene provides us with a unique test system; although the first characterized point mutations in this gene were biased by prior CpG site screening, the advent of more rapid methods of gene analysis (see Chapter 4) has now led to the identification of 451 independent (205 different) point mutations that together probably represent a fair cross-section of the point mutations causing haemophilia B (reviewed by Giannelli *et al.*, 1992). A comparison of the observed and predicted mutational spectra (Figure 6.5) confirms that our model has predictive value, although it performs better for CpG dinucleotides than for non-CpG dinucleotides. However, as it stands, MUTPRED is unable to predict known or probable hotspots of mutation in non-CpG dinucleotides in the F9 gene, namely Pro 55 (CCA→GCA), Ala 291 (GCT→ACT) and Ala 390 (GCA→GTA).

6.6.3 Disease prevalence and the relative rate of gene mutation

We speculate that, if the primary DNA sequence were indeed an important factor in determining the location and frequency of point mutations, then the mutability quotients, as calculated in Section 6.6.1, might correlate with the clinically observed mutation rates and/or the prevalence of inherited conditions resulting from the absence or alteration of the underlying gene products. Clearly, the prevalence of a given condition in the general population depends not only on the mutability of the underlying gene responsible for the disease phenotype, but also on whether one or two mutant alleles are required for the disease phenotype to be expressed (i.e. the 'mode of inheritance'). For any comparisons of this kind, it is therefore necessary to compare autosomal dominant, autosomal recessive and X-linked conditions separately. Table 6.8 summarizes a comparison of the relative prevalence of different coagulation factor deficiencies (C. Rizza, personal communication) with mutability quotients calculated from coagulation factor gene sequences.

The most comparable conditions listed in Table 6.8 are the haemophilias A and B, both X-linked recessive conditions that give rise to similar bleeding phenotypes as a consequence of the defective production of factors VIII and IX, respectively. Haemophilia A is 5.3 times more prevalent in the UK than haemophilia B, which is similar to the ratio of the mutability quotients (4.7:1). Expansion of the model to include other parameters such as gene length and number of splice junctions could in principle improve this correlation still further.

Similarly with the autosomal dominant conditions, the rank orders of disease prevalence and mutability quotient values are identical. The high mutability quotient for the von Willebrand factor gene is especially noteworthy in the light of the findings of Rodeghiero *et al.* (1987) who reported an extremely high incidence (0.82%) of mild autosomal dominant von Willebrand disease (vWD) in the general population. The mildness of the symptoms of the

Table 6.8. Coagulation factor deficiencies: prevalence and gene mutability

Disease	Mode of inheritance	Defective gene	Coding region (bp)	Mutability quotient*	Prevalence†
Haemophilia A	X-linked	F8	7053	1153	5195
Haemophilia B	recessive	F9	1383	243	982
vWD (mild)	Autosomal	VWF	8439	1736	2215
Fibrinogenaemia	dominant	FGG	4785	820	10
Prothrombin deficiency		F2	1995	402	2
Factor XIII deficiency	Autosomal	F13	4233	737	16
Factor XII deficiency	recessive	F12	1902	437	64
Factor X deficiency		F10	1584	290	37
Factor VII deficiency		F7	1578	319	35
Prekallikrein deficiency		KLK3	1971	327	3

*Explained in text. †Number of patients on UK Haemophilia Centre Director's National Register on 15 January 1988 (C. Rizza, personal communication). Most conditions listed give rise to clinically moderate/severe bleeding disorders. However, since factor XII deficiency, prekallikrein deficiency and mild vWD (von Willebrand disease) are virtually insignificant clinically, the prevalence figures given in the table are from chance detection and probably grossly underestimate the true prevalence of these conditions. The length of the coding region in base-pairs includes both the mature protein and leader peptide sequence. (Gene symbols not specified in text: VWF, von Willebrand factor; FGG, γ-fibrinogen.)

disease in the heterozygous form certainly accounts for the apparent lower prevalence of vWD in the UK than haemophilia A, since the former condition is much less likely to come to clinical attention. No correlation was noted for the autosomal recessive disorders. This is not at all surprising, because the prevalence of these rare conditions will be determined predominantly by factors such as founder effect, the degree of inbreeding, genetic drift and, possibly, heterozygote advantage in a given environment rather than the underlying mutation rate.

Since the best correlation found between disease prevalence and mutability quotients was observed for the haemophilias, the comparison was extended to calculated mutation rates associated with three other X-linked conditions, Duchenne muscular dystrophy, ornithine transcarbamylase deficiency and Lesch–Nyhan syndrome. In such X-linked recessive lethal conditions, the mutation rate may be easily calculated (reviewed by Vogel and Motulsky, 1986), since roughly one-third of all mutations will be new. The rank order of the calculated gene mutation rates again agrees well with that of the mutability quotients (Table 6.9).

Since MUTPRED does not consider the possibility of gene lesions other than point mutations (the proportion of other types of gene lesions may vary dramatically between different disorders, e.g. in Duchenne muscular dystrophy and haemophilia A, gene deletions account for approximately 60% and 2% of cases, respectively), it is perhaps a little surprising that mutability quotients correlate as well as they do with disease prevalence. Further, our value for the

Table 6.9. Sex-linked recessive 'lethal' conditions

Disease	Gene	Coding region (bp)	Mutation rate	Mutability quotient
Duchenne muscular dystrophy	DMD	11055	6×10^{-5}	1864
Haemophilia A	F8	7053	4.4×10^{-5}	1153
Haemophilia B	F9	1383	2.5×10^{-6}	243
Lesch–Nyhan syndrome	HPRT	656	2×10^{-6}	114
Ornithine transcarbamylase deficiency	OTC	1064	8×10^{-7}	182

The amino acid coding regions were obtained from GenBank, latest release. HPRT, hypoxanthine phosphoribosyltransferase.

relative mutability of a CpG dinucleotide is very much an average figure. In practice, CpG dinucleotides that are methylated will be more prone to mutation to TG or CA than the model would suggest, whereas those that are unmethylated will be much less so. Since the methylation patterns exhibited by different genes vary quite widely (see Gardiner-Garden and Frommer, 1987), this all-or-nothing mutational effect of cytosine methylation illustrates the importance of establishing the methylation status of individual CpG sites within specific genes in the germline [by e.g. genomic sequencing (Saluz *et al.*, 1986)]. The genomic architecture of the locus is undoubtedly also important. More specifically, the number of exons and splice junctions and the length and nature of intronic sequences (including the number and type of repetitive elements) will probably all play a role in determining the frequency, location and extent of types of lesion other than single base-pair substitutions and frameshift mutations. Finally, the 'private' characteristics of individual genes must not be ignored: DNA sequences encoding protein regions of structural and functional importance, e.g. those encoding proteolytic cleavage sites (which often contain CpG dinucleotides within Arg codons in coagulation factor genes), protein-binding sites, methylated CGA arginine codons (CGA → TGA creates a termination codon), etc.

6.7 Discrimination between recurrent mutation and identity by descent

When identical point mutations in a given gene responsible for a specific disease state are detected in apparently unrelated patients, it is often unclear whether they have arisen by recurrent mutation or whether they are instead identical by descent. In general, possession of the same haplotype background would argue in favour of the latter, whereas the occurrence of the mutation in a hypermutable CpG dinucleotide would provide support for the former postulate. Discrimination between these two alternative hypotheses is, however, very much case-dependent and, to be objective, some formal treatment is required. This will be attempted in the following section, with evidence in favour of one or the other hypothesis being based on the relative dinucleotide mutabilities calculated in Section 6.5.

6.7.1 Mutations in the cystic fibrosis (CFTR) gene

Our first example deals with cystic fibrosis (CF), one of the most frequent autosomal recessive diseases of Caucasians. The gene responsible for this condition was cloned by Rommens et al. (1989) by positional cloning (Section 5.4). Comparative studies of the deduced amino acid sequence revealed several homologies to protein domains of known function, leading to the adoption of the term cystic fibrosis transmembrane conductance regulator (CFTR) for the gene product (Riordan et al., 1989). A total of 27 exons have been identified within the CFTR gene (Tsui, 1990) and some of these, exons 9 to 12, are believed to encode a nucleotide binding fold (NBF) which interacts with ATP. This function is thought to be impaired by the predominant CF mutation, an in-frame deletion of three base-pairs resulting in the loss of a phenylalanine residue at position 508 (δF508; Kerem et al., 1989). Worldwide, δF508 is present on 68% of mutant chromosomes (Cystic Fibrosis Genetic Analysis Consortium, 1990), albeit with significant geographical variation (European Working Group on CF Genetics, 1990).

Whereas mutations other than δF508 were believed to be highly heterogeneous, Cutting et al. (1990) reported a tight cluster of point mutations affecting residues S549, G551, R553 and A559 within exon 11. In a German sample, Reiss et al. (1991) screened a total of 75 non-δF508 CF chromosomes for two of these aberrations, R553X and G551D, and found 10 chromosomes bearing the first mutation and four chromosomes bearing the second. These particular chromosomes were further typed for RFLPs at two CFTR-linked loci, namely D7S23 (KM19/PstI and XV2c/TaqI; Estivill et al., 1987; Feldman et al., 1988; Rosenbloom et al., 1989) and D7S8 (pJ3.11; Bartels et al., 1986; Northrup et al., 1989). Evaluation of homozygous alleles, family genotyping and consideration of a specific haplotype known to be δF508-associated (Krawczak et al. 1988; Wagner et al., 1990) revealed that R553X occurred together with 1(KM19)–1(XV2c)–2(pJ3.11) haplotypes on all chromosomes analysed. However, on two chromosomes from black American CF patients, R553X was observed on a 2(KM19)–2(XV2c) haplotype, one of which additionally carried a 1(pJ3.11) allele.

Of any two R553X-bearing chromosomes with different marker haplotypes, one must have originated either from a recurrent R553X substitution on a different haplotype background, or from recombination events involving (in our case) markers on both sides of the CFTR gene. Evidence in favour of one or the other hypothesis can be quantified approximately by calculating the relative likelihoods of the two possible haplotype origins. The recombination fractions between the flanking markers and CF are of the order of 10^{-4} for KM19 (Estivill et al., 1987) and 10^{-2} for pJ3.11 (Poustka et al., 1988). If we assume that the population frequency of R553X (10^{-3}) has remained relatively constant over a reasonable period of time, then the likelihood for a recombination event can be estimated as

$$L_i = 10^{-3} \times 10^{-4} \times 10^{-2} = 10^{-9} \text{ per meiosis}$$

neglecting RFLP allele frequencies.

The recurrent mutation hypothesis is supported by the location of the R553X mutation within a CpG dinucleotide; the $C \rightarrow T$ transition responsible is consistent with the model of methylation-mediated deamination. Assuming a generation time of 20 years for humans, $CG \rightarrow TG$ transitions occur at a rate of 3.3×10^{-7} per generation (Section 6.2.3). This value may be regarded as an estimate of L_{ii}, the likelihood of recurrent mutation. Comparison of L_i and L_{ii} demonstrates that recurrent mutation as a cause of the observed haplotype difference is approximately 300 times more likely than recombination affecting identical-by-descent chromosomes. This finding is independent of the time that has elapsed since the recombination/recurrent mutation event occurred.

The evidence provided here for recurrent mutation in two different racial groups is not trivial, since our conservative approach would yield only a 60:40 likelihood ratio in favour of recurrent mutation if the alleles of the flanking marker pJ3.11 were identical (the recombination fraction between KM19 and CF is estimated to be several orders of magnitude higher than the average mutation rate per generation, even for a CpG dinucleotide). Furthermore, Cutting et al. (1989) predicted that Caucasian CF genes might account for 50% or more of CF genes in American blacks.

The observation of recurrent mutation at a CpG site within the CFTR coding region suggests that other intragenic CpG sites could be targeted by a directed-search strategy (e.g. Pattinson et al., 1990) for the detection of novel point mutations. It also demonstrates that subsequent screening for such mutations, once detected, should not be limited to those CF patients possessing the same haplotype. The additional possibility of recurrent mutation within linked CpG-containing restriction sites (Cooper and Clayton, 1988) serves to emphasize this point.

In contrast to the situation with R553X, it can be demonstrated that all G551D mutations observed in the German sample have a high probability of being identical by descent. Three out of four G551D-carrying CF chromosomes bore the 2(KM19)-1(XV2c)-2(pJ3.11) haplotype. G551D mutations result from $GGT \rightarrow GAT$ substitutions, which occur at a rate of approximately 6.5×10^{-8} per generation (a figure derived from the relative dinucleotide mutabilities of Section 6.5 and a base mutation rate of $2.2 \times 10^{-9} \text{ year}^{-1}$). As before, were the mutations on the same marker haplotype to be traced back, either they must stem from the same ancestral chromosome or a recurrent mutation must have occurred.

If we assume random mating and a constant population growth of 1% per generation (Bodmer and Cavalli-Sforza, 1976), the probability of linking two lines of descent exactly n generations ago, given that they have neither joined before nor ended in mutations, is

$$p_n = 1.01^n / (1.01^n + 2N_0)$$

where N_0 denotes the present effective population size. For the Caucasian population, $N_0 = 1.5 \times 10^9$ (Bodmer and Cavalli-Sforza 1976) represents a conservative estimate for our purposes. Since in reality, N_0 tends to be smaller, p_n will actually be underestimated. The probability of at least one of the two lines of descent ending in a mutation is $q = 2 \times 6.5 \times 10^{-8} = 1.3 \times 10^{-7}$ in any generation, again given that they have neither joined nor ended before.

In the first generation, there is a likelihood of p_1 for linking the two lines together, q for a mutation and $1 - p_1 - q$ for neither event. In the second generation, these likelihoods are $p_2(1 - p_1 - q)$ for recombination, $q(1 - p_1 - q)$ for mutation and $(1 - p_1 - q)(1 - p_2 - q)$ for neither (and so on). In this progression, the 'neither event' likelihoods converge to zero, whereas the sum of 'mutation' likelihoods, 2.2×10^{-4}, equals the overall likelihood of the mutation hypothesis. This result, however, still represents an overestimate since random mating was assumed to hold over the entire time period. Founder effects, population 'bottlenecks' and changes in population structure, all of which would increase the probability of identity by descent, were thus neglected.

6.7.2 Mutations in the protein C gene

Protein C, a vitamin K-dependent glycoprotein and zymogen of a serine protease, fulfils an important regulatory role in haemostasis by inactivating factors Va and VIIIa in the presence of the cofactor protein S (reviewed by Stenflo, 1988). Hereditary protein C deficiency is usually but not always inherited as an autosomal dominant trait, heterozygotes being at risk for superficial thrombophlebitis, deep vein thrombosis and pulmonary embolism.

A CGA → TGA transition at codon 306 of the protein C gene was detected in a Swedish kindred with thrombotic disease whose members exhibited plasma protein C activity/antigen levels consistent with type I protein C deficiency (Grundy et al., 1992). This Swedish R306X mutation was identical to a lesion previously described in three Dutch families (Romeo et al., 1987, Reitsma et al., 1990; 1991).

In order to determine whether or not the Swedish and Dutch R306X mutations were identical by descent, family members were examined for the presence or absence of a polymorphic MspI site at nucleotide position 7932 (Foster et al., 1985) within intron 8 of the protein C gene. This site is present in 99% of European Caucasians (Koenhen et al., 1989), but was absent in the Dutch patients. Members of the Swedish family exhibited restriction fragment sizes that were consistent with the homozygous presence of the MspI site (i.e. the frequent allele) in all individuals tested.

The relative likelihoods of recurrent mutation at Arg 306 and identity by descent may be assessed as described in the previous section. To explain the results of RFLP typing under the assumption of identity by descent, either a recombination between the intron 8 MspI RFLP and the exon 9 mutation (a distance of 700 bp) or a mutation at the MspI site in one of the two lineages is required.

If it is assumed that a genetic distance of 1cM corresponds to approximately 10^6 bp and that the frequency of heterozygous protein C deficiency in the general population is approximately one in 200 (Miletich *et al.*, 1987), then the likelihood of recurrent mutation at Arg 306, 3.3×10^{-7} (see above), is one order of magnitude higher than the likelihood of recombination $(7 \times 10^{-6} \times 5 \times 10^{-3} = 3.5 \times 10^{-8})$.

Both the removal of an MspI site (i.e. CCGG) and the R306X mutation are explicable in terms of 5-methylcytosine deamination. However, since the MspI site mutation must have occurred almost certainly in the Dutch line, and since the hypothesis is therefore limited to only one out of two possible events, the posterior odds in favour of a recurrent mutation at Arg 306 are approximately 2:1.

Further genealogical evidence for a recurrent mutation having affected Arg 306 comes from the fact that the three Dutch families shared a common ancestor some 235 years ago (Reitsma *et al.*, 1991). Thus, if the Dutch and Swedish R306X mutations were identical by descent, the MspI site mutation must have occurred before 1757, the date of marriage of the Dutch common ancestor. This gives the recurrent mutation hypothesis a further 235 year 'start' over the competing MspI mutation hypothesis. Although this advantage becomes less important with time elapsed, a very ancient MspI mutation would have required the simultaneous persistence of two Arg 306 mutations in the population, despite prevailing natural selection. Although selective pressure is not readily quantifiable in thrombotic disorders, recurrent mutation remains the most likely scenario in this case.

6.8 Gene conversion

Gene conversion is the 'modification of one of two alleles by the other' (Vogel and Motulsky, 1986). The end result is very similar to that consequent on a double unequal crossing-over event (Figure 6.6). The difference between the two processes is, however, that the 'correction' of one allele brought about by gene conversion is non-reciprocal, leaving the other allele physically unchanged. In practice, it is usually not possible to distinguish the two mechanisms of interallelic recombination since, in humans, it would be highly unusual to be able to examine both recombination products. Moreover, the haplotypes created by gene conversion and double unequal crossing-over are expected to be identical. Intuitively, however, gene conversion, as a single event, may be expected to occur more frequently than the two independent events required for double unequal crossing-over.

The process of gene conversion may involve the whole or only a part of a gene and can occur either between allelic genes or between highly homologous but non-allelic genes. Examples of the latter include the G-γ (HBG2) and A-γ (HBG1) globin genes (Shen *et al.*, 1981; Stoeckert *et al.*, 1984; Powers and Smithies, 1986) and the α1- (HBGA1) and α2- (HBGA2) globin genes (Liebhaber *et al.*, 1981). The mechanism underlying gene conversion remains elusive but must presumably entail close physical interaction between the homologous DNA sequences; it may indeed involve heteroduplex formation followed

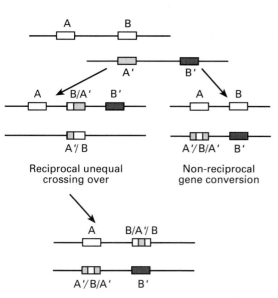

Figure 6.6. Gene conversion and double unequal crossing-over (from Vogel and Motulsky 1986; reproduced by permission of Springer Verlag). In the example given, a pair of homologous genes (A, A′ and B, B′) are arranged in tandem. In reciprocal unequal crossing-over, a recombination event occurs between B and A′, due to illegitimate alignment of the chromosomes, to produce duplicated and deleted chromosomes. A further additional recombination event between the two hybrid alleles then creates the double unequal crossing-over products shown. In gene conversion, part of the A′ gene is converted to the B sequence as a result of the illegitimate alignment. Unlike crossing-over, this event is non-reciprocal.

by mismatch repair. Powers and Smithies (1986) have suggested that gene conversion occurs during the zygotene and pachytene phases of meiosis, since it is known that single-stranded DNA is generated at this time and may interact with the double-stranded DNA from the homologous chromosome during pairing.

Gene conversion has been invoked in instances where it is necessary to account for the association of the same disease-causing mutation with two or more different haplotypes e.g. β^E-globin alleles in South-East Asian populations (Antonarakis *et al.*, 1982) and the β^s-globin mutation in African populations (Antonarakis *et al.*, 1984). In the latter example, the β^s mutation was found on 16 different haplotypes, which could be subdivided into four groups that could not be derived from each other by less than two crossing-over events. Similarly, Kazazian *et al.* (1984) and Pirastu *et al.* (1987) invoked gene conversion to explain the spread of the nonsense mutation at codon 39 of the β-globin (HBB) gene to a considerable number of different haplotypes in Mediterranean β-thalassaemia patients. Zhang *et al.* (1988) described five different β-globin gene mutations causing β-thalassaemia in the Chinese population that occurred on more than one haplotype. It was considered unlikely that all cases should have occurred either by recurrent mutation on different haplotypes or through multiple recombination events.

Matsuno *et al.* (1992) reported that a frameshift mutation at codons 41/42 in the β-globin gene occurred in association with two different haplotypes in two ethnically distinct groups — Chinese and South-East Asians. These authors pointed out that six of every seven β-thalassaemia mutations known to occur on very different haplotypes were located in a 451 bp region between codon 2 and position 16 of intron 2. Similarly, Powers and Smithies (1986) showed that gene conversion events between the G-γ and A-γ globin genes usually involve less than 300 bp in length. Matsuno et al. (1992) also noted the existence of a χ-like sequence (GCTGGTGG) (known to promote recombination both in E. coli and in mouse immunoglobulin genes; Smith, 1983), near the 5' end of exon 2 near to the site of the proposed gene conversion. Although evidence for the association is at present still circumstantial, it may be that such gene conversion events are mediated by χ or similar sequences (see also CYP21A/CYP21B genes below).

Harada et al. (1987) examined Japanese patients with steroid 21-hydroxylase deficiency and congenital adrenal hyperplasia by Southern blotting and found a 3.7 kb TaqI fragment encompassing the 21-OHase B (CYP21B) gene to be absent from the DNA of two unrelated patients. However, a 10.5 kb BglII fragment containing the CYP21B gene was still present in both patients. Restriction mapping and DNA sequencing demonstrated that the functional CYP21B gene of one of these patients had been converted to the closely linked and highly homologous (98%) pseudogene, 21-OHase A (CYP21A), resulting in chromosomes containing two CYP21A pseudogenes but lacking a normal functional CYP21B gene. Since the HLA haplotypes of the two patients were non-identical, two independent gene conversion events are thought to have occurred in these patients. Further probable examples of gene conversion involving a CYP21B gene by essentially the same mechanism as described above have been reported by Amor et al. (1988), Higashi et al. (1988), Morel et al. (1989) and Urabe et al. (1990). Amor et al. (1988) noted the presence of six χ-like sequences (GCTGGGG) in the region of the CYP21A and CYP21B genes which they speculated might play a role in the gene conversion events. Gene conversion is not, however, the most frequent cause of steroid 21-hydroxylase deficiency; White et al. (1988) noted only two of 15 patient chromosomes to be consistent with gene conversion events as opposed to gene deletions.

6.9 Point mutations in the mitochondrial genome

Wallace et al. (1991) reported a total of 20 different single base-pair substitutions in the human mitochondrial genome (Section 2.6) causing genetic disease: 10 A$\rightarrow$G, six G$\rightarrow$A, two T$\rightarrow$C, and one each of T$\rightarrow$G and C$\rightarrow$G. Thus 18 of 20 base changes were transitions, which represents a highly significant excess ($P < 10^{-5}$) over the expected proportion of one in three. When the observed frequencies of involvement in these mutational events are compared with expectation based on known nucleotide frequencies in the mitochondrial genome, mutations within C residues appear to be significantly under-represented ($\chi^2 = 6.41$). The high frequencies of mutation at A and G residues fail to attain significance since their χ^2 values (3.41 and 4.98) are smaller than 6.24, the appropriate threshold allowing for multiple testing ($P = 0.05$).

A similar analysis was performed for dinucleotides involved in the above-mentioned substitutions (each mutation was scored twice as two overlapping dinucleotides). Although it would not be meaningful to calculate χ^2 values with such a small sample size, mutations in the dinucleotide AA appear to be over-represented (observed 12 versus expected, 3.8). No dramatic excess of mutations in CpG dinucleotides was noted consistent with the lack of cytosine methylation (and hence methylation-mediated deamination) in the mitochondrial genome. In addition, the frequency of direct repeats, inverted repeats or symmetric elements (see Section 7.2) within 10 bp of each point mutation was not significantly elevated over expectation, suggesting that these elements are not involved in single base-pair substitutions in the mitochondrial genome.

References

Abadie V, Lyonnet S, Maurin N, Berthelon M, Caillaud C, Giraud F, Mattei J-F, Rey J, Rey F, Munnich A. (1989) CpG dinucleotides are mutation hotspots in phenylketonuria. *Genomics* **5**: 936–939.

Adams RLP, Eason R. (1984) Increased CpG content of DNA stabilizes CpG dinucleotides. *Nucleic Acids Res.* **12**: 5867–5877.

Adams RLP, Davis T, Rinaldi A, Easton R. (1987) CpG deficiency, dinucleotide distribution and nucleosome positioning. *Eur. J. Biochem.* **165**: 107–115.

Alber T. (1989) Mutational effects on protein stability. *Ann. Rev. Biochem.* **58**: 765–789.

Amor M, Parker KL, Globerman H, New MI, White PC. (1988) Mutation in the CYP21B gene (Ile→Asn) causes steroid 21-hydroxylase deficiency. *Proc. Natl. Acad. Sci. USA* **85**: 1600–1604.

Antonarakis SE, Boehm CD, Giardina PJ, Kazazian HH. (1982) Non-random association of polymorphic restriction sites in the β-globin gene cluster. *Proc. Natl. Acad. Sci. USA* **79**: 137–141.

Antonarakis SE, Boehm CD, Serjeant GR, Theisen CE, Dover GJ, Kazazian HH. (1984) Origin of the β^s-globin gene in Blacks: the contribution of recurrent mutation or gene conversion or both. *Proc. Natl. Acad. Sci. USA* **81**: 853–856.

Auerbach C. (1976) *Mutation Research: Problems, Results and Perspectives.* Chapman and Hall, London.

Bains W, Bains J. (1987) Rate of base substitution in mammalian nuclear DNA is dependent on local sequence context. *Mutat. Res.* **179**: 65–74.

Barker D, Schäfer M, White R. (1984) Restriction sites containing CpG show a higher frequency of polymorphism in human DNA. *Cell* **36**: 131–138.

Bartels I, Grzeschik KH, Cooper DN, Schmidtke J. (1986) Regional mapping of six cloned DNA sequences on human chromosome 7. *Am. J. Hum. Genet.* **38**: 280–287.

Behn-Krappa A, Hölker I, Sandaradura de Silva U, Doerfler W. (1991) Patterns of DNA methylation are indistinguishable in different individuals over a wide range of human DNA sequences. *Genomics* **11**: 1–7.

Benzer S. (1961) On the topography of the genetic fine structure. *Proc. Natl. Acad. Sci. USA* **47**: 403–417.

Bessman MJ, Reha-Krantz LJ. (1977) Studies on the biochemical basis of spontaneous mutation. V. Effect of temperature on mutation frequency. *J. Mol. Biol.* **116**: 115–123.

Bialek G, Nasheuer H-P, Goetz H, Grosse F. (1989) Exonucleolytic proofreading increases the accuracy of DNA synthesis by human lymphocyte DNA polymerase α DNA primase. *EMBO J.* **8**: 1833–1839.

Bird AP. (1980) DNA methylation and the frequency of CpG in animal DNA. *Nucleic Acids Res.* **8**: 1499–1504.

Bird AP. (1986) CpG-rich islands and the function of DNA methylation. *Nature* **321**: 209–213.

Bird AP. (1987) CpG islands as gene markers in the vertebrate nucleus. *Trends Genet.* **3:** 342–347.

Bodmer WF, Cavalli-Sforza LL. (1976) *Genetics, Evolution, and Man.* Freeman, San Francisco, California.

Bolden AH, Nalin CM, Ward CA, Poonian MS, Weissbach A. (1986) Primary DNA sequence determines sites of maintenance and *de novo* methylation by mammalian DNA methyltransferase. *Mol. Cell. Biol.* **6:** 1135–1140.

Bottema CDK, Ketterling RP, Yoon H-S, Sommer SS. (1990) The pattern of factor IX germ-line mutation in Asians is similar to that of Caucasians. *Am. J. Hum. Genet.* **47:** 835–841.

Bottema CDK, Ketterling RP, Li S, Yoon H-P, Phillips JA, Sommer SS. (1991) Missense mutations and evolutionary conservation of amino acids: evidence that many of the amino acids in factor IX function as 'spacer' elements. *Am. J. Hum. Genet.* **49:** 820–838.

Brennan SO, Arai K, Madison J, Laurell C-B, Galliano M, Watkins S, Peach R, Myles T, George P, Putnam FW. (1990) Hypermutability of CpG dinucleotides in the propeptide-encoding sequence of the human albumin gene. *Proc. Natl. Acad. Sci. USA* **87:** 3909–3913.

Britten RJ. (1986) Rates of DNA sequence evolution differ between taxonomic groups. *Science* **235:** 1393–1398.

Brown TC, Jiricny J. (1987) A specific mismatch repair event protects mammalian cells from loss of 5-methylcytosine. *Cell* **50:** 945–950.

Brown TC, Jiricny J. (1988) Different base/base mispairs are corrected with different efficiencies and specificities in monkey kidney cells. *Cell* **54:** 705–711.

Bullock P, Champoux JJ, Botchan M. (1985) Association of crossover points with topoisomerase I cleavage sites: a model for non-homologous recombination. *Science* **230:** 954–957.

Bulmer M, Wolfe KH, Sharp PM. (1991) Synonymous nucleotide substitution rates in mammalian genes: implications for the molecular clock and the relationship of mammalian orders. *Proc. Natl. Acad. Sci. USA* **88:** 5974–5978.

Cambareri EB, Jensen BC, Schabtach E, Selker EU. (1989) Repeat-induced G-C to A-T mutations in *Neurospora*. *Science* **244:** 1571–1575.

Castora FJ, Arnheim N, Simpson NN. (1980) Mitochondrial DNA polymorphism: evidence that variants detected by restriction enzymes differ in nucleotide sequence rather than in methylation. *Proc. Natl. Acad. Sci. USA* **77:** 6415–6419.

Cheng KC, Cahill DS, Kasai H, Nishimura S, Loeb LA. (1992) 8-Hydroxyguanine, an abundant form of oxidative DNA damage, causes $G \rightarrow T$ and $A \rightarrow C$ substitutions. *J. Biol. Chem.* **267:** 166–172.

Cooper DN, Clayton JF. (1988) DNA polymorphism and the study of disease associations. *Hum. Genet.* **78:** 299–312.

Cooper DN, Gerber-Huber S. (1985) DNA methylation and CpG suppression. *Cell Differ.* **17:** 199–205.

Cooper DN, Krawczak M. (1989) Cytosine methylation and the fate of CpG dinucleotides in vertebrate genomes. *Hum. Genet.* **83:** 181–189.

Cooper DN, Krawczak M. (1990) The mutational spectrum of single base-pair substitutions causing human genetic disease: patterns and predictions. *Hum. Genet.* **85:** 55–74.

Cooper DN, Schmidtke J. (1984) DNA restriction fragment length polymorphisms and heterozygosity in the human genome. *Hum. Genet.* **66:** 1–16.

Cooper DN, Schmidtke J. (1991) Diagnosis of genetic disease using recombinant DNA. Third edition. *Hum. Genet.* **87:** 519–560.

Cooper DN, Youssoufian H. (1988) The CpG dinucleotide and human genetic disease. *Hum. Genet.* **78:** 151–155.

Cooper DN, Errington LH, Clayton RM. (1983) Variation in the DNA methylation pattern of expressed and non-expressed genes in chicken. *DNA* **2:** 131–140.

Coulondre C, Miller JH, Farabaugh PJ, Gilbert W. (1978) Molecular basis of base substitution hotspots in *Escherichia coli*. *Nature* **274:** 775–780.

Cutting GR, Antonarakis SE, Buetow KH, Kasch LM, Rosenstein BJ, Kazazian HH. (1989) Analysis of DNA polymorphism haplotypes linked to the cystic fibrosis locus in North American black and Caucasian families supports the existence of multiple mutations of the cystic fibrosis gene. *Am. J. Hum. Genet.* **44:** 307–318.

Cutting GR, Kasch LM, Rosenstein BJ, Zielenski J, Tsui LC, Antonarakis SE, Kazazian HH. (1990) A cluster of cystic fibrosis mutations in the first nucleotide-binding fold of the cystic fibrosis conductance regulator protein. *Nature* **346:** 366–369.

Cystic Fibrosis Genetic Analysis Consortium. (1990) Worldwide survey of the δF508 mutation — report from the Cystic Fibrosis Genetic Analysis Consortium. *Am. J. Hum. Genet.* **47:** 354–359.

Drake JW. (1970) *The Molecular Basis of Mutation.* Holden Day, San Francisco, California.

Drobetsky EA, Grosovsky AJ, Glickman BW. (1987) The specificity of UV-induced mutations at endogenous loci in mammalian cells. *Proc. Natl. Acad. Sci. USA* **84:** 9103–9107.

Duncan BK, Miller JH. (1980) Mutagenic deamination of cytosine residues in DNA. *Nature* **287:** 560–561.

Ehrlich M, Norris KF, Wang RUH, Kuo KC, Gehrke CW. (1986) DNA cytosine methylation and heat-induced deamination. *Biosci. Rep.* **6:** 387–393.

Ehrlich M, Zhang X-Y, Inamdar NM. (1990) Spontaneous deamination of cytosine and 5-methylcytosine residues in DNA and replacement of 5-methylcytosine residues with cytosine residues. *Mutat. Res.* **238:** 277–286.

Epstein CJ. (1967) Non-randomness of amino-acid changes in the evolution of homologous proteins. *Nature* **215:** 355–359.

Estivill X, Farrall M, Scambler PJ, Bell GM, Hawley KMF, Lench NJ, Bates GP, Kruyer HC, Frederick PA, Stanier P, Watson EK, Williamson R, Wainwright BJ. (1987) A candidate for the cystic fibrosis locus isolated by selection for methylation-free islands. *Nature* **326:** 840–845.

European Working Group on CF Genetics. (1990) Gradient of distribution in Europe of the major CF mutation and of its associated haplotype. *Hum. Genet.* **85:** 436–445.

Feldman GL, Williamson R, Beaudet AL, O'Brien WE. (1988) Prenatal diagnosis of cystic fibrosis by DNA amplification for detection of KM-19 polymorphism. *Lancet* **ii:** 102.

Foster DC, Yoshitake S, Davie E. (1985) The nucleotide sequence of the gene for human protein C. *Proc. Natl. Acad. Sci. USA* **82:** 4673–4677.

Frederico LA, Kunkel TA, Shaw BR. (1990) A sensitive genetic assay for the detection of cytosine deamination: determination of rate constants and the activation energy. *Biochemistry* **29:** 2532–2537.

Gardiner-Garden M, Frommer M.. (1987) CpG islands in vertebrate genomes. *J. Mol. Biol.* **196:** 261–282.

Giannelli F, Green PM, High KA, Sommer S, Lillicrap DP, Ludwig DP, Olek K, Reitsma PH, Goossens M, Yoshioka A, Brownlee GG. (1992) Haemophilia B: database of point mutations and short additions and deletions — third edition. *Nucleic Acids Res. Suppl.* **20:** 2027–2063.

Grantham R. (1974) Amino acid difference formula to help explain protein evolution. *Science* **185:** 862–864.

Green PM, Montandon AJ, Bentley DR, Ljung R, Nilsson IM, Giannelli F. (1990) The incidence and distribution of CpG → TpG transitions in the coagulation factor IX gene: a fresh look at CpG mutational hotspots. *Nucleic Acids Res.* **18:** 3227–3231.

Green PM, Montandon AJ, Ljung R, Nilsson IM, Giannelli F. (1992) Haplotype analysis of identical factor IX mutants using PCR. *Thromb. Haemost.* **67:** 66–69.

Groot GSP, Kroon AM. (1979) Mitochondrial DNA from various organisms does not contain internally methylated cytosine in –CCGG– sequences. *Biochim. Biophys. Acta* **564:** 355–357.

Grundy CB, Schulman S, Krawczak M, Kobosko J, Kakkar VV, Cooper DN. (1992) Protein C deficiency and thromboembolism: recurrent mutation at Arg 306 in the protein C gene. *Hum. Genet.* **88:** 586–588.

Harada F, Kimura A, Iwanaga T, Shimozawa K, Yata J, Sasazuki T. (1987) Gene conversion-like events cause steroid 21-hydroxylase deficiency in congenital adrenal hyperplasia. *Proc. Natl. Acad. Sci. USA* **84:** 8091–8094.

Hare JT, Taylor JH. (1985) One role for DNA methylation in vertebrate cells is strand discrimination in mismatch repair. *Proc. Natl. Acad. Sci. USA* **82:** 7350–7354.

Harwood J, Tachibana A, Meuth M. (1991) Multiple dispersed spontaneous mutations: a novel pathway of mutation in a malignant human cell line. *Mol. Cell. Biol.* **11:** 3163–3170.

Higashi Y, Tanae A, Inoue H, Furjii-Kuriyama Y. (1988) Evidence for frequent gene conversion in the steroid 21-hydroxlase P-450C21 gene: implications for steroid 21 hydroxylase deficiency. *Am. J. Hum. Genet.* **42:** 17–25.

Holmes J, Clark S, Modrich P. (1990) Strand-specific mismatch correction in nuclear extracts of human and *Drosophila melanogaster* cell lines. *Proc. Natl. Acad. Sci. USA* **87:** 5837–5841.

Hsie AW, Recio L, Katz DS, Lee CQ, Wagner M, Shenley RL. (1986) Evidence for reactive oxygen species inducing mutations in mammalian cells. *Proc. Natl. Acad. Sci. USA* **83:** 9616–9620.

Hubrich-Kuhner K, Buhk H-J, Wagner H, Kroger H, Simon D. (1989) Non-CG recognition sequences of DNA cytosine-5-methyltransferase from rat liver. *Biochem. Biophys. Res. Commun.* **160:** 1175–1182.

Jones M, Wagner R, Radman M. (1987a) Repair of a mismatch is influenced by the base composition of the surrounding nucleotide sequence. *Genetics* **115:** 605–610.

Jones M, Wagner R, Radman M. (1987b) Mismatch repair of deaminated 5-methyl-cytosine. *J. Mol. Biol.* **194:** 155–159.

Jones PA, Rideout WM, Shen J-C, Spruck CH, Tsai YC. (1992) Methylation, mutation and cancer. *Bioessays* **14:** 33–36.

Josse J, Kaiser AD, Kornberg A. (1961) Enzymatic synthesis of deoxyribonucleic acid. VIII. Frequencies of nearest neighbour base sequences in deoxyribonucleic acid. *J. Biol. Chem.* **236:** 864–875.

Kazazian HH, Orkin SH, Markham AF, Chapman CR, Youssoufian H, Waber PG. (1984) Quantification of the close association between DNA haplotypes and specific β-thalassaemia mutations in Mediterraneans. *Nature* **310:** 152–154.

Keohavong P, Liu VF, Thilly WG. (1991) Analysis of point mutations induced by ultraviolet light in human cells. *Mutat. Res.* **249:** 147–159.

Kerem BS, Rommens JM, Buchanan JA, Markiewicz D, Cox TK, Chakravarti A, Buchwald M, Tsui LC. (1989) Identification of the cystic fibrosis gene: genetic analysis. *Science* **245:** 1073–1080.

Koeberl DD, Bottema CDK, Ketterling RP, Bridge PJ, Lillicrap DP, Sommer SS. (1990) Mutations causing hemophilia B: direct estimate of the underlying rates of spontaneous germline transitions, transversions and deletions in a human gene. *Am. J. Hum. Genet.* **47:** 202–217.

Koenhen E, Bertina RM, Reitsma PH. (1989) MspI RFLP in intron 8 of the protein C gene. *Nucleic Acids Res.* **17:** 8401.

Kramer B, Kramer W, Fritz HJ. (1984) Different base/base mismatches are corrected with different efficiencies by the methyl-directed DNA mismatch repair system of *E. coli. Cell* **38:** 879–887.

Krawczak M, Konecki DS, Schmidtke J, Dück M, Engel W, Nützenadel W, Trefz FK. (1988) Allelic association of the cystic fibrosis locus and two DNA markers, XV2c and KM19, in 55 German families. *Hum. Genet.* **80:** 78–80.

Krawczak M, Cooper DN. (1991) Gene deletions causing human genetic disease: mechanisms of mutagenesis and the role of the local DNA sequence environment. *Hum. Genet.* **86:** 425–441.

Kresnak MT, Davidson RL. (1992) Thymidine-induced mutations in mammalian cells: sequence specificity and implications for mutagenesis *in vivo. Proc. Natl. Acad. Sci. USA* **89:** 2829–2833.

Kunkel TA. (1984) Mutational specificity of depurination. *Proc. Natl. Acad. Sci. USA* **81:** 1494–1498.

Kunkel TA. (1985a) The mutational specificity of DNA polymerase-α during *in vitro* DNA synthesis. *J. Biol. Chem.* **260:** 5787–5796.

Kunkel TA. (1985b) The mutational specificity of DNA polymerases-α and -γ during *in vitro* DNA synthesis. *J. Biol. Chem.* **260:** 12866–12874.

Kunkel TA, Alexander PS. (1986) The base substitution fidelity of eukaryotic DNA polymerase. *J. Biol. Chem.* **261:** 160–166.

Kunkel TA, Bebenek K. (1988) Recent studies of the fidelity of DNA synthesis. *Biochim. Biophys. Acta* **951**: 1–15.

Kunkel TA, Soni A. (1988) Mutagenesis by transient misalignment. *J. Biol. Chem.* **263**: 14784–14789.

Kunkel TA, Schaaper RM, Beckmann RA, Loeb LA. (1981) On the fidelity of DNA replication. *J. Biol. Chem.* **256**: 9883–9889.

Kunkel TA, Schaaper RM, Loeb LA. (1983) Depurination-induced infidelity of DNA synthesis with purified DNA replication proteins *in vitro*. *Biochemistry* **22**: 2378–2384.

Landis CA, Masters SB, Spada A, Pace AM, Bourbe HR, Vallar L. (1989) GTPase inhibiting mutations activate the α chain of Gs and stimulate adenylyl cyclase in human pituitary tumours. *Nature* **340**: 692–696.

Li W-H, Tanimura M. (1987) The molecular clock runs more slowly in man than in apes and monkeys. *Nature* **326**: 93–96.

Li W-H, Wu C-I, Luo C-C. (1984) Non-randomness of point mutation as reflected in nucleotide substitutions in pseudogenes and its evolutionary implications. *J. Mol. Evol.* **21**: 58–71.

Liebhaber SA, Goossens M, Kan YW. (1981) Homology and concerted evolution at the $\alpha1$ and $\alpha2$ loci of human α-globin. *Nature* **290**: 26–29.

Lindahl T. (1982) DNA repair enzymes. *Ann. Rev. Biochem.* **51**: 61–87.

Lindahl T, Nyberg B. (1972) Rate of depurination of native deoxyribonucleic acid. *Biochemistry* **11**: 3610–3618.

Lindahl T, Nyberg B. (1974) Heat-induced deamination of cytosine residues in deoxyribonucleic acid. *Biochemistry* **13**: 3405–3410.

Lindsay S, Adams RLP, Monk M. (1989) Til 1 — a human lymphoblastoid cell line with minimal DNA methylation. *Hum. Genet.* **81**: 252–256.

Loeb LA. (1985) Apurinic sites as mutagenic intermediates. *Cell* **40**: 483–484.

Loeb LA. (1989) Endogenous carcinogenesis: molecular oncology into the twenty-first century. *Cancer Res.* **49**: 5489–5496.

Loeb LA, Kunkel TA. (1982) Fidelity of DNA synthesis. *Ann. Rev. Biochem.* **52**: 429–457.

Loeb LA, Preston BD. (1986) Mutagenesis by apurinic/apyrimidinic sites. *Ann. Rev. Genet.* **20**: 201–230.

Lu AL, Welsh K, Clark S, Su SS, Modrick P. (1984) Repair of DNA base-pair mismatches in extracts of *Escherichia coli*. *Cold Spring Harb. Symp. Quant. Biol.* **49**: 589–596.

McKusick VA. (1990) *Mendelian Inheritance in Man*, 9th Edn. Johns Hopkins University Press, Baltimore.

Maruyama R, Gojobori T, Aota S, Ikemura T. (1986) Codon usage tabulated from the GenBank genetic sequence data. *Nucleic Acids Res. Suppl.* **14**: r151–r197.

Mathews CK, Ji J. (1992) DNA precursor asymmetries, replication fidelity and variable genome evolution. *Bioessays* **14**: 295–301.

Matsuno Y, Yamashiro Y, Yamamoto K, Hattori Y, Yamamoto K, Ohba Y, Miyaji T. (1992) A possible example of gene conversion with a common β thalassaemia mutation and Chi sequence present in the β-globin gene. *Hum. Genet.* **88**: 357–358.

Mavilio F, Giampaolo A, Care A, Migliaccio G, Calandrini M, Russo G, Pagliardi GL, Mastroberardino G, Marinucci M, Peschle C. (1983) Molecular mechanisms of human hemoglobin switching; selective undermethylation and expression of globin genes in embryonic, fetal and adult erythroblasts. *Proc. Natl. Acad. Sci. USA* **80**: 6907–6911.

Mendelman LV, Boosalis MS, Petruska J, Goodman MF. (1989) Nearest neighbour influences on DNA polymerase insertion fidelity. *J. Biol. Chem.* **264**: 14415–14423.

Meuth M. (1989) The molecular basis of mutations induced by deoxynucleoside triphosphate pool imbalances in mammalian cells. *Exp. Cell Res.* **181**: 305–316.

Miletich J, Sherman L, Broze G. (1987) Absence of thrombosis in subjects with heterozygous protein C deficiency. *N. Engl. J. Med.* **317**: 991–996.

Miyamoto MM, Koop BF, Slightom JL, Goodman M, Tennant MR. (1988) Molecular systematics of higher primates: genealogical relations and classifications. *Proc. Natl. Acad. Sci. USA* **85**: 7627–7631.

Modrich P. (1987) DNA mismatch correction. *Ann. Rev. Biochem.* **56:** 435–466.

Monk M. (1988) Genomic imprinting. *Genes Dev.* **2:** 921–925.

Morel Y, David M, Forest MG, Betuel H, Hauptman G, Andre J, Bertrand J, Miller WL. (1989) Gene conversions and rearrangements cause discordance between inheritance of forms of 21-hydroxylase deficiency and HLA types. *J. Clin. Endocrinol. Metab.* **68:** 592–599.

Mullan M, Crawford F, Axelman K, Houlden H, Lilius L, Winblad B, Lannfelt L. (1992) A pathogenic mutation for probable Alzheimer's disease in the APP gene at the N-terminus of β-amyloid. *Nature Genetics* **1:** 345–347.

Nalbantoglu J, Goncalves O, Meuth M. (1983) Structure of mutant alleles of the *aprt* locus in Chinese hamster ovary cells. *J. Mol. Biol.* **167:** 575–594.

Nguyen T, Brunson D, Crespi CL, Penman BW, Wishnok JS, Tannenbaum SR. (1992) DNA damage and mutation in human cells exposed to nitric oxide *in vitro*. *Proc. Natl. Acad. Sci. USA* **89:** 3030–3034.

Northrup H, Rosenbloom C, O'Brien WE, Beaudet AL. (1989) Additional polymorphism for D7S8 linked to cystic fibrosis including detection by DNA amplification. *Nucleic Acids Res.* **17:** 1784.

Nussinov R. (1981a) Nearest neighbour nucleotide patterns: structural and biological implications. *J. Biol. Chem.* **256:** 8458–8462.

Nussinov R. (1981b) Eukaryotic dinucleotide preference rules and their implications for degenerate codon usage. *J. Mol. Biol.* **149:** 125–131.

Ohno S. (1988) Universal rule for coding sequence construction: TA/CG deficiency — TG/CT excess. *Proc. Natl. Acad. Sci. USA* **85:** 9630–9634.

Pakula AA, Sauer RT. (1989) Genetic analysis of protein stability and function. *Ann. Rev. Genet.* **23:** 289–310.

Pattinson JK, Millar DS, Grundy CB, Wieland K, Mibashan RS, Martinowitz U, McVey J, Tan-Un K, Vidaud M, Goossens M, Sampietro M, Krawczak M, Reiss J, Zoll B, Whitmore D, Bradshaw A, Wensley R, Ajani A, Mitchell V, Rizza C, Maia R, Winter P, Mayne EE, Schwartz M, Green PJ, Kakkar VV, Tuddenham EGD, Cooper DN. (1990) The molecular genetic analysis of hemophilia A: a directed-search strategy for the detection of point mutations in the human factor VIII gene. *Blood* **76:** 2242–2248.

Perry DJ, Carrell RW. (1989) CpG dinucleotides are 'hotspots' for mutation in the antithrombin III gene. *Mol. Biol. Med.* **6:** 239–243.

Perutz MF. (1990) Frequency of abnormal human haemoglobins caused by $C \rightarrow T$ transitions in CpG dinucleotides. *J. Mol. Biol.* **213:** 203–206.

Petruska J, Goodman MF. (1985) Influence of neighbouring bases on DNA polymerase insertion and proofreading fidelity. *J. Biol. Chem.* **260:** 7533–7539.

Phear G, Nalbantoglu J, Meuth M. (1987) Next-nucleotide effects in mutations driven by DNA precursor pool imbalances at the *aprt* locus of Chinese hamster ovary cells. *Proc. Natl. Acad. Sci. USA* **84:** 4450–4454.

Pirastu M, Galanello R, Doherty MA, Tuveri T, Cao A, Kan YW. (1987) The same β-globin gene mutation is present on nine different β-thalassaemia chromosomes in a Sardinian population. *Proc. Natl. Acad. Sci. USA* **84:** 2882–2885.

Poustka AM, Lehrach H, Williamson R, Bates G. (1988) A long-range restriction map encompassing the cystic fibrosis locus and its closely linked genetic markers. *Genomics* **2:** 337–345.

Powers PA, Smithies O. (1986) Short gene conversion in the human fetal globin gene region: a by-product of chromosome pairing during meiosis? *Genetics* **112:** 343–358.

Razin A, Szyf M, Kafri T, Roll M, Giloh H, Scarpa S, Carotti D, Cantoni GL. (1986) Replacement of 5-methylcytosine by cytosine: a possible mechanism for transient DNA demethylation during differentiation. *Proc. Natl. Acad. Sci. USA* **83:** 2827–2831.

Reiss J, Cooper DN, Bal J, Slomski R, Cutting GR, Krawczak M. (1991) Discrimination between recurrent mutation and identity by descent: application to point mutations in exon 11 of the CFTR gene. *Hum. Genet.* **87:** 457–461.

Reitsma PH, te Lintel Hekkert W, Koenhen E, van der Velden PA, Allaart CF, Deutz-Terlouw PP, Poort SR, Bertina RM. (1990) Application of two neutral MspI DNA polymorphisms in the analysis of hereditary protein C deficiency. *Thromb. Haemost.* **64:** 239–244.

Reitsma PH, Poort SR, Allaart CF, Briët E, Bertina RM. (1991) The spectrum of genetic defects in a panel of 40 Dutch families with symptomatic protein C deficiency type I: heterogeneity and founder effects. *Blood* **78:** 890–894.

Reitsma PH, Poort SR, Bernardi F, Gandrille S, Long GL, Sala N, Cooper DN. (1993) Protein C deficiency: a database of mutations. *Thromb. Haemost.* **69:** 77–84.

Reyland ME, Lehman IR, Loeb LA. (1988) Specificity of proofreading by the 3′→5′ exonuclease of the DNA polymerase-primase of *Drosophila melanogaster*. *J. Biol. Chem.* **263:** 6518–6524.

Richter C, Park J-W, Ames BN. (1988) Normal oxidative damage to mitochondrial and nuclear DNA is extensive. *Proc. Natl. Acad. Sci. USA* **85:** 6465–6467.

Rideout WM, Coetzee GA, Olumi AF, Jones PA. (1990) 5- Methylcytosine as an endogenous mutagen in the human LDL receptor and p53 genes. *Science* **249:** 1288–1290.

Riordan JR, Rommens JM, Kerem BS, Alon N, Rozmahel R, Grzelczak Z, Zielenski J, Lok S, Plavsic N, Chou JC, Drumm MC, Iannuzzi MC, Collins FL, Tsui LC. (1989) Identification of the cystic fibrosis gene: cloning and characterisation of complementary DNA. *Science* **245:** 1066–1073.

Roberts JD, Kunkel TA. (1986) Mutational specificity of animal cell DNA polymerases. *Environ. Mol. Mutagen.* **8:** 769–789.

Rodeghiero F, Castaman G, Dini E. (1987) Epidemiological investigation of the prevalence of von Willebrand's disease. *Blood* **69:** 454–459.

Romeo G, Hassan HJ, Staempfli S, Roncuzzi L, Ciannetti L, Leonardi A, Vicente V, Mannucci PM, Bertina R, Peschle C, Cortese R. (1987) Hereditary thrombophilia: identification of nonsense and missense mutations in the protein C gene. *Proc. Natl. Acad. Sci. USA* **84:** 2829–2832.

Rommens JM, Iannuzzi MC, Kerem BS, Drumm ML, Melmer G, Dean M, Rozmahel R, Cole JC, Kennedy D, Hideka N, Zsiga M, Buchwald M, Riordan JR, Tsui LC, Collins FS. (1989) Identification of the cystic fibrosis gene: chromosome walking and jumping. *Science* **245:** 1059–1065.

Rosenbloom CL, Kerem BS, Rommens JM, Tsui LC, Wainwright B, Williamson R, O'Brien WE, Beaudet AL. (1989) DNA amplification for detection of the XV-2c polymorphism linked to cystic fibrosis. *Nucleic Acids Res.* **17:** 7117.

Rüdiger HW. (1991) Clinical, genetic and regulatory consequences of exposure to mutagens. *Ann. Génét.* **34:** 173–178.

Sagher D, Strauss B. (1983) Insertion of nucleotides opposite apurinic/apyrimidinic sites in deoxyribonucleic acid during *in vitro* synthesis: uniqueness of adenine nucleotides. *Biochemistry* **22:** 4518–4526.

Saluz HP, Jiricny J, Jost JP. (1986) Genomic sequencing reveals a positive correlation between the kinetics of strand-specific DNA demethylation of the overlapping estradiol/glucocorticoid-receptor binding sites and the rate of avian vitellogenin mRNA synthesis. *Proc. Natl. Acad. Sci. USA* **83:** 7167–7171.

Schaaper RM, Kunkel TA, Loeb LA. (1983) Infidelity of DNA synthesis associated with bypass of apurinic sites. *Proc. Natl. Acad. Sci. USA* **80:** 487–491.

Seetharam S, Krämer KH, Waters HL, Seidman MM. (1991) Ultraviolet mutational spectrum in a shuttle vector propagated in xeroderma pigmentosum lymphoblastoid cells and fibroblasts. *Mutat. Res.* **254:** 97–105.

Setlow P. (1976) Nearest neighbour frequencies in deoxyribonucleic acids. In: *CRC Handbook of Biochemistry and Molecular Biology, Vol. 2: Nucleic Acids*, 3rd Edn. (ed. GD Fasman). CRC Press, Cleveland, Ohio, pp. 312–318.

Shearman CW, Loeb LA. (1979) The effects of depurination on the fidelity of DNA synthesis. *J. Mol. Biol.* **128:** 197–218.

Shen S, Slightom JL, Smithies O. (1981) A history of the human fetal globin gene duplication. *Cell* **26:** 191–203.

Shen J-C, Creighton S, Jones PA, Goodman MF. (1992a) A comparison of the fidelity of copying 5-methylcytosine and cytosine at a defined DNA template site. *Nucleic Acids Res.* **20:** 5119–5125.

Shen J-C, Rideout WM, Jones PA. (1992b) High frequency mutagenesis by a DNA methyltransferase. *Cell* **71:** 1073–1080.

Shenoy S, Ehrlich KC, Ehrlich M. (1987) Repair of thymidine–guanine and uracil–guanine mismatched base-pairs in bacteriophage M13 mp18 DNA heteroduplexes. *J. Mol. Biol.* **197:** 617–626.

Sibley CG, Ahlquist JE. (1984) The phylogeny of the hominoid primates as indicated by DNA–DNA hybridization. *J. Mol. Evol.* **20:** 2–15.

Skriver K, Radziejewska E, Silbermann JA, Donaldson VH, Bock SC. (1989) CpG mutations in the reactive site of human C1 inhibitor. *J. Biol. Chem.* **264:** 3066–3071.

Smith GR. (1983) Chi hotspots of generalized recombination. *Cell* **34:** 709–710.

Steinberg RA, Gorman KB. (1992) Linked spontaneous CG → TA mutations at CpG sites in the gene for protein kinase regulatory subunit. *Mol. Cell. Biol.* **12:** 767–772.

Stenflo J. (1988) The biochemistry of protein C. In: *Protein C and Related Proteins* (ed. RM Bertina). Churchill Livingstone, Edinburgh, pp. 21–54.

Stoeckert CJ, Collins FS, Weissman S. (1984) Human fetal globin DNA sequences suggest novel conversion event. *Nucleic Acids Res.* **12:** 4469–4479.

Sved J, Bird AP. (1990) The expected equilibrium of the CpG dinucleotide under a mutation model. *Proc. Natl. Acad. Sci. USA* **87:** 4692–4696.

Takeshita M, Chang C-N, Johnson F, Will S, Grollman A. (1987) Oligodeoxynucleotides containing synthetic abasic sites. *J. Biol. Chem.* **262:** 10171–10179.

Thacker J. (1985) The molecular nature of mutations in cultured mammalian cells: a review. *Mutat. Res.* **150:** 431–442.

Thomas DC, Roberts JD, Sabatino RD, Myers TW, Tan CK, Downey KM, So AG, Bambara RA, Kunkel-TA. (1991) Fidelity of mammalian DNA replication and replicative DNA polymerases. *Biochemistry* **30:** 11751–11759.

Topal MD, Fresco JR. (1976) Complementary base pairing and the origin of substitution mutations. *Nature* **263:** 285–289.

Toth M, Lichtenberg U, Doerfler W. (1989) Genomic sequencing reveals a 5-methylcytosine-free domain in active promoters and the spreading of preimposed methylation patterns. *Proc. Natl. Acad. Sci. USA* **86:** 3728–3732.

Tsui LC. (1990) Population analysis of the major mutation in cystic fibrosis. *Hum. Genet.* **85:** 391–392.

Tuddenham EGD, Cooper DN, Gitschier J, Higuchi M, Hoyer LW, Yoshioka A, Peake IR, Schwaab R, Olek K, Kazazian HH, Lavergne J-M, Giannelli F, Antonarakis SE. (1991) Haemophilia A: database of nucleotide substitutions, deletions, insertions and rearrangements of the factor VIII gene. *Nucleic Acids Res.* **19:** 4821–4833.

Urabe K, Kimura A, Harada F, Iwanaga T, Sasazuki T. (1990) Gene conversion in steroid 21-hydroxylase genes. *Am. J. Hum. Genet.* **46:** 1178–1186.

Vogel F, Kopun M. (1977) Higher frequencies of transitions among point mutations. *J. Mol. Evol.* **9:** 159–180.

Vogel F, Motulsky AG. (1986) *Human Genetics: Problems and Approaches*, 2nd Edn. Springer, Berlin.

Vogel F, Röhrborn G. (1965) Mutationsvorgänge bei der Entstehung von Hämoglobinvarianten. *Humangenetik* **1:** 635–650.

Vogel F, Kopun M, Rathenburg R. (1976) Mutation and molecular evolution. In: *Molecular Anthropology* (eds M Goodman, RE Tashian, JH Tashian). Plenum Press, New York, pp. 13–33.

Vulliamy TJ, D'Urso M, Battistuzzi G, Estrada M, Foulkes NS, Martini G, Calabro V, Poggi V, Giordano R, Town M, Luzzatto L, Persico MG. (1988) Diverse point mutations in the human glucose-6-phosphate dehydrogenase gene cause enzyme deficiency and mild or severe hemolytic anemia. *Proc. Natl. Acad. Sci. USA* **85:** 5171–5175.

Wada K, Wada Y, Doi H, Ishibashi F, Gojibori T, Ikemura T. (1991) Codon usage tabulated from the GenBank genetic sequence data. *Nucleic Acids Res. Suppl.* **19:** 1981–1986.

Wagner JR, Hu C-C, Ames BN. (1992) Endogenous oxidative damage of deoxycytidine in DNA. *Proc. Natl. Acad. Sci. USA* **89**: 3380–3384.

Wagner M, Schlösser M, Reiss J. (1990) Direct gene diagnosis of cystic fibrosis by allele-specific polymerase chain reactions. *Mol. Biol. Med.* **7**: 359–364.

Wallace DC, Lott MT, Torroni A, Shoffner JM. (1991) Report of the Committee on human mitochondrial DNA. *Cytogenet. Cell Genet.* **58**: 1103–1123.

Wang RYH, Kuo KC, Gehrke CW, Huang LH, Ehrlich M. (1982) Heat and alkali-induced deamination of 5-methylcytosine and cytosine residues in DNA. *Biochim. Biophys. Acta* **697**: 371–377.

White PC, Vitek A, Dupont B, New MI. (1988) Charactization of frequent deletions causing steroid 21-hydroxylase deficiency. *Proc. Natl. Acad. Sci USA* **85**: 4436–4440.

Wiebauer K, Jiricny J. (1989) *In vitro* correction of GT mispairs to GC pairs in nuclear extracts from human cells. *Nature* **339**: 234–236.

Wiebauer K, Jiricny J. (1990) Mismatch-specific thymine DNA glycosylase and DNA polymerase β mediate the correction of GT mispairs in nuclear extracts from human cells. *Proc. Natl. Acad. Sci. USA* **87**: 5842–5845.

Woodcock DM, Crowther PJ, Diver WP. (1987) The majority of methylated deoxycytidines in human DNA are not in the CpG dinucleotide. *Biochem. Biophys. Res. Commun.* **145**: 888–894.

Woodcock DM, Crowther PJ, Jefferson S, Diver WP. (1988) Methylation at dinucleotides other than CpG: implications for human maintenance methylation. *Gene* **74**: 151–152.

Wu C-I, Maeda N. (1987) Inequality in mutation rates of the two strands of DNA. *Nature* **327**: 169–170.

Young JZ. (1973) *The Life of Mammals*, 2nd Edn. Clarendon Press, Oxford.

Youssoufian H, Antonarakis SE, Bell W, Griffin AM, Kazazian HH. (1988) Nonsense and missense mutations in hemophilia A: estimate of the relative mutation rate at CG dinucleotides. *Am. J. Hum. Genet.* **42**: 718–725.

Zell R, Fritz JH. (1987) DNA mismatch-repair in *Escherichia coli* counteracting the hydrolytic deamination of 5-methylcytosine residues. *EMBO J.* **6**: 1809–1815.

Zhang J-Z, Cai S-P, He X, Lin H-X, Lin H-J, Huang Z-G, Chehab FF, Kan YW. (1988) Molecular basis of β thalassaemia in South China. *Hum. Genet.* **78**: 37–40.

Gene deletions

7.1 Gross gene deletions

Gene deletions in prokaryotes and viruses have been known for some time to occur non-randomly. Spontaneous deletions in the lacI gene of *Escherichia coli* have been shown to be flanked almost invariably by direct repeat sequences (Farabaugh *et al.*, 1978; Galas, 1978; Albertini *et al.*, 1982; Schaaper *et al.*, 1986; DasGupta *et al.*, 1987; Brunier *et al.*, 1988). Direct repeats have also been implicated in the generation of deletions in several viral systems, e.g. phage T4 (Singer and Westlye, 1988), phage T7 (Studier and Rosenberg, 1979) and murine minute virus (Hogan and Faust, 1984). Models to account for this type of lesion have usually been either replication or recombination-based (Streisinger *et al.*, 1966; Ripley, 1982; Glickman and Ripley, 1984) and have invoked direct repeats and/or palindromes (inverted repeats) as determinants of secondary structures which act as deletion intermediates.

The molecular events which underlie gene rearrangement in eukaryotes are still poorly understood, but have been widely assumed to be similar to those of their prokaryotic counterparts. Recent studies of human gene pathology have suggested that the local DNA sequence environment could be as important in the generation of gene deletions in humans as it is in bacteria and viruses. Indeed, the non-randomness of human gene deletion is readily apparent at two distinct levels. Firstly, in some X-linked recessive conditions of similar incidence, the frequency of gene deletion does not always correlate with the size and complexity of the underlying gene. For example, some 2.5% of haemophilia A patients possess deletions of the factor VIII (F8) gene (26 exons spanning 186kb genomic DNA; Millar *et al.*, 1991), whereas 84% of patients with steroid sulphatase (STS) deficiency possess deletions of their STS genes (10 exons spanning 146 kb genomic DNA; Ballabio *et al.*, 1989). Secondly, 'hotspots' for deletion breakpoints have been reported within several genes, namely the human Duchenne muscular dystrophy (DMD; Forrest *et al.*, 1987, 1988; Dunnen *et al.*, 1987; Wapenaar *et al.*, 1988; Hentemann *et al.*, 1990), growth hormone-1 (GH1; Vnencak-Jones and Phillips, 1990), low density lipoprotein receptor (LDLR; Langlois *et al.*, 1988) and α-globin (HBA1; Nicholls *et al.*, 1987) genes, and the hamster *aprt* (Phear *et al.*, 1989) and murine β2-microglobulin genes (Parnes *et al.*, 1986). These observations are consistent with deletional events in human genes being at least in part sequence directed, with the frequency of occurrence reflecting underlying structural differences between genes. In the following sections, we explore two basic types of recombination events in human genes causing genetic disease: homologous unequal recombination mediated either by related gene sequences or by repetitive sequence elements, and non-homologous recombination involving molecules with minimal sequence homology.

Gross gene deletions may arise through a number of different recombinational mechanisms. Unfortunately, some confusion has arisen through the variable use (and occasional misuse) of the different terms employed. These terms will therefore be defined here before examples of the different categories are given in the context of human genetic disease. *Recombination* involves the breakage of a double-stranded DNA molecule (chromatid) on each of two chromosomes and the reunion of the two fragments to yield a new recombinant DNA strand. *Homologous recombination* describes recombination between homologous chromosomes occurring at meiosis or mitosis between identical or very similar DNA sequences. *Homologous equal recombination* normally involves the cleavage and rejoining of non-sister chromatids at precisely the same position on the DNA molecules. Such 'allelic recombination' would generate fusion genes consisting of sequence elements from the two recombined alleles. Since no DNA sequence is deleted, these fusion genes could be functional; this mechanism (not unlike gene conversion in terms of its consequences for the gene) is thought to be responsible for generating new alleles (e.g. in the HLA system). Other types of recombination, however, do lead to gene deletion: *homologous unequal recombination* involves the cleavage and rejoining of non-sister chromatids at homologous but non-allelic DNA sequences. Although this mechanism can serve to generate fusion genes between closely linked and highly homologous sequences if the recombination breakpoints are intragenic, similar recombinational events occurring in a region between related genes can lead to sequence homogenization at these loci. *Non-homologous (illegitimate) recombination* occurs between two sites that show little or minimal sequence homology.

7.1.1 *Homologous unequal recombination between gene sequences*

This type of homologous recombination is thought to be one cause of deletions of the α-globin genes underlying α-thalassaemia. The $\alpha1$ (HBA1) and $\alpha2$ (HBA2) globin genes have evolved comparatively recently by gene duplication (Higgs *et al.*, 1989) and are thus virtually identical in sequence. These genes also possess flanking regions of homology (regions X and Z in Figure 7.1) whose sequence similarity may have been maintained during evolution by the processes of gene conversion and unequal crossing-over. These 'homology boxes' serve to potentiate homologous unequal recombination through incorrect chromosome alignment at meiosis. Recombinations between homologous X boxes which are 4.2 kb apart (the 'leftward crossover'; Figure 7.1) have been noted to give rise to chromosomes with a 4.2 kb deletion and only one α-globin gene (Embury *et al.*, 1980) and other chromosomes with three α-globin genes (Trent *et al.*, 1981). Recombinations between homologous

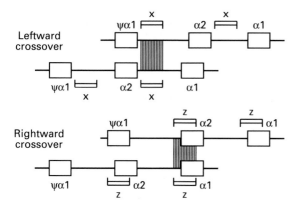

Figure 7.1. Homologous unequal recombination between the 'homology boxes' X and Z in the human α-globin gene region. The 'leftward crossover' is due to misalignment of the X boxes whereas the 'rightward crossover' is caused by misalignment of the Z boxes. The vertical lines illustrate the extent of the homology boxes.

Z boxes which are 3.7 kb apart (the 'rightward crossover'; Figure 7.1) generate chromosomes with a 3.7 kb deletion as well as the reciprocal product chromosomes with three α-globin genes (Goossens *et al.*, 1980).

Although we cannot be certain how frequent such recombination events are, they do not appear to be very rare events because their product chromosomes have been reported in many different ethnic groups (reviewed by Higgs *et al.*, 1989). Although the breakpoints differ within the X or Z homology boxes, the mechanism of homologous unequal recombination would appear to be the same. It is likely that this type of recombination event occurs frequently between other closely linked homologous gene loci, e.g. the G–γ (HBG2) and A–γ (HBG1) globin genes.

7.1.2 Homologous unequal recombination between repetitive sequence elements

Repetitive DNA sequences can give rise to gene deletions by promoting recombinational instability. Indeed, Alu sequences flanking deletion breakpoints have been noted in a considerable number of human genetic conditions involving defects in the genes for α-globin (HBA; Nicholls *et al.*, 1987), β-globin (HBB; Henthorn *et al.*, 1986), growth hormone (GH1; Vnencak-Jones *et al.*, 1988), apolipoprotein B (APOB; Huang *et al.*, 1989), β-hexosaminidase (HEXB; Myerowitz and Hogikyan, 1987), adenosine deaminase (ADA; Markert *et al.*, 1988; Berkvens *et al.*, 1990), α-galactosidase A (GLA; Kornreich *et al.*, 1990), C1 inhibitor (C1I; Stoppa-Lyonnet *et al.*, 1990) and low density lipoprotein receptor (LDLR; Hobbs *et al.*, 1986; Lehrman *et al.*, 1985, 1986, 1987) etc. A list of human inherited conditions caused by deletion in which Alu sequences appear to have played a role is given in Table 7.1. Although not intended to be fully comprehensive, this table does provide an indication of the variety of genes involved and hence the potential generality of the mutational mechanism.

It can be seen from Table 7.1 that Alu sequence-mediated deletions are of essentially three types: (i) recombination takes place between one Alu repeat

Table 7.1. Human genetic disease states caused by gene deletions in which Alu repeats have been located at one or both breakpoints

Disease	Gene	Deletion size (kb)	Alu repeats involved	Reference	Breakpoints*
Adenosine deaminase deficiency	ADA	3.2	5',3'	Markert et al., 1988	2, 6
Adenosine deaminase deficiency	ADA	3.2	5',3'	Berkvens et al., 1990	2, 6
Angioneurotic oedema	C1I	2	5',3'	Ariga et al., 1990	2, 6
Angioneurotic oedema	C1I	8.5	5',3'	Ariga et al., 1990	2, 6
Angioneurotic oedema	C1I	2.7	5',3'	Stoppa-Lyonnet et al., 1990	1, 6
Angioneurotic oedema	C1I	3.0	5',3'	Stoppa-Lyonnet et al., 1990	1, 6
Fabry disease	GLA	3.2	5',3'	Kornreich et al., 1990	2, 6
Fabry disease	GLA	4.6	3'	Kornreich et al., 1990	5
Haemophilia A	F8	57	3'	Woods-Samuels et al., 1991	
Hereditary persistence of fetal haemoglobin	HBB	> 15	5'	Jagadeeswaran et al., 1982	4
Hereditary persistence of fetal haemoglobin	HBB	48.5	5'	Henthorn et al., 1986	5
Hypercholesterolaemia	LDLR	5.5	5',3'	Lehrman et al., 1985	1, 6

Disease	Gene	Size (kb)	Breakpoints	Reference	Alu*
Hypercholesterolaemia	LDLR	0.8	5',3'	Hobbs et al., 1986	2, 7
Hypercholesterolaemia	LDLR	5	3'	Lehrman et al., 1986	4
Hypercholesterolaemia	LDLR	4	5',3'	Horsthemke et al., 1987	2, 6
Hypercholesterolaemia	LDLR	7.8	5',3'	Lehrman et al., 1987	2, 7
Hypobetalipoproteinaemia	APOB	0.7	5',3'	Huang et al., 1989	2, 6
Sandhoff disease	HEXB	16	5',3'	Neote et al., 1990	1, 6
Tay–Sachs disease	HEXA	7.6	3'	Myerowitz and Hogikyan, 1987	5
Thalassaemia-α	HBA	>30	3'	Nicholls et al., 1987	
Thalassaemia-α	HBA	62	5',3'	Nicholls et al., 1987	1, 6
Thalassaemia-α	HBA	20	3'	Nicholls et al., 1987	
Thalassaemia-α	HBA	21	5'	Nicholls et al., 1987	
Thalassaemia-α	HBA	18	3'	Nicholls et al., 1987	5
Thalassaemia-β	HBB	>14	5'	Ottolenghi and Giglioni, 1982	4
Thalassaemia-β	HBB	>42	5'	Vanin et al., 1983	4

Alu repeats at the 5' and 3' breakpoints are denoted by 5' and 3' respectively. *Breakpoints on: 1, left and right arms of Alu sequences respectively; 2, left arms of Alu sequences; 3, right arms of Alu sequences; 4, left arm of Alu sequence; 5, right arm of Alu sequence; Orientation of Alu sequences: 6, same; 7, opposite. For gene symbols, see text.

and a non-repetitive DNA sequence which may or may not possess sequence homology with the Alu repeat, (ii) recombination takes place between Alu sequences oriented in opposite directions and (iii) recombination takes place between Alu sequences oriented in the same direction. These different types of recombination event will now be examined in more detail.

In terms of the proportion of known deletions, the most dramatic examples of the involvement of Alu sequences occur in the LDLR and CII genes. The relative positions of the five LDLR gene deletions thought to be mediated by Alu sequences are shown in Figure 7.2. All but one of the break-points occur within an Alu repeat sequence (of which there are a total of 21 within the LDLR gene region). A closer look at the recombination junction of the 5.5 kb deletion is provided in Figure 7.3, and a possible mechanism for this

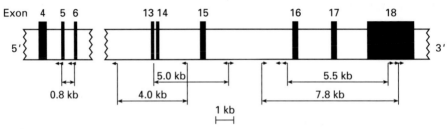

Figure 7.2. Deletions involving Alu sequences in the human LDLR gene causing hypercholesterolaemia (from data provided in Lehrman *et al.*, 1987 and Horsthemke *et al.*, 1987). Vertical bars denote exons. Horizontal arrows indicate the extent of the deletions. Arrowheads indicate the position and orientation of Alu sequences.

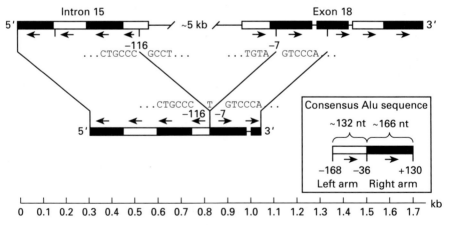

Figure 7.3. Recombination between Alu sequence elements generating a 5.5 kb deletion of the LDLR gene (from data provided by Lehrman *et al.*, 1985, 1987). Shaded and unshaded boxes denote right and left arms of Alu consensus sequences respectively. Orientations of the left and right arms of the Alu repeats are indicated by arrows. Joining of the two Alu sequences is accomplished as a staggered break and a novel T nucleotide is inserted at the deletion joint.

168

deletion is illustrated diagramatically in Figure 7.4; it involves the formation of a stem-loop structure mediated by inverted repeats on the *same* DNA strand and derived from the oppositely oriented Alu sequences in intron 15 and exon 18. A similar mechanism has been postulated for the 5.0 kb LDLR gene deletion (Figure 7.2) but, in this case, whereas the 3′ breakpoint lies within an Alu repeat, the 5′ breakpoint is located in exon 13; two pairs of inverted repeats (10/11 and 7/8 matches) flank the deletion breakpoints and are thought to potentiate the formation of the stem-loop structure (Lehrman *et al.*, 1986).

The remaining three LDLR gene deletions depicted in Figure 7.2 are bounded by Alu repeats of the same orientation. Here the recombinational event cannot be mediated by inverted repeats on the same DNA strand. Rather, deletion is proposed to occur by meiotic (or mitotic) recombination between chromosomes misaligned at the highly homologous Alu sequences. It

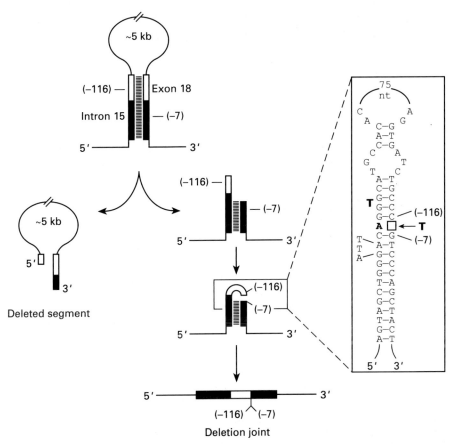

Figure 7.4. Possible mechanism for the 5.5 kb LDLR gene deletion involving the formation of a loop between inverted repeat sequences located on the same DNA strand. Shaded and unshaded boxes denote right and left arms of Alu consensus sequences respectively.

can be seen from Table 7.1 that, in the vast majority of cases in which two Alu sequences have been implicated in the deletion event, they occur in the same orientation. We may therefore surmise that homologous unequal recombination between similarly oriented Alu family members, misaligned at meiosis, is probably the most common mechanism of Alu-mediated deletion.

The clustering of deletion breakpoints within the left arm of Alu repeats was first noted by Lehrman *et al.* (1987). An adapted version of these authors' original figure is given in Figure 7.5. From the data collated in Table 7.1, it can be seen that this non-random distribution is still observed when a much larger sample size is considered. The reasons for this non-randomness are, however, less clear. Paolella *et al.* (1983) reported that the left arm is transcribed more efficiently *in vitro*. Lehrman *et al.* (1987) pointed out that the majority of the left arm breakpoints lie within the region bounded by the RNA polymerase III promoters A and B, and speculated that an open conformation brought about by promoter activity could increase the propensity for recombination to occur. Whilst breakpoints within the right arm of the Alu sequence are indeed much less common (Table 7.1), Ariga *et al.* (1990) have claimed that those breakpoints that do occur within the right arm are invariably located within the region that is homologous to the sequence between promoters A and B.

A similar situation to that found in the LDLR gene pertains in the C1I gene, which possesses a total of 17 Alu repeats within a 17 kb region (Carter *et al.*, 1991); Alu repeats therefore represent more than a third of the intronic sequence in this gene. Deletions and partial deletions of the C1I gene appear to account for 15–20% of the lesions which cause type 1 hereditary angioneurotic

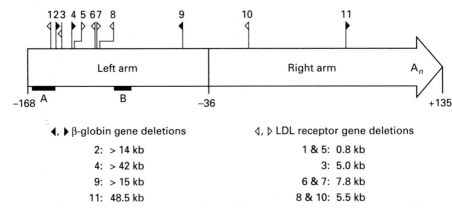

**, ▶ β-globin gene deletions   ◁, ▷ LDL receptor gene deletions

2: > 14 kb	1 & 5: 0.8 kb
4: > 42 kb	3: 5.0 kb
9: > 15 kb	6 & 7: 7.8 kb
11: 48.5 kb	8 & 10: 5.5 kb

Figure 7.5. Deletion breakpoints within the Alu consensus sequence for mutations in the LDLR and HBB gene loci (after Lehrman *et al.*, 1987). The locations of 11 deletion breakpoints (see Table 7.1) are shown within the Alu sequence as shaded (HBB) or unshaded (LDLR) arrowheads. The regions of the Alu sequence which correspond to the RNA polymerase III promoters A and B are shown as solid bars (Paolella *et al.*, 1983).

oedema, and a high proportion of these occur within Alu sequences. Clustering of breakpoints is evident; Stoppa-Lyonnet *et al.* (1991) have shown that 5/5 deletions/duplications occurred within the first Alu sequence element preceding exon 4. However, the breakpoints of these rearrangements were distributed over the entire Alu sequence element and were not themselves further clustered.

Finally, it should be mentioned that in many of the examples listed in Table 7.1 the recombinational join was not clean, in the sense that novel bases were often introduced and duplications of the target site were a frequent occurrence. These characteristics are commonly found with retrotransposed DNA.

We have thus seen that there are several examples of Alu-rich genes whose deletion breakpoints occur very frequently within members of this repeat family. There are, however, a number of counter examples which suggest that the extent of association between deletion breakpoints and Alu sequences is dependent upon the gene under study. Henthorn *et al.* (1990) collated data on over 30 deletions in the β-globin cluster but noted the presence of Alu sequences at only four breakpoints. They concluded that the occurrence of deletion breakpoints in Alu sequences within this region was not significantly different from that expected by chance alone. It could, however, be argued that this was due to the relative paucity of Alu sequences (only eight in 60 kb) within the gene cluster. The study of Kornreich *et al.* (1990) goes some way toward meeting this objection: these authors looked for an association between Alu sequences and deletion breakpoints in the gene (GLA) encoding α-galactosidase A, deficiency of which causes Fabry disease. Although 12 Alu repeats are found in the 12 kb gene region, deletions were relatively infrequent (only five of 130 patients possessed a partial gene deletion). Moreover, only three breakpoints occurred within an Alu sequence and only one resulted from an Alu–Alu recombination. This is rather a low proportion, considering that some 30% of the GLA gene comprises Alu repeat sequence. Finally, no correlation has been found between the locations of deletion breakpoints and Alu sequences in the human hypoxanthine phosphoribosyltransferase (HPRT) gene (Monnat *et al.*, 1992). These authors suggested that this might be because the 130–210 bp Alu repeats in the HPRT gene rarely exhibited more than 30 bp sequence identity, much lower than the 200–300 bp sequence identity normally required to promote efficient intrachromosomal recombination in mammalian cells (see Bollag *et al.*, 1989).

Not all deletions are, however, mediated by Alu repeat sequences. In the 66 kb human growth hormone gene cluster, some 48 Alu sequences are found, but these do not appear to be the cause of the high frequency of clustered GH1 gene deletions causing familial growth hormone deficiency (Vnencak-Jones *et al.*, 1988). Vnencak-Jones and Phillips (1990) studied 10 such patients and showed that in nine of these the crossovers had occurred within two 99% homologous 594 bp regions flanking the GH1 gene. Since these two sequences are longer and probably more similar than any two Alu repeats in the vicinity, it is thought that they may serve as recombination targets in preference to Alu repeats.

Other types of repetitive sequence element are also thought to mediate homologous unequal recombination. Approximately 90% of individuals with ichthyosis have a deletion at their steroid sulphatase (STS) locus (Shapiro *et al.*, 1989). Yen *et al.* (1990) reported that 24 of 26 STS deletion patients had breakpoints clustered within and around a number of S232-type repetitive sequences flanking the STS gene, suggesting that the high frequency of deletion at this locus may be due to recombination between these S232 sequences. The long terminal repeats of the RTVL-H family have also been found to mediate homologous unequal recombination events (Mager and Goodchild, 1989). In their study of some 30 deletions of the β-globin gene cluster, Henthorn *et al.* (1990) noted breakpoints within five LINE elements. However, this was no higher than random expectation and thus it is unnecessary to invoke an important role for LINE elements in the causation of deletions at this locus. Finally, sequence analysis of deletion breakpoints located within the intron 43 deletion hotspot in the dystrophin (DMD) genes of two unrelated Duchenne muscular dystrophy patients has revealed the presence of a transposon-like element belonging to the THE-1 family (Pizzuti *et al.*, 1992).

7.1.3 *Gene fusions caused by homologous unequal recombination*

The classic example of a gene fusion, arising from the deletional removal of intervening DNA sequence is that of haemoglobin Lepore. First reported by Gerald and Diamond (1958), this haemoglobin, which is synthesized in reduced amounts, is an abnormal molecule with the first 50–80 amino acid residues of δ-globin at its N terminal and the last 60–90 amino acid residues of β-globin at its C terminal. Heterozygotes for this rearrangement resemble β-thalassaemia trait in their phenotypes, whereas homozygotes are severely affected and possess increased levels of HbF and 15–25% Hb Lepore in the absence of normal β-chain synthesis. Three different examples of Hb Lepore have now been described in which the fusion junction occurs at different points (Baglioni, 1962; Barnabus and Muller, 1962; Ostertag and Smith, 1969). Southern blotting and DNA sequence analysis of the breakpoint junctions of Hb Lepore Boston genes have shown that the recombination has occurred within a 59 bp region of DNA (extending from codon 87 to the 11th nucleotide of intron 2) where the δ-and β-globin gene sequences are almost identical, resulting in the deletion of $\simeq 7$ kb of intervening DNA (Flavell *et al.*, 1978; Baird *et al.*, 1981; Chebloune and Verdier 1983; Mavilio *et al.*, 1983; Chebloune *et al.*, 1984; Metzenberg *et al.*, 1991). The reduction in globin synthesis is caused by the reduced synthesis of mRNA encoding the fusion product to a level intermediate between those of the δ- and β-globin genes (Ramirez *et al.*, 1979).

Three different haplotypes have been reported for Hb Lepore Boston chromosomes (Lanclos *et al.*, 1987; Fioretti *et al.*, 1992), strongly supporting the view that this gene rearrangement has occurred independently on several different occasions. A similar fusion of haemoglobins A–γ and β due to a 22.5 kb deletion has occurred in Hb Kenya (Huisman *et al.*, 1972; Kendall *et al.*, 1973; Ojwang *et al.*, 1983). These gene fusions appear to have arisen by homologous unequal recombination during meiosis between the globin locus on one chromosome and a misaligned globin locus on the other chromosome. The probable mechanism, shown in Figure 7.6, would predict the existence of a second abnormal chromosome: an anti-Lepore fusion gene encoding an N terminal β-globin fused to C terminal δ globin. Consistent with this interpretation, several anti-Lepore haemoglobins have been described (Lehmann and Charlesworth, 1970; Badr *et al.*, 1973; Honig *et al.*, 1978a, 1978b). Interestingly, the expression of β-δ anti-Lepore genes appears to be reduced to a level similar to that found in δ-β Lepore fusion genes.

Glucocorticoid-suppressible hyperaldosteronism (GSH) is an autosomal dominant form of hypertension, caused by the over-secretion of aldosterone. Pascoe *et al.* (1992) have demonstrated that some GSH patients possess hybrid genes generated by homologous unequal recombination between CYP11B1 and CYP11B2, two highly homologous cytochrome P450 genes which are closely linked on chromosome 8q22. CYP11B1, which is thought to reside some 13 kb downstream of CYP11B2, is normally expressed at high levels in the adrenal gland, is regulated by corticotrophin and is essential for cortisol synthesis. CYP11B2 is expressed at low levels in the adrenal gland, is regulated by angiotensin II but not corticotrophin, and is essential for aldosterone synthesis. All four GSH patients examined possessed hybrid genes containing the 5' regulatory and 5' coding regions from the CYP11B1 gene joined to the 3' coding region from the CYP11B2 gene; the breakpoints were located in

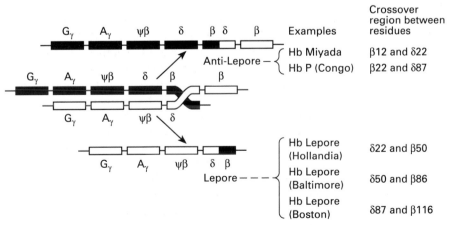

Figure 7.6. Probable mechanism for the generation of fusion genes encoding haemoglobins Lepore and anti-Lepore.

intron 2 (two cases), intron 3 and exon 4 respectively. *In vitro* expression studies with hybrid cDNAs containing up to the first three exons of the CYP11B1 gene synthesized aldosterone at levels normally characteristic of CYP11B2. Since replacement of the first three exons of CYP11B2 by CYP11B1 sequences leaves the 18-hydroxylase and 18-oxidase activities of CYP11B2 intact, Pascoe *et al.* (1992) inferred that GSH is caused by the expression of a hybrid CYP11B gene that is regulated like CYP11B1 yet able to synthesize aldosterone.

Another example of the creation of fusion genes by homologous unequal recombination is provided by visual dichromacy (red–green colour blindness). The genes involved are those encoding the red and green visual pigments (RCP and GCP respectively) which are highly homologous and linked in tandem on chromosome Xq28. G^-R^+ dichromats possess a fusion gene consisting of the 5' part of the GCP gene fused to the 3' part of the RCP gene in addition to a single copy of an intact RCP gene (Nathans *et al.*, 1986). This hybrid gene appears to include sufficient RCP sequence so that the spectral absorbance of its product is virtually identical to that of the red pigment. Conversely, G^+R^- dichromats possess a hybrid gene comprising the 5' portion of the RCP gene fused to the 3' portion of the GCP gene plus zero, one or two intact GCP genes (Nathans *et al.*, 1986). This hybrid gene may produce a green-like visual pigment. A fusion gene cDNA from a colour-blind individual has now been fully sequenced (Neitz *et al.*, 1989). Genotype–phenotype relationships associated with different types of fusion gene have been discussed by Deeb *et al.* (1992).

The same mechanism appears to have been responsible for the creation of a glucocerebrosidase (GBA) fusion gene created by homologous unequal recombination between the functional GBA gene and a pseudogene some 16 kb downstream (Zimran *et al.*, 1990). The patient, with type 1 Gaucher disease, was a compound heterozygote for the fusion gene and a missense mutation. Most of the functional gene was conserved by the recombination event which occurred somewhere between nucleotides 5933 and 6272 in a region of identity between the two sequences. This region of the pseudogene contains several single base-pair substitutions, which would be expected to disrupt the structure and/or function of the fusion product severely.

Tanigawa *et al.* (1990) have described the fusion of α- and β-myosin heavy chain genes (MYHCA and MYHCB) causing familial hypertrophic cardiomyopathy, a disease of the heart muscle. These genes encode proteins which are 95% homologous at the amino acid sequence level. The fusion gene appears to have arisen through homologous unequal recombination between the MYHCA and MYHCB genes within their exons 27; the precise location of the crossover is unclear owing to the high degree of DNA sequence homology in this region. The formation of an α/β hybrid molecule may adversely affect the formation of myosin heavy chain dimers or their assembly into myofilaments.

Homologous unequal recombination has also been held to account for the existence of a fusion between the proline-rich protein genes PRB1 and PRB2

(Azen *et al.*, 1992). Although not known to be associated with any disease phenotype, the recombination event responsible appears to have occurred within a 743 bp region of introns 3, which are identical save for a single base-pair mismatch.

Finally, Guioli *et al.* (1992) have reported a different mechanism for the generation of a fusion gene in a patient with Kallmann syndrome carrying an X;Y translocation. This translocation resulted from recombination between the Kallmann gene (KALX) at Xp22.3 and its homologue (KALY) at Yq11.21. The two sequences possess ~ 92% sequence homology and the breakpoint occurred within an identical 13 bp region. The KALX/Y fusion gene contained the entire KALX gene except the last exon, but no transcription of the novel gene was detectable.

7.1.4 Non-homologous recombination at sites with minimal homology

DNA rearrangements requiring at most only a bare minimum of sequence homology are also common in mammalian cells but are much more difficult to explain mechanistically. Examples of this type of non-homologous recombination include chromosomal translocation, gene amplification, retrotransposition and the developmental rearrangement of immunoglobulin genes (reviewed by Borst and Greaves, 1987). Many naturally occurring deletions observed in human genes have also arisen through non-homologous recombination between sequences that share little or no apparent homology.

Fodde *et al.* (1990) reported that the gross deletions responsible for Belgian $G-\gamma^{+}$ $(A-\gamma, \delta, \beta)^{\circ}$ thalassaemia and Indian HPFH have 3′ breakpoints within 4 bp of each other at the midpoint of a 160 bp palindrome (inverted repeat) which is potentially capable of forming a stem-loop structure. Since the 3′ breakpoints of two other deletions of the β-globin gene cluster are also thought to map to this position, it may represent a hotspot for recombination.

Another explanation put forward to account for this type of deletion has been that sequences originally remote from one another are brought into close proximity through their attachment to chromosome scaffolding. This hypothesis has been suggested as a means of explaining the observed periodicities in deletions, e.g. the similarity in size but not position of some α- and β-globin gene deletions (Vanin *et al.*, 1983: Nicholls *et al.*, 1987). However, Higgs *et al.* (1989) found no association between matrix-associated regions and the deletion breakpoints in either globin gene cluster.

Several types of junction have been noted in cases of non-homologous recombination: 'flush junctions' resulting from simple breakage and rejoining (e.g. Vanin *et al.*, 1983), 'insertional junctions' which contain novel nucleotides (e.g. Piccoli *et al.*, 1984) and 'junctions with limited homology' (e.g. Roth *et al.*, 1985; Gilman 1987). This last category of junction was first noted by Efstratiadis *et al.* (1980) in deletions involving the β-globin gene family. These authors proposed that short (2–8 bp) direct repeats flanking deletions were involved in their generation. Since these short regions of homology were deemed unlikely to be long enough to support meiotic recombination between chromosomes, it was postulated that the deletions arose instead by slipped mispairing during DNA replication. Consistent with this postulate, one direct repeat was usually lost in the deletion event.

No thorough quantitative analysis of gross gene deletions has yet been undertaken. An analysis of the type required is, however, attempted below (Section 7.2) for deletions of < 20 bp.

7.1.5 Double deletions: chance occurrence or premutation?

Occasional individuals have been reported with two distinct deletions in the same allele. For instance, Bartlett et al. (1989) described a Becker muscular dystrophy patient with two deletions, 1000 kb apart, in the dystrophin (DMD) gene; only one of the lesions, however, was found to be responsible for the disease phenotype. A further kindred has been reported in which a second lesion, a deletion, had arisen in the same dystrophin gene as carried a mutation causing a Becker muscular dystrophy phenotype (Laing et al., 1992). It is too early to say whether such double mutations occur periodically by chance alone (very unlikely), arise through the action of some unknown predisposing factor, or whether the first mutation somehow serves to increase the likelihood of (i.e. acts as a premutation to) a second lesion.

7.2 Short gene deletions

Gene deletions have so far been found to be responsible for at least 159 different inherited conditions in humans (Appendix 1). In the majority of cases, the extent of the deletion has not been precisely demarcated and sequence data are usually unavailable. Gene deletions may nevertheless be broadly (if crudely) categorized on the basis of the length of DNA deleted. Some deletions consist of only one or a few base-pairs, whereas others may span several hundred kilobases. This size continuum has so far proved difficult to dissect on account of our inability to draw clear boundaries between the categories or to infer a generative mechanism for a deletion simply from the nature of the deletion breakpoint.

In this section, we shall examine (i) the potential contribution of several postulated mechanisms of deletion mutagenesis to the spectrum of short human gene deletions and (ii) the sequence characteristics that might predispose a given gene to this type of mutation. This analysis greatly extends that first reported on a smaller sample of gene deletions (Krawczak and Cooper, 1991). A total of 219 human gene deletions of 20 bp or less are listed in Appendix 3; this size range was selected for several reasons.

Firstly, it was reasoned that deletion endpoints would be close enough together to simplify the task of locating the putative sequence elements involved in the deletion process.

Secondly, deletions arising by mechanisms other than homologous recombination were thought likely to predominate in this size range. Thus, for instance, the length of single-stranded DNA at the replication fork

(1000–2000 bp) is likely to impose strict physical limits on the length of mispaired sequence.

Finally, since most known short gene deletions have been discovered almost by chance during the course of DNA sequencing studies, our sample was considered unlikely to be biased by any parameter other than size.

The actual distribution of deletion lengths is given in Figure 7.7. Also included for every deletion in Appendix 3 are 10 bp DNA flanking the deletion breakpoints to permit the analysis of the local DNA sequence environment. Of the 219 deletions collated, 169 (77.2%) resulted in an alteration of the reading frame.

Excluded from Appendix 3 are deletions of the mitochondrial genome which, by virtue of its rapid replication time and own distinct DNA polymerase, may not be directly comparable to deletions occurring within the nuclear genome. A detailed analysis of deletions affecting mitochondrial genes is presented in Section 7.3.

Only one reported example of each deletion is included in Appendix 3. Whilst this policy was adopted in order to avoid the multiple inclusion of identical-by-descent mutations, there is a possibility that identical yet independently derived recurrent deletions could have been inadvertently excluded. Insertional junctions (Section 7.1.4) were not considered here, both because they are relatively uncommon and because their analysis would be considerably more complex than that required for flush junctions and/or junctions with limited homology.

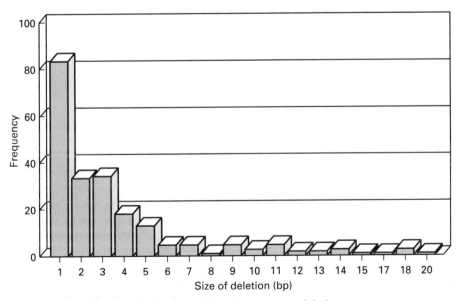

Figure 7.7. The size distribution of short human gene deletions.

7.2.1 The significance of DNA sequence characteristics

Some of the DNA sequences listed in Appendix 3 share specific properties that may predispose them to deletion-type mutation. To determine whether these properties could have occurred by chance alone, two alternative approaches to significance assessment were followed.

Firstly, simulation studies were carried out. In each simulation, 10 000 DNA sequences were generated randomly according to codon usage as reported for human genes by Wada *et al.* (1991). For the properties under study that concerned neighbouring codons, we made the simplifying assumption of a random composition of the simulated amino acid sequences. Thus, any conclusion as to the statistical significance of the corresponding results should be viewed with this assumption in mind. Within each simulated sequence, a deletion was assumed to start at position 10 spanning a number of base-pairs according to the size distribution of Figure 7.7. The length of each sequence was 20 bp plus the number of bases deleted. 'Random' sequences that exhibited the property under consideration were counted. The result divided by the total number of sequences (i.e. 10 000) was regarded as an estimate of how likely the property was to arise merely by chance.

Secondly, the frequency of the property of interest was determined in a collection of 29 human cDNA sequences from human genes (AT3, CFTR, DMD, HBB, F10, F11, F12, F13, F7, F8, F9, G6PD, HCF2, HPRT, INS, INSR, LAC1, OAT, OTC, PAH, PAP, PCI, PMG, PRK, PROC, PROS, PTH, TTPA, and VWF) comprising a total of 70 752 bp. Ready access to the computerized sequence data was the only criterion for a given gene to be included in this list. Along each sequence, a window was moved with variable size according to the distribution of deletion lengths depicted in Figure 7.7. The likelihood of chance occurrence was determined by counting as described for the simulation studies.

Finally, the actual observations made from the data in Appendix 3 were compared with the results from both the simulation and the reference sample studies, using a χ^2 test. Unless otherwise stated, observed frequencies were regarded as significantly different from chance expectation if comparison with the average 'expected' frequency yielded a significant χ^2 value.

7.2.2 The sequence environment of short gene deletions

We first attempted to ascertain whether or not the causative mechanism(s) underlying the deletions listed in Appendix 3 were sequence dependent by examining the composition of the surrounding DNA sequence. G + C richness is known to correlate with a high deletion frequency (Singer and Westlye, 1988), probably as a result of the increased stability of deletion intermediates facilitating a variety of endogenous mutational mechanisms. However, conclusions consistent with such observations could not be drawn from the analysis of the deleted human sequences listed in Appendix 3. These DNA sequences do exhibit mononucleotide frequencies different from those corresponding to tabulated codon usage (Wada *et al.*, 1991; $\chi^2 = 68.212$, 3 d.f., $P < 10^{-5}$). However, as can be inferred from Table 7.2, nucleotides T and A are over-represented whereas C and G are under-represented. Examination of the nucleotides immediately flanking the deletion breakpoints also revealed a significant excess of T ($\chi^2 = 17.870$) and a deficit of C residues ($\chi^2 = 10.072$).

Two codons were also found to be over-represented *in frame* within the DNA sequences listed in Appendix 3 (the appropriate limit for χ^2 values allowing for multiple testing was 11.28): TTT (50 versus 24.09 expected; $\chi^2 = 28.317$), and GAA (64 versus 40.35 expected; $\chi^2 = 14.239$).

We also studied the pattern of three and four base-pair motifs characteristic of the deletions and their 10 bp DNA sequence environments. Several motifs were found to be significantly over-represented (Table 7.3) when observed frequencies were compared with random expectation as described in Section 7.2.1.

7.2.3 Direct repeats and the generation of short deletions

A variety of different mechanisms for the generation of gene deletions involving the misalignment of short direct repeats have been proposed. Most replication-based models are essentially adaptations of the *slipped mispairing hypothesis* first proposed by Streisinger *et al.* (1966). This hypothesis was originally formulated to account for the common occurrence of deletions in T4 phage in regions bounded by direct repeats. The basic mechanism is presented in Figure 7.8. Two direct repeats (R1 and R2) occur in close proximity to one another with complementary sequences R1' and R2' on the other strand. As replication proceeds, the DNA duplex becomes single-stranded at the replication fork, permitting illegitimate pairing between R2 and the complementary R1' sequence. As a result, a single-stranded loop is formed containing the R1 repeat and sequence lying between R1 and R2. DNA repair enzymes may then excise this loop and rejoin the broken ends of the DNA strand. The next round of replication would then generate one deleted and one wild-type duplex.

Table 7.2. Mononucleotide frequencies in and around short human gene deletions

Nucleotide	Observed	Expected*	Individual χ^2 value
T	1298	1111.07	40.055
C	1209	1363.24	23.697
A	1400	1302.91	9.671
G	1265	1394.78	16.535

*Each expected frequency equals the product of the total number of nucleotides examined (5172 bp) and the nucleotide frequency resulting from tabulated codon usage (Wada *et al.*, 1991). The appropriate limit for χ^2 analysis allowing for multiple testing was 6.24; this was exceeded for all four nucleotides.

Table 7.3. Three and four base-pair motifs significantly over-represented near short human gene deletions

Motif	Obs.	Av. Exp.	χ^2‡	Expected	
				I*	II†
TTT	110	66.73	28.459	76.00	57.45
CTT	109	68.37	24.490	75.00	61.75
TCT	104	72.80	13.577	76.27	69.33
CTTT	37	17.44	21.999	19.23	15.66
TCTT	36	16.09	24.717	18.52	13.65
TTCT	42	19.68	25.401	23.19	16.18
CTTC	41	22.43	15.436	25.94	18.93
TTTG	37	18.47	18.644	22.61	14.33
TAAG	24	10.66	16.732	8.17	13.14
TTGG	36	17.43	19.834	19.48	15.38

Obs., observed frequency; Exp., expected frequency determined from *simulations based on tabulated codon usage, †a reference sample of cDNA sequences; Av., the average of I and II (see Section 7.2.1). ‡Individual χ^2 value. The appropriate limits for χ^2 analysis, allowing for multiple testing, were 11.28 (3 bp) and 13.87 (4 bp), respectively.

A search of the DNA sequences listed in Appendix 3 revealed that direct repeats (2 bp or more) could be found flanking and/or overlapping all gene deletions. The most frequent length of a direct repeat is 3 bp ($95/219 = 43.4\%$) whilst a sizable proportion ($108/219 = 49.3\%$) are between 4 and 11 bp (Figure 7.9). As can be inferred from Table 7.4, the length distribution for flanking and/or overlapping repeats is significantly different from that expected for random occurrence ($\chi^2 = 20.291$, 4 d.f., $P = 4.37 \times 10^{-4}$). Short repeats are obviously under-represented whereas direct repeats longer than 3 bp occur more often than expected by chance alone.

The frequency of slipped mispairing in prokaryotic genes has been shown to be proportional both to the length of the direct repeat motif and to the extent of homology between the direct repeats, but inversely proportional to the distance between them (Galas, 1978; Albertini et al., 1982; Singer and Westlye, 1988). Inspection of the data collated in Appendix 3 also reveals a strong positive correlation between the length of the direct repeat sequences and the amount of DNA deleted (Figure 7.10). For the flanking and/or overlapping longest direct repeats from Table 7.4, the Spearman rank correlation coefficient is $r = 0.6195$ ($P < 10^{-5}$). Furthermore, the likelihood of deletion increases with the length of the repeat motif, as is indicated by increasing ratios of observed/expected frequency of occurrence in Table 7.4. The distance between the 3′ and following 5′ ends of two component repeats, however, exhibits no significant correlation with deletion size ($r = 0.0344$, $P = 0.612$).

In summary, our observations are broadly consistent with the model of slipped mispairing. In accordance with the postulate of Efstratiadis et al.

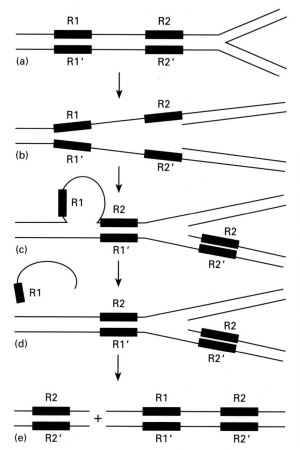

Figure 7.8. The slipped mispairing model for the generation of deletions during DNA replication (after Efstratiadis *et al.*, 1980). (a) Duplex DNA containing direct repeat sequence. (b) Duplex becomes single-stranded at replication fork. (c) R2 repeat base-pairs with complementary R1′ repeat producing a single-stranded loop. (d) Loop excised and rejoined by DNA repair enzymes. (e) Daughter duplexes, one of which contains only one of the two repeats and lacks the intervening sequence between R1 and R2.

(1980), the deletion of one whole repeat copy plus all the intervening sequence was observed in 73 of 135 (54.1%) of deletions spanning two or more base-pairs. Simulation and comparison with the cDNA reference sample indicate that this represents a highly significant excess over random expectation ($\chi^2 = 180.973$, 1 d.f., $P < 10^{-5}$).

For six deletions not readily explicable by slipped mispairing, we have noted that DNA sequence both 5′ and 3′ to the deleted bases also occurred as a contiguous sequence in a slightly different location (Table 7.5). This observation suggests a variation of the original slipped mispairing model, illustrated in Figure 7.11. Theoretically, misalignment between direct repeats might also occur between a specific contiguous sequence on one strand and a second homologous, yet interrupted, sequence on the other strand. The latter becomes capable of base-pairing only once the intervening non-homologous bases have looped out. It is proposed that slipped mispairing between the original and the newly created direct repeat copies is only transient, and deletion of one repeat does not follow as in the classic model. Rather, the mispairing lasts only long enough to template the formation of the second repeat copy, with excision of the intra-repeat loop serving to fix the deletion.

Slipped mispairing can in principle also account for the generation of minus-one-base frameshift mutations. The production of a frameshift error by these means must involve at least two separate steps: (i) a misalignment occurs

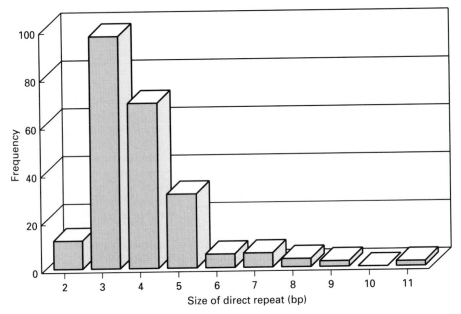

Figure 7.9. The size distribution of longest direct repeats flanking and/or overlapping short human gene deletions.

Table 7.4. Longest direct repeats flanking and/or overlapping short human gene deletions

	Length of direct repeat copies (bp)				
	2	3	4	5	>5
Observed	16	95	64	30	14
Expected average	27.50	103.73	61.56	19.96	6.25
Observed/expected	0.582	0.916	1.040	1.503	2.239
Expected I	31.27	107.88	58.47	17.03	4.34
Expected II	23.73	99.58	64.64	22.89	8.16

For the calculation of expected frequencies I, II and average, see Section 7.2.1.

within a run of identical bases followed by (ii) further incorporation events which fix the misaligned base(s). The initial formation of such misalignments may depend not only on the local DNA sequence environment (sequence composition and length of direct repeats or a run of bases) but probably also on the particular DNA polymerase involved. DNA polymerase β is much more error prone than DNA polymerase α. Polymerase β fulfils a role in the repair synthesis of short gaps or nicks, whereas polymerase α, which is solely respon-

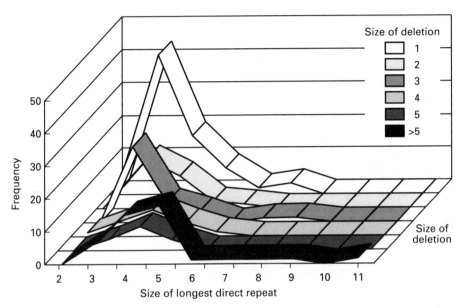

Figure 7.10. The relationship between the size of short human gene deletions and the longest direct repeats flanking and/or overlapping them.

Table 7.5. Short human gene deletions explicable by a modified slipped mispairing model

No.*	Gene	Deletion
56	CFTR	ATTCTGTTCTcaGTTTTCCTGG
86	OAT	TTTCTCTCCTgataggagtGGAGGCTGGA
97	F8	AAACACTGAAagaACAGTGAGTA
203	HBB	GACAAGCTGCacgTGGATCCTGA
207	HBB	CCACCAGTGCaggCTGCCTATCA
210	HBB	ATTCTGCCTAataaaAAACATTTAT
206†	HBB	ACCCCACCAGtGCAGGCTGCC

The longest direct repeat created by the deletion of the DNA sequence in lower case letters is underlined. *Number of deletion as given in Appendix 3. †The only single base-pair deletion explicable by the modified slipped mispairing model.

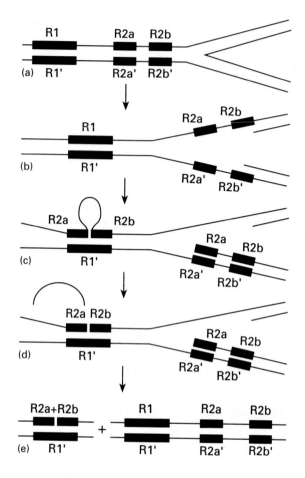

Figure 7.11. Modified slipped mispairing model of deletion mutagenesis. (For detail, see legend to Figure 7.8.)

sible for DNA synthesis at the replication fork, is more processive, does not bind to nicks and does not fill small gaps. Once formed, a misalignment must be stable enough to provide an efficient primer template for further elongation. This stability probably depends on the base composition of the misaligned sequences. Various lines of evidence from *in vitro* studies now support the validity of this model and demonstrate that deletions and frameshifts can arise during DNA synthesis:

(i) Vertebrate DNA polymerases α and β produce many more frameshifts at runs of bases than at non-runs (Kunkel, 1985a, 1985b). With polymerase β, mutation hotspots occur predominantly at runs of pyrimidines (particularly TTTT) rather than purines, although this effect is less pronounced with polymerase α.

(ii) The frequency of frameshift mutations is roughly proportional to the length of the run (Kunkel, 1985a). This is to be expected since the stability of the misalignment is enhanced by increased capacity for base-pairing.

(iii) The frequency of polymerase β-dependent frameshift mutation at a run sequence is decreased by experimental interruption of that run (Kunkel, 1986).

Kunkel and Soni (1988) have proposed a second alternative mechanism to account for the generation of frameshift mutations at DNA replication: if a nucleotide is misincorporated (perhaps due to a local imbalance in the nucleotide pool; Meuth, 1989) and this nucleotide happens to be complementary to the next base, then its translocation to the next position will lead to a frameshift if the misaligned intermediate is rapidly stabilized by further base-pairing. Evidence for the *in vivo* operation of this mechanism in bacteria has been presented (Bebenek and Kunkel, 1990).

We have tested the validity of the aforementioned models *in vivo* by screening all 84 minus-one-base frameshifts from Appendix 3 for the longest run of identical nucleotides overlapping the deletion. This analysis revealed that the deleted base is identical to one of its neighbours in 59 cases, representing a highly significant excess over expectation as based on simulation and reference sample cDNA data ($\chi^2 = 10.558$, 1 d.f., $P = 1.16 \times 10^{-3}$). Of these deletions, 25 possess a run of identical bases of 3 bp or more ($\chi^2 = 8.390$, 1 d.f., $P = 3.77 \times 10^{-3}$). Our data therefore suggest that a considerable proportion of minus-one-base frameshift mutations causing human genetic disease may indeed be due to slipped mispairing within runs of identical bases.

7.2.4 Palindromes (inverted repeats) and quasi-palindromes in the vicinity of short gene deletions

The slipped mispairing model both assumes and requires the presence of direct repeat sequences, but this model was unable to account for deletions in the *E. coli* lacI gene where no direct repeats were present and where the potential for misalignment was not obvious. Ripley (1982) therefore proposed a novel mechanism of deletion mediated by *quasi-palindromic* sequences. A palindrome by definition possesses self-complementarity within the same DNA strand, which allows this strand to fold back on itself to form a hairpin or cruciform structure. The imperfect self-complementarity of quasi-palindromic sequences allows them to form misaligned secondary structures. The non-palindromic portions of these structures then provide templates for frameshifts and short deletions through the exonucleolytic removal of unpaired bases followed by repair DNA synthesis (Figure 7.12). Thus if DNA synthesis in region B is templated by sequence A rather than by the sequence homologous to B on the complementary strand, the bases in region B that were non-complementary to sequence A will be deleted. This model has been shown to possess predictive value, at least in *E. coli* (DeBoer and Ripley, 1984).

Ripley (1982) proposed an alternative 'strand-switch' model for deletion mutagenesis which also requires palindromic or quasi-palindromic sequences. The strand switch occurs during DNA synthesis within the palindrome. When the switch is not precisely central, or if the sequence concerned is quasi-palindromic, deletions may occur through incorrect templating of the elongating DNA sequence, as in the secondary structure model outlined above.

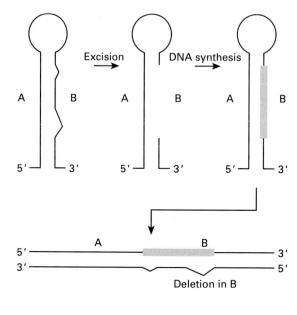

Figure 7.12. Model for the generation of deletions in a quasi-palindromic sequence by aberrantly templated DNA synthesis within a secondary structure (after Ripley, 1982).

Table 7.6. Longest inverted repeats flanking and/or overlapping short human gene deletions

| | Length of inverted repeat copies (bp) | | | |
	3	4	5	>5
Observed	98	50	24	9
Expected average	101.02	59.48	17.36	4.30
Observed/expected	0.970	0.841	1.383	2.093
Expected I	103.48	57.47	15.51	3.68
Expected II	98.56	61.49	19.20	4.91

For the calculation of expected frequencies I, II and average, see Section 7.2.1.

A search for palindromic sequences that could potentiate the looping out of single-stranded DNA revealed that 189 of 219 sequences listed in Appendix 3 contain at least one pair of inverted repeats of length 3 bp; these flank or span the deletion in 181 cases. The length distribution of the latter (Table 7.6) differs significantly from random expectation, albeit less dramatically than for direct repeats ($\chi^2 = 9.336$, 4 d.f., $P = 0.053$). However, as with direct repeats, the ratio of observed to expected frequency increases with increasing length of the inverted repeat copies, indicating that the longer the palindromes in the vicinity, the higher the likelihood of occurrence of deletion.

There are nine examples of flanking and/or overlapping inverted repeats of at least 6 bp, and these are listed in Table 7.7. The clearest case is provided by the 8 bp inverted repeat associated with the lactate dehydrogenase B (LDHB) gene deletion; one repeat was completely removed at the 5′ end of the

Table 7.7. Inverted repeats of at least 6 bp flanking and/or overlapping short human gene deletions

No.*	Gene	Deletion
2	APC	TAATGAAACTtTCATTTGATG
38	APOA1	ATCTGAGCACgCTCAGCGAGA
78	HEXA	TCATCTTGGAggaGATGAGGTTG
99	F8	TGGGGAAGAGtcTTCCACAAAG
140	LDHB	GGGCTATTGGactctctgtagcagatttggCAGAGAGTAT
143	MCAD	TGCAAATCAGttagCTACTGATGC
157	KIT	TCTGAACTCAaaGTCCTGAGTT
160	PROC	CGGCAGCTTCagctgcgactgccgcagcGGCTGGGAGG
161	PROC	CAGCTTCAGCtgcgactgccgcagcggcTGGGAGGGCC

Longest inverted repeats are underlined; deleted bases are indicated by lower case letters.
*Number of deletion in Appendix 3.

Table 7.8. Short human gene deletions explicable by the mispairing of quasi-palindromic sequences

No.*	Gene	Deletion
93	HPRT	CCCACGAAGTgttGGATATAAGC
132	LDLR	AGCGACAATCaccGCCGGGGTCG
161	PROC	CAGCTTCAGCtgcgactgccgcagcggcTGGGAGGGCC
210	HBB	ATTCTGCCTAataaaAAACATTTAT
216	PAX3	ATCCTGTGCAggtaccaggagactGGCTCCATAC

The longest inverted repeat created by deletion of the DNA sequence in lower case letters is underlined. *Number of deletion in Appendix 3.

deletion whereas the other abuts immediately upon the 3′ end of the deletion. However, in general, the exact location of the deleted base(s) was not predictable from the location of inverted repeats. The complexity of the local DNA sequence environment may contribute to this lack of predictability. Thus 47 sequences possessed both direct and inverted repeats of 4 bp or longer flanking and/or overlapping the deletion; the presence of the latter may influence the nature of the deletion regardless of whether it occurs through classical mispairing or via the intra-repeat loop mechanism.

A search for imperfect palindromes was also conducted, and in five cases it was possible to predict correctly (*a posteriori*) the excised bases from the structure of the partial hairpin loop generated by the imperfect self-complementarity of the quasi-palindromic sequence (Table 7.8). This, however, does not represent a significant excess over random expectation (5 versus 5.44)

In summary, the importance of palindromic sequences in the causation of human gene deletion remains unclear. Palindromic sequences are significantly over-represented in the vicinity of gene deletions but only five examples of a deletion potentially mediated by a quasi-palindromic sequence were found in our sample. It is probable that the majority of the deletions listed in Appendix 3 are too small to be caused by the deletion of an entire hairpin loop. Moreover, small hairpin loops require a large amount of energy to form and are consequently not favoured. It nevertheless remains possible that mechanisms invoking palindromes and quasi-palindromes may have explanatory value for larger gene deletions. The frequent co-occurrence of palindromes and direct repeats at sites of deletion has been reported before in prokaryotes (Glickman and Ripley, 1984). Although unlikely to be coincidental, this association has not been adequately tested statistically. Palindromes that occur internal to a direct repeat (e.g. in many transposable elements) might promote the emergence of secondary structures, thereby decreasing the effective distance between such short homologies and facilitating deletion. The presence of palindromic DNA sequence could also potentiate slipped mispairing involving $A + T$-rich sequences which would otherwise be less likely to be involved in such events (Singer and Westlye, 1988). Since such influences are likely to be very much sequence context-dependent, this could account for the unpredictability of the extent and location of deletions in which palindromes occur in association with direct repeats.

7.2.5 A role for symmetric elements?

Sequence motifs which we have termed 'symmetric elements' (Krawczak and Cooper, 1991) were noted in 180 of the sequences in Appendix 3. These elements possess an axis of internal symmetry (e.g. CTGAAGTC, GGACAGG) and vary in length between 5 and 13 bp. A search for the longest symmetric element overlapping the deletion yielded the size distribution given in Table 7.9. This distribution differs significantly from random expectation ($\chi^2 = 15.569$, 4 d.f., $P = 3.66 \times 10^{-3}$), and inspection of Table 7.9 indicates that short elements are under-represented whereas 'true' symmetric elements, i.e. those spanning 5 bp or more, are over-represented.

A considerable proportion of the deletions from our sample could not be unequivocally accounted for by invoking either direct repeats or palindromes

Table 7.9. Longest symmetric elements overlapping short human gene deletions

	Length of symmetric element (bp)				
	<5	5	6	7	>7
Observed	109	47	17	25	21
Expected average	135.13	39.41	14.55	16.27	13.65
Observed/expected	0.807	1.193	1.168	1.537	1.539
Expected I	137.44	39.11	13.32	16.14	12.99
Expected II	132.81	39.70	15.78	16.40	14.31

For the calculation of expected frequencies I, II and average, see Section 7.2.1.

because no such elements were present. In several cases, however, the site of deletion was covered by what we might term a 'quasi-symmetric' element. As with quasi-palindromes or interrupted direct repeats, these motifs are converted into perfect symmetric elements only when the bases that comprise the deletion are removed. If the criteria for inclusion are (i) a minimum element length of 7 bp, and (ii) an overlap of at least two bases on both sides of the deletion, then 10 of 84 single base-pair deletions fulfil these requirements, as do 17 of 135 deletions spanning 2 bp or more (Table 7.10).

Although our findings represent only a slight excess over expectation (10 and 17 observed versus 8.6 and 13.7 expected, respectively), the presence of quasi-symmetric elements at sites of gene deletion is intriguing. Could these elements somehow facilitate the formation of a secondary structure inter-mediate which would then increase the probability of a deletion event? We propose that this intermediate could be a Möbius loop-like structure (depicted in Figure 7.13) formed after strand separation and the twisting of one strand

Table 7.10. Short human gene deletions overlapped by quasi-symmetric elements

No.*	Gene	Deletion
10	APC	CTTCATC<u>ACA</u>g<u>AAACA</u>GTCAT
29	AT3	GCTGAT<u>GGAG</u>a<u>GTCGTG</u>TTCA
53	CFTR	CTCAGG<u>GTTC</u>t<u>TTGTGG</u>TGTT
62	CFTR	CAGA<u>AACAAA</u>a<u>AAACAA</u>TCTT
69	DMD	GACTCCCCC<u>CC</u>t<u>GAGCC</u>AGCCT
73	F10	AGT<u>TCTACAT</u>c<u>CTAAC</u>GGCAG
96	F8	TCAG<u>GTAAAT</u>t<u>GGAAG</u>AGTTT
121	F9	TAACAAC<u>ATGt</u>T<u>CTGTG</u>CTGG
139	IVD	ATGGGCC<u>GCT</u>t<u>TCTTCG</u>AGAT
173	RB1	CTGGACC<u>CTT</u>t<u>TCCAGC</u>ACAC
8	APC	<u>ATGAAATAAA</u>acaaa<u>GTGAGC</u>AAAG
12	APC	<u>AAATAAAAGG</u>aaaga<u>TTGGAA</u>CTAG
59	CFTR	<u>ATGATGAATA</u>ta<u>GATACA</u>GAAG
76	ALDB	TCCC<u>ACCCAT</u>Aggta<u>CCATGG</u>GGAA
83	OAT	GACGTT<u>GTCT</u>gct<u>ATCTCC</u>AGTT
95	HPRT	AATC<u>ATGTTT</u>gt<u>GTCATT</u>AGTG
104	F8	ATCTGG<u>GATA</u>aa<u>ACACAA</u>TATT
117	F9	TCGGG<u>TTGTT</u>ggt<u>GGAGAA</u>GATG
124	F9	AGGCAAA<u>TAT</u>ggaatatataccaa<u>GGTAT</u>CCCGG
159	PCCB	<u>ATACGGGGG</u>Catc<u>ATCCGG</u>CATG
176	CYP17	GCATAAC<u>AAC</u>ttc<u>TTCAAG</u>CTGC
178	HEXA	TCAAC<u>AAGAC</u>tg<u>AGATT</u>GAGGA
179	HEXA	AGACA<u>CTTCC</u>tctcc<u>TCTCCA</u>GGCT
180	HEXB	GAGCAC<u>ATTC</u>ttc<u>TTAGAA</u>GTCA
182	HBA	GGCCC<u>TGGAG</u>ag<u>GTGAGG</u>CTCC
202	HBB	ACACT<u>GAGTG</u>agctgcactgtgaca<u>AGCTGC</u>ACGT
215	PAX3	ATAGT<u>GGAGA</u>tggcccaccacggcatcc<u>GGCCCTGCGT</u>

Underlined bases constitute the two parts of the symmetric element that would be created by deletion of the bases identified by lower case letters. *Number of deletion in Appendix 3.

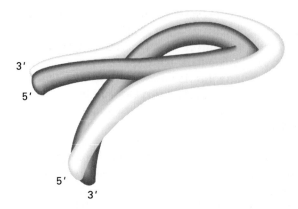

Figure 7.13. Conformation of a hypothetical secondary structure formed by the illegitimate pairing of a symmetric element after strand separation.

through a complete half-turn before re-annealing to the opposite strand in localized reverse orientation. If we consider the possibility of mismatches within the symmetric elements, the model becomes reminiscent of the quasi-palindromic model discussed in Section 7.2.4, which invoked mismatches in inverted repeats to generate deletions in secondary structure intermediates. It should be noted that there is no requirement for a nick or break in the DNA, only the potential to become single-stranded. Consistent with this model, the symmetric elements noted were 59% A+T rich (compared with 52% for sequences listed in Appendix 3); these sequences might thus be expected to be capable of remaining single-stranded long enough to permit a Möbius loop-like structure to form.

7.2.6 Deletion hotspots in human genes?

As we have seen in Sections 7.2.3–7.2.5, many models for deletion mutagenesis have been proposed but no one model alone appears to be sufficient to account for the spectrum of deletions observed in human genes. Another approach is to examine the similarities between deletions and then to attempt to account for this mechanistically. In so doing, we have previously identified a consensus sequence, TG(A/G)(A/G)(G/T)(A/C), which appears to be common to deletion 'hotspots' found in different human genes (Krawczak and Cooper, 1991). This consensus sequence is strikingly similar to the core motifs, TGGGG and TGAGC, found in the tandemly repeated immunoglobulin switch (Sμ) regions (Gritzmacher, 1989), and to putative arrest sites for polymerase α which often contain a GAG motif. [Indeed, one arrest site specifically mentioned by Weaver and DePamphilis (1982), (T/A)GGAG, fits perfectly with the deletion hotspot consensus sequence.] Larger deletions and translocations in human genes have also been reported which are flanked by similar sequences (Piccoli *et al.*, 1984; Besmer *et al.*, 1986; Anand *et al.*, 1988; Canning and Dryja, 1989; Lee *et al.*, 1989).

Polymerase arrest sites may fulfil one or more important biological functions such as the initial localization of the replication fork, the synchronization or termination of DNA replication or the promotion of recombination at the replication fork. Secondary structure appears to be important too, so it may be that the arrest of polymerase α at the replication fork may arise as a consequence of both primary and secondary structures acting in concert. All these factors suggest the possible involvement of DNA polymerase α arrest sites in the generation of human gene deletions.

By comparison with our previous study (Krawczak and Cooper 1991), the sample of short human gene deletions available for analysis has expanded by a factor of more than three. Re-screening for sequence motifs known to play a role in the breakage and rejoining of DNA molecules therefore appeared to be a meaningful exercise. A similar search, including also the deletion hotspot consensus sequence mentioned above, has been undertaken by Monnat et al. (1992) for 10 somatic deletions of the human HPRT gene causing Werner syndrome. The sequence motifs screened for by these authors are listed in Table 7.11, and the same collection was used for a computer search here. However, the statistical evaluation of the spatial association between motifs and deletion breakpoints was somewhat different from the approach adopted by Monnat et al. (1992). Whereas these authors employed a geometrical failure time equivalent, utilizing the complete HPRT cDNA sequence, we simply determined the number of entries in Appendix 3 for which a particular motif either overlaps with a deletion or is located no more than 2 bp from one of the deletion breakpoints. The observed frequency of occurrence was then compared to random expectation as described in Section 7.2.1.

Inspection of Table 7.11 reveals that only two of the 29 sequence motifs tested appear to be over-represented in the vicinity of short human gene deletions: polypyrimidine runs of at least 5 bp (YYYYY; $\chi^2 = 8.175$, 1 d.f., $P = 4.25 \times 10^{-3}$) and the deletion hotspot consensus sequence (TGRRKM; $\chi^2 = 17.157$, 1 d.f., $P = 3.45 \times 10^{-5}$). A detailed analysis of the YYYYY motifs yielded the maximum disparity between the observed and expected frequency of occurrence for the pentamer YTCYT (30 versus 12.65; $\chi^2 = 25.255$, 1 d.f., $P < 10^{-5}$). For the deletion hotspot consensus sequence, the significance of association with short gene deletions can be improved by some slight modifications: If the ambiguous symbol 'M' (A or C) at position 6 is replaced by 'R' (A or G), then the observed and expected numbers of matches are 42 versus 22.27 ($\chi^2 = 19.459$, 1 d.f., $P = 1.03 \times 10^{-5}$). Furthermore, 29 matches are characterized by adenine residues at position 6. When compared with random expectation (11.29) this represents an even more significant excess ($\chi^2 = 29.263$, 1 d.f., $P < 10^{-5}$). Shorter variations of the consensus sequence were consistently found to be less significant, whereas an extension by the ambiguous symbol 'R' (A or G) yielded 21 matches for TGRRKAR (6.55 expected; $\chi^2 = 32.900$, 1 d.f., $P < 10^{-5}$) and 30 matches for TGRRKRR (13.84 expected; $\chi^2 = 20.144$, 1 d.f., $P = 7.23 \times 10^{-5}$). In contrast to our findings, Monnat et al. (1992) observed a significant association with their HPRT deletion breakpoints only for the CTY vertebrate topoisomerase I cleavage site.

Table 7.11. DNA sequence motifs potentially associated with short human gene deletions

Motif	Sequence	Observed	Average	Expected	
				I	II
Vertebrate/plant topoisomerase I	CAT	36	34.61	32.76	36.47
consensus cleavage sites	CTY	73	65.12	63.33	66.91
	GTY	55	52.26	55.39	49.13
	RAT	62	67.24	64.78	69.70
DNA pol-α pause site core	GAG	46	47.30	49.08	45.52
motifs	GCS	35	62.29	71.88	52.71
	ACG	12	23.44	31.10	15.78
Murine MHC deletion hotspot	CAGG	13	16.04	16.07	16.00
Vaccinia topisomerase I cleavage consensus sequence	YCCTT	11	5.67	5.34	6.00
Polypyrimidine runs	YYYYY	71	52.89	50.79	54.99
Polypurine runs	RRRRR	79	74.79	67.71	81.87
Alternating purine–pyrimidine runs	RYRYR	35	51.30	53.70	48.90
Alternating pyrimidine–purine runs	YRYRY	33	47.85	50.70	45.00
Consensus Ig switch region	TGGGG	6	4.03	3.70	4.37
DNA pol-α frameshift hotspots	TCCCCC	3	0.76	0.96	0.56
	CTGGCG	1	0.82	0.99	0.66
DNA pol-β frameshift hotspots	ACCCWR	6	4.10	4.53	3.66
	TTTT	14	7.52	6.37	8.66
DNA pols-α/β frameshift hotspots	TGGNGT	4	3.53	3.22	3.83
	ACCCCA	1	1.29	0.83	1.74
Human deletion hotspot	TGRRKM	37	19.53	16.58	22.49
Murine parvovirus recombination hotspot	CTWTTY	1	2.66	2.63	2.70
Human Fra(X) breakpoint cluster	CGGCGG	0	0.52	0.70	0.35
Ig/TCR recombinase heptamer	CACAGTG	0	0.56	0.37	0.75
Chi and chi-like sequences	GCTGGTGG	1	0.23	0.15	0.31
	CCWCCWGC	0	0.73	0.46	1.01
Murine MHC recombination hotspot	CAGRCAGR	0	0.39	0.39	0.38
Ig/TCR recombinase nonamer	ACAAAAACC	0	0.02	0.00	0.05
Murine LTR recombination hotspot	TGGAAATCC	0	0.03	0.02	0.05

Ambiguous nucleotide symbols: R (A/G), Y (C/T), W (A/T), S (G/C), M (A/C), K (G/T), N (any base). For the calculation of expected frequencies I, II and average, see Section 7.2.1. MHC, major histocompatibility complex; Ig, immunoglobulin; TCR, T-cell receptor; LTR, long terminal repeat.

Analysis of the precise localization of the deletions listed in Appendix 3 revealed that 14 codons from six different genes could be identified as 'deletion hotspots'. To be classified as a deletion hotspot, the DNA sequence in and around a codon had to be affected by at least two different (and therefore independent) mutations. Consistent with the findings reported in the previous

Table 7.12. Hotspots for deletion mutagenesis found in six different human genes

Gene	Codon(s)	Motif
AT3	244	TGATGGA
F9	7/8	TGGAAGA
F9	182/183	TGGAGAA
PROC	76/77	TGGGAGG
HBA	30/31	TGGAGAG
HBB	4/5/7	TGAGGAG
HBB	42/43	TGGGGAT
HBB	125/126	TGCAGGC
CFTR	141/142	TTTTT
CFTR	506	TCTTT
CFTR	1175/1176	CCTACC
HBB	36/37	CCCTT
HBB	40	TTCTTT
HBB	140	TGCCCT

paragraph, either a deletion hotspot consensus-like motif or a run of at least five pyrimidines could be found in the vicinity of all deletion hotspots listed in Table 7.12.

That polypyrimidines are significantly associated with the sequences of Appendix 3 has already been noted in Section 7.2.2, where four of seven prevalent quadruplets did in fact consist of runs of C and T residues. This finding is not particularly surprising: the major enzyme of DNA repair synthesis *in vivo* is DNA polymerase β, which binds tightly to nicks in double-stranded DNA and is capable of incorporating a base into a single base gap. Polymerase β-associated deletions occur predominantly in pyrimidine runs and thus, if DNA repair synthesis were a significant cause of frameshift mutation *in vivo*, it would be expected that the mutational spectrum of human gene deletions might show similarities to the polymerase β-associated mutational spectrum observed *in vitro*. Nevertheless, several important differences between these mutational spectra are also apparent. Over 95% of polymerase β-associated frameshift deletions are 1 bp in length (Kunkel, 1985a), whereas only 38.4% of the deletions listed in Appendix 3 are of this size. Although 71 deletions included or flanked a pyrimidine run, only 25 (35%) of these represented losses of a single base-pair. This proportion compares to the deletions not associated with pyrimidine runs ($59/148 = 39.9\%$). Finally, whilst 76% of all non-run single base-pair losses *in vitro* involved a G residue, the corresponding figure for human gene mutations is 30.5% (i.e. not significantly higher than random expectation). It is therefore concluded that, were the over-representation of pyrimidine runs observed in Table 7.11 due to this mechanism of frameshift mutagenesis operating *in vivo*, the latter must manifest itself in a substantially different way in active chromatin.

The data presented in Table 7.11 confirm our previous observation that short human gene deletions are associated with a particular sequence motif,

TG(A/G)(A/G)(G/T)(A/C), which in turn resembles a number of known polymerase arrest sites and frameshift hotspots. Why can we assume that this homology is not purely coincidental? It has been shown that 86% of actual polymerase α arrest sites occurred within 16 bp of a palindromic (inverted repeat) sequence whereas long stretches of template which lacked palindromes were devoid of arrest sites (Weaver and DePamphilis, 1982). Since the DNA sequence environments of many deletions contain palindromic sequences, arrest of DNA synthesis may also be more likely to occur in such cases. The arrest of DNA synthesis at the replication fork, however, may then serve to increase the probability of occurrence either of a slipped mispairing event or the formation of secondary structure intermediates potentiated by the presence of inverted repeats or symmetric elements. Alternatively, if, as is thought, the polymerase tends to dissociate from the template strand at arrest sites, a strand-switch model (see Section 7.2.4) could also be considered.

Finally, Kunkel (1985b) suggested that energy released from phosphodiester bond cleavage of the dNTP substrate might be stored in the polymerase and used for the discriminative insertion of the next base. Were dissociation to occur, this stored energy would be lost and the next insertion after reassociation would be less accurate than subsequent insertions. Since misincorporation can lead to the generation of frameshift mutations (Kunkel and Soni, 1988), this type of lesion may be found at high frequency at polymerase α arrest sites where dissociation is very likely to occur.

7.2.7 Other mechanisms of deletion mutagenesis

DNA repair synthesis. In addition to classical and modified slipped mispairing models (Section 7.2.3), there is another possible deletional mechanism which requires the presence of direct repeats; the improper rejoining of DNA fragments after breakage. Roth *et al.* (1985) examined the extent of homology at crossover points associated with a large sample of non-homologous recombination events and demonstrated that ~ 20% of junctions contained significantly more homology than would have been predicted by random breakage and rejoining. This observation was explained by proposing a role for these short sequence homologies in directing the DNA joining reaction (Roth and Wilson, 1986). These authors went on to define three possible mechanisms for end-joining, namely single-strand, template-directed and post-repair ligations (Figure 7.14). Single-strand ligation serves to join together the protruding or blunt ends of single DNA strands; the gaps in the molecule are then repaired in a second reaction. This mechanism of end-joining does not require base-pairing and is thus independent of sequence homology. Template-directed ligation serves to join a protruding strand to a recessed strand and would appear to require homology between strands to effect correct base-pairing and positioning of the junction. Post-repair ligation is also homology dependent but, as the name suggests, ligation occurs only after repair has been completed. A role for short sequence homologies in the rejoining of DNA could account for the early observations of Ruley and Fried (1983) that multiple recombina-

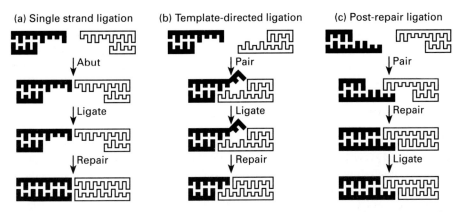

Figure 7.14. Three mechanisms for end-joining of DNA fragments (after Roth and Wilson, 1986). Only the template-directed and post-repair mechanisms are homology dependent.

tion events occurred within short regions and that short repeats were able to participate in the joining of two non-homologous sequences. It is possible therefore that direct repeat sequences not only permit a looping out of one misaligned repeat copy but may also play a role in the excision of the loop and the subsequent rejoining of the broken ends.

Recombination. Another alternative mechanism which must be considered is a recombination-based model involving the breakage and reunion of DNA under the control of enzymes such as DNA gyrase, ligase or the topoisomerases. The misalignment of direct repeats either within or between strands would precede and mediate an unequal crossing-over event (e.g. Marvo *et al.,* 1983). This mechanism may well be important for large gene deletions but, for several reasons, we consider that a recombination-based model is insufficient to account for the characteristics of the spectrum of short human gene deletions reported here:

(i) Direct repeats flanking the sites of deletion in Appendix 3 are considerably shorter than the 14 consecutive identical nucleotides said to be required for homologous recombination between chromatids to take place (Rubnitz and Subramani, 1984). It remains possible, however, that shorter repeats (4–5 bp) could under some circumstances mediate recombination events as reported by Ruley and Fried (1983) if other, as yet unspecified, factors are involved.

(ii) The size distribution of the deletions listed in Appendix 3 is severely skewed toward the range of 1–3 bp (Figure 7.7), longer deletions becoming progressively rarer. The shape of this distribution argues strongly for a generative mechanism other than homologous recombination which, as we have seen above, is known to be responsible for a considerable number of much larger deletions.

(iii) No sequence implicated in causing high-frequency recombination was found to be significantly represented in the sample of human gene deletions reported here.

It is concluded that the loss of one or a few base-pairs is more compatible with a replication-based model than with a recombination or repair hypothesis.

7.2.8 Studies of mutational spectra in cultured cells

Two basic approaches to studying the nature and frequency of spontaneous mutation in mammalian cells have been devised. The first employs exogenous genes introduced into mammalian cells and integrated into chromosomal DNA by means of retroviral shuttle vectors (reviewed by Dubridge and Calos, 1987). A variety of short deletions flanked by direct and/or inverted repeats have been reported from studies of the *E. coli* xanthine guanine phosphoribosyl-transferase (Ashman and Davidson, 1987) and human HPRT (Ikehata *et al.*, 1989) genes introduced into mouse cells in this way. In the former case, a very strong deletion hotspot was noted at a CTGGTTGA sequence strongly reminiscent of the lacI deletion hotspot of *E. coli* (CTGGCTGGCTGG). The second approach to the study of mammalian cell mutagenesis has been the analysis of the mutational spectra associated with naturally endogenous genes. The frequency of observed mutation is usually lower in these studies than for exogenously introduced genes, and may offer a more realistic view of spontaneous gene mutation. The best-studied system has been the adenosine phosphoribosyltransferase (aprt) gene in Chinese hamster cells, where a number of deletions flanked by short direct and/or inverted repeats have been reported (Nalbantoglu *et al.*, 1986, 1987; De Jong *et al.*, 1988; Grosovsky *et al.*, 1988). Deletions in the hamster aprt gene were observed to occur most frequently at TGAG and TGGAG sequences (Nalbantoglu *et al.*, 1986; Phear *et al.*, 1989) similar to the TG(A/G)(A/G)(G/T)(A/C) deletion hotspot consensus sequence discussed in Section 7.2.6.

7.2.9 Conclusions

In the preceding parts of Section 7.2, deletion breakpoint junction sequences were found to be non-random at a number of different levels. Direct repeats, which are a feature of several recombination, replication or repair-based models of deletion mutagenesis, were found in the vicinity of all deletions analysed. The influence of repeat length and inter-repeat length was studied in relation to both the location and extent of the deletions; results were broadly consistent with a slipped mispairing model or a modified version thereof. Palindromes (inverted repeats) were also found to be prevalent in the vicinity of gene deletions; these motifs may serve to promote instability by facilitating the formation of secondary structure intermediates. Symmetric elements were also noted to be significantly associated with sites of single base deletions. A new model to explain the involvement of quasi-symmetric elements in deletion mutagenesis was devised and successfully accounted for a substantial proportion of the deletions screened. Based on a three-fold larger sample than that previously employed, both a previously identified deletion hotspot consensus sequence and pyrimidine runs of five or more bases were shown to be preferentially associated with the sites of human gene deletions.

We may thus conclude that, as in bacteria (Papanicolaou and Ripley, 1989), multiple mechanisms may contribute to the observed spectrum of human gene deletions. Since deletions of different sizes can arise through quite different mechanisms, no one model can be all-encompassing and indeed effects may often be combinatorial. Moreover, our ability to utilize explanatory models to make predictions as to the probable location and frequency of gene deletions is hampered both by the diversity of sequence elements which might play a role in the generation of such mutations and by the complexity introduced by consideration of different aspects of DNA topology and metabolism. Other factors, such as the structure of chromatin or the presence of DNA binding proteins involved in the breakage, rejoining, unwinding etc of DNA duplexes will undoubtedly influence the nature and frequency of deletion-type mutation. Many more data must therefore become available, both on the parameters which determine secondary structure formation and on the biochemistry of DNA replication, recombination and repair before we are in a position to devise and adequately test predictive models.

7.3 Deletions in the mitochondrial genome

Some 40% of patients with mitochondrial myopathies exhibit a large deletion in at least a proportion of their muscle mitochondrial (mt) DNA. A large number of mtDNA deletions have now been reported, most commonly from patients with chronic external ophthalmoplegia and Kearns–Sayre syndrome (Wallace et al., 1991). Most deletions appear to be spontaneous, although a few cases of maternally inherited deletions have been reported (Wallace et al., 1991). Most deletions that occur, and which do not abolish replication, are probably detected clinically since, apart from the D-loop region, there are no non-coding sequences, implying that all deletions will occur in a functionally significant part of the mt genome.

Deletions of the mt genome are, however, largely confined to the 'major region' (from 5760 to 190). Fewer than 1% of known deletions are located in the 'minor region' (from 191 to 5730), which contains the origins of light and heavy chain replication. This is undoubtedly because deletion of either origin of replication would prevent the propagation of the mt DNA molecule and it would not survive to be characterized. Another factor is probably the nine-fold lower frequency of direct repeats reportedly found within the minor region compared with the major region (Johns and Cornblath, 1991). Shoffner et al. (1989) have claimed that the high frequency of direct repeats is due solely to the asymmetric distribution of cytosines and guanines between the L and H strands.

A considerable number of reports have now confirmed early observations that mtDNA deletions occur across flanking direct repeats (Holt *et al.*, 1989; Johns *et al.*, 1989; Schon *et al.*, 1989; Shoffner *et al.*, 1989; Poulton *et al.*, 1989; Tanaka *et al.*, 1989; Yuzaki *et al.*, 1989; Zeviani *et al.*, 1989; Mita *et al.*, 1990; Johns and Cornblath, 1991; Rötig *et al.*, 1991). Both the sizes of these deletions and their locations vary quite considerably.

Wallace *et al.* (1991) have collated published data on sequenced mtDNA deletions both in unrelated patients and for multiple deletions within the same individual. From these data, three hotspots for deletion are very apparent: a 9 bp deletion either from 8271 to 8281 or from 8280 to 8290 ($N > 262$), a deletion of 4977 bp (the 'common' deletion either from 8469 to 13447 or from 8482 to 13460 ($N > 128$) and a 7436 bp deletion from 8648 to 16085 ($N = 32$). The latter two large deletions are bounded by pairs of 13 bp and 12 bp direct repeats respectively, while the short deletion possesses two 10 bp overlapping direct repeats (Figure 7.15) at the site of deletion.

To assess whether the observed association with direct repeats is indeed a general phenomenon for mtDNA deletions, regions of ± 10 bp flanking the 85 pairs of deletion breakpoints reported by Wallace *et al.* (1991) were analysed. The distribution of the longest pairwise direct repeats found within these regions is given in Table 7.13. The observed figures were compared with the

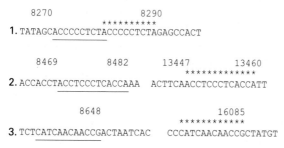

Figure 7.15. Breakpoints associated with three deletion hotspots in the mitochondrial genome (data derived from Wallace *et al.*, 1991). Members of pairs of direct repeats flanking the deletions are denoted by underlining and * respectively.

Table 7.13. Distribution of longest direct repeat lengths found within ± 10 bp of mtDNA deletion breakpoints

Longest direct repeat (bp)	Observed	Expected	χ^2
< 4	2	26.63	33.173*
4	20	35.45	11.561*
5	21	15.59	2.299
6	9	4.57	4.538
7	4	1.26	6.048
> 7	29	1.48	520.791*

Lengths marked * occur at frequencies significantly different from expectation, as based on the overall mtDNA sequence. The appropriate threshold of χ^2 values allowing for multiple testing was 6.96 ($P = 0.050$).

distribution of direct repeat lengths as expected in the overall mtDNA sequence. To this end, all possible pairs of 20 bp sequences, located at distances equal to that of the original breakpoints, were scanned, and the lengths of the longest direct repeats were collated. χ^2 analysis revealed that short lengths (i.e. <5 bp) are significantly under-represented near actual breakpoints, whereas long direct repeats are over-represented. A similar analysis was also performed for inverted repeats but failed to yield any significant results.

The involvement of direct repeats at deletion breakpoints is reminiscent of the mechanisms involved in unequal crossing-over during recombination and slipped mispairing during DNA replication, thought to be responsible for many deletions in the nuclear genome (see Section 7.1). Schon et al. (1989) suggested that recombination between homologous sequences might represent one mechanism of mtDNA deletion. However, there is scanty evidence for the occurrence of recombination in the mammalian mt genome and there are no reports of the reciprocal products expected from such unequal crossing-over events.

Instead, Shoffner et al. (1989) have proposed a model of slipped mispairing during mtDNA replication to account for the frequent proximity of direct repeats to deletion breakpoints; illustrated in Figure 7.16 is the 4977 bp 'common' deletion flanked by direct repeats at 13447–13459 (DR1) and 8470–8482 (DR2). Displacement of the H strand would permit the synthesis of a new daughter H strand to proceed, but could also have potentiated the mispairing of DR1 on the parental H strand with DR2 on the L strand once the latter had been exposed in single-stranded form by the moving replication fork. Breakage of the parental H strand at this juncture would permit replication to continue but would generate an mtDNA molecule with a deletion of the observed size. Replication of the parental L strand should generate a second (normal) mtDNA. A test of this hypothesis could involve an assessment of the amount of time any given location in the mt genome is obliged to remain single-stranded during replication. The probability of slipped mispairing might be expected to be related to this period of time as well as to the number and length of direct repeats in the vicinity.

A number of interesting homologies are apparent at the deletion breakpoints. Johns et al. (1989) sequenced the deletion junctions in three unrelated patients with progressive external ophthalmoplegia and noticed sufficient homology between them for a consensus sequence to be drawn up (Figure 7.17). This consensus sequence exhibits considerable similarity to sequences found in the core region of hypervariable minisatellite repeats (Jeffreys et al., 1985), which are thought to represent recombination signals in the human genome. It also exhibits some homology (in reverse complement) to the chi sequence (GCTGGTGG) known to represent a potent recombinogenic influence in E. coli.

Rötig et al. (1991) have pointed out that three deletion breakpoints characterized in patients with Pearson marrow–pancreas syndrome exhibit a high degree of homology with the binding site for an endoribonuclease, containing

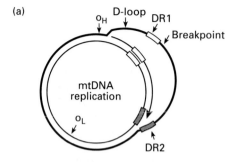

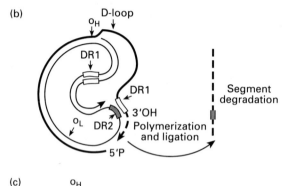

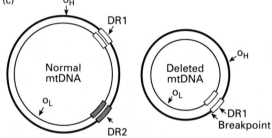

Figure 7.16. Model of slipped mispairing during mitochondrial DNA replication (after Shoffner *et al.*, 1989). (a) Mitochondrial DNA replication by displacement of the H strand. (b) Slipped mispairing of direct repeats DR1 and DR2 followed by H strand breakage. (c) Completion of mitochondrial DNA replication generates one normal and one deleted product. Heavy line, H strand; medium line, L strand; fine line, daughter H strand. Open and hatched boxes respectively denote direct repeats DR1 and DR2.

the nuclear-encoded MRP RNA, which is required for cleavage of the 7S RNA priming replication of the mtDNA from the D-loop (Figure 7.18). Incorrect recognition could somehow lead to cleavage and DNA loss at homologous sites within the mt genome.

Mita *et al.* (1990) characterized the deletions in 28 patients with progressive external ophthalmoplegia, 17 of whom possessed non-identical breakpoints: 16 of 17 deletions were clustered in a 6.3 kb region between 5835 and 12 112, whilst the 3′ breakpoints fell within a 3.3 kb region between 12 661 and 15 945. The deletions fell into two classes: Class I (nine deletions, 79% of patients) in which the deletion was flanked by perfect direct repeats (5–13 bp) and Class II (eight deletions, 29% of patients) in which the deletion was not immediately flanked by a repeat sequence. The existence of two distinct classes

```
       8472
          C T C C C T C A C C A
       13447
          C T C C C T C A C C A
       9345
          C T A - C T A A C C A
       13851
          C T A C C T A A C C A
       6332
          A G A C C T A A C C A
       13995
          A G A C C T A A C C T
          _____
Consensus     C T A C C T A A C C A

Hypervariable
                  C A
mini-satellite core  C T T  C C T G C C C A
region consensus
```

Figure 7.17. Comparison of the consensus deletion breakpoint sequence of Johns *et al.*, (1989) with a hypervariable minisatellite core region (reverse complement) consensus sequence (Jeffreys *et al.*, 1985).

```
Putative MRP RNA       310
recognition site        T C C C C C G C T
(D-loop, 310–318)
                       11233
                        T C C C C T A C T
Direct repeats at      8469
deletion breakpoints    T C C C T C A C C
                       10191
                        T C C C C C G C C
```

Figure 7.18. Sequence similarity between direct repeats at the sites of mtDNA deletions and the binding site for MRP RNA (after Rötig *et al.*, 1991).

of deletion argues for more than one mechanism for the generation of such deletions. Few clues are, however, apparent although a CCTCC motif was found at or near seven of nine of the Class II deletion breakpoints. In accord with this finding, inspection of the 170 (2×85) breakpoints reported by Wallace *et al.* (1991) reveals that, compared with the overall mtDNA, the frequencies of trinucleotides CCC, TCC and CCT are increased by more than 50% within ± 10 bp of the breakpoints. Further, Mita *et al.* (1990) claimed that sequences with some homology to *Drosophila* topoisomerase II recognition sequences [(A/G)N(T/C)NNCNNG(T/C)NG(G/T)TN(T/C)N(T/C); Spitzer and Muller, 1988] are non-randomly associated with deletion breakpoints, although no supporting statistical analysis was presented. Three of the breakpoints reported by Wallace *et al.* (1991), namely at positions 6329, 6330 and 6380, and a further two breakpoints at 12 102 and 12 103, possessed such a sequence motif in the immediate vicinity.

Zeviani *et al.* (1989, 1990) have described families with a mitochondrial myopathy which is not matrilineally inherited but rather manifests an auto-somal dominant mode of transmission. Multiple deletions were found in all patients examined and these deletions were invariably flanked by direct repeats. This suggests that, at least in some cases, mutational instability of the mt genome may be secondary to, and caused by, mutations in the nuclear genome.

References

Albertini AM, Hofer M, Calos MP, Miller JH. (1982) On the formation of spontaneous deletions: the importance of short sequence homologies in the generation of large deletions. *Cell* **29:** 319–328.

Anand R, Boehm CD, Kazazian HH, Vanin EF. (1988) Molecular characterization of a β^0-thalassemia resulting from a 1.4 kilobase deletion. *Blood* **72:** 636–641.

Ariga T, Carter PE, Davis AE. (1990) Recombinations between Alu repeat sequences that result in partial deletions within the C1 inhibitor gene. *Genomics* **8:** 607–613.

Ashman CR, Davidson RL. (1987) Sequence analysis of spontaneous mutations in a shuttle vector gene integrated into mammalian chromosomal DNA. *Proc. Natl. Acad. Sci. USA* **84:** 3354–3358.

Azen EA, O'Connell P, Kim H-S. (1992) PRB2/1 fusion gene: a product of unequal and homologous crossing-over between proline-rich protein (PRP) genes PRB1 and PRB2. *Am. J. Hum. Genet.* **50:** 842–851.

Badr FM, Lorkin PA, Lehmann H. (1973) Haemoglobin P-Nilotic containing a β–δ chain. *Nature* **242:** 107–110.

Baglioni C. (1962) The fusion of two peptide chains in hemoglobin Lepore and its interpretation as a genetic deletion. *Proc. Natl. Acad. Sci. USA* **48:** 1880–1886.

Baird M, Schreiner H, Driscoll C, Bank A. (1981) Localization of the site of recombination in the formation of the Lepore Boston globin gene. *J. Clin. Invest.* **58:** 560–564.

Ballabio A, Carrozzo R, Parenti G, Gil A, Zollo M, Persico MG, Gillard E, Affara N, Yates J, Ferguson-Smith MA, Frants RR, Eriksson AW, Andria G. (1989) Molecular heterogeneity of steroid sulfatase deficiency: a multicenter study on 57 unrelated patients at DNA and protein levels. *Genomics* **4:** 36–40.

Barnabus J, Muller CJ. (1962) Haemoglobin Lepore Hollandia. *Nature* **194:** 931–932.

Bartlett RJ, Walker AP, Laing NG, Koh J, Secore SL, Speer MC, Pericak-Vance MA, Hung W-Y, Yamaoka LH, Siddique T, Kandt R, Roses AD. (1989) Inherited deletion at Duchenne locus in normal male. *Lancet* **i:** 496–497.

Bebenek K, Kunkel TA. (1990) Frameshift errors initiated by nucleotide misincorporation. *Proc. Natl. Acad. Sci. USA* **87:** 4946–4950.

Berkvens TM, van Ormond H, Gerritsen EJA, Meera Khan P, van der Eb AJ. (1990) Identical 3250-bp deletion between two Alu1 repeats in the ADA genes of unrelated ADA-SCID patients. *Genomics* **7:** 486–490.

Besmer P, Murphy JE, George PC, Qiu F, Bergold PJ, Lederman L, Snyder HW, Brodeur D, Zuckerman EE, Hardy WD. (1986) A new acute transforming feline retrovirus and relationship of its oncogene *v-kit* with the protein kinase gene family. *Nature* **320:** 415–421.

Bollag RJ, Waldman AS, Liskay RM. (1989) Homologous recombination in mammalian cells. *Ann. Rev. Genet.* **23:** 199–225.

Borst P, Greaves DR. (1987) Programmed gene rearrangements altering gene expression. *Science* **235:** 658–667.

Brunier D, Michel B, Ehrlich SD. (1988) Copy choice illegitimate DNA recombination. *Cell* **52:** 883–892.

Canning S, Dryja TP. (1989) Short direct repeats at the breakpoints of deletions of the retinoblastoma gene. *Proc. Natl. Acad. Sci. USA* **86:** 5044–5048.

Carter PE, Duponchel C, Tosi M, Fothergill JE. (1991) Complete nucleotide sequence of the gene for human C1 inhibitor with an unusually high density of Alu elements. *Eur. J. Biochem.* **197:** 301–308.

Chebloune Y, Verdier G. (1983) The δ-β-crossing over site in the fusion gene of the Lepore–Boston disease might be localized in a preferential recombination region. *Acta Haematol.* **69:** 294–302.

Chebloune Y, Poncet D, Verdier G. (1984) S1-nuclease mapping of the genomic Lepore–Boston DNA demonstrates that the entire large intervening sequence of the fusion gene is of β-type. *Biochem. Biophys. Res. Commun.* **120:** 116–123.

Cooper DN, Schmidtke J. (1991) Diagnosis of human genetic disease using recombinant DNA. Third edition. *Hum. Genet.* **87:** 519–560.

DasGupta U, Weston-Hafer K, Berg DE. (1987) Local DNA sequence control of deletion formation in *Escherichia coli* plasmid pBR322. *Genetics* **115:** 41–49.

DeBoer JG, Ripley LS. (1984) Demonstration of the production of frameshift and base-substitution mutations by quasi-palindromic sequences. *Proc. Natl. Acad. Sci. USA* **81:** 5528–5531.

Deeb SS, Lindsey DT, Hibiya Y, Sanocki E, Winderickx J, Teller DY, Motulsky AG. (1992) Genotype-phenotype relationships in human red/green color vision defects: molecular and psychophysical studies. *Am. J. Hum. Genet.* **51:** 687–700.

De Jong PJ, Grosovsky AJ, Glickman BW. (1988) Spectrum of spontaneous mutation at the APRT locus of Chinese hamster ovary cells: an analysis at the DNA sequence level. *Proc. Natl. Acad. Sci. USA* **85:** 3499–3503.

Dubridge RB, Calos MP. (1987) Molecular approaches to the study of gene mutation in human cells. *Trends Genet.* **3:** 293–297.

Dunnen JT den, Bakker E, Klein Breteler EG, Pearson PL, van Ommen GJB. (1987) Direct detection of more than 50% of the Duchenne muscular dystrophy mutations by field inversion gels. *Nature* **329:** 640–642.

Efstratiadis A, Posakony JW, Maniatis T, Lawn RM, O'Connell C, Spritz RA, DeRiel JK, Forget BG, Weissman SM, Slightom JL, Blechl AE, Smithies O, Baralle FE, Shoulders CC, Proudfoot NJ. (1980) The structure and evolution of the human β-globin gene family. *Cell* **21:** 653–668.

Embury SH, Miller JA, Dozy AM, Kan YW, Chan V, Todd D. (1980) Two different molecular organizations account for the single α-globin gene of the α-thalassaemia-2 genotype. *J. Clin. Invest.* **66:** 1319–1324.

Farabaugh PJ, Schmeissner U, Hofer M, Miller JH. (1978) Genetic studies of the *lac* repressor. VII. On the molecular nature of spontaneous hotspots in the *lacI* gene of *Escherichia coli*. *J. Mol. Biol.* **126:** 847–863.

Fioretti G, De Angioletti M, Masciangelo F, Lacerra G, Scarallo A, de Bonis C, Pagano L, Guarino E, De Rosa L, Salvati F, Carestia C. (1992) Origin heterogeneity of Hb Lepore–Boston gene in Italy. *Am. J. Hum. Genet.* **50:** 781–786.

Flavell RA, Kooter JW, DeBoer E, Little PFR, Williamson R. (1978) Analysis of δ-β-globin gene in normal and Hb Lepore DNA: direct determination of gene linkage and intergene distance. *Cell* **15:** 25–41.

Fodde R, Losekoot M, Casula L, Bernini L. (1990) Nucleotide sequence of the Belgian G–γ^+ (A–γ, δ, β)°-thalassemia deletion breakpoint suggests a common mechanism for a number of such recombination events. *Genomics* **8:** 732–735.

Forrest SM, Cross GS, Speer A, Gardner-Medwin D, Burn J, Davies KE. (1987) Preferential deletion of exons in Duchenne and Becker muscular dystrophies. *Nature* **329:** 638–640.

Forrest SM, Cross GS, Flint T, Speer A, Robson KJH, Davies KE. (1988) Further studies of gene deletions that cause Duchenne and Becker muscular dystrophies. *Genomics* **2:** 109–114.

Galas DJ. (1978) An analysis of sequence repeats in the *lacI* gene of *Escherichia coli*. *J. Mol. Biol.* **126:** 858–863.

Gerald PS, Diamond LK. (1958) A new hereditary hemoglobinopathy (the Lepore trait) and its interaction with thalassemia trait. *Blood* **13:** 835–844.

Gilman JG. (1987) The 12.6 kilobase DNA deletion in Dutch β°-thalassaemia. *Br. J. Haematol.* **67:** 369–372.

Glickman BW, Ripley LS. (1984) Structural intermediates of deletion mutagenesis: a role for palindromic DNA. *Proc. Natl. Acad. Sci. USA* **81:** 512–516.

Goossens M, Dozy AM, Embury SH, Zachariades Z, Hadjiminas MG, Stamatoyannopoulos G, Kan YW. (1980) Triplicated α-globin loci in humans. *Proc. Natl. Acad. Sci. USA* **77:** 518–521.

Gritzmacher CA. (1989) Molecular aspects of heavy-chain class switching. *Crit. Rev. Immunol.* **9:** 173–200.

Grosovsky AJ, De Boer JG, De Jong PJ, Drobetsky EA, Glickman BW. (1988) Base substitutions, frameshifts and small deletions constitute ionizing radiation-induced point mutations in mammalian cells. *Proc. Natl. Acad. Sci. USA* **85**: 185–188.

Guioli S, Incerti B, Zanaria E, Bardoni B, Franco B, Taylor K, Ballabio A, Camerino G. (1992) Kallmann syndrome due to a translocation resulting in an X/Y fusion gene. Nature *Genetics* **1**: 337–340.

Hentemann M, Reiss J, Wagner M, Cooper DN. (1990) Rapid detection of deletions in the Duchenne muscular dystrophy gene by PCR amplification of deletion-prone exon sequences. *Hum. Genet.* **84**: 228–232.

Henthorn PS, Mager DL, Huisman THJ, Smithies O. (1986) A gene deletion ending within a complex array of repeated sequences 3' to the human β-globin gene cluster. *Proc. Natl. Acad. Sci. USA* **83**: 5194–5198.

Henthorn PS, Smithies O, Mager DL. (1990) Molecular analysis of deletions in the human β-globin gene cluster: deletion junctions and locations of breakpoints. *Genomics* **6**: 226–237.

Higgs DR, Vickers MA, Wilkie AOM, Pretorius I-M, Jarman AP, Weatherall DJ. (1989) A review of the molecular genetics of the human α-globin gene cluster. *Blood* **73**: 1081–1104.

Hobbs HH, Brown MS, Goldstein JL, Russell DW. (1986) Deletion of exon encoding cysteine-rich repeat of low-density lipoprotein receptor alters its binding specificity in a subject with familial hypercholesterolemia. *J. Biol. Chem.* **261**: 13114–13120.

Hogan A, Faust EA. (1984) Short direct repeats mediate spontaneous high frequency deletions in DNA of minute virus of mice. *Mol. Cell. Biol.* **4**: 2239–2242.

Holt IJ, Harding AE, Morgan-Hughes JA. (1989) Deletions of muscle mitochondrial DNA in mitochondrial myopathies: sequence analysis and possible mechanisms. *Nucleic Acids Res.* **17**: 4465–4469.

Honig GR, Mason RG, Tremaine LM, Vida LN. (1978a) Unbalanced globin chain synthesis by Hb Lincoln Park (anti-Lepore) reticulocytes. *Am. J. Hematol.* **5**: 335–340.

Honig GR, Shamsuddin M, Mason RG, Vida LN. (1978b) Hemoglobin Lincoln Park: a β-δ fusion (anti-Lepore) variant with an amino acid deletion in the δ chain-derived segment. *Proc. Natl. Acad. Sci. USA* **75**: 1475–1479.

Horsthemke B, Beisiegel U, Dunning A, Havinga JR, Williamson R, Humphries S. (1987) Unequal crossing-over between two Alu-repetitive DNA sequences in the low-density-lipoprotein-receptor gene. *Eur. J. Biochem.* **164**: 77–81.

Huang L-S, Ripps ME, Korman SH, Deckelbaum RJ, Breslow JL. (1989) Hypobetalipoproteinaemia due to an apolipoprotein B gene exon 21 deletion derived by Alu–Alu recombination. *J. Biol. Chem.* **264**: 11394–11400.

Huisman THJ, Wrightstone RN, Wilson JB, Schroeder WA, Kendall AG. (1972) Hemoglobin Kenya, the product of a fusion of γ and β polypeptide chains. *Arch. Biochem. Biophys.* **153**: 850–853.

Ikehata H, Akagi T, Kimura H, Akasaka S, Kato T. (1989) Spectrum of spontaneous mutations in a cDNA of the human hprt gene integrated in chromosomal DNA. *Mol. Gen. Genet.* **219**: 349–358.

Jagadeeswaran P, Tuan D, Forget BG, Weissman SM. (1982) A gene deletion ending at the midpoint of a repetitive DNA sequence in one form of hereditary persistence of fetal haemoglobin. *Nature* **296**: 469–470.

Jeffreys AJ, Wilson V, Thein SL. (1985) Hypervariable 'minisatellite' regions in human DNA. *Nature* **314**: 67–73.

Johns DR, Cornblath DR. (1991) Molecular insight into the asymmetric distribution of pathogenetic human mitochondrial DNA deletions. *Biochem. Biophys. Res. Commun.* **174**: 244–250.

Johns DR, Rutledge SL, Stine OC, Hurko O. (1989) Directly repeated sequences associated with pathogenic mitochondrial DNA deletions. *Proc. Natl. Acad. Sci. USA* **86**: 8059–8062.

Kendall AG, Ojwang PJ, Schroeder WA, Huisman THJ. (1973) Hemoglobin Kenya, the product of a γ-β fusion gene: studies of the family. *Am. J. Hum. Genet.* **25**: 548–563.

Kornreich R, Bishop DF, Desnick RJ. (1990) α-galactosidase A gene rearrangements causing Fabry disease. *J. Biol. Chem.* **265**: 9319–9326.

Krawczak M, Cooper DN. (1991) Gene deletions causing human genetic disease: mechanisms of mutagenesis and the role of the local DNA sequence environment. *Hum. Genet.* **86:** 425–441.

Kunkel TA. (1985a) The mutational specificity of DNA polymerase-β during *in vitro* DNA synthesis. *J. Biol. Chem.* **260:** 5787–5796.

Kunkel TA. (1985b) The mutational specificity of DNA polymerases α and γ during *in vitro* DNA synthesis. *J. Biol. Chem.* **260:** 12866–12874.

Kunkel TA. (1986) Frameshift mutagenesis by eukaryotic DNA polymerases *in vitro*. *J. Biol. Chem.* **261:** 13581–13587.

Kunkel TA, Soni A. (1988) Mutagenesis by transient misalignment. *J. Biol. Chem.* **263:** 14784–14789.

Laing NG, Layton MG, Johnsen RD, Chandler DC, Mears ME, Goldblatt J, Kakulas BA. (1992) Two distinct mutations in a single dystrophin gene: chance occurrence or premutation? *Am. J. Med. Genet.* **42:** 688–692.

Lanclos KD, Patterson J, Eframov GD, Wong SC, Villegas A, Ojwang PJ, Wilson JB, Kutlar F, Huisman THJ. (1987) Characterization of chromosomes with hybrid genes for Hb Lepore-Washington, Hb Lepore-Baltimore, Hb P-Nilotic, and Hb Kenya. *Hum. Genet.* **77:** 40–45.

Langlois S, Kastelein JJP, Hayden MR. (1988) Characterization of six partial deletions in the low density lipoprotein (LDL) receptor gene causing familial hypercholesterolemia (FH). *Am. J. Hum. Genet.* **43:** 60–68.

Lee B, Vissing H, Ramirez F, Rogers D, Rimoin D. (1989) Identification of the molecular defect in a family with spondyloepiphyseal dysplasia. *Science* **244:** 978–983.

Lehmann H, Charlesworth D. (1970) Observations on hemoglobin P (Congo type). *Biochem. J.* **119:** 43.

Lehrman MA, Schneider WJ, Suedhof TF, Brown MS, Goldstein JL, Russell DW. (1985) Mutation in LDL receptor: Alu-Alu recombination deletes exons encoding transmembrane and cytoplasmic domains. *Science* **227:** 140–146.

Lehrman MA, Russell DW, Goldstein JL, Brown MS. (1986) Exon-Alu recombination deletes 5 kilobases from the low density lipoprotein receptor gene producing a null phenotype in familial hypercholesterolemia. *Proc. Natl. Acad. Sci. USA* **83:** 3679–3683.

Lehrman MA, Russell DW, Goldstein JL, Brown MS. (1987) Alu-Alu recombination deletes splice acceptor sites and produces secreted low density lipoprotein receptor in a subject with familial hypercholesterolemia. *J. Biol. Chem.* **262:** 3354–3361.

Mager DL, Goodchild NL. (1989) Homologous recombination between the LTRs of a human retrovirus-like element causes a 5-kb deletion in two siblings. *Am. J. Hum. Genet.* **45:** 848–854.

Markert ML, Hutton JJ, Wiginton DA, States JC, Kaufman RE. (1988) Adenosine deaminase (ADA) deficiency due to deletion of the ADA gene promoter and first exon by homologous recombination between two Alu elements. *J. Clin. Invest.* **81:** 1323–1327.

Marvo SL, King SR, Jaskunas SR. (1983) Role of short regions of homology in intermolecular illegitimate recombination events. *Proc. Natl. Acad. Sci. USA* **80:** 2452–2456.

Mavilio F, Giampaolo A, Caré A, Sposi NM, Marinucci M. (1983) The δ-β crossover region in Lepore Boston hemoglobinopathy is restricted to a 59 base pairs region around the 5' splice junction of a large globin gene intervening sequence. *Blood* **62:** 230–233.

Metzenberg AB, Wurzer G, Huisman TH, Smithies O. (1991) Homology requirements for unequal crossing over in humans. *Genetics* **128:** 143–161.

Meuth M. (1989) The molecular basis of mutations induced by deoxyribonucleoside triphosphate pool imbalances in mammalian cells. *Exp. Cell Res.* **181:** 305–316.

Millar DS, Steinbrecher RA, Wieland K, Grundy CB, Martinowitz U, Krawczak M, Zoll B, Whitmore D, Stephenson J, Mibashan RS, Kakkar VV, Cooper DN. (1991) The molecular genetic analysis of haemophilia A: characterization of six partial deletions in the factor VIII gene. *Hum. Genet.* **86:** 219–227.

Mita S, Rizzuto R, Moraes CT, Shanske S, Arnaudo E, Fabrizi GM, Koga Y, DiMauro S, Schon EA. (1990) Recombination via flanking direct repeats is a major cause of large-scale deletions of human mitochondrial DNA. *Nucleic Acids Res.* **18:** 561–567.

Monnat RJ, Hackmann AFM, Chiaverotti TA. (1992) Nucleotide sequence analysis of human hypoxanthine phosphoribosyltransferase (HPRT) gene deletions. *Genomics* **13:** 777–787.

Myerowitz R, Hogikyan ND. (1987) A deletion involving Alu sequences in the β-hexosaminidase α-chain gene of French Canadians with Tay–Sachs disease. *J. Biol. Chem.* **262:** 15396–15399.

Nalbantoglu J, Hartley D, Phear G, Tear G, Meuth M. (1986) Spontaneous deletion formation at the aprt locus of hamster cells: the presence of short sequence homologies and dyad symmetries at deletion termini. *EMBO J.* **5:** 1199–1204.

Nalbantoglu J, Phear G, Meuth M. (1987) DNA sequence analysis of spontaneous mutations at the *aprt* locus of hamster cells. *Mol. Cell. Biol.* **7:** 1445–1449.

Nathans J, Piantanida TP, Eddy RL, Shows TB, Hogness DS. (1986) Molecular genetics of inherited variation in human color vision. *Science* **232:** 203–210.

Neitz J, Neitz M, Jacobs GH. (1989) Analysis of fusion gene and encoded photopigment of colour-blind humans. *Nature* **342:** 679–682.

Neote K, McInnes B, Mahuran DJ, Gravel RA. (1990) Structure and distribution of an Alu-type deletion mutation in Sandhoff disease. *J. Clin. Invest.* **86:** 1524–1531.

Nicholls RD, Fischel-Ghodsian N, Higgs DR. (1987) Recombination at the human α-globin gene cluster: sequence features and topological constraints. *Cell* **49:** 369–378.

Ojwang PJ, Nakatsuji T, Gardiner MB, Reese AL, Gilman JG, Huisman THJ. (1983) Gene deletion as the molecular basis for the Kenya–G-γ-HPFH condition. *Hemoglobin* **7:** 115–123.

Ostertag W, Smith EW. (1969) Hemoglobin–Lepore–Baltimore, a third type of a δ, β crossover (δ^{50}, β^{86}). *Eur. J. Biochem.* **10:** 371–376.

Ottolenghi S, Giglioni B. (1982) The deletion in a type of δ^0-β^0-thalassaemia begins in an inverted repeat. *Nature* **300:** 770–771.

Paolella G, Lucero MA, Murphy MH, Baralle FE. (1983) The Alu family repeat promoter has a tRNA-like bipartite structure. *EMBO J.* **2:** 691–696.

Papanicolaou C, Ripley LS. (1989) Polymerase-specific differences in the DNA intermediates of frameshift mutagenesis. *J. Mol. Biol.* **207:** 335–353.

Parnes JR, Sizer KC, Seidman JG, Stallings V, Hyman R. (1986) A mutational hot-spot within an intron of the mouse β2-microglobulin gene. *EMBO J.* **5:** 103–111.

Pascoe L, Curnow KM, Slutsker L, Connell JMC, Speiser PW, New MI, White PC. (1992) Glucocorticoid-suppressible hyperaldosteronism results from hybrid genes created by unequal crossovers between CYP11B1 and CYP11B2. *Proc. Natl. Acad. Sci. USA* **89:** 8327–8331.

Phear G, Armstrong W, Meuth M. (1989) Molecular basis of spontaneous mutation at the *aprt* locus of hamster cells. *J. Mol. Biol.* **209:** 577–582.

Piccoli SP, Caimi PG, Cole MD. (1984) A conserved sequence at *c-myc* oncogene chromosomal translocation breakpoints in plasmacytomas. *Nature* **310:** 327–331.

Pizzuti A, Pieretti M, Fenwick RG, Gibbs RA, Caskey CT. (1992) A transposon-like element in the deletion-prone region of the dystrophin gene. *Genomics* **13:** 594–600.

Poulton J, Deadman ME, Gardiner RM. (1989) Tandem direct duplications of mitochondrial DNA in mitochondrial myopathy: analysis of nucleotide sequence and tissue distribution. *Nucleic Acids Res.* **17:** 10223–10229.

Ramirez F, Mears JG, Nudel U, Bank A, Luzzato L, DiPrisco G, D'Avino R, Pepe G, Gambino R, Cimino R, Quattrin N. (1979) Defects in DNA and globin messenger RNA in homozygotes for hemoglobin Lepore. *J. Clin. Invest.* **63:** 736–742.

Ripley LS. (1982) Model for the participation of quasi-palindromic DNA sequences in frameshift mutation. *Proc. Natl. Acad. Sci. USA* **79:** 4128–4132.

Roth DB, Wilson JH. (1986) Nonhomologous recombination in mammalian cells: role for short sequence homologies in the joining reaction. *Mol. Cell. Biol.* **6:** 4295–4304.

Roth DB, Porter TN, Wilson JH. (1985) Mechanisms of nonhomologous recombination in mammalian cells. *Mol. Cell. Biol.* **5:** 2599–2607.

Rötig A, Cormier V, Koll F, Mize CE, Sauubray J-M, Veerman A, Pearson HA,

Munnich A. (1991) Site-specific deletions of the mitochondrial genome in the Pearson marrow–pancreas syndrome. *Genomics* **10:** 502–504.

Rubnitz J, Subramani S. (1984) The minimum amount of homology required for homologous recombination in mammalian cells. *Mol. Cell. Biol.* **4:** 2253–2258.

Ruley HE, Fried M. (1983) Clustered illegitimate recombination events in mammalian cells involving very short sequence homologies. *Nature* **304:** 181–184.

Schaaper RM, Danforth BN, Glickman BW. (1986) Mechanisms of spontaneous mutagenesis: an analysis of the spectrum of spontaneous mutation in the *Escherichia coli lacI* gene. *J. Mol. Biol.* **189:** 273–284.

Schon EA, Rizzuto R, Moraes CT, Nakase H, Zeviani M, DiMauro S. (1989) A direct repeat is a hotspot for large-scale deletion of human mitochondrial DNA. *Science* **244:** 346–349.

Shapiro LJ, Yen P, Pomerantz D, Martin E, Rolewic L, Mohandas T. (1989) Molecular studies of deletions at the human steroid sulphatase locus. *Proc. Natl. Acad. Sci. USA* **86:** 8477–8481.

Shoffner JM, Lott MT, Voljavec AS, Soueidan SA, Costigan DA, Wallace DC. (1989) Spontaneous Kearns–Sayre/chronic external ophthalmoplegia plus syndrome associated with a mitochondrial DNA deletion: a slip-replication model and metabolic therapy. *Proc. Natl. Acad. Sci. USA* **86:** 7952–7956.

Singer BS, Westlye J. (1988) Deletion formation in bacteriophage T4. *J. Mol. Biol.* **202:** 233–243.

Spitzer JR, Muller MT. (1988) A consensus sequence for cleavage by vertebrate DNA topoisomerase II. *Nucleic Acids Res.* **16:** 5533–5562.

Stoppa-Lyonnet D, Carter PE, Meo T, Tosi M. (1990) Clusters of intragenic Alu repeats predispose the human C1 inhibitor locus to deleterious rearrangements. *Proc. Natl. Acad. Sci. USA* **87:** 1551–1555.

Stoppa-Lyonnet D, Duponchel C, Meo T, Laurent J, Carter PE, Arala-Chaves M, Cohen JHM, Dewald G, Goetz J, Hauptmann G, Lagrue G, Lesavre P, Lopez-Trascasa M, Misiano G, Moraine C, Sobel A, Späth PJ, Tosi M. (1991) Recombinational biases in the rearranged C1-inhibitor genes of hereditary angioedema patients. *Am. J. Hum. Genet.* **49:** 1055–1062.

Streisinger G, Okada Y, Emrich J, Newton J, Tsugita A, Terzaghi E, Inouye M. (1966) Frameshift mutations and the genetic code. *Cold Spring Harb. Symp. Quant. Biol.* **31:** 77–84.

Studier FW, Rosenberg AH. (1979) Genetic and physical mapping in the early region of bacteriophage T7 DNA. *J. Mol. Biol.* **135:** 917–937.

Tanaka M, Sato W, Ohno K, Yamamoto T, Ozawa T. (1989) Direct sequencing of deleted mitochondrial DNA in myopathic patients. *Biochem. Biophys. Res. Commun.* **164:** 156–163.

Tanigawa G, Jarcho JA, Kass S, Solomon SD, Vosberg H-P, Seidman JG, Seidman CE. (1990) A molecular basis for familial hypertrophic cardiomyopathy: an α/β cardiac myosin heavy chain hybrid gene. *Cell* **62:** 991–998.

Trent RJ, Higgs DR, Clegg JB, Weatherall DJ. (1981) A new triplicated α-globin gene arrangement in man. *Br. J. Haematol.* **49:** 149–155.

Vanin EF, Henthorn PS, Kioussis D, Grosveld F, Smithies O. (1983) Unexpected relationships between four large deletions in the human β-globin gene cluster. *Cell* **35:** 701–709.

Vnencak-Jones CL, Phillips JA. (1990) Hot spots for growth hormone gene deletions in homologous regions outside of Alu repeats. *Science* **250:** 1745–1748.

Vnencak-Jones CL, Phillips JA, Chen EY, Seeburg PH. (1988) Molecular basis of human growth hormone deletions. *Proc. Natl. Acad. Sci. USA* **85:** 5615–5619.

Wada K, Wada Y, Doi H, Ishibashi F, Gojobori T, Ikemura T. (1991) Codon usage tabulated from the GenBank genetic sequence data. *Nucleic Acids Res.* **19** (Suppl.): 1981–1986.

Wallace DC, Lott MT, Torroni A, Shoffner JM. (1991) Report of the Committee on human mitochondrial DNA. *Cytogenet. Cell Genet.* **58:** 1103–1123.

Wapenaar MC, Kievits T, Hart KA, Abbs S, Blonden LAJ, Den Dunnen JT, Grootscholten PM, Bakker E, Verellen-Dumoulin C, Bobrow M, Van Ommen GJB,

Pearson PL. (1988) A deletion hot spot in the Duchenne muscular dystrophy gene. *Genomics* **2:** 101–108.

Weaver DT, DePamphilis ML. (1982) Specific sequences in native DNA that arrest synthesis by DNA polymerase α. *J. Biol. Chem.* **257:** 2075–2086.

Woods-Samuels P, Kazazian HH, Antonarakis SE. (1991) Nonhomologous recombination in the human genome: deletions in the human factor VIII gene. *Genomics* **10:** 94–101.

Yen PH, Li X-M, Tsai S-P, Johnson C, Mohandas T, Shapiro LJ. (1990) Frequent deletions of the human X chromosome distal short arm result from recombination between low copy repetitive elements. *Cell* **61:** 603–610.

Yuzaki M, Ohkoshi N, Kanazawa I, Kagawa Y, Ohta S. (1989) Multiple deletions in mitochodrial DNA at direct repeats of non-D-loop regions in cases of familial mitochondrial myopathy. *Biochem. Biophys. Res. Commun.* **164:** 1352–1357.

Zeviani M, Servidei S, Gellera C, Bertini E, DiMauro S. (1989) An autosomal dominant disorder with multiple deletions of mitochondrial DNA starting at the D-loop region. *Nature* **339:** 309–311.

Zeviani M, Bresolin N, Gellera C, Bordoni A, Pannacci M, Amati P, Moggio M, Servidei S, Scarlato G, DiDonato S. (1990) Nucleus driven multiple large-scale deletions of the human mitochondrial genome: a new autosomal dominant disease. *Am. J. Hum. Genet.* **47:** 904–914.

Zimran A, Sorge J, Gross E, Kubitz M, West C, Beutler E. (1990) A glucocerebrosidase fusion gene in Gaucher disease. *J. Clin. Invest.* **85:** 219–222.

Gene insertions, duplications and inversions

8.1 Small insertions

The vast majority of mutations causing human genetic disease are point mutations and deletions (Cooper and Schmidtke, 1991). However, a substantial proportion of the remainder involve short sequence duplications or insertions of novel bases, usually resulting in an alteration of the reading frame of the encoded protein, and most often causing termination of translation at some distance downstream. That insertional mutagenesis might be as intrinsically non-random as point mutations and gene deletions (Chapters 6 and 7) was strongly suggested, for example, by the findings of Fearon *et al.* (1990), who reported 10 independent examples of DNA insertion within the same 170 bp intronic region of the DCC gene (a locus which has been proposed to play an important role in human colorectal neoplasia).

The majority of well characterized (i.e. sequenced) gene insertions in humans appear to be of between one and a few base-pairs. We shall see later in this chapter that many of the mechanisms responsible for generating short gene deletions can also, in principle, be recruited to account for gene insertions. To this end, examples of short insertions leading to human genetic disease will be analysed to determine:

(i) Whether they indeed occur non-randomly
(ii) Whether this non-randomness, if it exists, is sequence-directed
(iii) Whether the non-randomness corresponds to mechanisms of mutagenesis similar to those involved in the generation of short gene deletions

Many of our conclusions have already been published elsewhere (Cooper and Krawczak, 1991).

Larger sequence insertions and partial gene duplications are considered in Sections 8.2 and 8.3, respectively. A sample of 20 short insertion-type mutations, i.e. insertions of fewer than 10 bp, were selected (Table 8.1). This is by no means a comprehensive listing, merely a selection of typical examples for the purposes of comparative analysis. Nearly half of these (nine of 20) were

Table 8.1. Insertions of <10 bp causing human genetic disease

Disease	Gene symbol	DNA sequence	Reference
1. $\alpha 2$ antiplasmin deficiency	AAP	Ala355 GGAGGCGGCGgcgGCGGCCACCA	Holmes et al., 1987
2. APRT deficiency	APRT	EXON 4|INTRON 4 CCACTGGTGGtTAAGGGTCTC	Hidaka et al., 1987
3. β-thalassaemia	HBB	Leu14 TACTGCCCTGgTGGGGCAAGG	Chan et al., 1988
4. β-thalassaemia	HBB	Cys93 AGCTGCACTGtgTGACAAGCTGCA	Ristaldi et al., 1990
5. Cystic fibrosis	CFTR	Ile809 GGATATATAtatTCAAGAAGGT	White et al., 1990
6. δ-thalassaemia	HBD	Glu90 GCTGAGTGAGCTtGCACTGTGACAAGC	Losekoot et al., 1990
7. DHPT deficiency	DHPT	Ala122 CATCTGGCTActaCCAAGCATCT	Howells et al., 1990
8. Elliptocytosis	SPTA	Leu148 TGACCAGTTGttgCTGCGGGCCC	Roux et al., 1989
9. Haemophilia B (Würzburg)	F9	Lys122 ACCAGAAGTCcCTGTGAACCA	Giannelli et al., 1992
10. Haemophilia B (Lincoln Park)	F9	Val401 TATACCAAGGTATC(CC)aaggtaccaaGGTATGTCAA	Giannelli et al., 1992

11.	Haemophilia B	F9	Ile408 CAACTGGATTgattAAGGAAAAAA Pro37	Bottema et al., 1989
12.	Hb Catonsville	HBA	GTCCTTCCCCgaaACCACCAAGA Asp17	Moo-Penn et al., 1989
13.	Lesch–Nyhan syndrome	HPRT	GTTATGACCTtTGATTTATTT Lys68	Davidson et al., 1989
14.	Lesch–Nyhan syndrome	HPRT	TGCTCAAGGGgGGGCTATAAA Thr141	Gibbs et al., 1989
15.	Lesch–Nyhan syndrome	HPRT	GGCAAAACAA(TGCAG)agcaaaACTTTGCTTT Thr291	Gibbs et al., 1989
16.	Oculocutaneous albinism	TYR	CCAGAACCCCcAAGGCTCCCC His1145	Tomita et al., 1989
17.	Osteogenesis imperfecta (2)	COL1A1	AAGGACAAGAGGCATtGTCTGGTTCG BPMS	Bateman et al., 1989
18.	Osteoporosis	CALCA	CACCTTGGGTtTCTGACACC Gly116	Alevizaki et al., 1989
19.	Serum cholinesterase deficiency	CHE2	GGTGGTGGag(T)TTTCAAACTG Ile425	Nogueira et al., 1990
20.	Tay–Sachs disease	HEXA	ACCGTATATCtatcCTATGGCCCT	Myerowitz and Costigan, 1988

Inserted bases are denoted by lower-case letters. Bases deleted in the process of the insertion are bracketed. BPMS, putative branchpoint migration sequence: APRT, adenosine phosphoribosyltransferase; CALCA, calcitonin-α; CFTR, cystic fibrosis transmembrane conductance regulator; COL1A1, α1(I) collagen; DHPT, dihydropteridine reductase; F9, factor IX; HBA, α-globin; HBB, β-globin; HEXA, hexosaminidase A; HPRT, hypoxanthine phosphoribosyltransferase; SPTA, α-spectrin; TYR, tyrosinase; other gene symbols are as specified in the text.

insertions of a single base. All mutations interrupted the reading frame of the protein except for the three examples of a three-base insertion (nos. 1, 8 and 12) where the novel codons were inserted between existing codons. Three of the insertions (nos. 10, 15 and, 19) were complex mutations since between one and five base-pairs were also deleted at the site of insertion.

8.1.1 Insertions due to slipped mispairing

In principle, slipped mispairing at the replication fork (Streisinger *et al.*, 1966; Efstratiadis *et al.*, 1980) mediated by direct repeats can account for insertion-just as for deletion-type mutations (see Section 7.2): an insertion takes place when the newly synthesized strand disconnects from the primer strand during replication synthesis and slips or folds back so that pairing between different direct repeat copies becomes possible. If synthesis is resumed so as to stabilize this mispairing, one extra copy plus DNA sequence from between the direct repeats is inserted behind the second repeat.

Runs of an identical base obviously represent a simple type of direct repeat, and slipped mispairing at such sequence motifs, producing minus-one base frameshift mutations, is known to be a relatively common mechanism of gene deletion causing human genetic disease (Krawczak and Cooper, 1991; see Chapter 7). Similarly, slipped mispairing can also account for the generation of plus-one base frameshift mutations, as is depicted in Figure 8.1. Empirical evidence for the relevance of plus-one base frameshifts for insertion muta-

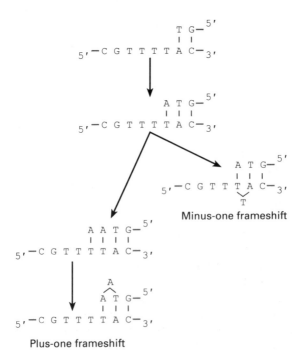

Figure 8.1. Pathway of frameshift mutagenesis leading to either plus-one or minus-one base incorporation errors (after Kunkel, 1986; reproduced by permission of The American Society for Biochemistry and Molecular Biology). Misalignment may occur at a run of identical bases by (i) disruption of hydrogen bonding between one of the base-pairs in the run, (ii) unstacking of a base to an extrahelical conformation, and (iii) reformation of hydrogen bonds on the 5′ side of the extrahelical base. A plus-one frameshift will occur if the extrahelical base is on the primer strand, and a minus-one frameshift will occur if the extrahelical base is on the template strand.

genesis was provided by Kunkel (1985a), who reported two insertions of a T into different strings of three T residues in an M13 substrate using purified rat polymerase β *in vitro*. Chick polymerase β yielded two insertions of a single C residue, one into a string of five Cs and one into a string of three Cs. A further insertion of a G residue into a string of three Gs occurred at a TGGGAA motif (which represents a near perfect deletion hotspot consensus sequence; see Section 7.2.6). Similar results were reported with human and calf polymerase α (Kunkel, 1985b).

Insertion-type mutations have also been shown to occur at a very low frequency in studies of spontaneous gene mutation in cultured cells. For example, Phear *et al.* (1989) reported one gene insertion in 89 adenosine phosphoribosyltransferase (APRT) mutants analysed in cultured hamster cells. Nevertheless, Ikehata *et al.* (1989) reported three independent cases of the insertion of a T residue into the same string of three Ts in the human HPRT gene integrated into the chromosomal DNA of VH12 cells. A study of mutations induced in the hamster APRT gene by ionizing radiation, however, yielded 16 point mutations but no insertions (Grosovsky *et al.*, 1988).

Thus, although insertions of a base occur much less frequently than changes or losses of a base, vertebrate DNA polymerases α and β appear to produce many more frameshifts at runs of bases than at non-runs. The frequency of frameshift mutations was found to be roughly proportional to the length of the run (Kunkel, 1985a; Kunkel *et al.*, 1989), which was to be expected since the stability of a misalignment is likely to be enhanced by increased capacity for base-pairing. Of the insertions listed in Table 8.1, at least three occurred within runs of the same base: nos. 7 (a T residue into three existing Ts), 14 (a G residue into six existing Gs) and 16 (a C residue into four existing Cs). These data are thus consistent with the model of slipped mispairing, although they are too sparse to confirm any relationship between the frequency of plus-one base frameshift mutations and the length of run or base composition. Furthermore, it is also not possible to distinguish polymerase α- from polymerase β-associated errors here. Although polymerase β is generally less accurate than polymerase α as far as frameshift mutations are concerned, polymerase β is actually five-fold more accurate than polymerase α at a run of five C residues (Kunkel, 1986). Mutation hotspots with polymerase β occur predominantly at runs of pyrimidines (particularly TTTT) rather than purines, but this effect is less pronounced with polymerase α (Kunkel, 1986). Pause sites for DNA polymerase α are nevertheless known to be hotspots for nucleotide insertion (Fry and Loeb, 1992).

Three insertions listed in Table 8.1 are duplications of tandemly repeated sequences (nos. 1, 4 and 5), and are thus also readily explicable in terms of the slipped mispairing hypothesis. In insertion no. 1, for example, slipped mispairing during DNA replication could have been mediated by the GCG direct repeat, the primer strand slipping back three bases with respect to the template strand to allow mispairing between one of the three GCG motifs and an adjacent complementary CGC copy. This would result in one strand with an extra GCG triplet which, once fixed, would yield an insertion mutation at the next round of replication. Such a mechanism could also account for the bases introduced in insertion nos. 4 (TG repeats) and 5 (AT repeats). A less than perfect example of an insertion mediated by slipped mispairing is probably provided by no. 20, where the TAT repeat is duplicated as expected, but only one of the two C nucleotides between the two original repeat copies is duplicated.

8.1.2 Insertions mediated by inverted repeats

Analogous to the process of slipped mispairing between direct repeats, the formation of temporary secondary DNA structures may also be mediated by neighbouring inverted repeats, i.e. sequence motifs that are complementary to each other. In this situation, the newly synthesized DNA strand is assumed to disconnect but, instead of annealing to a direct repeat copy on the primer strand, it snaps back and anneals to itself via the two inverted repeats. As with slipped mispairing, if DNA synthesis is then resumed, an insertion would result behind the second palindromic copy and the novel structure would be stabilized.

The above-mentioned mechanism has been proposed by Ohshima *et al.* (1992) to account for an *in vivo* duplication of a sequence in the ColE1 plasmid of *E. coli*. In Table 8.1, an example of an insertion likely to be mediated by inverted repeat copies is provided by insertion no. 10. If the inverted repeat ATACC/GGTAT is presumed to potentiate the formation of a hairpin loop just behind the advancing replication fork (Figure 8.2), continued DNA synthesis would be templated by the other strand, resulting in a duplication of the AAGGTA sequence. The mispaired CC dinucleotide would be deleted in the process. The model is, however, unable to account for the origin of the remaining CCAA of the duplicated sequence.

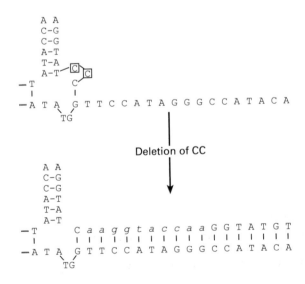

Figure 8.2. Insertional mutagenesis after inverted repeat-mediated hairpin loop formation on the nascent strand at DNA replication.

Although inverted repeat sequences are able to fold back upon themselves to form hairpin loops, imperfect self-complementarity can mediate formation of partially misaligned secondary structures (Ripley, 1982). The non-palindromic portions of these structures may then provide templates for either deletions (by endonucleolytic removal of bases; Chapter 7) or, putatively, insertions (by gap repair). In Table 8.1, the DNA sequences flanking two insertions (nos. 6 and 17) contain such quasi-palindromes, and would correctly predict the insertion of the appropriate base at the appropriate site (Figure 8.3). Two rather more complex mutations may also be explained in a similar fashion: insertion nos. 19 and 15 involve the deletion of one and three bases, respectively, in addition to the insertion of either two or four bases (Figure 8.3). Both the deletional and the insertional events are consistent with their having been templated by the base sequence within the hairpin loops. These sequence changes would be predicted to result in the increased stability of the hairpin loops (Figure 8.3).

8.1.3 Insertions mediated by symmetric elements

In our studies of the sequence context of short gene deletions, a significant excess of symmetric elements (e.g. CTGAAGTC) was noted in the vicinity of these lesions (Section 7.2.5). For this reason, we proposed that a Möbius loop-like structure, formed by two DNA strands during replication, could serve as an intermediate to potentiate the deletion of mismatched base-pairs within the

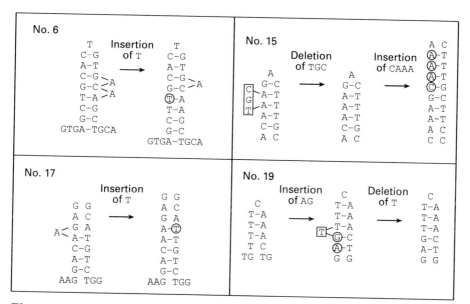

Figure 8.3. Partial self-complementarity exhibited by quasi-palindromic sequences flanking the sites of insertion. The insertion of a base or bases (circled) or deletion of a base or bases (surrounded by a square) serve to further stabilize the hairpin loop.

loop. Inspection of the insertions listed in Table 8.1 reveals that eight of 20 of these sequences also possess symmetric elements overlapping the site of insertion (nos.1, 2, 4, 5, 12, 14, 16 and 20). With one exception (no. 16), these insertions all represent inverted duplications of sequence motifs derived from either the 5′ or the 3′ end of the symmetric element. This finding is suggestive of a common endogenous mechanism of insertional mutagenesis, which is illustrated in Figure 8.4 for the case of insertion no. 20. If the Möbius loop (a) is partially resolved, either during its formation or separation, one of the two DNA strands may break, disconnect and make the loop partially single-stranded (b). Such a construct would clearly be a hotspot for DNA polymerase repair activity (c). Disconnection and repair of the broken strand would result in an inverted insertion of a sequence motif from one end of the symmetric element into the symmetric element on the broken strand (d).

In summary, the majority of insertions listed in Table 8.1 may be explained either by a model of slipped mispairing mediated by direct repeats, or by reference to neighbouring inverted repeats, imperfect inverted repeats or symmetric elements. All these sequence motifs appear to be capable of templating the misincorporation of novel bases by facilitating the formation of specific secondary structure intermediates. The mechanisms of mutagenesis proposed here thus provide us with a useful framework within which to study both the nature and the ultimate underlying causes of human gene insertions. One caveat must, however, be mentioned: even in cases where the bases inserted are fully consistent with the proposed mechanism, this does not in itself provide conclusive proof of the mechanism's validity. Indeed, in some cases, more than one mechanism may be invoked to explain the genesis of the

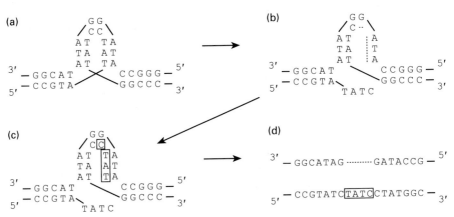

Figure 8.4. Möbius loop model of insertional mutagenesis demonstrated for insertion no. 20. (a) Re-annealing of the two single strands in an intermediate loop structure mediated by a symmetric element. (b) Partial resolution of the loop by disconnection and breakage of one strand. (c) Repair of single/double strand construct by DNA polymerase. (d) Complete resolution of the loop followed by reconnection of the two ends of the broken strand. A sequence motif from one side of the symmetric element is thus inserted in reverse orientation on the other side.

particular insertion in question. The complexity of some of the models considered implies that any conclusions drawn do not lend themselves easily to statistical scrutiny.

Three broad conclusions may nevertheless be stated:

(i) Insertional mutation involving the introduction of < 10 bp DNA sequence into a gene coding region is not a random process and appears to be highly dependent on the local DNA sequence context.

(ii) Mechanistic models which have explanatory value in the context of gene deletions also appear to be useful in accounting for the nature of gene insertions.

(iii) The majority of insertion-type mutations are consistent with an explanation which invokes an endogenous replication-associated mechanism of mutagenesis.

8.2 Large insertions

Are gross insertions of specific DNA sequences into human genes as nonrandom as short insertions? To date, the largest 'foreign' DNA sequence inserted into a gene is 220 kb into the Duchenne muscular dystrophy (DMD) gene (Bettecken and Müller, 1989). Unfortunately, neither the inserted sequence nor the breakpoint junctions have been further characterized.

One well characterized insertion is that of the highly repetitive LINE elements into the human factor VIII (F8) gene causing severe haemophilia A (Kazazian *et al.*, 1988). The insertion of these elements into exon 14 (at 3.1 kb, easily the largest exon) in the F8 genes of two patients, involved the duplication of the target sites, a normal occurrence in such cases (reviewed by Weiner *et al.*, 1986; Fanning and Singer, 1987) and consistent with a retrotransposition mechanism (see Section 2.1.3). Patient JH-27 was shown to possess a 3.8 kb truncated LINE element complete with 57 bp poly(A) tract. The LINE element in patient JH-28 was slightly shorter (2.3 kb) but more complex; one portion of LINE element sequence (nucleotides 4020–5114) was preceded by another (nucleotides 5115–6161) in reverse ($3' \rightarrow 5'$) orientation, both being associated with long $3'$ A-rich sequences.

Dombroski *et al.* (1991) have shown that the LINE element found in patient JH-27 is an exact but truncated copy of a full-length LINE element found at chromosome 22q11.1–q11.2. The latter progenitor element (L1.2B) is one of four LINE elements at this location and has been designated LRE1 (L1 retrotransposable element 1). It appears to have occupied this position for at least 6 million years. Since it is itself flanked by a target site duplication, it may also be the product of a retrotransposition event. Integrated LINE elements may therefore be capable of repeated cycles of transcription and retrotransposition or, alternatively, in the absence of appropriate regulatory sequence, they may remain quiescent. This self-propagation model is compatible with a number of active LINE elements producing both active and inactive progeny.

Although the two insertions described above were found in a screen of 240 unrelated haemophiliacs, no further examples were found in a study of over 500 unrelated haemophilia A patients (Millar *et al.*, 1990). The involvement of LINE elements in insertional mutagenesis has also been reported in two other human conditions, namely $G-\gamma^+(A-\gamma-\delta-\beta)^o$ thalassaemia (HBG1 gene; Mager *et al.*, 1985) and breast cancer (MYC gene; Morse *et al.*, 1988).

The highly repetitive Alu sequence family has also been shown to be capable of retrotransposition both *in vitro* (Lin *et al.*, 1988) and *in vivo*. Insertional inactivation of the NF1 gene by an Alu sequence causing neurofibromatosis type 1 was reported by Wallace *et al.* (1991). The insertion, which occurred *de novo*, was localized to intron 5, just 44 bp upstream of exon 6. The 320 bp Alu repeat was inserted in reverse orientation into a 26 bp stretch of A or T residues. Sequencing of reverse transcripts of the patient's mRNA revealed the skipping of exon 6. Although the exact mechanism responsible for this interference with splicing is not clear, these findings are consistent with a defect in branch-point recognition. An insertion of a ~ 300 bp Alu sequence into the human MLVI2 oncogene associated with haematopoietic neoplasia has also been reported by Economou-Pachnis and Tsichlis (1985).

The *de novo* insertion of an Alu sequence into exon V of the factor IX (F9) gene has also been reported as a cause of severe haemophilia B (Vidaud *et al.*, 1993). Insertion of the 322 bp Alu repeat (in a sense direction) was associated with a target site duplication and served to interrupt the factor IX reading frame at Glu 96, giving rise to a premature termination codon. The insertion event, which probably occurred in a grandpaternal gamete, appears to have involved the retrotransposition of a putative source gene.

A completely different type of insertional inactivation mediated by an Alu repeat has been noted by Mitchell *et al.* (1991). Analysis of the ornithine δ-aminotransferase (OAT) mRNA of a patient with gyrate atrophy revealed a 142 nucleotide insertion at the junction of exons 3 and 4. The patient possessed a much reduced level (5%) of abnormal mRNA in his fibroblasts and an even smaller amount of normally sized mRNA. An Alu sequence is normally present in intron 3 of the OAT gene, 150 bp downstream of exon 3. The Alu sequence found in the cDNA was identical to this one, except that the patient was homozygous for a C→G transversion in the right arm of the Alu repeat which served to create a new 5' splice site. This activated an upstream cryptic 3' splice site [the poly(T) complement of the Alu poly(A) tail followed by an AG dinucleotide] and a new 'exon', containing the majority of the right arm of the Alu sequence, was recognized by the splicing apparatus and incorporated into the mRNA. The 'splice-mediated insertion' of an Alu sequence in reverse orientation may yet prove to be no unusual mechanism of insertional mutagenesis, since (i) Alu sequences are interspersed through many coding sequences, (ii) the sequence requirements for a functional 3' splice site are far from stringent and (iii) the reverse complement of a consensus Alu repeat contains at least two cryptic 3' splice sites and several potential 5' splice sites.

The observation that both Alu sequences (Kariya *et al.*, 1987) and LINE elements (Kazazian *et al.*, 1988) exhibit a preference for integration at AT-rich sequences is reminiscent of the AT-rich insertional target sequences of retroviruses (Umlauf and Cox, 1988; Shih *et al.*, 1988). Indeed, we have noted that the two LINE element target sites in the factor VIII (F8) gene (Kazazian *et al.*, 1988) are 80% homologous to a 10 nucleotide motif (GAAGACATAC) present in one of the highly favoured retroviral insertion target sequences reported by Shih *et al.* (1988). If the generality of this observation is supported by further data, insertions of specific DNA sequences will have been shown to be as non-random as the insertion of a few base-pairs.

Although large insertions are individually rare events, a substantial proportion of patients with some disorders may bear an insertion mutation through a founder effect. Such an example is provided by a 2 kb insertion into the lipoprotein lipase (LPL) gene which has been noted in four of 11 families with LPL deficiency (Langlois *et al.*, 1989). Although geographically separated, these patients possessed the same haplotype, consistent with the identity by descent of these alleles. The insertion resulted in the production of catalytically defective LPL. The insertion has not been well characterized but restriction mapping suggested that it was neither the result of a local gene duplication nor the insertion of a LINE element.

8.3 Gene duplications

The duplication of either whole genes or their constituent exons has played an important role in the evolution of the mammalian genome. Gene duplication events may, however, also result in disease (reviewed by Hu and Worton, 1992) and their contribution to human genome pathology is described here in some detail. Two distinct mechanisms are currently envisaged: (i) homologous unequal recombination between either homologous chromosomes or sister chromatids and (ii) non-homologous recombination at sites with minimal homology.

A proportion of the small insertions (< 20 bp) described in Section 8.1 have effectively been very short duplications of DNA sequence. Although a very arbitrary distinction, for practical purposes we have defined duplications as involving in excess of 20 bp DNA. Various examples of gene duplications causing human genetic disease are listed in Table 8.2.

One of the best characterized pathological gene duplications to date is also one of the most interesting. For this reason, it will be described in some detail. This partial factor VIII (F8) gene duplication has been reported (Gitschier, 1988) from the family of a haemophilia A deletion patient identified as H96 (Gitschier *et al.*, 1985). The patient himself possessed a deletion of 39 kb encompassing exons 23–25 of the F8 gene (Figure 8.5). One of his sisters was also heterozygous for the deletion, whilst two non-haemophilic brothers and two sisters exhibited a normal hybridization band pattern. However, the proband's mother and one sister, both phenotypically normal, showed a rather

Table 8.2. Characterized gene duplications and partial duplications (> 20 bp) causing human genetic disease

Disease	Gene	Duplication	Reference
Angioneurotic oedema	C1I	3.2 kb (exon 4)	Stoppa-Lyonnet et al., 1990, 1991
Apolipoprotein E3 Leiden	APOE3	21 bp (exon 4)	Maagdenberg et al., 1989
Elevated Hb F (asymptomatic)	HBG2	5.2 kb (entire γ-globin gene)	Trent et al., 1981
Fabry disease	GLA	8.1 kb (exons 2–6)	Kornreich et al., 1990
GM1-gangliosidosis	GLB1	165 bp (exon ?)	Yoshida et al., 1991
	GLB1	23 bp (exon 3)	Oshima et al., 1992
Haemophilia A	F8	23 kb (intron 22)	Gitschier, 1988
Haemophilia A	F8	<3.8 kb (exon 13)	Casula et al., 1990
Hypercholesterolaemia	LDLR	14 kb (exons 2–8)	Lehrman et al., 1987
	LDLR	? kb (exons 9–12)	Top et al., 1990
	LDLR	? kb (exons 13–15)	Lelli et al., 1991
Lesch–Nyhan syndrome	HPRT	16–20 kb (exons 2 and 3)	Yang et al., 1988
Lipoprotein lipase deficiency	LPL	2 kb (partial exon 6)	Devlin et al., 1990
Muscular dystrophy (DMD/BMD)	DMD	(exons 8, 9)	Hu et al., 1988, 1990, 1991
	DMD	(exons 3–11)	
	DMD	(exons 38–43)	
	DMD	(exons 50–52)	
	DMD	(exons 3, 4)	
	DMD	(exons 45–51)	
	DMD	(exons 20–41)	
	DMD	(exons 2–7)	
	DMD	(exons 22–27)	
	DMD	(exons 13–42)	Angelini et al., 1990
	DMD	(exons 5–11)	Roberts et al., 1991
Osteogeneis imperfecta Type II	COL1A1	0.6 kb (exons ?)	Byers et al., 1988
Spondyloepiphyseal dysplasia	COL2A1	45 bp (most of exon 48)	Tiller et al., 1990

Gene symbols not specified in text: APOE3, apolipoprotein E3; C1I, C1 inhibitor; COL1A1, α1(I) collagen; COL2A1, α2(I) collagen; GLA, α-galactosidase; GLB1, β-galactosidase-1; HBG2, G-γ globin; HPRT, hypoxanthine phosphoribosyltransferase; LDLR, low density lipoprotein receptor; LPL, lipoprotein lipase.

different pattern: 23 kb of intron 22 had been duplicated and re-inserted between exons 23 and 24 (Figure 8.5). Thus a direct repeat of 23 kb was separated by a 6 kb stretch of DNA containing exon 23. Since both the duplicated sequence and the site of insertion were intronic, it is perhaps not surprising that carriers of this sequence duplication were phenotypically normal. Since the mother passed on a 39 kb deletion allele to two of her offspring, she must have been a germline mosaic for the normal, deletion and duplication alleles.

The 39 kb deletion in patient H96 was larger than the entire region of duplication in the maternal gene by 3 kb in an upstream direction and by 7 kb

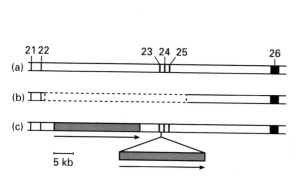

Figure 8.5. Diagram of the deletion/duplication lesions in the factor VIII (F8) gene causing haemophilia A reported by Gitschier (1988). Only the portion of the F8 gene spanning exons 21–26 is shown. (a) Wild-type gene. (b) 39 kb deletion of intron 22 and exons 23–25 (deleted region indicated by dotted lines). (c) Duplication of 23 kb of intron 22 inserted into intron 23 (duplicated region indicated by cross-hatching lines).

in a downstream direction. Since both copies of the duplicated sequence were lost in the deletion, it was thought unlikely that the duplication and deletion were products of a reciprocal recombination event. Indeed, RFLP data for the linked extragenic St14 (DXS52) probe were consistent with the interpretation that the deletion and duplication events had occurred on one and the same chromosome. Gitschier (1988) suggested a model in which the duplication had occurred first (creating, in effect, a type of highly unstable premutation), either in a grandpaternal gamete or during the mother's early embryogenesis. The deletion then occurred, probably mediated by the close proximity of the 23 kb direct repeats, through intramolecular recombination. The mother would thus appear to be a mosaic as far as both her gametes (inferred from the pedigree) and her somatic cells are concerned.

The duplicated sequence possessed an adenine-rich tract preceded by a polyadenylation motif reminiscent of a retroposon-like sequence. The significance of this observation, together with that of the discovery of a CpG island-like sequence in intron 22 which is capable of being transcribed, is not clear. The deletion occurred at a pair of CATT sequences normally 39 kb apart in the F8 gene. Both copies of the CATT sequence were retained at the deletion boundary and were separated by a new 9 bp sequence generating an 11 bp direct repeat. Short repeated sequences are known to mediate recombination events in vertebrate genomes; both $(CAGA)_n$ and $(CAGG)_n$ repeats have been noted in the region of the recombination hotspots found within the murine MHC gene complex (Steinmetz et al., 1987).

A further F8 gene duplication has been described by Casula et al. (1990). This duplication of exon 13, giving rise to mild haemophilia A, also appears to have arisen as a result of a non-homologous recombination event involving two misaligned X chromosomes. The additional exon may well undergo normal splicing, producing an elongated mRNA. Since no alteration in reading frame would be expected, an abnormal protein of higher than normal molecular weight would be predicted. The breakpoint region was sequenced and contained various AT-rich sequences.

Several possible topoisomerase I cleavage sites were noted in the vicinity of the F8 gene duplication desribed by Casula *et al.* (1990). Topoisomerase activity has been implicated in several cases of non-homologous recombination (Bullock *et al.*, 1985). Other examples of topoisomerase cleavage sites have been reported to be associated with gene duplications (Kornreich *et al.*, 1990; Hu *et al.*, 1991); potential sites for topoisomerases I and II were found exactly coincident with the breakpoints of a duplication in the dystrophin gene (Hu *et al.*, 1991). The significance of these findings remains to be elucidated.

The largest duplication reported to date is a 400 kb internal duplication of the dystrophin (DMD) gene involving exons 13–42 (Angelini *et al.*, 1990). Interestingly, despite this gross alteration in the structure of the gene (and of the resulting protein: ~ 600 kDa instead of 400 kDa), the patient manifested the relatively mild Becker form of muscular dystrophy. The duplication appears to be stable since it is also present in the patient's mother.

A number of other gene duplications and partial duplications have been reported and these are summarized in Table 8.2. They vary in size from 45 bp (COL2A1) to 20 kb (HPRT), from a part of an exon (LPL) to an entire gene (HBG2). Usually, the duplicated material exists in tandem with the original sequence (e.g. C1I duplication of exon 4) but the HPRT gene duplication is highly unusual in that a segment of the gene containing exons 2 and 3 has been placed in the middle of an intron 1 fragment. Although this is exactly analogous to the F8 gene duplication described above, an explanatory mechanism is far from evident.

One frequent mechanism of gene duplication is homologous unequal recombination. This may take different forms depending on the nature of the DNA sequence at the breakpoints. Thus homologous unequal recombination in the β-globin gene cluster occurs between the G–γ (HBG2) and A–γ (HBG1) genes whereas, in the LDLR and C1I genes, it occurs between pairs of Alu sequences. This process is depicted diagrammatically (for the LDLR gene duplication) in Figure 8.6. Regarding the COL2A1 gene duplication, alignment of two copies of the duplicated exon, in the manner that must have preceded the recombination event, demonstrated 78% nucleotide sequence homology around the recombination site (Tiller *et al.*, 1990). In principle, unequal crossing-over caused by homologous recombination between repetitive sequence elements could lead to either the deletion or the duplication of exons. That the exons duplicated in the C1I and COL2A1 genes have also been found to be deleted in other patients with deficiencies of these proteins would seem to lend support to this model of mutagenesis.

Other duplication junctions appear, however, to possess little or no homology with each other (e.g. GLA, Kornreich *et al.*, 1990; F8, Murru *et al.*, 1990; DMD, Hu *et al.*, 1991). In the LPL gene, recombination has occurred between an Alu sequence and a region of exon 6 but the sequenced breakpoints exhibited no obvious homology with one another (Devlin *et al.*, 1990).

The frequency of gene duplication is difficult to assess on account of the relatively small sample size. As with gene deletions, the frequency of gene duplication is likely to vary very dramatically between genes. However, several

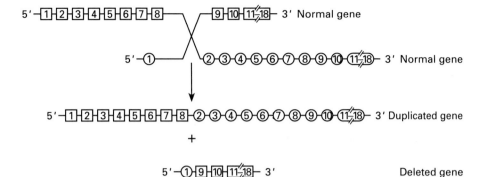

Figure 8.6. Unequal crossing-over in the low density lipoprotein receptor (LDLR) gene creating a 14 kb duplication spanning exons 2–8 (modified from Lehrman *et al.*, 1987; reproduced with permission of Cell Press. ©Cell Press). Two normal copies of the LDLR gene recombine to create a duplication and a (hypothetical) deletion. Exons from the two normal alleles are indicated by squares or circles.

estimates of the frequency of (partial) gene duplication are available for the dystrophin gene from large studies of patients with Duchenne/Becker muscular dystrophy (DMD/BMD): 6.7% (Den Dunnen *et al.*, 1989), 5.5% (Hu *et al.*, 1990) and 1.5% (Cooke *et al.*, 1990). Thus, for the DMD gene, the duplication frequency is probably 5–10% of the deletion frequency. A much higher frequency of duplication (uncharacterized and evidenced only by hybridization band intensity) may be found in the CYP21B gene causing 21-hydroxylase deficiency: Haglund-Stengler *et al.* (1990) found 11 gene deletions and nine gene duplications in their study of 43 unrelated patients. However, at other loci, where gene deletions are much less frequent, gene duplications may well be so rare as not to be found.

One intriguing finding has been the localization of a *de novo* partial gene duplication in the dystrophin (DMD) gene in a patient two of whose relatives exhibit either a deletion or an undefined lesion at a similar location (Miciak *et al.*, 1992). It is possible that this is a hotspot for recombination, since the chromosomes involved appear to be different.

It is interesting to ponder the question as to why gene duplications are usually so much rarer than deletions, for this is clearly a general finding whichever gene one cares to consider. One possibility is that deletions are on average more likely to be deleterious and hence more likely to come to clinical attention. This is thought to be unlikely, since with DMD/BMD, for example, it is the maintenance of the reading frame or otherwise that determines the disease phenotype, rather than the nature of the lesion itself (Angelini *et al.*, 1990; Hu *et al.*, 1990; Roberts *et al.*, 1991; Hu and Worton, 1992). A second possibility is that not all mechanisms involved in deletion creation would generate duplications as reciprocal products. Finally, it is possible that duplications are relatively unstable and revert or 'decay' to deletions quite rapidly. The F8 partial gene deletion is a case in point. Another example is that of the exon $2 + 3$ duplication in the HPRT gene; cells bearing this patient's gene lesion reverted to wild-type in culture through the loss of the duplicated exons (Yang *et al.*, 1988; Monnat *et al.*, 1992). Two similar HPRT gene duplications have been reported as spontaneous mutations in the human myeloid leukaemia cell line HL60 (Monnat *et al.*, 1992) and these were also found to be highly unstable, exhibiting a reversion rate ~ 100-fold higher than the rate of gene duplication. It would therefore seem that, once duplicated, the enlarged DNA sequence provides the substrate (a premutation) for further rounds of homologous unequal recombination. However, not all duplications appear to be this unstable. Hu *et al.* (1990) have reported that, in three families, the mother carried the same DMD gene duplication as the *propositus* and, in one case, so did the maternal grandfather.

8.4 Inversions

Inversions appear to be an extremely unusual form of gene mutation. Two examples involving the β-globin gene cluster will be given here: the first is a complex rearrangement of the β-globin gene cluster found in a patient with Indian A-γ-δ-β thalassaemia (Jennings *et al.*, 1985). Details of this rearrangement are given in Figure 8.7. Two segments, 0.83 kb and 7.46 kb respectively, were deleted, whereas the intervening segment was inverted and reintroduced between the A-γ (HBG1) and δ (HBD) globin gene loci. Jennings *et al.* (1985) suggested that this unique mutation may have been made possible by the chromatin folding pattern of the cluster region bringing the A-γ gene into close proximity with the δ (HBD) and β (HBB) globin genes. These authors have argued that the Alu and LINE repeat elements in the vicinity are perfectly placed to explain the nature of the observed rearrangement by virtue of their stabilization of the folding pattern long enough for recombination to occur (Figure 8.8). Interestingly, this rearrangement serves to enhance the expression of the upstream fetal G-γ globin (HBG2) gene.

The second case concerns a Turkish patient with δ-β° thalassaemia and a complex rearrangement of the β-globin gene cluster (Kulozik *et al.*, 1992). The

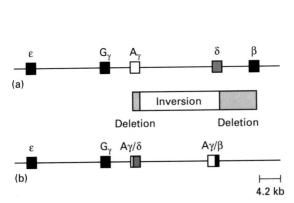

Figure 8.7. Rearrangement of the β-globin gene cluster in a patient with Indian A-γ-δ-β-thalassaemia (from Jennings *et al.*, 1985; by permission of Oxford University Press). (a) Wild-type arrangement of the β-globin gene cluster. Shaded boxes denote the extent of deletions whilst open boxes denote the position of the inverted segment. (b) Patient β-globin gene region showing inversion of a 15.5 kb A-γ/δ globin gene fragment.

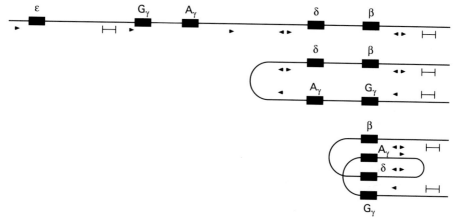

Figure 8.8. Proposed folding model of the β-globin gene cluster to generate the rearrangement found in Indian A-γ-δ-β thalassaemia (modified from Jennings *et al.*, 1985; with permission of Oxford University Press). Alu sequences and LINE elements are shown as arrows and lines respectively.

rearrangement consists of a deletion of 11.5 kb including the β- and δ-globin genes, a second 1.6 kb deletion downstream of the first and a 7.6 kb inversion of the intervening sequence, including the LINE element downstream of the β-globin gene. The absence of obvious sequence homologies at the breakpoints suggests that the underlying causative mechanism may be non-homologous recombination.

A third example of an inversion has been reported in the apolipoprotein A1/C3/A4 gene cluster in a patient with premature atherosclerosis and a deficiency of both apoAI and apoCIII (Karathanasis *et al.*, 1987). The inversion was 6 kb in length with breakpoints in exon 4 of the APOA1 gene and intron 1 of the APOC3 gene. This inversion resulted in the reciprocal fusion of portions of the two genes and contains exons 1-3 and part of exon 4 from the APOA1 gene plus exons 2-4 and intron 1 from the APOC3 gene; the fusion gene is expressed as a stable mRNA. In the process of inversion, however, 9 bp from the APOA1 and 21 bp from the APOC3 gene were deleted. Since Alu sequences were also noted in the vicinity of the breakpoints of this inversion, Karathanasis *et al.* (1987) speculated that they might be involved in the stabilization of a stem-loop structure prior to the inversion event.

8.5 Expansion of unstable repeat sequences

A novel insertional/duplicational mechanism of mutation has recently been shown to arise through the instability of certain trinucleotide repeat sequences (reviewed by Caskey *et al.*, 1992 and Rousseau *et al.*, 1992). This mechanism was first reported as a cause of the fragile X syndrome, the most frequent cause of inherited mental retardation, which is associated with the presence of a fragile site on the X chromosome at q27.3. The genetics of this disorder had long been a puzzle, since about 20% of males bearing the fragile X chromosome are phenotypically normal (although they may have fully penetrant grandsons) whereas 35% of carrier females exhibit some symptoms of mental retardation. However, mental retardation is very rare among the daughters of normal transmitting males. To explain these observations, two distinct types of mutation have been proposed (Pembrey et al., 1985; Nussbaum et al., 1986; Laird, 1987). The first, a 'premutation', would not be clinically expressed but could be converted to a second form, the pathological 'full mutation', with high frequency when transmitted by a woman. With the cloning of the fragile X gene and its molecular analysis in affected families, this explanation has now been shown to be correct.

The gene underlying the fragile X syndrome, FMR1, was first isolated and identified through its association with a CpG island, the occurrence of abnormal methylation patterns in the vicinity, by the presence within the FMR1 gene of the fragile X site-induced breakpoint cluster region and by the greatly reduced levels of FMR1 mRNA seen in fragile X patients (Oberlé et al., 1991; Pieretti et al., 1991; Verkerk et al., 1991; Yu et al., 1991). The brain-expressed FMR1 gene was found to contain (putatively upstream of the Met initiation codon and 250 bp downstream of the CpG island) a highly unusual ~90 bp CGG repeat sequence encoding a stretch of ~30 arginine residues (Verkerk et al., 1991). A length variation in the region was also noted (Oberlé et al., 1991; Yu et al., 1991) which appeared to correlate with the expression of the fragile X phenotype. This region of instability was localized to the CGG repeat sequence. Indeed, the $(CGG)_n$ repeat exhibited copy number variation of between 6 and 54 ($N = 492$ chromosomes; Kremer et al., 1991) in normal healthy controls, although the bulk of individuals possessed between 25 and 35 repeat copies (Fu et al., 1991). By contrast, phenotypically normal transmitting males exhibited a repeat copy number of between 52 and >200 (the 'premutation') whilst affected males possessed 300 and sometimes in excess of 1000 copies (the 'full mutation'; Dobkin et al., 1991; Fu et al., 1991; Hirst et al., 1991; Rousseau et al., 1991; Pergolizzi et al., 1992). The intrinsic instability of both the premutation and the mutation is further exemplified by the existence of somatic mosaicism for different copy number alleles in some individuals (Fu et al., 1991; Yu et al., 1992). Thus a continuum exists between a copy number polymorphism present in the general population, the asymptomatic premutation [which involves limited expansion of CGG copy number] and the full mutation (which appears to require copy number expansion beyond a certain threshold value).

The studies of Rousseau et al. (1991) and Fu et al. (1991) allowed several important conclusions to be drawn about the expansion of repeat copy number during genetic transmission: alleles with a repeat copy number <46 exhibit no meiotic instability. The premutation represents a comparatively small increase in CGG copy number but is not associated with methylation of the gene region, nor with mental impairment (at least not in 97% of cases, a proportion comparable to that in the general population). However, individuals bearing the premutation exhibit a high probability of having either affected children or affected grandchildren. Expansion of premutations to full mutations occurs only during female meiotic transmission. For alleles with 52–113 repeat copies, the premutation expanded to the full mutation in 70% of transmissions, whereas the corresponding figure for alleles with >90 repeat copies was 100%. The probability of repeat expansion thus correlates with the repeat copy number in the premutation allele. The tendency was to increase repeat copy number rather than to decrease it; the ratio of probabilities was given as 64:3 (Fu *et al.*, 1991). The alteration of allele size with every genetic transmission through a female (an obligate mutation) is quite without precedent and implies a special mechanism.

Since the premutation must precede the appearance of the full mutation, all mothers of affected children carried either a full mutation or a premutation; no case of direct conversion of normal copy number to full mutation has been observed (Rousseau *et al.*, 1991). In affected offspring of women with the premutation, 83% had the full mutation and 17% had the premutation. The full mutation was not detected in daughters of normal transmitting males, even although small increases in CGG copy number were observed in the daughters. All male patients with the fragile X syndrome possessed the full mutation and all individuals with the full mutation were retarded. Moreover, 53% of females carrying the full mutation exhibited symptoms of mental retardation. Although the transition from premutation to full mutation was always associated with the expansion of the $(CGG)_n$ repeat, examples of contraction were also observed and were reportedly associated with regression from a full mutation to a premutation (Rousseau *et al.*, 1991; Fu *et al.*, 1991).

Fu *et al.* (1991) reported a 'normal' mother from the general population with a 54 copy repeat allele, within the normal range of the premutation. The authors estimated that about one in 500 members of the general population might possess a repeat copy number within the premutation range. All the mother's children inherited alleles of expanded size, indicating the meiotic instability of the 54 copy repeat allele. On the other hand, a 'normal' family with a 46 copy repeat allele transmitted it unchanged. The boundary between stability and instability would therefore appear to lie between 46 and 54 copy repeats. Richards *et al.* (1992) have presented evidence for a founder haplotype in the normal population which is associated with a much higher than average CGG repeat copy number.

Affected individuals appear to possess abnormally high methylation of the FMR1 region (Rousseau *et al.*, 1991). Whether this is a cause or a consequence of the possession of a full mutation is still unclear, but methylation of the associated CpG island correlates with the loss of expression of the FMR1 mRNA (Pieretti *et al.*, 1991; Sutcliffe *et al.*, 1992). Laird (1987) proposed that the X chromosome bearing the fragile X gene is inactivated through lyonization in a female carrier (a process thought to involve DNA methylation of CpG islands) but is reactivated prior to oogenesis. Methylation would therefore precede and could even facilitate copy number expansion, thereby providing an explanation of why the transition from premutation to mutation must take place in a female. Interestingly, even in the absence of methylation, poly(CG)-containing sequences are known to be recombinogenic (Slightom *et al.*, 1980).

It should be pointed out that the fragile X syndrome is not invariably caused by CGG repeat amplification: Gedeon *et al.* (1992) have reported a patient with typical clinical features of the disease but lacking cytogenetic expression of the fragile X phenotype. This patient exhibited a gross deletion both of the FMR1 gene and the CGG repeat. Similarly, Wöhrle *et al.* (1992) reported a deletion of <250 kb, which included at least five exons of the FMR1 gene. It would thus appear that removal or partial removal of the FMR1 gene results in the same phenotypic dysfunction as $(CGG)_n$ repeat amplification over a certain threshold.

A second example of a disease that exhibits expansion of unstable repeat sequences is myotonic dystrophy. This progressive disorder of muscle weakness is inherited as an autosomal dominant trait and exhibits a unique property termed 'anticipation' to denote the earlier onset and increasing severity of the disease in successive generations. Mildly affected patients have cataracts whereas severe cases exhibit muscular hypoplasia and mental retardation. Novel restriction fragments have been found to be associated with the myotonic dystrophy (DM) gene in a majority of patients (Harley *et al.*, 1992a, 1992b; Buxton *et al.*, 1992). The size increase correlated with increasing severity and, contrary to the situation observed in the fragile X syndrome, band enlargement was seen after transmission by either sex. In pedigrees exhibiting anticipation, the fragment size increased in successive generations.

These findings were confirmed by sequence analysis of the DM gene in both patients and controls (Brook *et al.*, 1992; Fu *et al.*, 1992; Harper *et al.*, 1992; Mahadevan *et al.*, 1992; Tsilfidis *et al.*, 1992). The molecular basis of the instability was shown to derive from a $(CTG)_n$ repeat sequence within the 3' untranslated region (UTR) of the myotonin protein kinase (DM) gene 500 bp from the polyadenylation site. Some 40% of normal controls were found to possess five CTG repeats, most of the remainder bearing between 10 and 14 repeats and a few with any number up to 27 repeats. By contrast, minimally affected myotonic dystrophy patients possessed at least 50 CTG repeats, whereas the more severe cases exhibited expansion of the repeat sequence up to 5 kb (Suthers *et al.*, 1992). The size of the $(CTG)_n$ repeat correlated both with severity and age of onset; indeed, families in which the severity of the disease had increased in successive generations exhibited a dramatic parallel expansion in repeat copy number. Similarly, infants with severe congenital myotonic dystrophy and their mothers exhibit a greater degree of amplification of CTG repeats than the non-congenital patient population. In one reported case, transmission of the affected chromosome from father to son was associated with a contraction rather than an expansion of repeat size (Shelbourne *et al.*, 1992). As in the analogous cases reported in the fragile X syndrome (see above), the son appears asymptomatic. This may therefore provide an explanation for the incomplete penetrance manifested by myotonic dystrophy. Interestingly, patients often exhibit somatic heterogeneity in the number of CTG repeats, a finding which may be relevant to the clinical phenotype. It is too early to say whether or not a premutation is involved in myotonic dystrophy — if it is, such mildly affected individuals may not have come to clinical attention.

As with the fragile X syndrome, linkage disequilibrium is apparent in heterogeneous populations between myotonic dystrophy and DNA polymorphisms in the vicinity (Harley et al., 1992a; Mahadevan et al., 1992) implying either the existence of only one or at most a few mutations, or that the polymorphisms are not neutral but rather predispose the individual concerned to mutation at the DM locus. Assuming that the former explanation is the more likely, then it may be that the disease allele is present as a premutation in the asymptomatic general population, which would thereby serve as a continual source of new full mutations. Since linkage disequilibrium has been reported between the same polymorphic alleles in both Japanese and Caucasian populations (Yamagata et al., 1992), myotonic dystrophy patients from these populations may share a common ancestor.

Mahadevan et al. (1992) reported that two of 98 myotonic dystrophy patients examined failed to exhibit any expansion of the $(CTG)_n$ repeat. These individuals may possess mutations in the DM gene coding sequence rather than in the $(CTG)_n$ repeat.

How expansion of the $(CTG)_n$ repeat within the 3' UTR causes the myotonic dystrophy phenotype is of course still unclear. If it abolishes expression of the mutant allele, myotonic dystrophy might arise through the level of the DM gene product falling below a certain threshold level. Alternatively, the repeat expansion might prevent the binding of a protein involved in the negative regulation of DM gene expression.

A third example of the involvement of the expansion and contraction of unstable repeat sequences in disease pathology is provided by X-linked spinal and bulbar muscular atrophy (Kennedy disease). This adult-onset form of motor neuron disease is sometimes associated with signs of androgen insensitivity. La Spada et al. (1991) reported the increased size of a polymorphic tandem $(CAG)_n$ repeat encoding polyglutamine within exon 1 of the androgen receptor (AR) gene, which was strongly associated with the disease. Whereas healthy controls exhibited copy number variation in this trinucleotide repeat $(21 \pm 2$, range 17–26), 24 unrelated patients examined possessed copy numbers of between 40 and 52. Similar results were reported by Yamamoto et al. (1992) on ethnically distinct patients (range 44–55) whilst Biancalana et al. (1992) reported an increase in CAG repeat number from 46 to 53 on transmission from a parent to a child. These latter authors also noted that the tendency of the repeat to increase in size was greater during male transmission, that decreases in repeat length occasionally occurred and that the abnormal allele sometimes exhibited somatic instability. Expansion of the $(CAG)_n$ repeat appears to occur regardless of whether the mutation is passed through the male or the female germline. It is at present unclear whether this instability is progressive in these families, i.e. whether, as in the fragile X syndrome, progression to a clinical phenotype associated with the full mutation must first pass through a premutation stage. The CAG trinucleotide exhibits some homology with one of the recombinational hotspots reported in the mouse MHC gene cluster [$(CACA)_n$ and $(CAGG)_n$; Steinmetz *et al.*, 1987].

Intriguingly, contraction of the $(CAG)_n$ repeat in the AR gene may be associated with a completely different condition, testicular feminization syndrome. McPhaul *et al.* (1991) reported that a patient with inherited resistance to androgens possessed only 12 CAG repeats (compared with 20–22 in their control population).

The number of examples of this type of mutation will almost certainly increase and may provide explanations at the molecular level for a variety of intriguing phenomena in human genetics, such as variable expression and multifactorial inheritance (Sutherland *et al.*, 1991). As to the *in vivo* mechanism of instability manifested by these trinucleotide repeats, slipped mispairing would appear to be one possibility, an assertion supported by the observed expansion of the repeat in multiples of 3 bp. However, this mechanism does not account for the clustering of repeat lengths noted in myotonic dystrophy, nor does it explain how, in fragile X syndrome, it occurs obligatorily (above a certain copy number) at every female meiosis. This may suggest that the length and simple sequence of the repeat may pose an insurmountable obstacle for the replication apparatus, perhaps involving cycles of termination and reinitiation of DNA synthesis. The losses of repeat copies noted *in vitro* both in cloning (Yu *et al.*, 1991; Kremer *et al.*, 1991) and in PCR amplification (Yamamoto *et al.*, 1992; Brook *et al.*, 1992) may, however, be caused by simple slipped mispairing. In microsatellites, mutability is proportional to copy number (Weber, 1990) and thus expansion of a sequence can itself lead to further expansion, a process termed 'dynamic mutation' by Richards *et al.* (1992).

Richards and Sutherland (1992) have noted that a number of human genes contain $(CGG)_n$ repeats (between 3 and 17 copies), very often within their 5' untranslated regions. They further suggested that, were these repeats to represent binding sites for transcription factors, a change in repeat copy number would alter the number of available binding sites, which might affect the transcriptional activity of the gene. The three different trinucleotide repeat units so far reported to be involved in expansion all possess a 5' C and a 3' G residue. Finally, Riggins *et al.* (1992) have reported that a number of human genes including those encoding N-cadherin (CDHN), chronic myeloid leukaemia breakpoint cluster region (BCR), glutathione-S-transferase-1 (GST1) and Na^+/K^+ ATPase β subunit (ATP1B1) contain either CGG or CAG repeats. These repeats are highly polymorphic and may represent further (sub-clinical) examples of the expansion of trinucleotide repeats. In the context of mutation, it may also be pertinent to note that a short duplication/insertion in the α2-antiplasmin gene (presented in Section 8.1) involved the insertion of a GCG trinucleotide into a pre-existing $(CGG)_3$ repeat.

References

Alevizaki M, Stevenson JC, Girgis SI, MacIntyre I, Legon S. (1989) Altered calcitonin gene in a young patient with osteoporosis. *Br. Med. J.* **298:** 1215–1216.

Angelini C, Beggs AH, Hoffman EP, Fanin M, Kunkel LM. (1990) Enormous dystrophin in a patient with Becker muscular dystrophy. *Neurology* **40**: 808–812.

Bateman JF, Lamande SR, Dahl H-HM, Chan D, Mascara T, Cole WG. (1989) A frameshift mutation results in a truncated nonfunctional carboxyl-terminal pro α1(I) propeptide of type I collagen in osteogenesis imperfecta. *J. Biol. Chem.* **264**: 10960–10964.

Bettecken T, Müller CR. (1989) Identification of a 220 kb insertion into the Duchenne gene in a family with an atypical course of muscular dystrophy. *Genomics* **4**: 592–596.

Biancalana V, Serville F, Pommier J, Julien J, Hanauer A, Mandel JL. (1992) Moderate instability of the trinucleotide repeat in spino bulbar muscular atrophy. *Hum. Mol. Genet.* **1**: 255–258.

Bottema CDK, Ketterling RP, Cho HI, Sommer SS. (1989) Hemophilia B in a male with a four-base insertion that arose in the germline of his mother. *Nucleic Acids Res.* **17**: 10139.

Brook JD, McCurrach ME, Harley HG, Buckler AJ, Church D, Aburatani H, Hunter K, Stanton VP, Thirion J-P, Hudson T, Sohn R, Zemelman B, Snell RG, Rundle SA, Crow S, Davies J, Shelbourne P, Buxton J, Harper PS, Shaw DJ, Housman DE. (1992) Molecular basis of myotonic dystrophy: expansion of a trinucleotide (CTG) repeat at the 3′ end of a transcript encoding a protein kinase family member. *Cell* **68**: 799–808.

Bullock P, Champoux JJ, Botchan M. (1985) Association of cross-over points with topoisomerase I cleavage sites: a model for nonhomologous recombination. *Science* **230**: 954–958.

Buxton J, Shelbourne P, Davies J, Jones C, Van Tongeren T, Aslanidis C, de Jong P, Jansen G, Anvret M, Riley B, Williamson R, Johnson K. (1992) Detection of an unstable fragment of DNA specific to individuals with myotonic dystrophy. *Nature* **355**: 547–548.

Byers PH, Starman BJ, Cohn DH, Horwitz AL. (1988) A novel mutation causes a perinatal lethal form of osteogenesis imperfecta. *J. Biol. Chem.* **263**: 7855–7861.

Caskey CT, Pizzuti A, Fu Y-H, Fenwick RG, Nelson DL. (1992) Triplet repeat mutations in human disease. *Science* **256**: 784–789.

Casula L, Murru S, Pecorara M, Ristaldi MS, Restagno G, Mancuso G, Morfini M, DeBiasi R, Baudo F, Carbonara A, Mori PG, Cao A, Pirastu M. (1990) Recurrent mutations and three novel rearrangements in the factor VIII gene of hemophilia A patients of Italian descent. *Blood* **75**: 662–670.

Chan V, Chan TK, Kan YW, Todd D. (1988) A novel β-thalassaemia frameshift mutation (codon 14/15), detectable by direct visualization of abnormal restriction fragment in amplified genomic DNA. *Blood* **72**: 1420–1423.

Cooke A, Lanyon WG, Wilcox DE, Dornan ES, Kataki A, Gillard EF, McWhinnie AJM, Morris A, Ferguson-Smith MA, Connor JM. (1990) Analysis of Scottish Duchenne and Becker muscular dystrophy families with dystrophin cDNA probes. *J. Med. Genet.* **27**: 292–297.

Cooper DN, Krawczak M. (1991) Mechanisms of insertional mutagenesis in human genes causing genetic disease. *Hum. Genet.* **87**: 409–415.

Cooper DN, Schmidtke J. (1991) Diagnosis of human genetic disease using recombinant DNA. Third edition. *Hum. Genet.* **87**: 519–560.

Davidson BL, Tarlé SA, Palella TD, Kelley WN. (1989) Molecular basis of hypoxanthine-guanine phosphoribosyltransferase deficiency in ten subjects determined by direct sequencing of amplified transcripts. *J. Clin. Invest.* **84**: 342–346.

Den Dunnen JT, Grootscholten PM, Bakker E, Blonden LAJ, Ginjaar HB, Wapenaar MC, van Paassen HMB, van Broeckhoven C, Pearson PL, van Ommen GJB. (1989) Topography of the Duchenne muscular dystrophy (DMD) gene: FIGE and cDNA analysis of 194 cases reveals 115 deletions and 13 duplications. *Am. J. Hum. Genet.* **45**: 835–847.

Devlin RH, Deeb S, Brunzell J, Hayden MR. (1990) Partial gene duplication involving exon-Alu interchange results in lipoprotein lipase deficiency. *Am. J. Hum. Genet.* **46**: 112–119.

Dobkin CS, Ding X-H, Jenkins EC, Krawczun MS, Brown WT, Goonewardena P, Willner WT, Benson C, Heitz D, Rousseau F. (1991) Prenatal diagnosis of fragile X syndrome. *Lancet* **338**: 957–958.

Dombroski BA, Mathias SL, Nanthakumar E, Scott AF, Kazazian HH. (1991) Isolation of an active human transposable element. *Science* **254**: 1805–1807.

Economou-Pachnis A, Tsichlis PN. (1985) Insertion of an Alu SINE in the human homologue of the *Mlvi-2* locus. *Nucleic Acids Res.* **13:** 8379–8387.

Efstratiadis A, Posakony JW, Maniatis T, Lawn RM, O'Connell C, Spritz RA, DeRiel JK, Forget BG, Weissman SM, Slightom JL, Blechl AE, Smithies O, Baralle FE, Shoulders CC, Proudfoot NJ. (1980) The structure and evolution of the human β-globin gene family. *Cell* **21:** 653–668.

Fanning TG, Singer MF. (1987) LINE-1: A mammalian transposable element. *Biochim. Biophys. Acta* **910:** 203–212.

Fearon ER, Cho KR, Nigro JM, Kern SE, Simons JW, Ruppert JM, Hamilton SR, Preisinger AC, Thomas G, Kinzler KW, Vogelstein B. (1990) Identification of a chromosome 18q gene that is altered in colorectal cancers. *Science* **247:** 49–56.

Fry M, Loeb LA. (1992) A DNA polymerase α pause site is a hotspot for nucleotide misinsertion. *Proc. Natl. Acad. Sci. USA* **89:** 763–767.

Fu Y-H, Kuhl DPA, Pizzuti A, Pieretti M, Sutcliffe JS, Richards S, Verkerk AJMH, Holden JJA, Fenwick RG, Warren ST, Oostra BA, Nelson DL, Caskey CT. (1991) Variation of the CGG repeat at the fragile X site results in genetic instability: resolution of Sherman paradox. *Cell* **67:** 1047–1058.

Fu Y-H, Pizzuti A, Fenwick RG, King J, Rajnarayan S, Dunne PW, Dubel J, Nasser GA, Ashizawa T, De Jong P, Wieringa B, Korneluk R, Perryman MB, Epstein HF, Caskey CT. (1992) An unstable triplet repeat in a gene related to myotonic muscular dystrophy. *Science* **255:** 1256–1258.

Gedeon AK, Baker E, Robinson H, Partington MW, Gross B, Manca A, Korn B, Poustka A, Yu S, Sutherland GR, Mulley JC. (1992) Fragile X syndrome without CCG amplification has an FMR1 deletion. *Nature Genetics* **1:** 341–344.

Giannelli F, Green PM, High KA, Sommer SS, Lillicrap DP, Ludwig M, Olek K, Reitsma PH, Goossens M, Yoshioka A, Brownlee GG. (1992) Haemophilia B: database of point mutations and short additions and deletions — Third edition, 1992. *Nucleic Acids Res. Suppl.* **20:** 2027–2063.

Gibbs RA, Nguyen P-N, McBride LJ, Koepf SM, Caskey CT. (1989) Identification of mutations leading to the Lesch–Nyhan syndrome by automated direct DNA sequencing of *in vitro* amplified cDNA. *Proc. Natl. Acad. Sci. USA* **86:** 1919–1923.

Gitschier J. (1988) Maternal duplication associated with gene deletion in sporadic hemophilia. *Am. J. Hum. Genet.* **43:** 274–279.

Gitschier J, Wood WI, Tuddenham EGD, Shuman MA, Goralka TM, Chen EY, Lawn RM. (1985) Detection and sequence of mutations in the factor VIII gene of haemophiliacs. *Nature* **315:** 427–430.

Grosovsky AJ, De Boer JG, De Jong PJ, Drobetsky EA, Glickman BW. (1988) Base substitutions, frameshifts and small deletions constitute ionizing radiation-induced point mutations in mammalian cells. *Proc. Natl. Acad. Sci. USA* **85:** 185–188.

Haglund-Stengler R, Ritzen EM, Luthman H. (1990) 21-Hydroxylase deficiency: disease-causing mutations categorized by densitometry of 21-hydroxylase-specific deoxyribonucleic acid fragments. *J. Clin. Endocrinol. Metab.* **70:** 43–48.

Harley HG, Brook JD, Rundle SA, Crow S, Reardon W, Buckler AJ, Harper PS, Housman DE, Shaw DJ. (1992a) Expansion of an unstable DNA region and phenotypic variation in myotonic dystrophy. *Nature* **355:** 545–546.

Harley HG, Rundle SA, Reardon W, Myring J, Crow S, Brook JD, Harper PS, Shaw DJ. (1992b) Unstable DNA sequence in myotonic dystrophy. *Lancet* **339:** 1125–1128.

Harper PS, Harley HG, Reardon W, Shaw DJ. (1992) Anticipation in myotonic dystrophy: new light on an old problem. *Am. J. Hum. Genet.* **51:** 10–16.

Hidaka Y, Palella TD, O'Toole TE, Tarlé SA, Kelley WN. (1987) Human adenine phosphoribosyltransferase: identification of allelic mutations at the nucleotide level as a cause of complete deficiency of the enzyme. *J. Clin. Invest.* **80:** 1409–1415.

Hirst M, Knight S, Davies K, Cross G, Ocraft K, Raeburn S, Heeger S, Eunpu D, Jenkins EC, Lindenbaum R. (1991) Prenatal diagnosis of fragile X syndrome. *Lancet* **338:** 956–957.

Holmes WE, Lijnen HR, Nelles L, Kluft C, Nieuwenhuis HK, Rijken DC, Collen D. (1987) α2-Antiplasmin Enschede: alanine insertion and abolition of plasmin inhibitory activity. *Science* **238:** 209-211.

Howells DW, Forrest SM, Dahl H-HM, Cotton RGH. (1990) Insertion of an extra codon for threonine is a cause of dihydropteridine reductase deficiency. *Am. J. Hum. Genet.* **47:** 279-285.

Hu X, Worton RG. (1992) Partial gene duplication as a cause of human disease. *Human Mutation* **1:** 3-12.

Hu X, Burghes AHM, Ray PN, Thompson MW, Murphy EG, Worton RG. (1988) Partial gene duplication in Duchenne and Becker muscular dystrophies. *J. Med. Genet.* **25:** 369-376.

Hu X, Ray PN, Murphy EG, Thompson MW, Worton RG. (1990) Duplicational mutation at the Duchenne muscular dystrophy locus: its frequency, distribution, origin and phenotype/genotype correlation. *Am. J. Hum. Genet.* **46:** 682-695.

Hu X, Ray PN, Worton RG. (1991) Mechanisms of tandem duplication in the Duchenne muscular dystrophy gene include both homologous and nonhomologous intrachromosomal recombination. *EMBO J.* **10:** 2471-2477.

Ikehata H, Akagi T, Kimura H, Akasaka S, Kato T. (1989) Spectrum of spontaneous mutations in a cDNA of the human *hprt* gene integrated in chromosomal DNA. *Mol. Gen. Genet.* **219:** 349-358.

Jennings MW, Jones RW, Wood WG, Weatherall DJ. (1985) Analysis of an inversion within the human β globin gene cluster. *Nucleic Acids Res.* **13:** 2897-2906.

Karathanasis SK, Ferris E, Haddad IA. (1987) DNA inversion within the apolipoproteins AI/CIII/AIV-encoding gene cluster of certain patients with premature atherosclerosis. *Proc. Natl. Acad. Sci. USA* **84:** 7198-7202.

Kariya Y, Kato K, Hayashizaki Y, Himeno S, Tarui S, Matsubara K. (1987) Revision of consensus sequence of human Alu repeats: a review. *Gene* **53:** 1-10.

Kazazian HH, Wong C, Youssoufian H, Scott AF, Phillips DG, Antonarakis SE. (1988) Haemophilia A resulting from *de novo* insertion of L1 sequences represents a novel mechanism for mutation in man. *Nature* **332:** 164-166.

Kornreich R, Bishop DF, Desnick RJ. (1990) α-Galactosidase A gene rearrangements causing Fabry disease. *J. Biol. Chem.* **265:** 9319-9326.

Krawczak M, Cooper DN. (1991) Gene deletions causing human genetic disease: mechanisms of mutagenesis and the role of the local DNA sequence environment. *Hum. Genet.* **86:** 425-441.

Kremer EJ, Pritchard M, Lynch M, Yu S, Holman K, Baker E, Warren ST, Schlessinger D, Sutherland GR, Richards RI. (1991) Mapping of DNA instability at the fragile X to a trinucleotide repeat sequence p(CCG)$_n$. *Science* **252:** 1711-1714.

Kulozik AE, Bellan-Koch A, Kohne E, Kleihauer E. (1992) A deletion/inversion rearrangement of the β-globin gene cluster in a Turkish family with δ-β-thalassemia intermedia. *Blood* **79:** 2455-2459.

Kunkel TA. (1985a) The mutational specificity of DNA polymerase-β during *in vitro* DNA synthesis. *J. Biol. Chem.* **260:** 5787-5796.

Kunkel TA. (1985b) The mutational specificity of DNA polymerases α and γ during *in vitro* DNA synthesis. *J. Biol. Chem.* **260:** 12866-12874.

Kunkel TA. (1986) The base substitution fidelity of eukaryotic DNA polymerases. *J. Biol. Chem.* **261:** 160-166.

Kunkel TA, Hamatake RK, Motto-Fox J, Fitzgerald MP, Sugino A. (1989) Fidelity of DNA polymerase I and the DNA polymerase I-DNA primase complex from *Saccharomyces cerevisiae*. *Mol. Cell. Biol.* **9:** 4447-4458.

La Spada AR, Wilson EM, Lubahn DB, Harding AE, Fischbeck KH. (1991) Androgen receptor gene mutations in X-linked spinal muscular atrophy. *Nature* **352:** 77-79.

Laird CD. (1987) Proposed mechanism of inheritance and expression of the human fragile X syndrome of mental retardation. *Genetics* **117:** 587-599.

Langlois S, Deeb S, Brunzell JD, Kastelein JJ, Hayden MR. (1989) A major insertion accounts for a significant proportion of mutations underlying human lipoprotein lipase deficiency. *Proc. Natl. Acad. Sci. USA* **86:** 948-952.

Lehrman MA, Goldstein JL, Russell DW, Brown MS. (1987) Duplication of seven exons in LDL receptor gene caused by Alu–Alu recombination in a subject with familial hypercholesterolemia. *Cell* **48:** 827–835.

Lelli N, Ghisellini M, Calandra S, Gaddi A, Ciarrocchi A, Coviello DA, Bertolini S. (1991) Duplication of exons 13, 14 and 15 of the LDL-receptor gene in a patient with heterozygous familial hypercholesterolemia. *Hum. Genet.* **86:** 359–362.

Lin CS, Goldthwait DA, Samols D. (1988) Identification of Alu transposition in human lung carcinoma cells. *Cell* **54:** 153–159.

Losekoot M, Fodde R, Giordano PC, Bernini LF. (1989) A novel δ°-thalassemia arising from a frameshift insertion, detected by direct sequencing of enzymatically amplified DNA. *Hum. Genet.* **83:** 75–78.

Maagdenberg AM van den, de Knijff P, Stalenhoef AF, Gevers-Leuven JA, Haverkes LM, Frants RR. (1989) Apolipoprotein E3–Leiden allele results from a partial gene duplication in exon 4. *Biochem. Biophys. Res. Commun.* **165:** 157–163.

McPhaul MJ, Marcelli M, Tilley WD, Griffin JE, Isidro-Gutierrez RF, Wilson JD. (1991) Molecular basis of androgen resistance in a family with a qualitative abnormality of the androgen receptor and responsive to high-dose androgen therapy. *J. Clin. Invest.* **87:** 1413–1421.

Mager DL, Henthorn PS, Smithies O. (1985) A Chinese G $\gamma^+(\text{A-}\gamma\text{-}\delta\text{-}\beta)^\circ$ thalassaemia deletion: comparison to other deletions in the human β-globin gene cluster and sequence analysis of the breakpoints. *Nucleic Acids Res.* **13:** 6559–6564.

Mahadevan M, Tsilfidis C, Sabourin L, Shutler G, Amemiya C, Jansen G, Neville C, Narang M, Barceló J, O'Hoy K, Leblond S, Earle-MacDonald J, De Jong PJ, Wieringa B, Korneluk RG. (1992) Myotonic dystrophy mutation: an unstable CTG repeat in the 3′ untranslated region of the gene. *Science* **255:** 1253–1255.

Miciak A, Keen A, Jadayel D, Bundey S. (1992) Multiple mutation in an extended Duchenne muscular dystrophy family. *J. Med. Genet.* **29:** 123–126.

Millar DS, Steinbrecher RA, Wieland K, Grundy CB, Martinowitz U, Krawczak M, Zoll B, Whitmore D, Stephenson J, Mibashan RS, Kakkar VV, Cooper DN. (1990) The molecular genetic analysis of haemophilia A: characterization of six partial deletions in the factor VIII gene. *Hum. Genet.* **86:** 219–227.

Mitchell GA, Labuda D, Fontaine G, Saudubray JM, Bonnefont JP, Lyonnet S, Brody LC, Steel G, Obie C, Valle D. (1991) Splice-mediated insertion of an Alu sequence inactivates ornithine δ-aminotransferase: a role for Alu elements in human mutation. *Proc. Natl. Acad. Sci. USA* **88:** 815–819.

Monnat RJ, Chiaverotti TA, Hackmann AFM, Maresh GA. (1992) Molecular structure and genetic stability of human hypoxanthine phosphoribosyltransferase (HPRT) gene duplications. *Genomics* **13:** 788–796.

Moo-Penn WF, Swan DC, Hine TK, Baine RM, Jue DL, Benson JM, Johnson MH, Virshup DM, Zinkham WH. (1989) Hb Catonsville [Glutamic acid inserted between Pro-37(C2)α and Thr-38(C3)α]. *J. Biol. Chem.* **264:** 21454–21457.

Morse J, Rothberg PG, South VJ, Spandorfer JM, Astrin SM. (1988) Insertional mutagenesis of the *myc* locus by a LINE-1 sequence in a human breast carcinoma. *Nature* **333:** 87–89.

Murru S, Casula L, Pecorara M, Mori P, Cao A, Pirastu M. (1990) Illegitimate recombination produced a duplication within the FVIII gene in a patient with mild hemophilia A. *Genomics* **7:** 115–118.

Myerowitz R, Costigan FC. (1988) The major defect in Ashkenazi Jews with Tay–Sachs disease is an insertion in the gene for the α chain of β-hexosaminidase. *J. Biol. Chem.* **263:** 18587–18589.

Nogueira CP, McGuire MC, Graeser C, Bartels CF, Arpagaus M, Van der Spek AFL, Lightstone H, Lockridge O, La Du BN. (1990) Identification of a frameshift mutation responsible for the silent phenotype of human serum cholinesterase, Gly 117 (GGT → GGAG). *Am. J. Hum. Genet.* **46:** 934–942.

Nussbaum RL, Airhart SD, Ledbetter DH. (1986) Recombination and amplification of pyrimidine-rich sequences may be responsible for initiation and progression of the Xq27 fragile site. *Am. J. Med. Genet.* **23:** 715-721.

Oberlé I, Rousseau F, Heitz D, Kretz C, Devys D, Hanauer A, Boué J, Bertheas MF, Mandel JL. (1991) Instability of a 550 base pair DNA segment and abnormal methylation in fragile X syndrome. *Science* **252:** 1097-1102.

Ohshima A, Inouye S, Inouye M. (1992) *In vivo* duplication of genetic elements by the formation of stem-loop DNA without an RNA intermediate. *Proc. Natl. Acad. Sci. USA* **89:** 1016-1020.

Oshima A, Yoshida K, Ishizaki A, Shimmoto M, Fukuhara Y, Sakuraba H, Suzuki Y. (1992) GM1-gangliosidosis: tandem duplication within exon 3 of β-galactosidase gene in an infantile patient. *Clin. Genet.* **41:** 235-238.

Pembrey MR, Winter WM, Davies KE. (1985) A premutation that generates a defect at crossing over explains the inheritance of fragile X mental retardation. *Am. J. Med. Genet.* **21:** 709-718.

Pergolizzi RG, Erster SH, Goonewardena P, Brown WT. (1992) Detection of full fragile X mutation. *Lancet* **339:** 271-272.

Phear G, Armstrong W, Meuth M. (1989) Molecular basis of spontaneous mutation at the *aprt* locus of hamster cells. *J. Mol. Biol.* **209:** 577-582.

Pieretti M, Zhang F, Fu Y-H, Warren ST, Oostra BA, Caskey CT, Nelson DL. (1991) Absence of expression of the FMR-1 gene in fragile X syndrome. *Cell* **66:** 817-822.

Richards RI, Sutherland GR. (1992) Dynamic mutations: a new class of mutations causing human disease. *Cell* **70:** 709-712.

Richards RI, Holman K, Friend K, Kremer E, Hillen D, Staples A, Brown WT, Goonewardena P, Tarleton J, Schwartz C, Sutherland GR. (1992) Evidence of founder chromosomes in fragile X syndrome. *Nature Genetics* **1:** 257-260.

Riggins GJ, Lokey LK, Chastain JL, Leiner HA, Sherman SL, Wilkinson KD, Warren ST. (1992) Human genes containing polymorphic trinucleotide repeats. *Nature Genet.* **2:** 186-191.

Ripley LS. (1982) Model for the participation of quasi-palindromic DNA sequences in frameshift mutation. *Proc. Natl. Acad. Sci. USA* **79:** 4128-4132.

Ristaldi MS, Pirastu M, Murru S, Casula L, Loudianos G, Cao A, Sciarrata GV, Agosti S, Parodi MI, Leone D, Melesendi C. (1990) A spontaneous mutation produced a novel elongated β-globin chain structural variant (Hb Agnana) with a thalassemia-like phenotype. *Blood* **75:** 1378-1380.

Roberts RG, Barby TFM, Manners E, Bobrow M, Bentley DR. (1991) Direct detection of dystrophin gene rearrangements by analysis of dystrophin mRNA in peripheral blood lymphocytes. *Am. J. Hum. Genet.* **49:** 298-310.

Rousseau F, Heitz D, Biancalana V, Blumenfeld S, Kretz C, Boué J, Tommerup N, Van der Hagen C, DeLozier-Blanchet C, Croquette M-F, Gilgenkrantz S, Jalbert P, Voelckel M-A, Oberlé I, Mandel J-L. (1991) Direct diagnosis by DNA analysis of the fragile X syndrome of mental retardation. *N. Engl. J. Med.* **325:** 1673-1681.

Rousseau F, Heitz D, Mandel J-L. (1992) The unstable and methylatable mutations causing the fragile X syndrome. *Hum. Mutat.* **1:** 91-96.

Roux A-F, Morlé F, Guetarni D, Colonna P, Sahr K, Forget BG, Delaunay J, Godet J. (1989) Molecular basis of sp α 1/65 hereditary elliptocytosis in North Africa: insertion of a TTG triplet between codons 147 and 149 in the α-spectrin gene from five unrelated families. *Blood* **73:** 2196-2201.

Shelbourne P, Winquist R, Kunert E, Davies J, Leisti J, Thiele H, Bachmann H, Buxton J, Williamson B, Johnson K. (1992) Unstable DNA may be responsible for the incomplete penetrance of the myotonic dystrophy phenotype. *Hum. Mol. Genet.* **1:** 467-473.

Shih C-C, Stoye JP, Coffin JM. (1988) Highly preferred targets for retrovirus integration. *Cell* **53:** 531-537.

Slightom JL, Blechl AE, Smithies O. (1980) Human fetal G-γ and A-γ globin genes: complete nucleotide sequences suggest that DNA can be exchanged between these duplicated genes. *Cell* **21:** 627-638.

Steinmetz M, Uematsu Y, Lindahl KF. (1987) Hotspots of homologous recombination in mammalian genomes. *Trends Genet.* **3:** 7–10.

Stoppa-Lyonnet D, Carter PE, Meo T, Tosi M. (1990) Clusters of intragenic Alu repeats predispose the human C1 inhibitor locus to deleterious rearrangements. *Proc. Natl. Acad. Sci. USA* **87:** 1551–1555.

Stoppa-Lyonnet D, Duponchel C, Meo T, Laurent J, Carter PE, Arala-Chaves M, Cohen JHM, Dewald G, Goetz J, Hauptmann G, Lagrue G, Lesavre P, Lopez-Trascasa M, Misiano G, Moraine C, Sobel A, Späth PJ, Tosi M. (1991) Recombination biases in the rearranged C1-inhibitor genes of hereditary angioedema patients. *Am. J. Hum. Genet.* **49:** 1055–1062.

Streisinger G, Okada Y, Emrich J, Newton J, Tsugita A, Terzaghi E, Inouye M. (1966) Frameshift mutations and the genetic code. *Cold Spring Harb. Symp. Quant. Biol.* **31:** 77–84.

Sutcliffe JS, Nelson DL, Zhang F, Pieretti M, Caskey CT, Saxe D, Warren ST. (1992) DNA methylation represses FMR-1 transcription in fragile X syndrome. *Hum. Mol. Genet.* **1:** 397–400.

Sutherland GR, Haan EA, Kremer E, Lynch M, Pritchard M, Yu S, Richards RI. (1991) Hereditary unstable DNA: a new explanation for some old genetic questions? *Lancet* **338:** 289–292.

Suthers GK, Huson SM, Davies KE. (1992) Instability versus predictability: the molecular diagnosis of myotonic dystrophy. *J. Med. Genet.* **29:** 761–765.

Tiller GE, Rimoin DL, Murray LW, Cohn DH. (1990) Tandem duplication within a type II collagen gene (COL2A1) exon in an individual with spondyloepiphyseal dysplasia. *Proc. Natl. Acad. Sci. USA* **87:** 3889–3893.

Tomita Y, Takeda A, Okinaga S, Tagami H, Shibahara S. (1989) Human oculocutaneous albinism caused by single base insertion in the tyrosinase gene. *Biochem. Biophys. Res. Commun.* **164:** 990–996.

Top B, Koelman BP, Gevers-Leuven JA, Havekes LM, Frants RR. (1990) Rearrangements in the LDL receptor gene in Dutch familial hypercholesterolemic patients and the presence of a common 4kb deletion. *Atherosclerosis* **83:** 127–136.

Trent RJ, Bowden DK, Old JM, Wainscoat JS, Clegg JB, Weatherall DJ. (1981) A novel rearrangement of the human β-like globin gene cluster. *Nucleic Acids Res.* **9:** 6723–6733.

Tsilfidis C, Mackenzie AE, Mrttler G, Barceló J, Korneluk RG. (1992) Correlation between CTG trinucleotide repeat length and frequency of severe congenital myotonic dystrophy. *Nature Genetics* **1:** 192–195.

Umlauf SW, Cox MM. (1988) The functional significance of DNA sequence structure in a site-specific genetic recombination reaction. *EMBO J.* **7:** 1845–1852.

Verkerk AJMH, Pieretti M, Sutcliffe JS, Fu Y-H, Kuhl DPA, Pizzuti A, Reiner O, Richards S, Victoria MF, Zhang F, Eussen BE, Van Ommen GJB, Blonden LAJ, Riggins GJ, Chastain JL, Kunst CB, Galjaard H, Caskey CT, Nelson DL, Oostra BA, Warren ST. (1991) Identification of a gene (FMR-1) containing a CGG repeat coincident with a breakpoint cluster region exhibiting length variation in fragile X syndrome. *Cell* **65:** 905–914.

Vidaud D, Vidaud M, Bahnak BR, Siguret V, Sanchez SG, Laurian Y, Meyer D, Goossens M, Lavergne JM. (1993) Hemophilia B due to a *de novo* insertion of a human-specific Alu subfamily member within the coding region of the factor IX gene. *Eur. J. Hum. Genet.* **1:** 30–36.

Wallace MR, Andersen LB, Saulino AM, Gregory PE, Glover TW, Collins FS. (1991) A *de novo* Alu insertion results in neurofibromatosis type 1. *Nature* **353:** 864–866.

Weber JL. (1990) Informativeness of human $(dC-dA)_n/(dG-dT)_n$ polymorphisms. *Genomics* **7:** 524–530.

Weiner AM, Deininger PL, Efstratiadis A. (1986) Nonviral retroposons: genes, pseudogenes and transposable elements generated by the reverse flow of genetic information. *Ann. Rev. Biochem.* **55:** 631–661.

White MB, Amos J, Hsu JMC, Gerrard B, Finn P, Dean M. (1990) A frame-shift mutation in the cystic fibrosis gene. *Nature* **344:** 665–667.

Wöhrle D, Kotzot D, Hirst MC, Manca A, Korn B, Schmidt A, Barbi G, Rott H-D, Poustka A, Davies KE, Steinbach P. (1992) A microdeletion of less than 250 kb, including the proximal part of the FMR-1 gene and the fragile-X site, in a male with the clinical phenotype of fragile-X syndrome. *Am. J. Hum. Genet.* **51:** 299–306.

Yamagata H, Miki T, Ogihara T, Nakagawa M, Higuchi I, Osame M, Shelbourne P, Davies J, Johnson K. (1992) Expansion of unstable DNA region in Japanese myotonic dystrophy patients. *Lancet* **339:** 692.

Yamamoto Y, Kawai H, Nakahara K, Osame M, Nakatsuji Y, Kishimoto T, Sakoda S. (1992) A novel primer extension method to detect the number of CAG repeats in the androgen receptor gene in families with X-linked spinal and bulbar muscular atrophy. *Biochem. Biophys. Res. Commun.* **182:** 507–513.

Yang TP, Stout JT, Konecki DS, Patel PI, Alford RL, Caskey CT. (1988) Spontaneous reversion of novel Lesch–Nyhan mutation by HPRT gene rearrangement. *Somat. Cell Mol. Genet.* **14:** 293–303.

Yoshida K, Oshima A, Shimmoto M, Fukuhara Y, Sakaraba H, Yanagisawa N, Suzuki Y. (1991) Human β-galactosidase gene mutations in Gm1-gangliosidosis: a common mutation among Japanese adult/chronic cases. *Am. J. Hum. Genet.* **49:** 435–442.

Yu S, Pritchard M, Kremer E, Lynch M, Nancarrow J, Baker E, Holman K, Mulley JC, Warren ST, Schlessinger D, Sutherland GR, Richards RI. (1991) Fragile X genotype characterized by an unstable region of DNA. *Science* **252:** 1179–1181.

Yu S, Mulley J, Loesch D, Turner G, Donnelly A, Gedeon A, Hillen D, Kremer E, Lynch M, Pritchard M, Sutherland GR, Richards RI. (1992) Fragile-X syndrome: unique genetics of the heritable unstable element. *Am. J. Hum. Genet.* **50:** 968–980.

Single base-pair substitutions in human gene mRNA splice junctions and their phenotypic consequences

In Chapters 6–8, we have shown that point mutations, deletions and insertions within human gene coding sequences are both non-randomly distributed and DNA sequence directed. In this chapter, we shall demonstrate that human gene mutations affecting mRNA splicing are also non-randomly distributed, and we shall investigate how this non-randomness can be related to the phenotypic consequences of mutation (for a detailed description of the mechanisms of mRNA splicing, see Section 2.2). Many of our conclusions have already been published elsewhere (Krawczak *et al.*, 1992).

That the location of mutations affecting mRNA splicing is inherently non-random has already been suggested by empirical data. For example, three mutations in the protein C (PROC) gene responsible for familial venous thrombosis have been found to occur at position +5 in the 5′ splice site of exon 5 (Appendix 4, Table 1); since these three lesions were different, identity by descent could clearly be excluded. Similarly, Mitchell *et al.* (1986) reported that three mutations of the dihydrofolatereductase (DHFR) gene arising spontaneously in cultured CHO cells occurred in the 5′ and 3′ splice sites flanking exon 5.

Naturally occurring mutations that affect mRNA splicing can be assumed to fall into three main categories:

(i) Mutations within a 5′ or 3′ splice site. Such lesions usually reduce the amount of mature mRNA generated and/or activate so-called 'cryptic' (i.e. alternative) splice sites in the vicinity. The utilization of cryptic splice sites results in the production of mRNAs which either lack a portion of the coding sequence or which instead contain additional sequence of intronic origin. According to the exon definition model proposed by Robberson *et al.* (1990), exons are recognized and defined as distinct units by the initial binding of protein factors to the 3' end of the intron followed by a search for a downstream 5' splice site. Thus an alternative consequence of splice site mutation could be for an exon to be no longer recognized as such, and as a result to be excluded from the mature mRNA transcript — a process termed 'exon skipping'.

(ii) Mutations within an intron. These mutations may serve to activate cryptic splice sites, leading to the production of aberrant mRNA species.

(iii) Mutations within a branch-point sequence.

In this chapter, following a brief review of relevant *in vitro* studies, both the location and the relative frequency of splice site mutations causing human genetic disease will be explored and their consequences for mRNA splicing analysed. The major advantage of this approach is two-fold: without extensive studies, it is often impossible to say whether an altered splicing efficiency observed for a given mutation *in vitro* will be of any functional and/or clinical significance *in vivo*. By contrast, the deleterious effects of *in vivo* mutations may already be assumed since the clinical phenotype must have been severe enough to have come to clinical attention. Secondly, only a small number of *in vitro* systems have as yet been examined in any depth (most notably β-globin), and conclusions drawn as to the effect of specific mutations have often proved to be relevant only to that one system. With naturally occurring splice site mutations, however, gene-specific effects can be minimized because a variety of genes are considered.

9.1 Splice junction mutations and their effect on pre-mRNA splicing *in vitro*

One approach to learning about the phenotypic consequences of splice site mutation has been to study the *in vitro* expression of synthetic gene constructs containing a range of different base substitutions within a specific exon–intron junction. Following this approach, Aebi *et al.* (1986, 1987) determined the effects of all possible mutations of the invariant GT dinucleotide at the 5' splice site of the rabbit β-globin intron 2:

(i) Mutation to GA, GG or AT dramatically reduced or abolished normal splicing. Although these point mutations did not prevent cleavage at the 5' splice site, exon joining was blocked. The accumulation of the lariat intermediate indicated that these mutations allowed branch formation to take place but prevented cleavage and exon joining at the 3' splice site.

(ii) Transitions to GC did not impair splicing significantly, an experimental finding not inconsistent with the occasional natural occurrence of GC instead of GT at this position (for references, see reviews by Green, 1986; Aebi and Weissmann, 1987; Shapiro and Senapathy, 1987; Jackson, 1991).

(iii) Mutations to either TT or CT shifted the cleavage site one base upstream but nevertheless permitted the formation of a spliced mRNA product.

These findings obviously suggest that the precise location of the 5′ splice site is not determined by the strictly conserved GT doublet alone. Nevertheless, its conservation is thought to reflect a strict requirement for the binding of the pre-mRNA to the U1 snRNP by base-pairing between complementary regions (Figure 2.5). Ohshima and Gotoh (1987) showed that the highest predicted stability of base-pairing with U1 snRNA was exhibited by actual 5′ splice sites as opposed to other sequences in the vicinity which were not normally utilized. Aebi *et al.* (1986) demonstrated that most mutations analysed that affected splicing efficiency at the 5′ splice site of rabbit β-globin intron 2, actually reduced its complementarity to U1 snRNA. Finally, Lear *et al.* (1990) have reported a strong correlation between the intrinsic strength of 5′ splice sites and the stability of their interactions with U1 snRNA.

The study of Aebi *et al.* (1986) also illustrated the extent to which the consequences of a given mutation for mRNA splicing are critically dependent on the type of study system employed. These authors used a HeLa cell-derived nuclear extract as an *in vitro* system and transient expression in transfected HeLa cells as an '*in vivo*' system. *In vitro*, all but two of the mutations of the invariant 5′ GT dinucleotide resulted in exon skipping. *In vivo*, however, most mutations resulted in the utilization of cryptic splice sites, although no decrease in the level of spliced product was observed. This observation may be accounted for by the explanation of Pikielny and Rosbash (1985), who speculated that the level of spliced mRNA may be relatively normal *in vivo* even if splicing is partially inhibited, since a build-up of pre-mRNA may drive the reaction.

The results of *in vitro* studies of mutation in 3′ splice sites are somewhat contradictory and, as with 5′ splice sites, differ from those noted *in vivo*. Whereas mutations in the invariant AG of the human β-globin intron 1 decreased the efficiency of lariat formation without entirely abolishing it (Reed and Maniatis, 1985; Ruskin and Green, 1985a), similar experiments with rabbit β-globin intron 2 resulted in inhibition of both lariat formation (Aebi *et al.*, 1986) and spliceosome assembly (Lamond *et al.*, 1987).

Mutations of the invariant AG which abolished splicing *in vitro* gave rise to alternative splicing at cryptic splice sites *in vivo* (Aebi *et al.*, 1986). This apparent discrepancy may be in part explained by experimental findings demonstrating an important role for the pyrimidine tract found at the 3′ ends of introns (Reed, 1989). If this tract is short (e.g. 14 bases), the presence of the invariant AG within the adjacent 3′ splice site appears to be essential for efficient splicing. If, however, the tract is somewhat longer (e.g. 26 bases), then an AG does not seem to be an absolute requirement. Deletions of the pyrimidine tract have been shown to abolish lariat formation and spliceosome assembly *in vitro* (Frendewey and Keller, 1985; Reed and Maniatis, 1985; Ruskin and Green, 1985b), even although the length of the tract can be reduced quite substantially before splicing is impaired (Smith *et al.*, 1989).

Mutation of mammalian branch-points (Section 2.2) dramatically reduces the efficiency of mRNA splicing *in vitro*, and may also lead to an activation of cryptic splice sites (Padgett *et al.*, 1985; Ruskin *et al.*, 1985). Splicing may, however, continue at a reduced rate even in the absence of a branch-point sequence, provided that alternative A residues are present at the appropriate distance from the 3′ splice site to permit the formation of lariats (Padgett *et al.*, 1985; Reed and Maniatis, 1985; Ruskin *et al.*, 1985; Hornig *et al.*, 1986). *In vivo*, the selection of 3′ splice sites is substantially altered by branch-point mutation even though spliceosome assembly is not itself abolished (Reed and Maniatis, 1988).

9.2 Splice junction mutations causing human genetic disease

Splicing defects are not an uncommon cause of human genetic disease. The study of naturally occurring mRNA splice site mutations is important since their phenotypic consequences can be studied within the context of the entire gene in its natural chromosomal location, without being affected by such *in vitro* experimental artefacts as might arise owing, for example, to the juxtaposition of vector sequence within synthetic gene constructs.

The vast majority of known genetic lesions that affect splicing are single base-pair substitutions (point mutations) within 5′ and 3′ splice sites. This is undoubtedly because such lesions are comparatively frequent, but also because they are both readily detectable and highly likely to result in a severe clinical phenotype. For this reason, and because point mutations are better understood in terms of their relative frequencies and underlying causative mechanisms (Chapter 6), the following analysis is confined exclusively to this category of lesion. For other types of splice site mutation, such as deletions, insertions or duplications, the reader is referred to the original research papers, e.g. Hidaka *et al.* (1987), Dlott *et al.* (1990) and Koeberl *et al.* (1990). Mutations of the pyrimidine tract and branch-point sequence, although clearly important in any consideration of mRNA splicing mutations, will also not be considered in any detail here since the weak consensus sequence derived for the branch-point sequence and the considerable length of many pyrimidine tracts (Ohshima and Gotoh, 1987) argue that *in vivo*, mutations are more likely to be deletions rather than point mutations.

A search of the literature based upon the above criteria revealed 101 different examples of point mutation in the vicinity of exon–intron splice junctions of human genes, which have been held to alter the accuracy or efficiency of mRNA splicing and to be responsible for a specific disease phenotype. These reports are listed in Appendix 4; mutations in 5′ and 3′ splice sites are presented separately, as are examples of the creation of novel splice sites. For the mutations listed, evidence for a defect in mRNA splicing has been direct or indirect or both. In some cases, aberrant mRNA species have been detected and characterized. In the remainder, the mutation reported was the sole deviation from the wild-type sequence that could not be accounted for by

DNA polymorphism; co-segregation with the disease phenotype through the family pedigree was usually demonstrated.

Point mutations that occurred within the exonic portion of a splice site consensus sequence were also included in Appendix 4, although in some cases it is not easy to disentangle the resulting deleterious effects on protein structure and function from those on mRNA splicing. A specific mutation at a given site was listed only once in order to avoid multiple inclusion of identical-by-descent mutations. One consequence of this policy has been to neglect consideration of recurrent mutation. There are, however, only three examples of *proven* (by extreme geographical separation, independent somatic mutation and/or proof of *de novo* mutation) recurrent mutation in splice junctions: at position $+1$ of the $5'$ splice site of the retinoblastoma (RB1) gene exon 12 (Dunn *et al.*, 1989), at position $+1$ of the $5'$ splice site of exon 6 of the $\alpha2(I)$ collagen (COL1A2) gene causing Ehlers–Danlos syndrome type VII (Weil *et al.*, 1990; Vasan *et al.*, 1991), and at position -1 of the $3'$ splice site of exon 7 in the factor IX (F9) gene causing severe haemophilia B (Matsushita *et al.*, 1989; Chen *et al.*, 1991). A further two splice site mutations in the β-globin (HBB) gene, both causing β-thalassaemia, are probably recurrent on the basis of RFLP haplotyping although identity-by-descent/recombination cannot be formally excluded (Atweh *et al.*, 1987; Wong *et al.*, 1989).

9.2.1 The relative frequency of occurrence of splicing mutations

Do splice site mutations contribute disproportionately to human gene mutation? The 101 different point mutations within or adjacent to mRNA splice junctions quoted in Appendix 4 were reported in the literature before June 1991, at which time 558 different point mutations were known to occur within human gene coding sequences. Point mutations causing a defect in mRNA splicing therefore appear to represent some 15% of all point mutations causing human genetic disease. This is only slightly higher than the frequency of splice site (including cryptic splice site) mutation observed in the factor IX (F9) gene causing haemophilia B ($30/278 = 10.8\%$; Giannelli *et al.*, 1992).

A rough estimate of the expected frequency of splice site mutation can be arrived at by calculation of relative target sizes. If the 'average' gene possesses 10 exons, the splice site target will approximate to $9\times(6+3)=81$, where 6 and 3 are the numbers of evolutionarily conserved bases at the $5'$ and $3'$ splice sites, respectively, which are known when mutated to result in a disease phenotype. The size of the target proffered by a gene coding sequence can be estimated to be $1500 \times 2/3 = 1000$, where 1500 represents the average length of a human coding sequence, and $2/3$ allows for the one-third of mutations that are silent (see also Section 6.2.1). The ratio of the two target sizes, i.e. $81/1000 = 8\%$, is a little smaller than the observed proportion of point mutations affecting splice sites. This is due in part to cryptic splice site mutations not being considered in the calculation, but probably also to underestimation of either the number of 'mutation-sensitive' bases within splice sites or of the phenotypic consequences of splice site mutation which ensure clinical detection.

9.2.2 Are splice sites involved in mutations representative of the 'average' splice site?

Of the 101 different splice site mutations collated in Appendix 4, 62 affected 5′ splice sites (Table 1), 26 were located in 3′ splice sites (Table 2) and 13 resulted in the creation of novel splice sites in the vicinity of existing ones (Table 3). Position-wise comparison of the spectrum of splice sites observed in a reference sample of primate genes (Mount, 1982; Shapiro and Senapathy, 1987; see Section 2.2) with nucleotide frequencies from the wild-type (i.e. unmutated) splice sites in Appendix 4 yielded only one significant difference (Table 9.1): at intronic position − 5 in 3′ sites, adenine occurs at a significantly increased frequency whereas pyrimidines are under-represented ($\chi^2 = 15.47$).

Included in Appendix 4 are so-called 'consensus values' (CVs; Shapiro and Senapathy, 1987), calculated both for the wild-type (CVN) and mutated (CVM) splice sites. These CVs reflect the similarity of any one splice site to the sequence spectrum presented in Table 9.1. To compute the CV of a given splice site, each of its positions was scored with the corresponding mononucleotide frequency in the reference sample. The CV was then obtained by subtracting from the sum of these scores its smallest possible value and dividing the result by the difference between the largest and smallest possible value. This

Table 9.1. Consensus nucleotide frequency patterns at eight positions within 5′ and 3′ splice sites

Position	A	C	G	T	χ^2
5′ splice sites					
− 2	0.58 (24)	0.12 (9)	0.15 (4)	0.15 (10)	4.945
− 1	0.10 (5)	0.04 (4)	0.78 (33)	0.08 (5)	3.184
+ 1	0.00 (0)	0.00 (0)	1.00 (47)	0.00 (0)	0.000
+ 2	0.00 (0)	0.00 (0)	0.00 (0)	1.00 (47)	0.000
+ 3	0.57 (26)	0.02 (1)	0.39 (16)	0.02 (4)	10.285
+ 4	0.71 (35)	0.08 (1)	0.12 (5)	0.09 (6)	2.919
+ 5	0.05 (1)	0.06 (2)	0.84 (40)	0.05 (4)	2.179
+ 6	0.16 (5)	0.15 (9)	0.22 (5)	0.47 (28)	5.723
3′ splice sites					
− 6	0.06 (0)	0.39 (7)	0.06 (1)	0.47 (11)	1.660
− 5	0.06 (5)	0.40 (8)	0.08 (0)	0.46 (6)	15.470†
− 4	0.23 (7)	0.29 (2)	0.23 (2)	0.23 (8)	8.119
− 3	0.03 (1)	0.74 (11)	0.01 (0)	0.22 (7)	3.083
− 2	1.00 (19)	0.00 (0)	0.00 (0)	0.00 (0)	0.000
− 1	0.00 (0)	0.00 (0)	1.00 (19)	0.00 (0)	0.000
+ 1	0.28 (5)	0.13 (2)	0.49 (10)	0.10 (2)	0.165
+ 2*	0.17 (1)	0.22 (3)	0.24 (6)	0.37 (9)	2.879

Data from Shapiro and Senapathy (1987) and *Mount (1982). Values in parentheses are the observed numbers among the wild-type splice sites from Tables 1–2 of Appendix 4 (each splice site was only considered once). Compared with the consensus, only the position marked † yielded an individual χ^2 value > 12.36, which is the appropriate limit allowing for multiple testing (8 comparisons, 3 d.f., $P<0.05$).

implies that a splice site containing the least frequent bases at each position would yield a CV of zero, whereas splices sites containing only the most frequent bases would have a CV of unity. [Note that, in this context, frequency data for exonic position +2 in 3′ splice sites were taken from the study of Mount (1982) because this position was not considered by Shapiro and Senapathy (1987).]

The observed distributions of wild-type CVs (CVNs) are presented in Figure 9.1 together with their random expectations. Expected distributions were calculated assuming that the likelihood of occurrence of any given splice site is proportional to the product of the corresponding mononucleotide frequencies from Table 9.1. As can be inferred from Figure 9.1, CVNs for the splice sites included in Appendix 4 (Tables 1 and 2) are not distributed as expected. When compared by a Kolmogorov–Smirnov test, significant differences between observed and expected distributions were found for both 5′

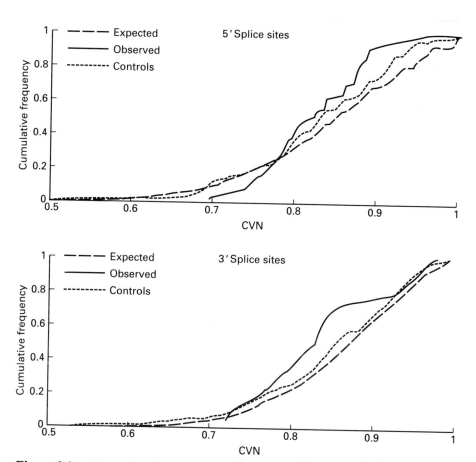

Figure 9.1. Observed and expected distributions of Shapiro–Senapathy consensus values (CVN) in the 5′ (a) and 3′ (b) splice sites of Appendix 4.

($P=0.008$) and $3'$ ($P=0.029$) splice sites. Although average CVNs are not much different from expectation (0.825 versus 0.847 for $5'$ splice sites, and 0.840 versus 0.851 for $3'$ splice sites), the observed variance appears to be smaller: sequences with either extremely small or extremely high CVNs are lacking. [CVNs of $5'$ splice sites affected by mutations outside the invariant GT dinucleotide are distributed similarly to the total but fail to differ significantly from expectation ($P=0.116$), most probably due to the small sample size.] In summary, our findings suggest that (i) splice sites that are already less than optimal in terms of their similarity to the consensus sequence are especially prone to the deleterious effects of mutation, but that (ii) splice sites with an already extremely low degree of similarity are not further functionally impaired by single base changes.

Since it cannot be immediately excluded that splice sites with extreme CVs are generally depleted (and that the above finding therefore merely reflects inappropriate assumptions made about expected distributions), CVs of a total of 406 $5'$ and $3'$ splice sites from a selection of 29 human genes were analysed (the only criterion for inclusion being ready library access). The distributions of CVs as derived from this sample are also included in Figure 9.1, demonstrating that there is only a small difference in CVs between 'control' splice sites and expectation. Although mean CVs appear to be slightly smaller among control sequences, the variances appear comparable.

An analysis similar to the one performed on CVNs can also be conducted for the mutated splice sites: every hypothetical base change within the splice sites included in Appendix 4 can be allocated a corresponding CV, and the distribution of CVMs as expected in the present sample is then obtained by weighting each possible (mutant) CV by the likelihood of the corresponding base change (likelihoods of point mutations were calculated as described in Chapter 6). Expected and observed distributions of CVMs are presented in Figure 9.2, showing that for both $5'$ splice sites and $3'$ splice sites, the observed CVMs are considerably smaller than expected. When both distributions are compared by a Kolmogorov–Smirnov test, differences turn out to be highly significant, with error probabilities of $P=8.12 \times 10^{-6}$ for $5'$ splice sites and $P=1.26 \times 10^{-6}$ for $3'$ splice sites. These results indicate that both the location and the spectrum of point mutations within splice sites are very different from predictions based on the mutation data derived from gene coding regions reported in Chapter 6. This topic will be examined in more detail in the following section.

9.2.3 The location and spectrum of splice site mutations

To test whether the location of point mutations within splice sites is compatible with point mutation data from human gene coding regions, the number of mutations observed at particular splice site positions may be compared with their corresponding expectations: relative dinucleotide mutabilities (Section 6.5) allow one to calculate the relative likelihood of any possible base change within the splice sites listed in Tables 1 and 2 of Appendix 4. (For a detailed

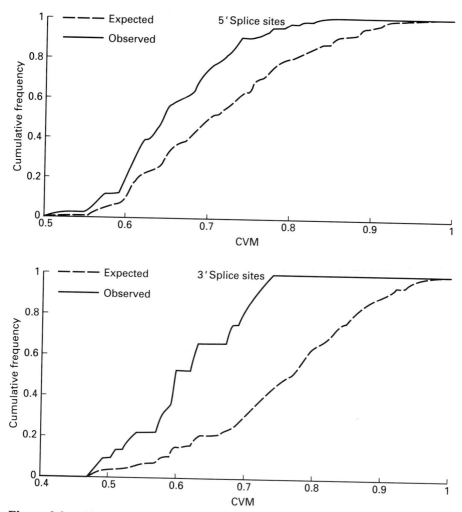

Figure 9.2. Observed and expected distributions of Shapiro–Senapathy consensus values (CVM) in the mutated 5′ and 3′ splice sites of Appendix 4.

description of the calculus, see Chapter 6.) By appropriate summation of these figures, the relative likelihood of mutation at any given position can be obtained for either table. This relative likelihood, when multiplied by the total number of mutations included in the table, yields the number of mutations expected at that position. The results of these calculations, together with observed numbers and χ^2 values, are given in Tables 9.2 and 9.3. As may be inferred from Table 9.2, the location of point mutations within 5′ splice sites differs significantly from expectation based on data from human gene coding regions ($\chi^2 = 37.356$, 7 d.f., $P < 10^{-5}$). Comparison of observed and expected frequencies of occurrence at individual positions indicates that point mutations are significantly over-represented at position $+1$ ($\chi^2 = 18.706$). By and large,

Table 9.2. Observed and expected frequencies of point mutations at different positions in 5′ splice sites

Position	Observed	Expected	χ^2	Individual χ^2 value	P (1 d.f.)
−2	0	6.42	6.420	7.175	7.37×10^{-3}
−1	6	11.84	2.881	3.574	5.88×10^{-2}
+1	29	14.59	14.232	18.706	$1.53 \times 10^{-5*}$
+2	8	3.85	4.473	4.775	2.90×10^{-2}
+3	3	5.58	1.193	1.313	2.52×10^{-1}
+4	0	4.43	4.430	4.777	2.88×10^{-2}
+5	13	9.05	1.724	2.024	1.55×10^{-1}
+6	2	5.24	2.003	2.192	1.39×10^{-1}
	61		37.356	($P < 10^{-5}$, 7 d.f.)	

*Position +1 yielded an individual χ^2 value > 7.48, which is the appropriate limit of significance allowing for multiple testing ($P < 0.05$).

Table 9.3. Observed and expected frequencies of point mutations at different positions in 3′ splice sites

Position	Observed	Expected	χ^2	Individual χ^2 value	P (1 d.f.)
−6	0	2.56	2.560	2.881	8.97×10^{-2}
−5	0	3.15	3.150	3.650	5.61×10^{-2}
−4	0	2.66	2.660	3.008	8.28×10^{-2}
−3	3	2.51	0.096	0.107	7.40×10^{-1}
−2	10	1.26	60.625	64.139	$< 10^{-5*}$
−1	10	3.52	11.929	14.085	$1.75 \times 10^{-4*}$
+1	0	3.95	3.950	4.769	2.90×10^{-2}
+2	0	3.38	3.380	3.962	4.66×10^{-2}
	23		88.350	($P < 1.00 \times 10^{-5}$, 7 d.f.)	

*Positions −2 and −1 yielded an individual χ^2 value > 7.48, which is the appropriate limit of significance allowing for multiple testing ($P < 0.05$).

the relative frequencies of observed *in vivo* mutations at the different positions within 5′ splice sites reflect broadly the evolutionary conservation apparent in the consensus sequence presented in Table 9.1.

In addition to their unusual localization pattern 5′ splice sites also exhibit a *spectrum* of mutation that deviates significantly from randomness. Fifty cases (81%) involve the substitution of a G residue (six at position −1, 29 at position +1, two at position +3, 13 at position +5). In 64% of these cases, the substituting base was an A. Even if CG to CA mutations are excluded because of their known hypermutability (Section 6.2), the excess of G to A transitions over transversions to either C or T still remains highly significant ($\chi^2 = 14.552$, 2 d.f., $P = 6.92 \times 10^{-4}$). No mutations were noted at positions −2 and +4 despite a clear preference in the consensus sequence for A residues at these sites.

Mutations in 3' splice sites were found to occur much less frequently than in 5' splice sites. This is consistent with the smaller target size of the former as evidenced by the much greater redundancy exhibited by the 3' splice site consensus sequence (Table 9.1). However, as with 5' splice sites, point mutations in 3' splice sites were found to be distributed differently from expectation based on relative dinucleotide mutabilities (Table 9.3; $\chi^2 = 88.350$, 7 d.f., $P < 10^{-5}$). This deviation from expectation was due to the over-representation of mutations at positions -2 ($\chi^2 = 64.139$) and -1 ($\chi^2 = 14.085$). Position -2 is expected to be the least prone to point mutations yet is actually involved in 10 of 23 mutations scored. Mutations at other positions do not occur at frequencies significantly different from expectation. Of the substitutions at position -2, eight were to a G, which is expected with a probability of less than 3.38×10^{-3} if substitutions to G, T and C are equally likely.

In the previous section, we noted that the *mutated* splice sites in Appendix 4 exhibited a significantly lower degree of similarity to the consensus sequences than expected, as measured by means of the CVMs. Now, we are able to demonstrate that this deviation is indeed due to an over-representation of point mutations at positions where the expected reduction of CVMs is largest. To this end, mean CVMs, as expected from mutation at a particular position, were calculated using the aforementioned expected distributions (Figure 9.2). For both 5' and 3' splice sites, these mean expected CVMs correlate negatively with the position-wise differences between observed and expected numbers of mutations (Figure 9.3). The Spearman rank correlation coefficients were $r = -0.707$ ($P < 0.05$) for 5' splice sites and $r = -0.778$ ($P < 0.025$) for 3' splice sites. Almost identical results were obtained when, instead of CVM values, the absolute or percentage changes from CVN to CVM were considered (data not shown).

9.2.4 Why is the in vivo splice site mutational spectrum non-random?

It appears very likely that the observed non-randomness of mutation within splice sites is a reflection of relative phenotypic severity (and hence detection bias) rather than any intrinsic difference in the underlying frequency of mutation.

The replacement of G residues at positions $+1$ and $+5$ of 5' splice sites would be predicted to reduce significantly the stability of base-pairing of the splice site with the complementary region of U1 snRNA. This also holds true for the six guanine replacements observed at position -1. However, it should be remembered that (i) the reduction in CV expected from mutations at this position is no higher than for other positions outside the invariant GT dinucleotide, and (ii) mutations at position -1 are severely under-represented [a total of 11 hypermutable CG dinucleotides were found in the 5' splice sites listed in Appendix 4 (all overlapping position -1) but none of these was

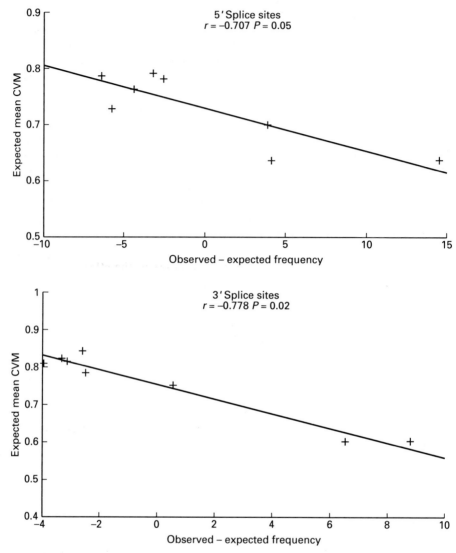

Figure 9.3. Correlation between the expected mean Shapiro–Senapathy consensus value (CV) and the difference between observed and expected frequency of mutation at eight positions in the 5′ and 3′ splice sites of Appendix 4. *r*, Spearman rank correlation coefficient.

affected by a mutation. This explains the large excess of expected over observed mutations at this position.]

Only three examples of mutations at the +3 residue were noted; the corresponding residue in U1 snRNA is pseudouridine rather than a cytosine (see Figure 2.5). No examples of mutation were found at the +4 A residue whose U1 counterpart is also pseudouridine. Thus, the spectrum of 5′ splice site mutations observed *in vivo* also suggests an important role for U1 sRNA binding and is therefore consistent with interpretations based on, and deduced from, *in vitro* data. The only exception to this concordance is the T to C substitution at position $+2$, which did not appear to impair splicing *in vitro* yet was serious enough in at least two cases *in vivo* to have come to clinical attention.

Three *in vivo* mutations have so far been detected in the 3′ splice site-associated pyrimidine tracts of the steroid 21-hydroxylase B (CA21HB) and β-globin (HBB) genes causing adrenal hyperplasia and β-thalassaemia respectively (Appendix 4, Table 2c, Nos. 4–6). It is not immediately clear how and why these mutations, at nucleotides -7, -8 and -13 respectively, exert a pathological influence on efficient mRNA splicing. However, two of these lesions occur within the pyrimidine tract of the 3′ splice site of the HBB exon 2; the pyrimidine tract (16 of 17 residues are C or T) is comparatively short at this location, as indeed it is at the 3′ splice site of exon 2 of the CA21HB gene (14 of 15 residues are C or T) where the remaining lesion was found. Again, it may be that some 3′ splice sites are more susceptible to the effects of pyrimidine loss than others by virtue of the relative length of the pyrimidine tract (see also Section 9.1).

9.3 Mutations causing human genetic disease through the creation of novel splice sites

A different category of mutation affecting mRNA splicing is provided by single base-pair substitutions outside actual splice sites, which create novel splice sites that substitute for the wild-type sites. A total of 13 such lesions have been reported (Appendix 4, Table 3); in all but one case, the novel splice site was situated upstream of the original wild-type site. One intriguing finding for mutations creating novel 3′ acceptor splice sites should be noted: all six mutations introduced an A at position -2, but never a G at position -1. Since the A nucleotide at position -2 is also over-represented with respect to its relative frequency of mutation, this may further reflect a particular requirement for an adenine residue at this position.

CVs for the activated cryptic splice sites (CVAs) were calculated wherever possible (Table 3, Appendix 4); in eight of 12 cases, the CVA was as high or higher than the wild-type CVN, suggesting that the novel splice sites successfully compete with the wild-type sites for splicing factors. For mutations in the vicinity of 3′ splice sites, the relative proportion of cryptic splice site-utilizing mRNAs appears to correlate positively with the CVA:CVN ratio (see nos. 8, 9 and 11 from Table 3, Appendix 4) whereas, at 5′ splice sites, the distance to the wild-type site may also play an important role (see especially No. 7).

Mutations creating novel splice sites are the most difficult to detect and characterize using currently available techniques. Firstly, very few sequence data exist for introns compared with coding regions and, secondly investigation of the mRNA (instead of the DNA) is a prerequisite for assessing the phenotypic consequences of an observed base change located outside the coding sequence and the normal splice sites. There are, however, two reasons to expect an increased frequency of detection of this type of mutation in the future: (i) especially in complex genes, molecular analyses will increasingly exploit ectopic transcription in peripheral blood lymphocytes to study RNA rather than genomic DNA sequence (see Berg *et al.*, 1992; Parkinson and Thakker, 1992; Ramus *et al.*, 1992 and review in Section 4.3.2); (ii) a large proportion of the existing mutations in most complex disease genes have not hitherto been identified.

9.4 The phenotypic consequences of splice site mutation *in vivo*: exon skipping or cryptic splice site utilization?

The phenotypic consequences of naturally occurring point mutation in the (internal) 5' splice sites of seven human genes were studied by Talerico and Berget (1990), who observed exon skipping in six cases compared with only one case (β-globin) of cryptic splice site usage. These initial results suggested that exon skipping might be the preferred *in vivo* phenotype, an assertion confirmed by the much larger sample presented in Appendix 4 (Table 1): 21 of the point mutations reported for 5' splice sites resulted in exon skipping, whereas only 12 mutations were definitely characterized by cryptic splice site utilization. In five cases, both exon skipping and cryptic splice site utilization occurred, with the relative proportion of each differing quite widely. Although exon skipping was thus found to occur at higher frequency, a detection bias is possible because a single exon-skipped transcript might be easier to detect or identify than a number of less frequent transcripts each resulting from the use of a different cryptic splice site. Several instances of the detection of small amounts of residual wild-type mRNA from the cells of patients with a 5' splice site defect have also been reported. Remarkably, all these involve the mutation of bases outside the invariant GT dinucleotide (Appendix 4, Table 1c), suggesting that normal splicing is still possible in such cases, albeit at greatly reduced efficiency.

Four clear examples of exon skipping have been reported as a result of mutation in 3' splice sites (Appendix 4, Table 2), whereas five mutations resulted in cryptic splice site utilization.

9.4.1 The multiplicity of exon skipping products

Naylor *et al.* (1991) reported that although the predominant transcription product in a patient with a 3' splice site mutation in intron 5 of the factor VIII (F8) gene lacked exon 6, various minor splicing products were also detected which lacked different combinations of neighbouring exons. Although Naylor *et al.* (1991) made this observation on ectopically transcribed mRNA (see Section 4.3.2), evidence for variable (and unpredictable) aberrant splicing products has also emerged from the study of the consequences of splice site mutations in expressing tissues, e.g. in the 5' splice site of exon 5 of the β-hexosaminidase (HEXA) gene causing Tay–Sachs disease (Akli *et al.*, 1990); the predominant mRNA species detected lacked exon 5, but two minor species were also detectable which lacked either exon 4 or both exons 4 and 5. Thus, a multiplicity of aberrant mRNA products may well be the rule rather than the exception; they have only ever been detected by highly sensitive PCR-based assays rather than by Northern blotting. This notwithstanding, the data presented in Appendix 4 reveal that, when exon skipping occurs, one major mRNA species is usually observed, and that this species lacks an exon either upstream of the mutated 5′ splice site or downstream of the mutated 3′ splice site.

The extent of exon skipping resulting from a specific splice site mutation may be influenced by various factors including, among others, the host cell type. For example, a mutation at position +5 of the 5′ splice site of the α1(I) collagen (COL1A1) gene causing osteogenesis imperfecta (Bonadio *et al.*, 1990) resulted in inefficient exon skipping both *in vivo* and in cultured fibroblasts. However, exon skipping was nearly 100% when the mutant gene was expressed in COS cells. Some evidence for the effect of temperature at which the mutant cells are grown has been reported for three different 5′ splice site mutations (Bonadio *et al.*, 1990; Weil *et al.*, 1990; Lee *et al.*, 1991), suggesting that the extent to which these mutations (which did not involve the invariant GT dinucleotide) affected spliceosome assembly was temperature dependent, possibly through the efficiency of base-pairing to U1 snRNP. Kaneko *et al.* (1991) also reported an alteration in the proportion of exon-skipped mRNA splicing product of the albumin gene in Nagase analbuminaemic rats with aging.

9.4.2 The potential for cryptic splice site utilization

The choice between exon skipping and cryptic splice site usage may be visualized merely as a decision as to whether to utilize the next available legitimate splice site or the next best, albeit illegitimate, sequence in the immediate vicinity. This choice may be made on the basis of the presence or absence of sites capable of competing with the mutated splice site for splicing factors. Since it may therefore be supposed that the potential for cryptic splice site utilization is strongly dependent on the DNA sequence environment in the vicinity of a splice site, it appeared worthwhile to study the regions both upstream and downstream of the mutations reported in Appendix 4, Tables 1 and 2, to attempt to correlate their structural properties with the observed phenotypic consequences of mutation.

Unfortunately, sufficient data on intronic DNA sequence are available for only a small number of genes. Of the human genes listed in Appendix 4 for which phenotypic data were available, the complete DNA sequence has been established only in the case of the β-globin (HBB) gene. The distribution of mutations between the two 5′ splice sites of the HBB gene is dramatically skewed. Nine out of 10 mutations affect the splice site adjacent to the first exon, although both sites are estimated to be equally mutable (Chapter 6). The exon 1 site, as can be inferred from Figure 9.4a, has a comparatively low CV (0.792), and is surrounded by three other sequence motifs with similar or even

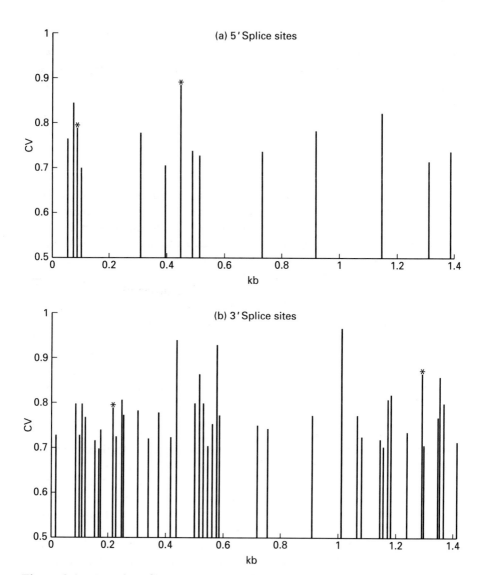

Figure 9.4. Location of potential cryptic splice sites in the HBB gene (CV > 0.700). The positions of the original splice sites are marked by asterisks.

higher CVs (0.765, 38 bp upstream; 0.843, 16 bp upstream; 0.700, 12 bp downstream). For the splice site at the second exon, however, the CV is considerably higher (0.889) and potential cryptic splice sites with lower CVs are located at more distant positions (0.706, 47 bp upstream; 0.739, 48 bp downstream; 0.728, 95 bp downstream). These (numerical) characteristics can be represented by a single quantity, termed the PCU value (potential of cryptic splice site utilization) of a normal splice site:

$$\text{PCU} = \Sigma \text{CVC/CVN} \times [1 - \text{abs}(\text{LOC}_N - \text{LOC}_C)/100]$$

CVN and CVC represent the Shapiro–Senapathy CV values of the normal and cryptic splice sites respectively, whereas LOC_N and LOC_C are their locations given in base-pairs. Summation is over all cryptic splice sites within a distance of 100 bp or less from the normal site, and with $CVC > 0.700$. The PCU value is higher:

(i)   The more cryptic sites are located in the vicinity of a splice site
(ii) The closer they are to the normal site
(iii) The higher the CVC values of the cryptic sites are as compared with the CVN values.

The first $5'$ splice site in the HBB gene, characterized by cryptic splice site utilization as the only abnormal phenotypic consequence of mutation reported, has a PCU value of 2.271. Clearly, skipping of the upstream exon 1 is not feasible here and so cryptic splice site utilization is probably the only possible option. For the second site, the PCU value is smaller, 1.108; exon skipping was also reported for the single mutation known to affect this site. Analysis of the DNA sequence surrounding two mutations in the uroporphyrinogen decarboxylase (UROD) and $\alpha2(I)$ collagen (COLIA2) genes, both characterized by 100% exon skipping, yielded PCU values of 1.196 and 0.000 respectively. Similar results were obtained for three $5'$ splice sites in the $\alpha1(3)$ collagen (COL3A1) gene: PCU values appear to correlate perfectly with the relative ratio of exon skipping versus cryptic splice site usage for mutations affecting these sites (Kuivaniemi et al., 1990). Thus we may conclude that, in cases of mutation, the extent of cryptic splice site usage is greater the more cryptic sites with relatively high CVs are located in the vicinity of a $5'$ splice site. If no alternative sites with sufficient homology to the consensus sequence are present, then either exon skipping or a greatly reduced production of normal transcripts appears to be the predominant phenotypic consequence.

For $3'$ splice sites, data are more sparse, and no obvious relationship between PCU value and phenotypic consequence is apparent. Three out of four mutations in the HBB gene were observed at the $3'$ splice site downstream of intron 2, which was estimated to be as mutable as that adjacent to intron 1 (Chapter 6). However, PCU values are 3.691 for the first and 2.003 for the second site (Figure 9.4b). For the $3'$ splice site of intron 2, cryptic splice site usage was reported for two mutations. Information regarding the phenotypic consequences of the remaining mutations was not available. The only $3'$ splice site mutation that resulted in exon skipping and for which sufficient sequence information could be obtained was observed in the COLIA2 gene: the PCU value of this site was calculated to be 3.378.

No obvious sequence-dependent explanation for cryptic splice site activation can thus be found in the case of $3'$ splice sites. We surmise that recognition and correct usage of the $3'$ splice site requires less homology to the conserved consensus sequence than is necessary at the $5'$ splice site, and is probably influenced more heavily by other factors such as the nature of the branch-point and/or the length of the pyrimidine tract (see Goux-Pelletan et al., 1990; Mullen et al., 1991; Steingrimsdottir et al., 1992). Deshler and Rossi

(1991) have demonstrated that 3′ splice site selection in the actin gene of the yeast *Kluyveromyces lactis* is potentiated by the formation of specific secondary pre-mRNA structures. Even though the normal splice site remained unchanged, point mutations introduced *in vitro* between the branch-point and the original 3′ splice site resulted in the use of an alternative neighbouring splice site with a much smaller Shapiro–Senapathy CV. The authors therefore concluded that 3′ splice site selection is not simply a consequence of linear directional scanning, but requires correct positioning relative to the branch-point.

The accuracy and efficiency of splicing is also known to be affected by the length and/or sequence composition of exons at some distance from the normal splice junction (Somasekhar and Mertz, 1985; Furdon and Kole, 1986, 1988; Reed and Maniatis, 1986; Matsuo *et al.*, 1991; Steingrimsdottir *et al.*, 1992) perhaps again as a result of higher-order RNA structure considerations (Solnick, 1985; Ohshima and Gotoh, 1987).

The accurate and efficient selection of both 5′ and 3′ splice sites is clearly a complex process. We have seen here that the accuracy of this process is optimized by integrating multiple cues such as those given by the splice site itself, the branch-point, the length of the exon and pyrimidine tract (Dominski and Kole, 1991), the local nucleotide sequence environment, and perhaps even chromatin structure (see, for example, Beckmann and Trifonov, 1991). Knowing the hierarchy of cues and how they each contribute to the process of splice site selection will be important not merely for future studies of gene mutation but also for our emerging understanding of the mechanisms underlying alternative splicing and the means by which genes have evolved through the recruitment and subsequent exploitation of novel exons.

9.5 Conclusions

A total of 101 different examples of point mutations, which lie in the vicinity of mRNA splice junctions and which have been held to be responsible for a human genetic disease by altering the accuracy or efficiency of mRNA splicing, were collated. These data comprised 62 mutations at 5′ splice sites, 26 at 3′ splice sites and 13 that resulted in the creation of novel splice sites. It was estimated that some 10–15% of all point mutations causing human genetic disease result in an mRNA splicing defect. Of the 5′ splice site mutations, 60% involved the invariant GT dinucleotide; mutations were found to be non-randomly distributed with an excess over expectation at position +1 and an apparent deficiency at position −2. Of the 3′ splice site mutations, 87% involved the invariant AG dinucleotide; an excess of mutations over expectation was noted at position −2 and −1. This non-randomness of mutation reflects the evolutionary conservation apparent in splice site consensus sequences and is probably attributable to detection bias resulting from the differing phenotypic severity of specific lesions.

The spectrum of point mutations was also found to be drastically skewed: purines were significantly over-represented as substituting nucleotides, perhaps because of steric hindrance (e.g. in U1 snRNA binding at 5′ splice sites). Further, splice sites affected by point mutations resulting in human genetic disease were markedly different from the splice site consensus sequences. When similarity was quantified by a 'consensus value', both extremely low and extremely high values were notably absent from the wild-type sequences of the mutated splice sites. Splice sites of intermediate similarity to the consensus sequence may thus be more prone to the deleterious effects of mutation. Regarding the phenotypic effects of mutations on mRNA splicing, exon skipping occurred more frequently than cryptic splice site usage; one major mRNA species was usually observed and this invariably lacked an exon either upstream of the mutated 5′ splice site or downstream of the mutated 3′ splice site. Evidence was presented which indicates that, at least for 5′ splice site mutations, cryptic splice site usage is favoured under conditions where (i) a number of such sites are present in the immediate vicinity and (ii) these sites exhibit sufficient homology to the splice site consensus sequence for them to be able to compete successfully with the mutated splice site. The novel concept of a 'potential for cryptic splice site usage' value was introduced in an attempt to quantify these characteristics and to predict the relative proportion of exon skipping versus cryptic splice site utilization consequent to the introduction of a mutation at a normal splice site.

References

Aebi M, Weissmann C. (1987) Precision and orderliness in splicing. *Trends Genet.* **3:** 102–107.

Aebi M, Hornig H, Padgett RA, Reiser J, Weissmann C. (1986) Sequence requirements for splicing of higher eukaryotic nuclear pre-mRNA. *Cell* **47:** 555–565.

Aebi M, Hornig H, Weissmann C. (1987) 5′ cleavage site in eukaryotic pre-mRNA splicing is determined by the overall 5′ splice region, not by the conserved 5′ GU. *Cell* **50:** 237–246.

Akli S, Chelly J, Mezard C, Gandy S, Kahn A, Poenaru L. (1990) A G to A mutation at position −1 of a 5′ splice site in a late infantile form of Tay–Sachs disease. *J. Biol. Chem.* **265:** 7324–7330.

Atweh GF, Wong C, Reed R, Antonarakis SE, Zhu D, Ghosh PK, Maniatis T, Forget B, Kazazian HH. (1987) A new mutation in IVS-1 of the human β-globin gene causing β-thalassaemia due to abnormal splicing. *Blood* **70:** 147–151.

Beckmann JS, Trifonov EN. (1991) Splice junctions follow a 205-base ladder. *Proc. Natl. Acad. Sci. USA* **88:** 2380–2383.

Berg L-P, Grundy CB, Thomas F, Millar DS, Green PJ, Slomski R, Reiss J, Kakkar VV, Cooper DN. (1992) *De novo* splice site mutation in the antithrombin III (AT3) gene causing recurrent venous thrombosis: demonstration of exon skipping by ectopic transcript analysis. *Genomics* **13:** 1359–1361.

Bonadio J, Ramirez F, Barr M. (1990) An intron mutation in the human α1(I) collagen gene alters the efficiency of pre-mRNA splicing and is associated with osteogenesis imperfecta type II. *J. Biol. Chem.* **265:** 2262–2268.

Chen S-H, Zhang M, Thompson AR, Bray GL, Scott CR. (1991) Splice junction mutations in factor IX gene resulting in severe hemophilia B. *Nucleic Acids Res.* **19:** 1172.

Deshler JO, Rossi JJ. (1991) Unexpected point mutations activate cryptic splice sites by perturbing a natural secondary structure within a yeast intron. *Genes Dev.* **5:** 1252–1263.

Dlott B, d'Azzo A, Quon DVK, Neufeld EF. (1990) Two mutations produce intron insertion in mRNA and elongated β-subunit of human β-hexosaminidase. *J. Biol. Chem.* **265:** 17921–17927.

Dominski Z, Kole R. (1991) Selection of splice sites in pre-mRNAs with short internal exons. *Mol. Cell. Biol.* **11:** 6075–6083.

Dunn JM, Phillips RA, Zhu X, Becker A, Gallie BL. (1989) Mutations in the RB1 gene and their effects on transcription. *Mol. Cell. Biol.* **9:** 4596–4604.

Frendewey D, Keller W. (1985) Stepwise assembly of a pre-mRNA splicing complex requires U-snRNPs and specific intron sequences. *Cell* **42:** 355–367.

Furdon PJ, Kole R. (1986) Inhibition of splicing but not cleavage at the 5′ splice site by truncating human β-globin pre-mRNA. *Proc. Natl. Acad. Sci. USA* **83:** 927–931.

Furdon PJ, Kole R. (1988) The length of the downstream exon and the substitution of specific sequences affect pre-mRNA splicing *in vitro*. *Mol. Cell. Biol.* **8:** 860–866.

Giannelli F, Green PM, High KA, Sommer S, Lillicrap DP, Ludwig M, Olek K, Reitsma PH, Goossens M, Yoshioka A, Brownlee GG. (1992) Haemophilia B: database of point mutations and short additions and deletions — third edition. *Nucleic Acids Res.* **20:** 2027–2063.

Goux-Pelletan M, Libri D, d'Aubenton-Carafa Y, Fiszman M, Brody E, Marie J. (1990) *In vitro* splicing of mutually exclusive exons from the chicken β-tropomyosin gene: role of the branch point location and very long pyrimidine stretch. *EMBO J.* **9:** 241–249.

Green MR. (1986) Pre-mRNA splicing. *Ann. Rev. Genet.* **20:** 671–708.

Hidaka H, Palella TD, O'Toole TE, Tarlé SA, Kelley WN. (1987) Human adenine phosphoribosyltransferase: identification of allelic mutations at the nucleotide level as a cause of the complete deficiency of the enzyme. *J. Clin. Invest.* **80:** 1409–1415.

Hornig H, Aebi M, Weissmann C. (1986) Effect of mutations at the lariat branch acceptor site on β-globin pre-mRNA splicing *in vitro*. *Nature* **324:** 589–591.

Jackson IJ. (1991) A reappraisal of non-consensus mRNA splice sites. *Nucleic Acids Res.*, **19:** 3795–3798.

Kaneko T, Shima H, Esumi H, Ochiai M, Nagase S, Sugimura T, Nagao M. (1991) Marked increases of two kinds of two-exon-skipped albumin mRNAs with aging and their further increase by treatment with 3′-methyl-4-dimethylaminoazobenzene in Nagase analbuminemic rats. *Proc. Natl. Acad. Sci. USA* **88:** 2707–2711.

Koeberl DD, Bottema CDK, Ketterling RP, Bridge PJ, Lillicrap DP, Sommer SS. (1990) Mutations causing hemophilia B: direct estimate of the underlying rates of spontaneous germ-line transitions, transversions and deletions in a human gene. *Am. J. Hum. Genet.* **47:** 202–217.

Krawczak M, Reiss J, Cooper DN. (1992) The mutational spectrum of single base-pair substitutions in mRNA splice junctions of human genes: causes and consequences. *Hum. Genet.* **90:** 41–54.

Kuivaniemi H, Kontusaari S, Tromp G, Zhao M, Sabol C, Prockop DJ. (1990) Identical G + 1 to A mutations in three different introns of the type III procollagen gene (COL3A1) produce different patterns of RNA splicing in three variants of Ehlers–Danlos syndrome type IV. *J. Biol. Chem.* **265:** 12067–12074.

Lamond AI, Konarska MM, Sharp PA. (1987) A mutational analysis of spliceosome assembly: evidence for splice site collaboration during spliceosome formation. *Genes Dev.* **1:** 532–543.

Lear AL, Eperon LP, Wheatley IM, Eperon IC. (1990) Hierarchy for 5′ splice site preference determined *in vivo*. *J. Mol. Biol.* **211:** 103–115.

Lee B, Vitale E, Superti-Furga A, Steinmann B, Ramirez F. (1991) G to T transversion at position + 5 of a splice donor site causes skipping of the preceding exon in the type III procollagen transcripts of a patient with Ehlers–Danlos syndrome type IV. *J. Biol. Chem.* **266:** 5256–5259.

Matsuo M, Masumura T, Nishio H, Nakajima T, Kitoh Y, Takumi T, Koga J, Nakamura H. (1991) Exon skipping during splicing of dystrophin mRNA precursor due to an intraexon deletion in the dystrophin gene of Duchenne muscular dystrophy Kobe. *J. Clin. Invest.* **87:** 2127–2131.

Matsushita T, Tanimoto M, Yamamoto K, Sugiura I, Hamaguchi M, Takamatsu J, Saito H. (1989) Nucleotide sequence analysis of hemophilia B with the inhibitor phenotype. *Blood Suppl.* **74:** 251a.

Mitchell PJ, Urlaub G, Chasin L. (1986) Spontaneous splicing mutations at the dihydrofolate reductase locus in Chinese hamster ovary cells. *Mol. Cell. Biol.* **6:** 1926–1935.

Mount SM. (1982) A catalogue of splice junction sequences. *Nucleic Acids Res.* **10:** 459–472.

Mullen MP, Smith CWJ, Patton JG, Nadal-Ginard B. (1991) α-tropomyosin mutually exclusive exon selection: competition between branchpoint/polypyrimidine tracts determines default exon choice. *Genes Dev.* **5:** 642–655.

Naylor JA, Green PM, Montandon AJ, Rizza CR, Giannelli F. (1991) Detection of three novel mutations in two haemophilia A patients by rapid screening of whole essential region of factor VIII gene. *Lancet* **337:** 635–639.

Ohshima Y, Gotoh Y. (1987) Signals for the selection of a splice site in pre-mRNA: computer analysis of splice junction sequences and like sequences. *J. Mol. Biol.*, **195:** 247–259.

Padgett RA, Konarska MM, Aebi M, Hornig H, Weissmann C, Sharp PA. (1985) Non-consensus branch-site sequences in the *in vitro* splicing of transcripts of mutant rabbit β-globin genes. *Proc. Natl. Acad. Sci. USA* **82:** 8349–8353.

Parkinson DB, Thakker RV. (1992) A donor splice site mutation in the parathyroid hormone gene is associated with autosomal recessive hypoparathyroidism. *Nature Genetics* **1:** 149–152.

Pikielny CW, Rosbash M. (1985) mRNA splicing efficiency in yeast and the contribution of nonconserved sequences. *Cell* **41:** 119–126.

Ramus SJ, Forrest SM, Cotton RGH. (1992) Illegitimate transcription of phenylalanine hydroxylase for detection of mutations in patients with phenylketonuria. *Hum. Mutat.* **1:** 154–158.

Reed R. (1989) The organization of 3′ splice-site sequences in mammalian introns. *Genes Dev.* **3:** 2113–2123.

Reed R, Maniatis T. (1985) Intron sequences involved in lariat formation during pre-mRNA splicing. *Cell* **41:** 95–105.

Reed R, Maniatis T. (1986) A role for exon sequences and splice-site proximity in splice site selection. *Cell* **46:** 681–690.

Reed R, Maniatis T. (1988) The role of the mammalian branchpoint sequence in pre-mRNA splicing. *Genes Dev.* **2:** 1268–1276.

Robberson BL, Cote GJ, Berget SM. (1990) Exon definition may facilitate splice site selection in RNAs with multiple exons. *Mol. Cell. Biol.* **10:** 84–94.

Ruskin B, Green MR. (1985a) Role of the 3′ splice site consensus sequence in mammalian pre-mRNA splicing. *Nature* **317:** 732–734.

Ruskin B, Green MR. (1985b) Specific and stable intron-factor interactions are established early during *in vitro* pre-mRNA splicing. *Cell* **43:** 131–142.

Ruskin B, Greene JM, Green MR. (1985) Cryptic branch point activation allows accurate *in vitro* splicing of human β-globin intron mutants. *Cell* **41:** 833–844.

Shapiro MB, Senapathy P. (1987) RNA splice junctions of different classes of eukaryotes: sequence statistics and functional implications in gene expression. *Nucleic Acids Res.* **15:** 7155–7174.

Smith CWJ, Porro EB, Patton JG, Nadal-Ginard B. (1989) Scanning from an independently specified branch point defines the 3′ splice site of mammalian introns. *Nature* **342:** 243–247.

Solnick D. (1985) Alternative splicing caused by RNA secondary structure. *Cell* **43:** 667–676.

Somasekhar MB, Mertz JE. (1985) Exon mutations that affect the choice of splice sites used in processing the SV40 late transcripts. *Nucleic Acids Res.* **13:** 5591–5609.

Steingrimsdottir H, Rowley G, Dorado G, Cole J, Lehmann AR. (1992) Mutations which alter splicing in the human hypoxanthineguanine phosphoribosyltransferase gene. *Nucleic Acids Res.* **20:** 1201–1208.

Talerico M, Berget SM. (1990) Effect of 5′splice site mutations on splicing of the preceding intron. *Mol. Cell. Biol.* **10:** 6299–6305.

Vasan NS, Kuivaniemi H, Vogel BE, Minor RR, Wootton JAM, Tromp G, Weksberg R, Prockop DJ. (1991) A mutation in the pro α2(I) gene (COL1A2) for type I procollagen in Ehlers–Danlos syndrome type VII: evidence suggesting that skipping of exon 6 in RNA splicing may be a common cause of the phenotype. *Am. J. Hum. Genet.* **48:** 305–317.

Weil D, D'Alessio M, Ramirez F, Steinmann B, Wirtz MK, Glanville RW, Hollister DW. (1990) Temperature-dependent expression of a collagen splicing defect in the fibroblasts of a patient with Ehlers–Danlos syndrome type VII. *J. Biol. Chem.* **264:** 16804–16809.

Wong C, Antonarakis SE, Goff SC, Orkin SH, Forget BG, Nathan DG, Giardina PJV, Kazazian HH. (1989) β-thalassaemia due to two novel nucleotide substitutions in consensus acceptor splice sequences of the β-globin gene. *Blood* **73:** 914–918.

Regulatory mutations

Most pathological lesions underlying human genetic disease lie within gene coding regions. Such mutations usually result in amino acid substitutions, alteration of the translational reading frame or truncation of the encoded protein, either through deletion or via the premature introduction of a termination codon. A different class of molecular lesion is, however, represented by regulatory mutations, and it is this category of lesion that will be reviewed here. These mutations disrupt the normal processes of gene activation and transcriptional initiation and serve either to increase or decrease the level of mRNA/gene product synthesized, rather than altering its nature. The vast majority of regulatory mutations so far described are found in gene promoter regions — the 5′ regulatory sequences which contain constitutive promoter elements, enhancers, repressors, the determinants of tissue-specific gene expression and other responsive elements. The most cogent reason for studying such mutations and their effects on control element function is therefore to gain insight into the various processes that regulate the normal expression of human genes.

10.1 Promoter mutations causing β- and δ-thalassaemia

In humans, the β-globin gene cluster is located on chromosome 11p15.5 and comprises five active genes [two adult (β, δ), two fetal (G-γ, A-γ) and one embryonic (ε)] and one inactive pseudogene [$\psi\beta1$] (Figure 10.1). These genes are differentially regulated and expressed during human development, a process which leads to the replacement of fetal haemoglobin (HbF) [α_2, γ_2] with adult haemoglobins HbA [α_2, β_2] and HbA2 (α_2, δ_2) during the perinatal period. Defects in these genes are many and varied. In the case of the β-globin gene, lesions may either alter the structure of the protein product or the amount of protein produced. The latter class includes the β^+ thalassaemias, where a reduced amount of β-globin is synthesized, and the β^0 thalassaemias, in which β-globin synthesis is completely abolished.

Single base-pair substitutions that occur in the promoter region 5′ to the β-globin (HBB) gene causing β-thalassaemia give rise to a moderate reduction in globin synthesis; the known naturally occurring mutations are highly clustered (Table 10.1). Two regions in particular have been implicated in the regulation of the human β-globin gene by virtue of the phenotypic and clinical

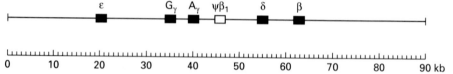

Figure 10.1. Organization of the human β-globin gene cluster on chromosome 11 containing the genes encoding the ε-(HBE1), G-γ-(HBG2), A-γ-(HBG1), δ-(HBD) and β-(HBB) globins and the ψ-β1-pseudogene. The scale is shown in kilobases.

Table 10.1. Mutations in the β-globin (HBB) gene promoter region causing β^+-thalassaemia

Mutation	Nucleotide	Origin	% Normal transcription*	Reference
C→T	−101	Turkish, Bulgarian, Italian	?	Gonzalez-Redondo et al., 1989
C→T	−92	Mediterranean	?	Huisman, 1992
C→T	−90	Portuguese	?	Faustino et al., 1992
C→A	−88	Kurdish	?	Huisman, 1992
C→T	−88	Black, Indian	40	Orkin et al., 1984 Baklouti et al., 1989
C→G	−87	Mediterranean	10	Orkin et al., 1982 Treisman et al., 1983
C→T	−87	German/Italian	45–51	Kulozik et al., 1991
C→A	−87	Yugoslav, Black	?	Huisman, 1992
C→A	−86	Italian	?	Meloni et al., 1992
C→G	−86	Lebanese	?	Huisman, 1992
C→A	−32	Taiwanese	?	Lin et al., 1992a
A→G	−31	Japanese	55	Takihara et al., 1986
T→A	−30	Turkish, Bulgarian	8–10	Fei et al., 1988
T→C	−30	Chinese	?	Cai et al., 1989
A→G	−29	Black, Chinese	25	Huang et al., 1986 Antonarakis et al., 1984
A→C	−28	Kurdish	?	Poncz et al., 1983
A→G	−28	Chinese	10	Orkin et al., 1983

*Defined as the reduction in mutant allele-specific β-globin gene transcription as assessed by *in vitro* expression studies.

effects of these mutations (Myers *et al.*, 1986). One is a CACCC motif located between −91 and −86 relative to the transcriptional initiation site and the other is the TATA box found at about −30 (Figure 10.2). The CACCC box is a highly conserved promoter element (Dierks *et al.*, 1983; Collins and Weissman, 1984; Myers *et al.*, 1986) and appears to bind one or more erythroid-specific nuclear factors which may be involved in the developmental activation of β-globin gene transcription. Such binding is abolished by the −87 C→G mutation (Mantovani *et al.*, 1988b). The TATA box is present 25–30 bp upstream of the transcriptional initiation site in a large number of (but not all) genes and is thought to bind the protein TFIID (Sawadago and Roeder, 1985).

```
   -108            *              -93*   *   * * *         -80
 A G A C C T C A C C C T G T G G A G C C A C A C C C T A G G G T T

   -35     * * * * *              -20
 T G G G C A T A A A A G T C A G G
```

Figure 10.2. Promoter region of the human β-globin (HBB) gene. The TATA box (ATAAAA) and conserved CACCC motif are in bold type. The sites of known mutations are marked with a *.

This protein probably serves to position the start site for mRNA synthesis and may also facilitate interactions with other DNA binding proteins to create a stable transcriptional complex. It is certainly not surprising that mutations in these important promoter elements severely reduce transcription efficiency.

These regions are, however, not the only ones involved in the control of β-globin gene expression. The -101 mutation occurs in a second upstream CACCC motif between -105 and -101. In addition to known mutations in the remote promoter element known as the 'locus control region' (LCR; see Section 10.5), Berg *et al.* (1991) have reported a $+ATA/-T$ mutation at -530 which is associated with reduced β-globin synthesis. This lesion reportedly results in a nine-fold increase in the binding capacity of BP1, a protein which may therefore possess the properties of a repressor (see also Section 12.3).

Defects of the δ-globin gene causing δ-thalassaemia are not usually associated with clinical symptoms since HbA2 ($\alpha_2 \delta_2$) is a minor component of adult Hb. A few mutations causing δ-thalassaemia are, however, known: a G→A transition 69 bp $3'$ to the polyadenylation site of the δ-globin gene appears to be responsible for drastically reducing the expression of the δ-globin gene causing δ-thalassaemia (Moi *et al.*, 1992). The lesion occurs within a motif homologous to the consensus recognition sequence for the erythroid-specific DNA binding protein GATA-1. Gel retardation assays showed that a DNA fragment containing the G→A lesion exhibited increased binding affinity for GATA-1 (Moi *et al.*, 1992). Matsuda *et al.* (1992) have reported a T→C transition at position -77 $5'$ to the δ-globin gene in Japanese patients with δ-thalassaemia. The lesion occurs in an inverted binding motif for GATA-1 (TTATCT); gel retardation assays demonstrated the binding of GATA-1 to the region spanning -61 to -90. Competition experiments showed that GATA-1 binding can be competed out by a wild-type oligonucleotide but not by the mutant oligonucleotide. CAT expression assays demonstrated that a construct containing the mutant promoter region was expressed ~ 20-fold less than a construct containing the wild-type promoter. The -77 lesion therefore appears to impair δ-globin gene expression by abolishing GATA-1 binding to its recognition sequence.

10.2 Hereditary persistence of fetal haemoglobin

The switch from fetal haemoglobin (HbF; α_2, γ_2) to adult haemoglobin (HbA; α_2, β_2) synthesis normally occurs perinatally. The hereditary persistence of fetal haemoglobin (HPFH) is usually a heterozygous condition in which inherited gene lesions cause a marked but variable increase in HbF (α_2, γ_2) synthesis above the normal adult level of $<1\%$. Unlike β-thalassaemia, HPFH heterozygotes do not exhibit an imbalance between the relative amounts of α and non-α (β and γ) chains synthesized. This is because the continued production of fetal γ chains compensates for the lack of β chains. For this reason, HPFH is often only of clinical significance in combination with a heterozygous thalassaemia allele or with sickle cell trait. However, individuals with significant levels of HbF appear to be protected to some extent from the normal clinical effects of these conditions.

The molecular genetic analysis of HPFH has revealed both allelic and non-allelic (locus) heterogeneity, which has helped to account for the observed phenotypic heterogeneity characteristic of this condition. In one form of HPFH, the δ-and β-globin genes may be deleted. A non-deletion form of HPFH also exists, caused by point mutations within the highly homologous promoter regions of the G-γ (HBG2) or A-γ globin (HBG1) genes. From a functional point of view, these lesions are much more interesting than gross gene deletions. Thus, although well reviewed by Ottolenghi *et al.* (1989), this type of lesion will be covered here in some detail.

Some of these point mutations (summarized in Table 10.2) are clustered, providing good (albeit circumstantial) evidence that these substitutions are directly responsible for the raised HbF levels observed in these patients.

Table 10.2. Promoter mutations associated with the A-γ (HBG1) and G-γ (HBG2) globin genes in non-deletion hereditary persistence of fetal haemoglobin (HPFH)

Gene	Nucleotide change/position		% Hb F in heterozygote*	Origin	Reference
HBG1	C→T	−114	3–5	Black	Öner *et al.*, 1991
HBG1	G→A	−117	10–20	Greek	Collins *et al.*, 1985
					Gelinas *et al.*, 1985
HBG1	T→C	−175	38	Black	Stoming *et al.*, 1989
HBG1	C→G	−195	4–7	Brazilian	Costa *et al.*, 1990
HBG1	C→T	−196	10–20	Italian	Gelinas *et al.*, 1986
					Giglioni *et al.*, 1984
				Chinese	Ottolenghi *et al.*, 1987
HBG1	T→C	−198	3–10	British	Tate *et al.*, 1986
HBG1	C→T	−202	1.6–3.9	Black	Gilman *et al.*, 1988
HBG2	C→T	−114	11–14	Japanese	Fucharoen *et al.*, 1990
HBG2	C→T	−158	2–4	Black	Gilman and Huisman, 1985
					Labie *et al.*, 1985
				Saudi	Miller *et al.*, 1986
HBG2	G→A	−161	1–2	Black	Gilman *et al.*, 1988
HBG2	T→C	−175	18–20	Black	Ottolenghi *et al.*, 1988
					Surrey *et al.*, 1988
HBG2	C→G	−202	15–25	Black	Collins *et al.*, 1984

*HbF is normally $<1\%$ of total haemoglobin in healthy adult humans.

Further, in most cases, the observed lesions were shown to be the only mutations detected within the gene regions and had never been found before in control individuals. Their independent origin in geographically separate populations also argued for their authenticity. Finally, three examples are known of HPFH mutations at homologous positions in the HBG1 and HBG2 genes (at -114, -175 and -202), a finding which argues strongly for the functional significance of the surrounding regions. From the data presented in Table 10.2, it is difficult to discern any immediate association between location of the lesion and the amount of HbF synthesized. However, as discussed below, *in vitro* expression experiments have shown that such mutations are indeed responsible for increasing the level of γ-globin gene transcription.

The -202 mutation occurs within a GGGGCCCC motif (Figure 10.3) reminiscent of the GC box (GGGCGG) that serves as a binding site for the transcription factor Sp1 (La Thangue and Rigby, 1988). Interestingly, individuals heterozygous for the C→T mutation at -202 of the HBG1 gene had 5–10 times less HbF than those with the C→G mutation at -202 of the HBG2 gene (Gilman *et al.*, 1988). Gumucio *et al.* (1991) have shown that this position normally acts as a weak binding site for Sp1. Using mobility shift assays, Sykes and Kaufman (1990) studied the effect of the C→T and C→G mutations on Sp1 binding: the C→T transition, which decreases the similarity of the motif to an Sp1 binding site, did not serve to enhance Sp1 binding but did alter the interaction with other normally bound protein factors. The C→G mutation, on the other hand, which increases the similarity of the motif to an Sp1 binding site, increased Sp1 binding affinity some 5–10-fold over that of the wild type and also reduced the binding of other normally bound protein factors. It is possible, therefore, that the much higher level of HbF found associated with the C→G mutation is due specifically to this effect on Sp1 binding. In contrast to the above results, however, Lin *et al.* (1992b) have reported only a small effect on promoter function to result from the mutation of nucleotides between -200 and -190.

Three different mutations occurred between -195 and -198 in the HBG1 gene. This region possesses a TCCCCAC motif similar to the TC motif of the SV40 viral enhancer (Figure 10.3). Rixon and Gelinas (1988) failed to note any difference in promoter strength between the -196 mutant and its

```
      -205     * -200    *    *  *        -190
  G G G G G C C C C T T C C C C A C A C T A T C

      -180           *        -170      -165      *       *    -155
  T C A A T G C A A A T A T C T G T C T G A A A C G G T T C C T G G

      -120      *        *        -110
  T T G C C T T G A C C A A T A G C
```

Figure 10.3. Promoter sequence upstream of the homologous human γ-globin genes. The GGGGCCCC and CCTTGA motifs are in bold type. The ATGCAAAT (octamer) motif and distal CCAAT box are underlined. The sites of known mutations are marked with a *.

wild-type counterpart *in vitro*. By contrast, the T→C mutation at −198 reportedly resulted in a greatly increased binding capacity for Sp1 (Fischer and Nowock, 1990; Gumucio *et al.*, 1991).

T→C mutations at −175 have been found in both HBG1 and HBG2 genes. This base occurs within an ATGCAAAT motif (−182 to −175) known as the octamer. The octamer is found in the promoters of a number of human genes inluding those encoding immunoglobulins, histones and snRNAs. It is known to bind a range of regulatory proteins which exert both positive and negative transcriptional effects (reviewed by La Thangue and Rigby, 1988).

The −175 lesion has been shown to increase the strength of the promoter between three- and 20-fold *in vitro* but only in erythroid cells (Lloyd *et al.*, 1989; Martin *et al.*, 1989; Nicolis *et al.*, 1989; Gumucio *et al.*, 1990; McDonagh *et al.*, 1991). This lesion appears to reduce or abolish the ability of the ubiquitous octamer binding protein (OTF-1) to bind at this site (Gumucio *et al.*, 1988; Mantovani *et al.*, 1988a; Nicolis *et al.*, 1989; O'Neill *et al.*, 1990) and alters the binding of the erythroid-specific protein, GATA-1 (Mantovani *et al.*, 1988a; Martin *et al.*, 1989; Nicolis *et al.*, 1989; McDonagh *et al.*, 1991; see also Section 10.1). DNase I footprinting and gel mobility shift assays have provided evidence for the binding of OTF-1 and GATA-1 to the −194 to −172 region such that their 'footprints' overlap (O'Neill *et al.*, 1990). GATA-1 recognizes the consensus sequence (A/T)GA(T/C)A(G/A)G that is present from −167 to −175 and from −185 to −190 (on the antisense strand). It is not clear whether GATA-1 is a dimeric protein or whether these sequence motifs represent alternative binding sites for GATA-1. It is thought that OTF-1 may act as a repressor of γ-globin gene transcription and compete with GATA-1 for the −175 binding site. Stoming *et al.* (1989) noted a difference in the relative amount of Hb F in a patient with an HBG1 gene T→C mutation at −175 as compared with the patient exhibiting an HBG2 gene lesion reported by Surrey *et al.* (1988). This could arise from promoter-specific effects or from an additive effect of the HBG2 gene mutation (T→C at −158) also found in the patient with the HBG1 gene lesion.

One of the HPFH mutations (−117) occurred within the highly conserved CCTTGA motif (Figure 10.3) immediately upstream of the distal CCAAT box (a second CCAAT box is found at −88) of the HBG1 gene. This motif occurs in mammalian globin genes expressed during the embryonic or fetal developmental periods but is not found in adult-type β-globin gene promoters (Collins *et al.*, 1985). *In vitro* expression experiments have shown that the −117 mutation is associated with a variable degree of overexpression of the HBG1 gene (Stoeckert *et al.*, 1987; Rixon and Gelinas, 1988). Mutation of −117 greatly reduces the binding of erythroid-specific factors GATA-1 and NFE-3 (Mantovani *et al.*, 1988a; Superti-Furga *et al.*, 1988; Berry *et al.*, 1992). Although this mutation has also been reported as increasing the affinity of the ubiquitous CCAAT-binding factor CP1 for its binding site (Gumucio *et al.*, 1988; Superti-Furga *et al.*, 1988), this was not confirmed by Berry *et al.* (1992). GATA-1 and NFE-3 may therefore normally act as repressors of γ-globin gene activity in adult erythroid cells.

Employing mice transgenic for an HBG1 gene bearing the -117 mutation, Berry *et al.* (1992) reported a decrease in β-globin (HBB) gene expression concomitant with a persistent high-level expression of the HBG1 gene. The lowered expression of the HBB gene in *cis* to the HPFH allele has also been reported by Giglioni *et al.* (1984) and may be due to competition between the γ and β genes for activation by the locus control region (Behringer *et al.*, 1990; Hanscombe *et al.*, 1991; see Section 10.5).

$C \rightarrow T$ mutations have been found within the distal CCAAT box at -114 in both HBG1 and HBG2 genes. The amount of HbF produced is, however, considerably higher for the HBG2 mutation, a situation paralleling that involving the two homologous -202 mutations. Using gel retardation assays, Fucharoen *et al.* (1990) have demonstrated that the -114 mutation abolishes the binding of CP1 to the distal CCAAT motif of the HBG2 gene, although the lesion does not affect the binding of erythroid-specific factors. This finding would tend to argue against a role for CP1 in the developmental regulation of fetal globin gene expression.

Gelinas *et al.* (1988) have reported a Seattle variant of HPFH in which no pathological lesions were found in any of the four γ-globin gene promoter regions. However, analysis of the enhancer region, located $3'$ to the HBG1 gene, on the putative HPFH chromosome revealed three single base-pair substitutions consistent with an alteration of enhancer function.

The characterization of mutations in the promoter regions of the human γ-globin genes has thus resulted in the recognition of a number of important sequence motifs which are thought to be involved in the control of fetal to adult haemoglobin switching through interaction with a variety of *trans*-acting factors. Some of these factors appear to be repressors; known mutations within their binding sites which reduce their binding affinity therefore up-regulate γ-globin gene expression. Other factors are probably activators; known mutations within their recognition sites increase their binding affinity and hence also serve to up-regulate γ-globin gene expression.

10.3 Hereditary persistence of α-fetoprotein

The hereditary persistence of α-fetoprotein (HPAFP) is a clinically harmless autosomal dominant trait which is characterized by the continued expression of the fetally expressed α-fetoprotein (AFP) gene into adult life. Normally AFP is produced at a high level in fetal liver but declines rapidly after birth and is barely detectable in the adult. In humans, the AFP gene is located on chromosome 4q11–q13, very closely linked to the evolutionarily related albumin (ALB) gene. (By contrast, the ALB gene is expressed in both fetal and adult tissues.)

McVey *et al.* (1993) have reported the molecular genetic analysis of a child and its family with HPAFP. Sequencing of the promoter region of the AFP gene revealed a $G \rightarrow A$ substitution at position -119. This lesion co-segregated with the HPAFP phenotype through the multigenerational pedigree. *In vitro* expression experiments were conducted with artificial constructs, comprising mutant and wild-type promoters placed upstream of the chloramphenicol acetyltransferase (CAT) reporter gene, being used to transfect HepG2 cells. A construct bearing the -119 mutation was found to direct a higher level of CAT expression than its wild-type counterpart. This difference in expression, very reminiscent of HPFH, was accentuated by treatment with dexamethasone.

The -119 G$\rightarrow$A mutation occurred within a GTTAATTATTGGC motif (from -130 to -118) which possesses strong homology to the HNF1 binding site consensus sequence (GTTAATNATTAAC) of Courtois et al. (1988). Interestingly, the observed mutation renders the motif more similar to the consensus sequence than the original wild-type sequence. The murine AFP gene also possesses an HNF1 binding site at the homologous position in the promoter, and Feuerman et al. (1989) have demonstrated by in vitro transfection assays that mutation of this HNF1 binding site results in a significant reduction in AFP gene transcription.

Also present within this sequence is an inverted CCAAT box starting at position -119. It is tempting to speculate that the observed mutation enhances transcription of the AFP gene by increasing the affinity of the HNF1 binding site, perhaps through displacement of the normally bound negative regulatory proteins. However, further protein binding studies will be required to establish the exact mechanism of transcriptional enhancement and the identity of the various proteins involved.

10.4 Haemophilia B Leyden

Haemophilia B Leyden is a fascinating example of how the study of a group of regulatory mutations can provide insights into functional questions. This Dutch factor IX variant is characterized by severe childhood haemophilia, which is ameliorated at puberty probably under the influence of testosterone (Briët et al., 1982). The amelioration in clinical phenotype is foreshadowed by an increase in plasma factor IX activity/antigen values from $<1\%$ to between 30 and 60% of normal. These observations suggested that the causative lesion might reside in a regulatory rather than a structural region of the factor IX (F9) gene. Sequencing of 600 bp of $5'$ non-coding region of the F9 gene (Reitsma et al., 1988) initially revealed two changes at nucleotide positions -20 and -423 (relative to the transcriptional initiation site). The latter change is now considered to be a common polymorphism (Tsang et al., 1988) but the former, a T$\rightarrow$A transversion, is located within a possible TATA box and is presumed to be the underlying regulatory mutation. Evidence for this assertion initially came from the observation that no such variant had previously been found in other F9 gene sequences determined from either normal alleles or alleles from other types of haemophilia B. Further, the T$\rightarrow$A change co-segregated with the disease phenotype in at least two apparently unrelated Dutch pedigrees. Finally, this T residue is highly conserved in the F9 gene promoters of five mammalian species (Pang et al., 1990).

Four further patients with the haemophilia B Leyden phenotype, of Greek, American and British origin, exhibited different mutations at nucleotide +13: the deletion of an A in one and an identical A→G transition in the other three (Bottema *et al.*, 1989; Crossley *et al.*, 1989; Reitsma *et al.*, 1989). The +13 residue is also conserved between five mammalian species (Pang *et al.*, 1990). Hirosawa *et al.* (1990) and Crossley *et al.* (1990) have both independently reported CG→CA base changes at nucleotide −6 which segregate with the Leyden phenotype through three-generation families, whereas Gispert *et al.* (1989) have noted a G→C transversion at −6 with a similar phenotype. The −6 G residue is also found in the macaque F9 gene but is substituted by an A residue in the mouse, rat and dog F9 gene promoters (Pang *et al.*, 1990). Royle *et al.* (1991) have noted a *de novo* T→C mutation at position +8 in a New Zealand family of Anglo-Irish origin, while Freedenberg and Black (1991) have reported a T→A point mutation at position +6. Picketts *et al.* (1992) have described a sporadic case of mild haemophilia B in a 3-year-old boy with 3% factor IX activity and an A→T transversion at position −5.

Reitsma *et al.* (1989) noted sequence similarity within the F9 gene promoter spanning the region in which the above lesions occurred. These authors showed that the region from −5 to +23 possesses significant homology with the region immediately upstream from −31 to −6 (Figure 10.4). This has been termed the Leyden-specific (LS) region by Hirosawa *et al.* (1990). All mutated sites occur within the region of homology.

Crossley and Brownlee (1990) demonstrated by DNase I footprinting that the +13 mutation lies within a binding site (+1 to +18) for the CCAAT/enhancer binding protein (C/EBP) and serves to abolish binding of C/EBP to this site. Further, C/EBP was shown to be capable of transactivating a co-transfected normal F9 promoter but not the mutant promoter. Whatever the underlying mechanism here, it must be distinct from that involving the −6 mutation; this substitution did not affect the C/EBP footprint in any way.

In an *in vitro* reporter gene expression system, Reijnen *et al.* (1992) demonstrated that the −20 lesion was associated with a ~17-fold reduction in CAT activity as compared with the wild-type sequence. Using gel retardation analysis, Crossley *et al.* (1992) demonstrated that a DNA fragment from −40 to −9 formed complexes with two rat liver proteins. One of these proteins appeared to be LF-A1/HNF4. A sequence very similar to the consensus binding site for LF-A1/HNF4 (TGGACTTTGGCCC) is evident between −27 and −15. Since an oligonucleotide specific for the −20 mutation was not able to compete for binding, it was inferred that this lesion disrupts the LF-A1/HNF4 binding site, thus impairing F9 promoter activity.

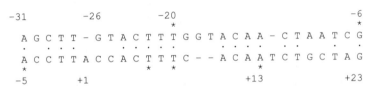

Figure 10.4. Leyden-specific region of the human factor IX (F9) gene promoter. Aligned bases are denoted by dots while the sites known to be mutated in haemophilia B Leyden-like phenotypes are marked with a *.

Since the post-pubertal manufacture of testosterone apparently serves to increase factor IX production, the characterization of upstream testosterone-responsive elements was clearly very important. Crossley et al. (1989) noted that a perfect palindrome at -20 exhibited similarities with a testosterone-responsive element characterized in mouse mammary tumour virus (MMTV). Hirosawa et al. (1990) pointed out homology between the sequence from -20 to -6 and the glucocorticoid-responsive element consensus sequence.

A possible explanatory model for the Leyden phenotype is suggested by the observation that the progesterone-responsive element is able to stimulate the rate of transcription of a gene in the absence of a functional TATA box (Thomson et al., 1990). This finding indicates how exposure to a steroid hormone could serve to override an existing mutation in a constitutive promoter element. Consistent with this postulate, in vitro expression studies (Hirosawa et al., 1990) demonstrated that mutations at -20 and -6 were associated with lowered expression of the F9 gene and that restoration of expression in a concentration-dependent fashion was observed upon treatment of the cultured cells with androgen. Gel retardation assays provided good evidence for the binding of two proteins, termed LSP-1 and LSP-2, to the region between -32 and $+8$ (Hirosawa et al., 1990).

Crossley et al. (1992) reported several lines of evidence to support the view that an AGCTCAGCTTGTACT motif between -36 and -22, with strong homology to the androgen-responsive element (ARE) consensus sequence, is functional. Firstly, the F9 ARE, linked to the Herpes virus TK gene promoter and CAT reporter gene, was transactivated in HeLa cells by a co-transfected androgen receptor gene in the presence of testosterone. A threshold effect was observed such that one, two and four copies of the ARE produced a zero, three-fold and >50-fold transactivation of the TK promoter respectively. Secondly, the F9 ARE was shown by gel retardation analysis to be capable of binding androgen receptor protein in vitro. The -20 mutation, which is located within the LF-A1/HNF4 binding site but outside the ARE, was capable of supporting transactivation in the above system. This suggested that, although the lesion disrupts the LF-A1/HNF4 binding site, its effects could still be overriden by ARE-mediated transcriptional enhancement. The -20 mutation did not affect binding of androgen receptor to the F9 promoter. A second mutation [G→C at position -26 (Haemophilia B Brandenburg)] also markedly reduced transcription of the F9 gene. This lesion occurs in the region of overlap between the LF-A1/HNF4 binding site and the ARE and thus disrupts both elements. As a consequence, the -26 mutation abolished binding of the androgen receptor and did not support transactivation. These in vitro results are sufficient to account for the in vivo phenotype in this patient, namely no increase in factor IX activity and no amelioration of bleeding tendency at puberty.

In summary, it would appear that, before puberty, several transcription factors (including C/EBP, LF-A1/HNF4 and a further protein which binds to the -6 site) are involved in potentiating the expression of the F9 gene. Since mutations interfering with the binding of any of these factors lead to the abolition of F9 gene transcription, these proteins probably act in concert. It is assumed that at puberty, when a testosterone-dependent mechanism mediated by the ARE comes into play, the binding of all three transcription factors ceases to be an absolute requirement for transcription to occur.

10.5 Mutation in remote promoter elements

The first hint that mutations at some considerable distance 5' to the transcriptional initiation site could affect the expression of a downstream gene came from the study of Van der Ploeg *et al.* (1980): a >40 kb deletion of the G–γ (HBG2), A–γ (HBG1) and δ-globin (HBD) genes was found to have been responsible for a Dutch case of γ–δ–β-thalassaemia, but this deletion had left the β-globin (HBB) gene intact together with at least 2.5 kb 5' flanking sequence. The implication was that the removal of sequences far upstream of the HBB gene had resulted in suppression of its transcriptional activity. Kioussis *et al.* (1983) then showed that, although the HBB gene in this patient was identical in sequence to that of the wild-type, the surrounding chromatin appeared to be in an inactive conformation as judged by DNaseI sensitivity and methylation analysis.

Curtin *et al.* (1985) reported a 90 kb deletion of the β-globin gene cluster in an English γ–δ–β thalassaemia patient. The ε-globin (HBE1) gene and part of the HBG2 gene were deleted but the HBG1, $\psi\beta$, HBD and HBB genes were still intact. A deletion more than 25 kb upstream of the HBB gene therefore served to abolish its expression. As if to emphasize this point, Driscoll *et al.* (1989) described a 25kb deletion in an Hispanic patient with γ–δ–β thalassaemia. The deletion was located between 9.5 kb and 39 kb upstream of the HBE1 gene and included three of the four erythroid cell-specific DNaseI hypersensitive sites 5' to the HBE1 gene. These sites are present prior to transcriptional activation of the globin genes and are developmentally stable. All the globin genes, including HBE1, and the DNaseI hypersensitive site 6.1 kb 5' to it, remained intact. The HBB gene, some 60 kb downstream from the 3' deletion breakpoint, was nevertheless rendered non-functional. The three deletions quoted are shown in Figure 10.5.

Grosveld *et al.* (1987) showed that DNA containing the four erythroid-specific hypersensitive sites was capable of directing a high level of position-

Figure 10.5. Map of the β-globin gene cluster showing the extents of the deletions in three cases of γ–δ–β thalassaemia. Dotted lines indicate uncertainty of deletion endpoints.

independent HBB gene expression *in vitro*. The location of the putative 'locus control region' (LCR) or 'locus-activating region' has now been further narrowed down to a 0.8 kb DNA fragment, between 10.2 kb and 11 kb 5' to the HBE1 gene, and is believed to contain an enhancer capable of directing the expression of downstream sequences in an erythroid-specific fashion (Tuan *et al.*, 1989). The region around the second hypersensitive site (HS2) has been shown by experiments in transgenic mice to be both necessary and sufficient for developmental regulation of the human β-globin gene cluster (Morley *et al.*, 1992). Further, HBB gene expression is abolished by the targeted insertional inactivation of the LCR in a mouse/human hybrid erythroid cell line (Kim *et al.*, 1992).

Forrester *et al.* (1990) studied the chromatin structure and timing of DNA replication of both the normal β-globin gene cluster and that containing the Hispanic (25 kb) deletion. As far as chromatin structure was concerned, the deletion conferred DNaseI resistance upon the region as far as 100 kb 3' to the HBB gene. The globin locus on the Hispanic chromosome replicates late, in contrast to the early replication exhibited by the wild-type chromosome, suggesting that the LCR may contain an origin of replication. Since the effect on chromatin conformation appeared to be unidirectional and that on replication timing bidirectional, it is likely that these properties of the LCR are separable and that the LCR contains a variety of different regulatory elements.

The LCR therefore serves both to organize the β-globin gene cluster into an active chromatin domain and to enhance the transcription of individual globin genes. Haemoglobin gene switching is now thought to come about through competition between the different globin genes for access to the LCR. Thus, while the transcription of the HBE1 gene is enhanced by the closely linked LCR in the embryo, HBE1 gene expression is suppressed in the fetus through the activation of a silencer element. Expression of the γ-globin genes then becomes dominant.

A similar situation may pertain in the α-globin gene cluster at chromosome 16pter-p13.3. Hatton *et al.* (1990) reported a 62 kb deletion causing α-thalassaemia encompassing the embryonic α-like $\zeta 2$ (HBZ) globin gene but which left the other genes and pseudogenes of the α-globin gene cluster intact (Figure 10.6). Although the sequences of the two α genes [$\alpha 1$ (HBA1) and $\alpha 2$ (HBA2)] were found to be normal, they nevertheless appeared to be transcriptionally inactive. Several other examples of similar deletions 5' to the α-globin gene cluster have now been reported: Wilkie *et al.* (1990) described a case of α-thalassaemia involving the truncation of chromosome 16 to a position 50 kb upstream of the α-globin genes. A more extensive deletion, from ~ 17 kb upstream of the HBA2 gene to the 16p telomere, has been reported by Romao *et al.* (1992). Liebhaber *et al.* (1990) reported a 35 kb deletion with its 3' breakpoint 30 kb upstream of the α-globin genes. Finally, Romao *et al.* (1991) described an extensive (> 105 kb) deletion whose 3' endpoint was located 27 kb upstream of the α-globin genes. These deletions exhibit an area of overlap between 30 and 50 kb upstream of the α-globin genes (Figure 10.6). Since the patients concerned do not exhibit any obvious phenotypic differences, it may

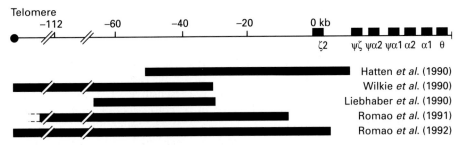

Figure 10.6. Deletions 5′ to the α-globin gene cluster causing α-thalassaemia. Shown are the ζ-2-globin (HBZ), α-2-globin (HBA2), α-1-globin (HBA1) and θ-1-globin (HBQ1) genes and three pseudogenes. Dotted lines show region of uncertainty.

be inferred that regions outside the area of overlap are incapable of influencing α-globin gene expression significantly. This region contains several DNaseI hypersensitive sites (two erythroid-specific) and is capable of directing the high-level expression of an α-globin gene both in stably transfected mouse erythroleukaemia cells and when integrated into the genomes of transgenic mice (Higgs *et al.*, 1990; Vyas *et al.*, 1992). The regulatory element has been further localized to a 350 bp stretch and the presence of functional binding sites for the transcription factors GATA-1 and AP-1 confirmed by DNase footprinting and gel retardation assays (Jarman *et al.*, 1991). It is therefore clear that an LCR, analogous to that found upstream of the β-globin gene cluster, is also present upstream of the α-globin gene cluster.

How frequent are LCRs in human genes? This question is important diagnostically since mutation in LCRs would not be detectable by routine sequencing of the coding regions plus exon–intron boundaries. Unfortunately, few data are as yet available. However, enhancer elements required for normal tissue-specific expression have been found ~3.5 kb upstream of the human α-fetoprotein (AFP) gene (Watanabe *et al.*, 1987) and as far as 11 kb upstream of the rat ornithine transcarbamylase (OAT) gene (Murakami *et al.*, 1990). Candidate genes for possession of an LCR must include cases where mutations are not readily apparent in a substantial proportion of patients screened by the sequencing of exons and splice junctions. One example of the latter phenomenon is that of haemophilia A: no mutation appears to be detectable within the factor VIII (F8) gene coding sequence in ~50% of patients with severe haemophilia A, although such mutations are invariably found in mild and moderate cases (Higuchi *et al.*, 1991). However, this example is perhaps potentially misleading since evidence is now emerging for a highly unusual clustering of mutations in the vicinity of intron 22 of the F8 gene, which appear to result in defective splicing of exons 22 and 23 in the mRNA transcript (Naylor *et al.*, 1992). Anecdotal reports from other disease states suggest that failure to detect all pathological lesions associated with a given disease state may be more common than hitherto realized.

10.6 Promoter mutations causing retinoblastoma

Two single base-pair substitutions have been reported to occur in the promoter region of the retinoblastoma (RB1) gene (Sakai *et al.*, 1991). The first was a G → T transversion 189 bp upstream of the Met translational initiation codon. This occurred in a GTGAC<u>G</u>T motif which is homologous to the consensus sequence for ATF, a DNA binding protein of the CREB family of transcription factors. The second lesion was a G → A transition, 198 bp upstream of the initiation codon within a GGGC<u>G</u>G motif homologous to the Sp1 binding protein consensus sequence. Neither lesion was found in a screen of over 100 normal controls. Using a nuclear extract from a monkey kidney cell line and oligonucleotides corresponding to the mutant and wild-type sequences, Sakai *et al.* (1991) carried out gel retardation assays to determine whether or not these sequences could bind nuclear proteins. They concluded that nuclear factors including Sp1 could indeed complex with the wild-type sequences but not with those of the mutants. This finding was consistent with the two mutations being the pathological lesions responsible for the retinoblastoma phenotype.

10.7 Promoter polymorphisms that exert a phenotypic effect

In the preceding sections of this chapter, a considerable number of promoter mutations have been described which serve to alter the normal expression of the downstream gene in such a way that a pathological effect on clinical phenotype can be recognized. The question naturally arises as to whether gene promoters might also harbour DNA sequence polymorphisms which, instead of being phenotypically and clinically neutral as normally expected of polymorphisms (see Section 5.5), could exert some influence on the transcriptional activity of the downstream gene. Such comparatively minor effects on transcription might not always be immediately apparent but could still assume clinical significance in combination with another sequence change, whether it be another polymorphism or a true mutation. Several examples of promoter polymorphisms of possible or probable phenotypic importance are described below.

Elevated levels of apolipoprotein AI (ApoAI), the major constituent of high density lipoprotein (HDL), are associated with a reduced risk of coronary artery disease. A (G/A) polymorphism upstream of the human APOA1 gene, at position −75, may be of some clinical importance: the A allele has been found to be strongly associated with elevated levels of HDL cholesterol and ApoAI in UK males (Jeenah *et al.*, 1990), Icelandic males (Sigurdsson *et al.*, 1992), Italian females (Pagani *et al.*, 1990) and Belgian boys and young men (Paul-Hayase *et al.*, 1992). In the latter study, the G → A substitution was associated with 3.6% of the variance in ApoAI concentration. To confirm that the (G/A) polymorphism is itself functionally significant rather than merely in linkage disequilibrium with some other sequence change, *in vitro* expression studies have been performed: constructs containing 330 bp APOA1 gene promoter and the CAT reporter gene were used to transfect Hep3B liver cells (Tuteja *et al.*, 1992). Contrary to expectation, an A→G transition served to *increase* promoter activity ~ two-fold. However, when 1469 bp APOA1 gene promoter sequence was used, no difference in promoter activity between A and G forms was observed. Similar experiments in another laboratory have, however, yielded the opposite result, the A allele being associated with higher transcriptional activity than the G allele (S. E. Humphries, personal communication). The (G/A) polymorphism is located between a CCACAT sequence at -105 and the TAAATA box at -30. The G→A change, consistent with a methylation-mediated deamination event, creates a 6 bp direct repeat [CAGGGCC(A/G)GGGC]. Recently, DNase footprinting analysis has demonstrated protein binding to the region -128 to -77 (Papazafiri *et al.*, 1991). It is possible that the (G/A) polymorphism differentially affects the binding affinity of such a protein, resulting in a change in the transcriptional activity of the APOA1 gene.

Olansky *et al.* (1992) have reported a copy number polymorphism between -322 and -315 upstream of the human insulin (INS) gene. The polymorphism consists of either one or two copies of an octanucleotide motif (TGGTCTAA) and appears to be confined to the Black population. These authors found the larger allele to be present in five of 100 patients with non-insulin-dependent diabetes mellitus (NIDDM), but in only one of 100 non-diabetic individuals. In Mauritian Creoles, the larger allele was found in three of 41 NIDDM patients but in none of 41 non-diabetic controls. In at least one family, however, possession of the larger allele was found not to be necessary for diabetes to occur. The relative activities of the two types of gene promoter were then compared in both hamster and mouse insulinoma cells transfected with insulin promoter/firefly luciferase reporter gene constructs. The larger allele was associated with ~ 38–49% reduction in promoter activity as compared with the shorter allele. Taken together, these data suggest that a naturally occurring insulin gene promoter polymorphism in the Black population could contribute to the development of diabetes in ~ 5% of NIDDM patients.

Dawson *et al.* (1993) have studied a common insertion/deletion polymorphism at position -675 in the plasminogen activator inhibitor-1 (PAI1) gene. The polymorphism involves the addition or loss of a single G residue in a sequence [TGAGGGG(G)TGC] with perfect homology to the deletion hotspot consensus sequence (Chapter 7). Gel retardation assays suggested that the *ins* allele contains a protein binding site not found in the *del* allele. Oligonucleotide competition experiments suggested that this protein might be related to NF-κB, a ubiquitous transcription factor which has been implicated in the regulation of genes by interleukin-1. *In vitro* expression studies in liver cells using CAT reporter gene constructs showed that transcriptional activity associated with the *del* allele increased six-fold in response to treatment with interleukin-1 whereas no increase in mRNA production was noted from the *ins* allele. In a sample of 107 patients with a history of myocardial infarction, individuals homozygous for the *del* allele exhibited a significantly higher plasma PAI-1 activity level than those heterozygous or homozygous for the *ins* allele. Taken together, these results suggest that individuals homozygous for the *del* allele possess higher plasma PAI-1 levels and may exhibit an altered PAI-1 response during the acute phase.

Finally, DNA sequence polymorphisms upstream of the β-globin (HBB) gene and within the β-globin gene cluster LCR appear to be capable of modulating β-globin gene expression, thereby ameliorating the clinical severity of sickle cell disease. This phenomenon is discussed in detail in Section 12.3.

10.8 Conclusion

A considerable number of regulatory mutations causing human genetic disease have now been described. These lesions occur within gene promoters at very different distances from the downstream sites of transcriptional initiation, and are located within or span a variety of different DNA sequence motifs. What these lesions have in common is their characteristic ability to alter or even abolish the binding capacity of *cis*-acting DNA sequence motifs for the *trans*-acting protein factors that normally interact with them. The exact effect on protein binding is determined by the precise location of the lesion with respect to the binding site as well as by the nature of the lesion itself. The clinical phenotype observed is determined firstly by the identity of the gene involved, and secondly by the normal regulatory function of the *trans*-acting factor whose binding is perturbed, and by whether the ability of this factor to perform its function is increased or decreased as a consequence of the lesion. The study of regulatory mutations is thus not only providing new insights into the intricacies of gene regulation but is also helping to explain some of the more puzzling clinical phenotypes associated with human inherited disease.

References

Antonarakis SE, Orkin SH, Cheng T-C, Scott AF, Sexton JP, Trusko SP, Charache S, Kazazian HH. (1984) β-thalassemia in American blacks: novel mutations in the 'TATA' box and an acceptor splice site. *Proc. Natl. Acad. Sci. USA* **81:** 1154–1158.

Baklouti F, Ouazana R, Gonnet C, Lapillonne A, Delaunay J, Godet J. (1989) β^+-thalassaemia in *cis* of a sickle gene: occurrence of a promoter mutation on a β^s chromosome. *Blood* **74:** 1817–1822.

Behringer RR, Ryan TM, Palmiter RD, Brinster RL, Townes TM. (1990) Human γ- to β-globin switching in transgenic mice. *Genes Dev.* **4:** 380–389.

Berg PE, Mittelman M, Elion J, Labie D, Schechter AN. (1991) Increased protein binding to a -530 mutation of the human β-globin gene associated with decreased β-globin synthesis. *Am. J. Hematol.* **36:** 42–47.

Berry M, Grosveld F, Dillon N. (1992) A single point mutation is the cause of the Greek form of hereditary persistence of fetal haemoglobin. *Nature* **358:** 499–502.

Bottema CDK, Koeberl DD, Sommer SS. (1989) Direct carrier testing in 14 families with haemophilia B. *Lancet* **ii:** 526–529.

Briët E, Bertina RM, van Tilburg NH, Veltkamp JJ. (1982) Haemophilia B Leyden: a sex-linked hereditary disorder that improves after puberty. *N. Engl. J. Med.* **306:** 788–792.

Cai S-P, Zhang J-Z, Doherty M, Kan YW. (1989) A new TATA box mutation detected at prenatal diagnosis for β-thalassemia. *Am. J. Hum. Genet.* **45:** 112–114.

Collins FS, Weissman SM. (1984) The molecular genetics of human hemoglobin. *Prog. Nucl. Acid Res. Mol. Biol.* **31:** 315–353.

Collins FS, Stoeckert CJ, Serjeant GR, Forget BG, Weissman SM. (1984) G-γ β+ hereditary persistence of fetal hemoglobin: cosmid cloning and identification of a specific mutation 5′ to the G-γ gene. *Proc. Natl. Acad. Sci. USA* **81:** 4894–4898.

Collins FS, Metherall JE, Yamakawa M, Pan J, Weissman SM, Forget BG. (1985) A point mutation in the A-γ globin gene promoter in Greek hereditary persistence of fetal haemoglobin. *Nature* **313:** 325–326.

Costa FF, Zago MA, Cheng G, Nechtman JF, Stoming TA, Huisman THJ. (1990) The Brazilian type of nondeletional A-γ fetal hemoglobin has a C → G substitution at nucleotide − 195 of the A-γ globin gene. *Blood* **76:** 1896–1897.

Courtois G, Baumhueter S, Crabtree GR. (1988) Purified hepatocyte nuclear factor 1 interacts with a family of hepatocyte-specific promoters. *Proc. Natl. Acad. Sci. USA* **85:** 7937–7941.

Crossley M, Brownlee GG. (1990) Disruption of a C/EBP binding site in the factor IX promoter is associated with haemophilia B. *Nature* **345:** 444–446.

Crossley M, Winship P, Brownlee GG. (1989) Functional analysis of the normal and an aberrant factor IX promoter. P.51. In *Regulation of liver gene expression.* Cold Spring Harbor Laboratory, New York.

Crossley M, Winship PR, Austen DEG, Rizza CR, Brownlee GG. (1990) A less severe form of haemophilia B Leyden. *Nucleic Acids Res.* **18:** 4633.

Crossley M, Ludwig M, Stowell KM, De Vos P, Olek K, Brownlee GG. (1992) Recovery from hemophilia B Leyden: an androgen-responsive element in the factor IX promoter. *Science* **257:** 377–379.

Curtin P, Pirastu M, Kan YW, Gobert-Jones JA, Stephens AD, Lehmann H. (1985) A distant gene deletion affects β-globin gene function in an atypical γ-δ-β-thalassemia. *J. Clin. Invest.* **76:** 1554–1558.

Dawson SJ, Wiman B, Hamsten A, Green F, Humphries S, Henney AM. (1993) The two allele sequences of a common polymorphism in the promoter of the plasminogen activator inhibitor-1 (PAI-1) gene respond differently to IL-1 in HepG2 cells. *J. Biol. Chem.* **268:** 10739–10745.

Dierks P, Van Ooyen A, Cochran MD, Dobkin C, Reiser J, Weissman C. (1983) Three regions upstream from the cap site are required for efficient and accurate transcription of the rabbit β-globin gene in mouse 3T6 cells. *Cell* **32:** 695–701.

Driscoll MC, Dobkin CS, Alter BP. (1989) γ-δ-β-thalassemia due to a *de novo* mutation deleting the 5′ β-globin gene activation-region hypersensitive sites. *Proc. Natl. Acad. Sci. USA* **86:** 7470–7474.

Faustino P, Osório-Almeida L, Barbot J, Espirito-Santo D, Gonçalves J, Romao L, Martins MC, Marques MM, Lavinha J. (1992) Novel promoter and splice junction defects add to the genetic, clinical or geographic heterogeneity of β-thalassaemia in the Portuguese population. *Hum. Genet.* **89:** 573–576.

Fei YJ, Stoming TA, Efremov GD, Efremov DG, Battacharia R, Gonzalez-Redondo JM, Altay C, Gurgey A, Huisman THJ. (1988) β-Thalassemia due to a T → A mutation within the ATA box. *Biochem. Biophys. Res. Commun.* **153:** 741–747.

Feuerman MH, Godbout R, Ingram RS, Tilghman SM. (1989) Tissue-specific transcription of the mouse α-fetoprotein gene promoter is dependent on HNF-1. *Mol. Cell. Biol.* **9:** 4204–4212.

Fischer KD, Nowock J. (1990) The T → C substitution at − 198 of the A gamma-globin gene associated with the British form of HPFH generates overlapping recognition sites for two DNA-binding proteins. *Nucleic Acids Res.* **18:** 5685–5693.

Forrester WC, Epner E, Driscoll MC, Enver T, Brice M, Papayannopoulou T, Groudine M. (1990) A deletion of the human β-globin locus activation region causes a major alteration in chromatin structure and replication across the entire β-globin locus. *Genes Dev.* **4:** 1637–1649.

Freedenberg DL, Black B. (1991) Altered developmental control of the factor IX gene: a new T to A mutation at position +6 of the FIX gene resulting in hemophilia B Leyden. *Thromb. Haemost.* **65:** 964.

Fucharoen S, Shimizu K, Fukumaki Y. (1990) A novel C→T transition within the distal CCAAT motif of the G-γ globin gene in the Japanese HPFH: implication of factor binding in elevated fetal globin expression. *Nucleic Acids Res.* **18:** 5245–5253.

Gelinas R, Endlich B, Pfeiffer C, Yagi M, Stamatoyannopoulos G. (1985) G to A substitution in the distal CCAAT box of the A-γ globin gene in Greek hereditary persistence of fetal haemoglobin. *Nature* **313:** 323–324.

Gelinas R, Bender M, Lotshaw C, Waber P, Kazazian H, Stamatoyannopoulos G. (1986) Chinese A-γ fetal hemoglobin: C to T substitution at position −196 of the A-γ gene promoter. *Blood* **67:** 1777–1779.

Gelinas RE, Rixon M, Magis W, Stamatoyannopoulos G. (1988) Gamma gene promoter and enhancer structure in Seattle variant of hereditary persistence of fetal hemoglobin. *Blood* **71:** 1108–1112.

Giglioni B, Casini C, Mantovani R, Merli S, Comi P, Ottolenghi S, Saglio G, Camaschella C, Mazza U. (1984) A molecular study of a family with Greek hereditary persistence of fetal hemoglobin and β-thalassaemia. *EMBO J.* **3:** 2641–2645.

Gilman JG, Huisman THJ. (1985) DNA sequence variation associated with elevated fetal G-γ globin production. *Blood* **66:** 783–787.

Gilman JG, Mishima N, Wen XJ, Kutlar F, Huisman THJ. (1988) Upstream promoter mutation associated with a modest elevation of fetal hemoglobin expression in human adults. *Blood* **72:** 78–81.

Gispert S, Vidaud M, Vidaud D, Gazengel C, Boneu B, Goossens M. (1989) A promoter defect correlates with an abnormal coagulation factor IX gene expression in a French family (hemophilia B Leyden). *Am. J. Hum. Genet.* **45:** (Suppl.): A189.

Gonzalez-Redondo JM, Stoming TA, Kutlar A, Kutlar F, Lanclos KD, Howard EF, Fei YJ, Aksoy M, Altay C, Gurgey A, Basak AN, Efremov GD, Petkov G, Huisman THJ. (1989) A C→T substitution at nt −101 in a conserved DNA sequence of the promoter region of the β-globin gene is associated with 'silent' β-thalassemia. *Blood* **73:** 1705–1711.

Grosveld F, van Assendelft GB, Greaves DR, Kollias G. (1987) Position-independent high-level expression of the human β-globin gene in transgenic mice. *Cell* **51:** 975–985.

Gumucio DL, Rood KL, Gray TA, Riordan MF, Sartor CI, Collins FS. (1988) Nuclear proteins that bind the human γ-globin gene promoter: alterations in binding produced by point mutations associated with hereditary persistence of fetal hemoglobin. *Mol. Cell. Biol.* **8:** 5310–5322.

Gumucio DL, Lockwood WK, Weber JL, Saulino AM, Delgrosso K, Surrey S, Schwartz E, Goodman M, Collins FS. (1990) The −175 T→C mutation increases promoter strength in erythroid cells: correlation with evolutionary conservation of binding sites for two *trans*-acting factors. *Blood* **75:** 756–761.

Gumucio DL, Rood KL, Blanchard-McQuate KL, Gray TA, Saulino A, Collins FS. (1991) Interaction of Sp1 with the human γ globin promoter: binding and transactivation of normal and mutant promoters. *Blood* **78:** 1853–1863.

Hanscombe O, Whyatt D, Fraser P, Yannoutsos N, Greaves D, Dillon N, Grosveld F. (1991) Importance of globin gene order for correct developmental expression. *Genes Dev.* **5:** 1387–1394.

Hatton CSR, Wilkie AOM, Drysdale HC, Wood WG, Vickers MA, Sharpe J, Ayyub H, Pretorius IM, Buckle VJ, Higgs DR. (1990) α-thalassemia caused by a large (62 kb) deletion upstream of the human α globin gene cluster. *Blood* **76:** 221–227.

Higgs DR, Wood WG, Jarman AP, Sharpe J, Lida J, Pretorius IM, Ayyub H. (1990) A major positive regulatory region located far upstream of the human α-globin gene locus. *Genes Dev.* **4:** 1588–1593.

Higuchi M, Kazazian HH, Kasch L, Warren TC, McGinniss MJ, Phillips JA, Kasper C, Janco R, Antonarakis SE. (1991) Molecular characterization of severe hemophilia A suggests that about half the mutations are not within the coding regions and splice junctions of the factor VIII gene. *Proc. Natl. Acad. Sci. USA* **88**: 7405-7409.

Hirosawa S, Fahner JB, Salier J-P, Wu C-T, Lovrien EW, Kurachi K. (1990) Structural and functional basis of the developmental regulation of human coagulation factor IX gene: factor IX Leyden. *Proc. Natl. Acad. Sci. USA* **87**: 4421-4425.

Huang S-Z, Wong C, Antonarakis SE, Ro-lein T, Lo WHY, Kazazian HH. (1986) The same TATA box β-thalassemia mutation in Chinese and US blacks: another example of independent origin of mutation. *Hum. Genet.* **74**: 162-164.

Huisman THJ. (1992) The β- and δ-thalassemia repository. *Hemoglobin* **16**: 237-258.

Jarman AP, Wood WG, Sharpe JA, Gourdon G, Ayyub H, Higgs DR. (1991) Characterization of the major regulatory element upstream of the human α-globin gene cluster. *Mol. Cell. Biol.* **11**: 4679-4689.

Jeenah M, Kessling A, Miller N, Humphries S. (1990) G to A substitution in the promoter region of the apolipoprotein AI gene is associated with elevated serum apolipoprotein AI and high density lipoprotein cholesterol concentrations. *Mol. Biol. Med.* **7**: 233-241.

Kim CG, Epner EM, Forrester WC, Groudine M. (1992) Inactivation of the human β-globin gene by targeted insertion into the β-globin locus control region. *Genes Dev.* **6**: 928-938.

Kioussis D, Vanin E, deLange T, Flavell RA, Grosveld FG. (1983) β-globin gene inactivation by DNA translocation in γ-β-thalassaemia. *Nature* **306**: 662-666.

Kulozik AE, Bellan-Koch A, Bail S, Kohne E, Kleihauer E. (1991) Thalassemia intermedia: moderate reduction of β globin gene transcriptional activity by a novel mutation of the proximal CACCC promoter element. *Blood* **77**: 2054-2058.

Labie D, Dunda-Belkhodja O, Rouabhi F, Pagnier J, Ragusa A, Nagel RL. (1985) The −158 site 5' to the G-γ gene and G-γ expression. *Blood* **66**: 1463-1465.

La Thangue NB, Rigby PWJ. (1988) *Trans*-acting protein factors and the regulation of eukaryotic transcription. In: *Transcription and Splicing* (eds BD Hames, DM Glover). IRL Press, Oxford.

Liebhaber SA, Griese E-U, Weiss I, Cash FE, Ayyub H, Higgs DR, Horst J. (1990) Inactivation of human α-globin gene expression by a *de novo* deletion located upstream of the α-globin gene cluster. *Proc. Natl. Acad. Sci. USA* **87**: 9431-9435.

Lin L-L, Lin K-S, Lin K-H, Cheng T-Y. (1992a) A novel −32 (C-A) mutant identified in amplified genomic DNA of a Chinese β-thalassemic patient. *Am. J. Hum. Genet.* **50**: 237-238.

Lin HJ, Han C-Y, Nienhuis AW. (1992b) Functional profile of the human fetal γ-globin gene upstream promoter region. *Am. J. Hum. Genet.* **51**: 363-370.

Lloyd JA, Lee RF, Lingrel JB. (1989) Mutations in two regions upstream of the A γ globin gene canonical promoter affect gene expression. *Nucleic Acids Res.* **17**: 4339-4352.

McDonagh KT, Lin HJ, Lowrey CH, Bodine DM, Nienhuis AW. (1991) The upstream region of the human γ-globin gene promoter: identification and functional analysis of nuclear protein binding sites. *J. Biol. Chem.* **266**: 11965-11974.

McVey JH, Michaelides K, Hansen LP, Ferguson-Smith M, Tilghman SM, Krumlauf R, Tuddenham EGD. (1993) A G → A substitution in an HNF1 binding site in the human α-fetoprotein gene is associated with hereditary persistence of α-fetoprotein (HPAFP). *Hum. Mol. Genet.* **2**: 379-384.

Mantovani R, Malgaretti N, Nicolis S, Ronchi A, Giglioni B, Ottolenghi S. (1988a) The effects of HPFH mutations in the human γ-globin promoter on binding of ubiquitous and erythroid-specific nuclear factors. *Nucleic Acids Res.* **16**: 7783-7797.

Mantovani R, Malgaretti N, Nicolis S, Giglioni B, Comi P, Capellini N, Bertero MT, Caligaris-Cappio F, Ottolenghi S. (1988b) An erythroid specific nuclear factor binding to the proximal CACCC box of the β-globin gene promoter. *Nucleic Acids Res.* **16**: 4299-4313.

Martin DIK, Tsai S-F, Orkin SH. (1989) Increased γ-globin expression in a nondeletion HPFH mediated by an erythroid-specific DNA-binding factor. *Nature* **338**: 435-438

Matsuda M, Sakamoto N, Fukumaki Y. (1992) δ-thalassemia caused by disruption of the site for an erythroid-specific transcription factor, GATA-1, in the δ-globin gene promoter. *Blood* **80**: 1347-1351.

279

Meloni A, Rosatelli MC, Faà V, Sardu R, Saba L, Murru S, Sciarratta GV, Baldi M, Tannoia N. (1992) Promoter mutations producing mild β-thalassaemia in the Italian population. *Br. J. Haematol.* **80:** 222–226.

Miller BA, Salameh M, Ahmed M, Wainscoat J, Antognetti G, Orkin S, Weatherall D, Nathan D. (1986) High fetal hemoglobin production in sickle cell anemia in the Eastern province of Saudi Arabia is genetically determined. *Blood* **67:** 1404–1410.

Moi P, Loudianos G, Lavinha J, Murru S, Cossu P, Casu R, Oggiano L, Longinotti M, Cao A, Pirastu M. (1992) δ-thalassemia due to a mutation in an erythroid-specific binding protein sequence 3' to the δ-globin gene. *Blood* **79:** 512–516.

Morley BJ, Abbott CA, Sharpe JA, Lida J, Chan-Thomas PS, Wood WG. (1992) A single β-globin locus control region element (5' hypersensitive site 2) is sufficient for developmental regulation of human globin genes in transgenic mice. *Mol. Cell. Biol.* **12:** 2057–2066.

Murakami T, Nishiyori A, Takiguchi M, Mori M. (1990) Promoter and 11kb upstream enhancer elements responsible for hepatoma cell-specific expression of the rat ornithine transcarbamylase gene. *Mol. Cell. Biol.* **10:** 1180–1191.

Myers RM, Tilly K, Maniatis T. (1986) Fine structure genetic analysis of a β-globin promoter. *Science* **232:** 613–618.

Naylor JA, Green PM, Rizza CR, Giannelli F. (1992) Factor VIII gene explains all cases of haemophilia A. *Lancet* **340:** 1066–1067.

Nicolis S, Ronchi A, Malgaretti N, Mantovani R, Giglioni B, Ottolenghi S. (1989) Increased erythroid-specific expression of a mutated HPFH γ-globin promoter requires the erythroid factor NFE-1. *Nucleic Acids Res.* **17:** 5509–5516.

O'Neil D, Kaysen J, Donovan-Peluso M, Castle M, Bank A. (1990) Protein–DNA interactions upstream from the human A γ globin gene. *Nucleic Acids Res.* **18:** 1977–1982.

Olansky L, Welling C, Giddings S, Adler S, Bourey R, Dowse G, Serjeantson S, Zimmet P, Permutt MA. (1992) A variant insulin promoter in non-insulin-dependent diabetes mellitus. *J. Clin. Invest.* **89:** 1596–1602.

Öner R, Kutlar F, Gu L-H, Huisman THJ. (1991) The Georgia type of nondeletional hereditary persistence of fetal hemoglobin has a C→T mutation at nucleotide −114 of the A-γ globin gene. *Blood* **77:** 1124–1128.

Orkin SH, Kazazian HH, Antonarakis SE, Goff SC, Boehm CD, Sexton JP, Waber PG, Giardina PJV. (1982) Linkage of β-thalassaemic mutations and β-globin gene polymorphisms with DNA polymorphisms in the human β-globin gene cluster. *Nature* **296:** 627–631.

Orkin SH, Sexton JP, Cheng T-C, Goff SC, Giardina PJV, Lee JI, Kazazian HH. (1983) ATA box transcription mutation in β-thalassemia. *Nucleic Acids Res.* **11:** 4727–4734.

Orkin SH, Antonarakis SE, Kazazian HH. (1984) Base substitution at position −88 in a β-thalassemic globin gene: further evidence for the role of distal promoter element ACACCC. *J. Biol. Chem.* **259:** 8679–8681.

Ottolenghi S, Giglioni B, Pulazzini A, Comi P, Camaschella C, Serra A, Guerrasio A, Saglio G. (1987) Sardinian δ β^0 thalassemia: a further example of a C to T substitution of position −196 of the A-γ globin gene promoter. *Blood* **69:** 1058–1061.

Ottolenghi S, Nicolis S, Taramelli R, Malgaretti N, Mantovani R, Comi P, Giglioni B, Longinotti M, Dore F, Oggiano L, Pistidda P, Serra A, Camaschella C, Saglio G. (1988) Sardinian G-γ HPFH: a T→C substitution in a conserved 'octamer' sequence in the G-γ globin promoter. *Blood* **71:** 815–817.

Ottolenghi S, Mantovani R, Nicolis S, Ronchi A, Giglioni B. (1989) DNA sequences regulating human globin gene transcription in nondeletional hereditary persistence of fetal hemoglobin. *Hemoglobin* **13:** 523–541.

Pagani F, Sidoli A, Guidici GA, Barenghi L, Vergani C, Baralle FE. (1990) Human apolipoprotein AI promoter polymorphism: association with hyperalphalipoproteinaemia. *J. Lipid Res.* **31:** 1371–1377.

Pang C-P, Crossley M, Kent G, Brownlee GG. (1990) Comparative sequence analysis of mammalian factor IX promoters. *Nucleic Acids Res.* **18:** 6731.

Papazafiri P, Ogami K, Ramji DP, Nicosia A, Monaki P, Cladaras C, Zannis VI. (1991)

Promoter elements and factors involved in hepatic transcription of the human apoA1 gene positive and negative regulators bind to overlapping sites. *J. Biol. Chem.* **266:** 5790–5797.

Paul-Hayase H, Rosseneu M, Robinson D, Van Bervliet JP, Deslypere JP, Humphries SE. (1992) Polymorpisms in the apolipoprotein (apo) AI–CIII–AIV gene cluster: detection of genetic variation determining plasma apoAI, apoCIII and apoAIV concentrations. *Hum. Genet.* **88:** 439–446.

Picketts DJ, D'Souza C, Bridge PJ, Lillicrap D. (1992) An A to T transversion at position −5 of the factor IX promoter results in hemophilia B. *Genomics* **12:** 161–163.

Poncz M, Ballantine M, Solowiejczyk D, Barak I, Schwartz E, Surrey S. (1983) β-thalassemia in a Kurdish Jew. *J. Biol. Chem.* **257:** 5994–5996.

Reijnen MJ, Sladek FM, Bertina RM, Reitsma PH. (1992) Disruption of a binding site for hepatocyte nuclear factor 4 results in hemophilia B Leyden. *Proc. Natl. Acad. Sci. USA* **89:** 6300–6303.

Reitsma PH, Bertina RM, Ploos van Amstel JK, Riemans A, Briët E. (1988) The putative factor IX gene promoter in hemophilia B Leyden. *Blood* **72:** 1074–1076.

Reitsma PH, Mandalaki T, Kasper CK, Bertina RM, Briët E. (1989) Two novel point mutations correlate with an altered developmental expression of blood coagulation factor IX (hemophilia B Leyden phenotype). *Blood* **73:** 743–746.

Rixon MW, Gelinas RE. (1988) A fetal globin gene mutation in A γ nondeletion hereditary persistence of fetal hemoglobin increases promoter strength in a non-erythroid cell. *Mol. Cell. Biol.* **8:** 713–721.

Romao L, Osorio-Almeida L, Higgs DR, Lavinha J, Liebhaber SA. (1991) α-thalassemia resulting from deletion of regulatory sequences far upstream of the α-globin structural genes. *Blood* **78:** 1589–1595.

Romao L, Cash F, Weiss I, Liebhaber S, Pirastu M, Galanello R, Loi A, Paglietti E, Ioannou P, Cao A. (1992) Human α-globin gene expression is silenced by terminal truncation of chromosome 16p beginning immediately 3′ of the ζ-globin gene. *Hum. Genet.* **89:** 323–328.

Royle G, van de Water NS, Berry E, Ockelford PA, Browett PJ. (1991) Haemophilia B Leyden arising *de novo* by point mutation in the putative factor IX promoter region. *Br. J. Haematol.* **77:** 191–194.

Sakai T, Ohtani N, McGee TL, Robbins PD, Dryja TP. (1991) Oncogenic germ-line mutations in Sp1 and ATF sites in the human retinoblastoma gene. *Nature* **353:** 83–86.

Sawadago M, Roeder RG. (1985) Interaction of a gene-specific transcription factor with the adenovirus major late promoter upstream of the TATA box region. *Cell* **43:** 165–175.

Sigurdsson G, Gudnason V, Sigurdsson G, Humphries SE. (1992) Interaction between a polymorphism of the apolipoprotein AI promoter region and smoking determines plasma levels of high density lipoprotein and apolipoprotein AI. *Aterio. Thromb.* **12:** 1017–1022.

Stoeckert CJ, Metherall JE, Yamakawa M, Weissman SM, Forget BG. (1987) Expression of the affected A γ globin gene associated with Greek nondeletion hereditary persistence of fetal hemoglobin. *Mol. Cell. Biol.* **7:** 2999–3003.

Stoming TA, Stoming GS, Lanclos KD, Fei YJ, Altay C, Kutlar F, Huisman THJ. (1989) A A-γ type of nondeletional hereditary persistence of fetal hemoglobin with a T → C mutation at position −175 to the Cap site of the A-γ globin gene. *Blood* **73:** 329–333.

Superti-Furga G, Barberis A, Schaffner G, Busslinger M. (1988) The −117 mutation in Greek HPFH affects the binding of three nuclear factors to the CCAAT region of the γ-globin gene. *EMBO J.* **7:** 3099–3107.

Surrey S, Delgrosso K, Malladi P, Schwartz E. (1988) A single base change at position −175 in the 5′ flanking region of the G-γ globin gene from a black with G-γ-β⁺ HPFH. *Blood* **71:** 807–810.

Sykes K, Kaufman R. (1990) A naturally occurring γ globin gene mutation enhances SP1 binding activity. *Mol. Cell. Biol.* **10:** 95–102.

Takihara Y, Nakamura T, Yamada H, Takagi Y, Fukumaki Y. (1986) A novel mutation in the TATA box in a Japanese patient with β⁺-thalassemia. *Blood* **67:** 547–550.

Tate VE, Wood WG, Weatherall DJ. (1986) The British form of hereditary persistence of fetal hemoglobin results from a single base mutation adjacent to an S1 hypersensitive site 5' to the A–γ globin gene. *Blood* **68:** 1389–1393.

Thomson AA, Ham J, Bakker O, Parker MG. (1990) The progesterone receptor can regulate transcription in the absence of a functional TATA box element. *J. Biol. Chem.* **265:** 16709–16712.

Treisman R, Orkin SH, Maniatis T. (1983) Specific transcription and RNA splicing defects in five cloned β-thalassaemia genes. *Nature* **302:** 591–596.

Tsang CT, Bentley DR, Mibashan RS, Giannelli F. (1988) A factor IX mutation, verified by direct genomic sequencing, causes haemophilia B by a novel mechanism. *EMBO J.* **7:** 3009–3015.

Tuan DYH, Solomon WB, London IM, Lee DP. (1989) An erythroid-specific, developmental-stage-independent enhancer far upstream of the human 'β-like globin' genes. *Proc. Natl. Acad. Sci. USA* **86:** 2554–2558.

Tuteja R, Tuteja N, Melo C, Casari G, Baralle FE. (1992) Transcription efficiency of human apolipoprotein A-I promoter varies with naturally occurring A to G transition. *FEBS Lett.* **304:** 98–101.

Van der Ploeg LHT, Konings A, Oort M, Roos D, Bernini L, Flavell RA. (1980) γ-β-Thalassaemia studies showing that deletion of the γ- and δ-genes influences β-globin gene expression in man. *Nature* **283:** 637–642.

Vyas P, Vickers MA, Simmons DL, Ayyub H, Craddock CF, Higgs DR. (1992) *Cis*-acting sequences regulating expression of the human α-globin cluster lie within constitutively open chromatin. *Cell* **69:** 781–793.

Watanabe K, Saito A, Tamaoki T. (1987) Cell-specific enhancer activity in a far upstream region of the human α-fetoprotein gene. *J. Biol. Chem.* **262:** 4812–4818.

Wilkie AOM, Lamb J, Harris PC, Finney RD, Higgs DR. (1990) A truncated human chromosome 16 associated with α-thalassaemia is stabilized by addition of telomeric repeat (TTAGGG). *Nature* **346:** 868–871.

Mutations affecting RNA processing and translation

Mutations affecting mRNA processing and translation may exert their pathological effects at any one of the various stages in the expression pathway between transcriptional initiation and translation (see Section 2.8). Mutations affecting mRNA splicing have already been covered separately (Chapter 9). Examples of the other types of lesion in this category and their phenotypic consequences are described here.

11.1 Cap site mutants

The transcription of an mRNA is initiated at the cap site ($+1$), so named on account of the post-transcriptional addition of 7-methylguanine at this position as a means to protect the transcript from exonucleolytic degradation. Wong *et al.* (1987) have described an A → C transversion at the cap site in the β-globin (HBB) gene of an Indian patient with β-thalassaemia. Since no other lesion was detected in this patient and since it has not been previously reported in a large number of sequenced β-globin genes, it would appear to represent the pathological lesion. Kozak (1984) collated known eukaryotic mRNA sequence data and showed that the cap site is an adenine in 76% of cases; a C residue at position $+1$ was noted in only 6% of cases. It is not, however, clear whether it is transcription of the β-globin gene *per se* that is severely reduced in the above patient or whether transcriptional initiation occurs efficiently but at a different, incorrect site. In the latter case, the resulting transcript could be either incomplete or unstable. An A → G transition in the mouse β-globin gene cap site results in a 50% decrease in the steady-state level of β-globin mRNA in an *in vitro* transient expression system (Myers *et al.*, 1986).

11.2 Polyadenylation/cleavage signal mutations

All polyadenylated mRNAs in higher eukaryotes possess the sequence AAUAAA, or a close homologue, 10–30 nucleotides upstream of the polyadenylation site. This motif is thought to play a role in 3' end formation through endonucleolytic cleavage and polyadenylation of the mRNA transcript. Several single base-pair substitutions are now known in the cleavage/polyadenylation signal sequences of the $\alpha 2$- (HBA2) and β-globin (HBB) genes (Table 11.1): all cause a relatively mild form of thalassaemia due to the reduction of Hb A_2 synthesis to 3–5% of the normal level.

As far as the HBB gene mutants are concerned, cleavage and polyadenylation at the normal site are markedly reduced; however, HbA_2 does still occur at not much less than 10% of the normal level as judged by both *in vivo* and *in vitro* assays (Orkin *et al.*, 1985; Jankovic *et al.*, 1990a). These mutants are characterized by a novel species of β-globin mRNA: 1500 nucleotides in length, 900 nucleotides larger than the wild-type transcript. This results from the use of an alternative cleavage/polyadenylation site (AATAAAA) 900 bp 3' to the mutated site — polyadenylation occurs within 15 nucleotides of this cryptic site. This abnormal mRNA may be highly unstable since it has proved to be extremely difficult to isolate. Several other polyadenylated mRNA species up to 2900 bp in length have been reported in an Israeli patient with a polyadenylation site mutation (Rund *et al.*, 1992); the β^+-thalassaemia phenotype exhibited by this patient was consistent with the translation of these extended mRNA species.

One of the cleavage/polyadenylation signal mutants noted in the HBA2 gene caused a mild α-thalassaemia (Higgs *et al.*, 1983; Thein *et al.*, 1988). The level of HBA2 mRNA detectable in erythroid cells was 5% of normal. As was the case with the HBB mutations, readthrough transcripts extending beyond the normal wild-type poly(A) addition site were detected in HeLa cells transfected with the mutant HBA2 gene. However, these transcripts were not detected *in vivo* probably either because they were highly unstable or because abnormal mRNAs might not have been transported to the cytoplasm. The second HBA2 gene mutation occurred in association with a $\alpha 1$-globin (HBA1) gene deletion, resulting in Hb H disease (Yüregir *et al.*, 1992).

An unusual T→C substitution causing β-thalassaemia has been found at position +1570 of the HBB gene, 12 bp upstream of the AATAAA poly-

Table 11.1. Cleavage/polyadenylation signal sequence mutations causing thalassaemia

Gene	Mutation	Origin	% Normal Hb A_2	Reference
HBB	AATAAA→AACAAA	US Black	3.1	Orkin *et al.*, 1985
HBB	AATAAA→AATAGA	Malaysian	4.3	Jankovic *et al.*, 1990a
HBB	AATAAA→AATGAA	Greek	3.9	Jankovic *et al.*, 1990a
HBB	AATAAA→AATAAG	Kurdish	?	Kazazian and Boehm, 1988
		Israeli	~10	Rund *et al.*, 1992
HBA2	AATAAA→AATAAG	Saudi	5	Higgs *et al.*, 1983
				Thein *et al.*, 1988
HBA2	AATAAA→AATGAA	Turkish	0.5–1.4	Yüregir *et al.*, 1992

adenylation signal, in an Irish family (Cai *et al.*, 1992). It is thought that this lesion may serve to destabilize the HBB mRNA.

11.3 Mutation in termination codons

The first reported example of a mutation in a termination codon was that in the α2-globin (HBA2) gene causing haemoglobin Constant Spring, an abnormal haemoglobin that occurs frequently in South-East Asia (Clegg *et al.*, 1971; Milner *et al.*, 1971). The associated α-globin chain is 172 amino acids in length, rather longer than the normal 141 amino acids, as a result of a TAA→CAA transition in the termination codon. In this patient, translation extends into the 3′ non-coding region of the α2-globin (HBA2) mRNA. The Constant Spring HBA2 mRNA is highly unstable, resulting in low production of haemoglobin in the red cells of heterozygous carriers (Hunt *et al.*, 1982). In the homozygous state, the clinical phenotype is more severe than α-thalassaemia caused by the deletion of two α-globin genes. This appears to be due to a much reduced red cell lifespan caused by the spleen recognizing and removing circulating erythrocytes made abnormal through the proteolytic destruction of excess β-globin chain dimers and monomers (Derry *et al.*, 1984). Several other mutations are known to occur in the HBA2 termination codon (Table 11.2): a similar phenotype to Hb Constant Spring is observed (Bunn, 1978).

Elongated proteins may also be generated by a second mechanism: a frameshift mutation close to the natural termination codon which results in the extension of translation until the next available downstream termination codon. A number of examples of this type of lesion are known to cause β-thalassaemia (Beris *et al.*, 1988; Kazazian *et al.*, 1989; Fucharoen *et al.*, 1990; Ristaldi *et al.*, 1990; Thein *et al.*, 1990; Murru *et al.*, 1991). All give rise to an imbalance in α- and β-globin chain synthesis and inclusion body (containing precipitated α and β chains) formation. All are associated with the dominant form of the disease.

11.4 Mutation in initiation codons

A number of examples of mutations in Met (ATG) translational initiation codons have been reported (Table 11.3); a preponderance of Met→Val substitutions is apparent. The consequences for mRNA transcription and translation have not been well studied but one or two salient points can nevertheless be summarized.

A few examples are also known of deletions which encompass or flank the initiation codon, e.g. the deletion of two bases at positions −2 and −3 relative to the Met initiation codon of the α1-globin (HBA1) gene causing α-thalassaemia (Morlé *et al.*, 1985). Such mutations presumably alter the surrounding consensus sequence and prevent proper recognition of the initiation site.

As far as the point mutations are concerned, it is particularly useful to compare and contrast the ATG mutations reported in the HBA1 and HBA2

Table 11.2. Mutations in termination codons

Gene	Nucleotide substitution	Codon	Globin	Reference
HBA2	TAA → CAA	142	Constant Spring	Clegg *et al.*, 1971
HBA2	TAA → AAA	142	Icaria	Clegg *et al.*, 1974
HBA2	TAA → TCA	142	Koya Dora	De Jong *et al.*, 1975
HBA2	TAA → GAA	142	Seal Rock	Bradley *et al.*, 1975

Table 11.3. Mutations in translational initiation codons

Disease	Gene	Nucleotide substitution	Amino acid substitution	Reference
Albright's osteodystrophy	GSA	cATG → GTG	Met → Val	Patten *et al.*, 1990
Apolipoprotein C2 deficiency	APOC2	tATG → GTG	Met → Val	Fojo *et al.*, 1989a
Gyrate atrophy	OAT	ATGt → ATA	Met → Ile	Mitchell *et al.*, 1988
HPRT deficiency	HPRT	ATGg → ATA	Met → Ile	Tarlé *et al.*, 1991
Leukocyte adhesion deficiency	CD18	ATG → AAG	Met → Lys	Sligh *et al.*, 1992
Phenylketonuria	PAH	cATG → GTG	Met → Val	John *et al.*, 1989
Sphingolipid activator protein deficiency	SAP1	tATG → TTG	Met → Leu	Schnabel *et al.*, 1992
Tay–Sachs disease	HEXA	cATG → GTG	Met → Val	Mules *et al.*, 1992
Thalassaemia-α	HBA2	ATG → ACG	Met → Thr	Pirastu *et al.*, 1984
Thalassaemia-α	HBA1	gATG → GTG	Met → Val	Moi *et al.*, 1987
Thalassaemia-β	HBB	ATG → AGG	Met → Arg	Lam *et al.*, 1990
Thalassaemia-β	HBB	cATG → GTG	Met → Val	Hattori *et al.*, 1991
Thalassaemia-β	HBB	ATG → ACG	Met → Thr	Jankovic *et al.*, 1990b

Bases 5′ and 3′ to the mutated base are given in lower case. GSA, G protein adenylate cyclase; APOC2, apolipoprotein C2; OAT, ornithine δ-aminotransferase; HPRT, hypoxanthine phosphoribosyltransferase; PAH, phenylalanine hydroxylase; HEXA, hexosaminidase A. Other gene symbols are as specified in the text.

genes. The HBA1 gene mutation was associated with a reduction in the steady-state HBA1 mRNA level to one-quarter of normal (Moi *et al.*, 1987) whereas the corresponding HBA2 mRNA level consequent to the HBA2 gene lesion was similarly reduced to one-third of normal (Pirastu *et al.*, 1984). The HBA2 gene mutation results in a greater reduction in α-globin synthesis and a more severe α-thalassaemia phenotype than its HBA1 counterpart. This is presumably because, in normal individuals, the ratio of $\alpha 2 : \alpha 1$ mRNA produced from the two genes is 2.6, reflecting the relative importance of the HBA2 gene in α-globin synthesis.

The observed reductions in steady-state mRNA levels are reminiscent of the consequences of nonsense mutations (Section 11.5). Presumably the mechanism is the same, with failure to initiate translation and premature termination exerting similar effects on either mRNA transport or stability. As with nonsense mutations, however, the exceptions may well prove the rule:

Mitchell *et al.* (1988) reported a normal amount of ornithine δ-aminotransferase (OAT) mRNA transcripts from their gyrate atrophy patient with an initiation codon mutation.

Given that some mRNA is still transcribed, is it translated? The answer to this question is likely to be determined by a complex interplay of the different structural features of an mRNA that serve to modulate its translation (reviewed by Kozak, 1991). Until fairly recently it was thought that an AUG codon was an absolute requirement for translational initiation in mammals. However, a handful of exceptions are now known, e.g. ACG, CUG (reviewed by Kozak, 1991), indicating that some mutations may be tolerated more readily than others. The scanning model of translational initiation predicts that the 40S ribosomal subunit initiates at the first AUG codon to be encountered within an acceptable sequence context [GCC (A/G) CCAUGG is believed to be optimal; Kozak, 1991]. Ribosomes may be capable of utilizing mutated AUG codons, albeit with reduced efficiency, or they may be able to initiate translation at the next best available site downstream (Neote *et al.*, 1990). Three studies listed in Table 11.3 failed to detect an abnormal protein (Fojo *et al.*, 1989a; Lam *et al.*, 1990; Schnabel *et al.*, 1992) but Patten *et al.* (1990) provided evidence for an abnormal protein species possibly synthesized as a result of initiation at a downstream site. The phenotypic consequences of a given ATG mutation are thus likely to depend on (i) the nature of the mutational lesion, (ii) the tolerance of the ribosome with respect to translational initiation codon recognition, (iii) the presence of alternative downstream ATG codons complete with flanking translational initiation site consensus sequence, and (iv) the functional importance of the absent amino terminal end of the protein.

Another type of mutation that interferes with correct initiation is the creation of a cryptic ATG codon in the vicinity of the one normally used. An example of this type of lesion is provided by the G→A transition at position +22 (relative to the cap site) of the β-globin gene causing β-thalassaemia intermedia (Cai *et al.*, 1992). This cryptic initiation codon is 26 bp 5' to the normal ATG codon and its use would lead to a frameshift and premature termination 36 bp downstream. Although the relative extent of utilization of the two AUG codons in this patient is not known, the comparatively mild clinical phenotype suggests that at least some β-globin is correctly initiated and translated.

11.5 Nonsense mutations and their effect on mRNA levels

Inspection of the data in Appendix 2 provides a direct demonstration of the importance of nonsense mutations in human genes as a cause of genetic disease. Their dire consequences for translation are reflected in the increased likelihood that they will come to clinical attention (see Section 6.5.2).

Benz *et al.* (1978) first noticed that some β-thalassaemia patients exhibited very low levels (< 1% of normal) of β-globin mRNA in their peripheral blood cells. Since these observations were first made, a considerable number of nonsense or frameshift mutations from a variety of different genes have been shown to be associated with dramatic reductions in the steady-state level of cytoplasmic mRNA (Table 11.4).

This rule is not, however, completely inviolable; a few nonsense mutations are associated with normal levels of cytoplasmic mRNA, which appears to be efficiently translated to generate a truncated protein [e.g. low density lipoprotein receptor (LDLR), Lehrman *et al.*, 1987; apolipoprotein C2 (APOC2), Fojo *et al.*, 1989b; *β*-globin (HBB), Liebhaber *et al.*, 1987]. Moreover, some considerable variation in mRNA levels is apparent between different nonsense codons within the same gene. Thus, measured reticulocyte HBB mRNA varies from <1%, normal in a *β*-thalassaemia patient with a 1 bp frameshift deletion at codon 44 (Kinniburgh *et al.*, 1982) to 15% normal in a patient with a nonsense mutation in codon 17 (Chang and Kan, 1979). These discrepancies notwithstanding, it would still appear as if, by and large, the closer a termination codon is to the 3′ end of a gene, the higher the level of mRNA transcripts is likely to be.

Table 11.4. Nonsense mutations for which associated *in vivo* mRNA levels are known

Gene	Codon	Exons*	Mutation	mRNA	Reference
APOC2	37	3/4	TAA	Normal	Fojo *et al.*, 1989b
CFTR	553	11/27	TGA	<2%	Hamosh *et al.*, 1991
CFTR	1316	21/27	TGA	<2%	Hamosh *et al.*, 1991
C1I	400	8/8	Del T (TGA)	Elevated	Frangi *et al.*, 1991
C1I	401	8/8	Ins A (TAA)	Normal	Frangi *et al.*, 1991
HBA2	116	3/3	TAG	Normal	Liebhaber *et al.*, 1987
HBB	17	1/3	TAG	15%	Chang and Kan, 1979
HBB	39	2/3	TAG	5%	Trecartin *et al.*, 1981
HBB	43	2/3	TAG	<3%	Atweh *et al.*, 1988
HBB	44	2/3	Del C (TGA)	<1%	Kinniburgh *et al.*, 1982
HBB	121	3/3	TAA	>0.1%†	Adams *et al.*, 1990
HBB	145	3/3	TAA/TAG	Normal	Winslow *et al.*, 1976
INSR	372	5/22	TGA	5–15%	Longo *et al.*, 1992
LDLR	660	14/18	TGA	Normal	Lehrman *et al.*, 1987
OAT	64	4/11	Del AG (TGA)	0–10%	Mashima *et al.*, 1992
OAT	192	6/11	Del exon 6 (TGA)	0%	Akaki *et al.*, 1992
OAT	209	6/11	TAA	0%	Mashima *et al.*, 1992
OAT	299	8/11	TAG	20–40%	Mashima *et al.*, 1992
OAT	426	11/11	TGA	80–90%	Mashima *et al.*, 1992
TPI	189	7/7	TGA	25%	Daar and Maquat, 1988
VWF	2535	45/51	TGA	<1%	Eikenboom *et al.*, 1991

*The number of the exon in which the termination codon occurred is given as well as the total number of exons within the gene. Either the specific termination codon created by the mutation is included or the next downstream termination codon in the case of a frameshift mutation. The mRNA level relative to that of wild-type controls is given. C1I, C1 inhibitor; INSR, insulin receptor; VWF, von Willebrand factor. Other gene symbols are as specified in the text. †Estimate based on measurement of truncated globin protein present in patient red blood cells.

Several groups have attempted to explore this phenomenon further by using *in vitro* expression systems. The expression of transfected mutant genes can thus be compared with their wild-type counterparts. Decreased *in vitro* accumulation of cytoplasmic mRNA has been reported to be associated with several nonsense mutations in the HBB gene but not with missense mutations (Takeshita *et al.*, 1984; Humphries *et al.*, 1984; Atweh *et al.*, 1988; Baserga and Benz, 1988, 1992). However, the amounts of mRNA produced from the mutant genes relative to wild-type controls were some 2–4 fold higher than *in vivo*.

One obvious potential explanation for the observed effect of nonsense mutations on mRNA metabolism is that mRNAs that are not completely translated are not protected properly from RNase digestion on the ribosome and are therefore likely to exhibit an increased turnover rate (Losson and Lacroute, 1979). Consistent with this postulate, the HBB mRNA bearing the codon 44 mutation appears to be highly unstable (Maquat *et al.*, 1981). Moreover, Daar and Maquat (1988) reported that all triosephosphate isomerase (TPI) gene nonsense and frameshift mutations tested *in vitro* exhibited a reduced mRNA stability but did not alter the rate of transcription. However, at least for the HBB codon 39 mutation, the decreased steady-state levels of both nuclear and cytoplasmic mRNA have been shown not to be due to increased mRNA instability in the cytoplasm (Humphries *et al.*, 1984; Takeshita *et al.*, 1984; Baserga and Benz, 1992).

The mechanism by which a newly created in-frame termination codon results in a decrease in concentration of steady-state cytoplasmic mRNA is not at all understood. In principle, any one or more of several parameters could be affected: the transcription rate, the efficiency of mRNA processing or transport to the cytoplasm or mRNA stability. Urlaub *et al.* (1989) showed that, whereas nonsense mutations in the dihydrofolate reductase (DHFR) gene located prior to the final exon resulted in drastically reduced (10–20-fold) mRNA levels, nonsense mutations in the last exon of the gene yielded normal levels of DHFR mRNA. Nuclear run-on studies and experiments with the transcriptional inhibitor actinomycin D demonstrated that the low mRNA levels did not result from either a reduced rate of transcription or decreased mRNA stability. Very similar results were obtained for nonsense mutations artificially introduced into the TPI gene and expressed *in vitro* (Cheng *et al.*, 1990). On the basis of these and previous results, Urlaub *et al.* (1989) proposed two explanatory models which imply some form of coupling between processing and/or transport of the mRNA and translation:

(i) *Translational translocation model.* This model proposes that translation of the mRNA on the ribosome would begin as soon as the mRNA emerged from the nuclear pore and would serve to physically pull the pre-mRNA through the splicing apparatus and through the pores in the nuclear membrane. Nonsense mutations would halt the pulling process, leaving the RNA molecule vulnerable to RNase digestion. However, nonsense mutations occurring in the last exon would not be recognized until the translocation of the mRNA from the nucleus was virtually complete.

(ii) *Nuclear scanning of translation frames model.* In this model, pre-mRNAs are scanned within the nucleus for nonsense mutations prior to their translocation through the nuclear membrane. Detection of an in-frame termination codon would then result in a slowing down of mRNA splicing/translocation. Such a mechanism might be an intrinsic part of the mRNA splicing process since open reading frame recognition could be an important cue for exon definition.

The translational translocation model would predict a probability gradient from 5′ to 3′, with a gradually increasing likelihood that an mRNA containing a termination codon would be successfully transported across the nuclear membrane. In support of this hypothesis are the several examples of normal levels of mRNA transcripts derived from genes bearing termination codons in their 3′-most exons (Table 11.4). However, counter examples such as the HBB gene codon 17 and 44 nonsense mutations quoted above argue against its validity in all cases, since they are inconsistent with a perfect linear relationship between the relative position of the nonsense mutation and the level of mRNA produced by the mutant allele.

The translational translocation model certainly appears convincing for the TPI and DHFR genes and may imply links between pre-mRNA splicing, mRNA transport and translation. The problem with invoking any one model alone is that it cannot adequately explain the observed inconsistencies between studies regarding (i) the possible position effect associated with nonsense mutations *in vivo* and (ii) the role of changes in mRNA stability if they occur. The different explanatory models may not necessarily be mutually exclusive but one model might be more relevant in the context of a particular gene transcript than the other. After all, mRNAs may be directed specifically to membrane-bound, cytoskeletal or cytosolic polysomes (Hesketh and Pryne, 1991) and translational mechanisms may vary accordingly.

Recently, Lim *et al.* (1992) have shown that nonsense and frameshift mutations within exons 1 or 2 of the human HBB gene give rise to an increased rate of HBB mRNA degradation, generating a number of discrete mRNA products lacking sequences from exons 1 and/or 2. However, no correlation was noted between the site of translation termination and the termini of the degradation products. The generation of these small mRNAs was shown to be a cytoplasmic process and had no effect on nuclear RNA metabolism. It therefore appears likely that nucleolytic cleavage of the mRNA is dependent on association of the mRNA with the ribosome, thus permitting recognition of the nonsense codon.

In practical terms, the common finding of greatly reduced or absent cytoplasmic mRNA associated with nonsense mutations ('allelic exclusion') has important implications for mutation screening. Attempts to obtain mRNA for reverse transcription/PCR amplification and DNA sequencing (e.g. Ploos van Amstel *et al.*, 1991; Peerlinck *et al.*, 1992) may be thwarted in patients with nonsense mutations by a cellular mechanism that links mRNA processing/transport to translation.

References

Adams JG, Steinberg MH, Kazazian HH. (1990) Isolation and characterization of the translation product of a β-globin gene nonsense mutation (β121 GAA → TAA). *Br. J. Haematol.* **75:** 561–567.

Akaki Y, Hotta Y, Mashima Y, Murakami A, Kennaway NG, Weleber RG, Inana G. (1992) A deletion in the ornithine aminotransferase gene in gyrate atrophy. *J. Biol. Chem.* **267:** 12950–12954.

Atweh GF, Brickner HE, Zhu X-X, Kazazian HH, Forget BG. (1988) New amber mutation in a β-thalassemic gene with nonmeasurable levels of mutant messenger RNA *in vivo. J. Clin. Invest.* **82:** 557–561.

Baserga SJ, Benz EJ. (1988) Nonsense mutations in the human β-globin gene affect mRNA metabolism. *Proc. Natl. Acad. Sci. USA* **85:** 2056–2060.

Baserga SJ, Benz EJ. (1992) β-Globin nonsense mutation: deficient accumulation of mRNA occurs despite normal cytoplasmic stability. *Proc. Natl. Acad. Sci. USA* **89:** 2935–2939.

Benz EJ, Forget BG, Hillman DG, Cohen-Solal M, Pritchard J, Cavallesco C, Prensky W, Housman D. (1978) Variability in the amount of β-globin mRNA in β^0-thalassemia. *Cell* **14:** 299–312.

Beris PH, Miesher PA, Diaz-Chico JC, Hans IS, Kutlar A, Hu H, Wilson HB, Huisman TJH. (1988) Inclusion body β-thalassaemia trait in a Swiss family is caused by an abnormal hemoglobin (Geneva) with an altered and extended β-chain carboxy terminus due to a modification in codon β114. *Blood* **72:** 801–807.

Bradley TB, Wohl RC, Smith GJ. (1975) Elongation of the α globin chain in a black family: interaction with Hb G Philadelphia. *Clin. Res.* **23:** 1314–1319.

Bunn HF. (1978). Mutant hemoglobins having elongated chains. *Hemoglobin* **2:** 1978–1987.

Cai S-P, Eng B, Francombe WH, Olivieri NF, Kendall AG, Waye JS, Chui DHK. (1992) Two novel β-thalassemia mutations in the 5' and 3' noncoding regions of the β-globin gene. *Blood* **79:** 1342–1346.

Chang JC, Kan YW. (1979) β^0 thalassemia, a nonsense mutation in man. *Proc. Natl. Acad. Sci. USA* **76:** 2886–2889.

Cheng J, Fogel-Petrovic M, Maquat LE. (1990) Translation to near the distal end of the penultimate exon is required for normal levels of spliced triosephosphate isomerase mRNA. *Mol. Cell. Biol.* **10:** 5215–5225.

Clegg JB, Weatherall DJ, Milner PG. (1971) Haemoglobin Constant Spring — a chain termination mutant? *Nature* **234:** 337–340.

Clegg JB, Weatherall DJ, Contopoulos-Griva I, Caroutsos K, Poungouras P, Tsevrenis H. (1974) Haemoglobin Icaria, a new chain termination mutant which causes α-thalassaemia. *Nature* **251:** 245–248.

Daar IO, Maquat LE. (1988) Premature translation termination mediates triosephosphate isomerase mRNA degradation. *Mol. Cell. Biol.* **8:** 802–813.

De Jong WW, Khan PM, Bernini LF. (1975) Hemoglobin Koya Dora: high frequency of a chain termination mutant. *Am. J. Hum. Genet.* **27:** 81–87.

Derry S, Wood WG, Pippard M, Clegg JB, Weatherall DJ, Wickramasinghe SN, Darley J, Fucharoen S, Wasi P. (1984) Hematologic and biosynthetic studies in homozygous hemoglobin Constant Spring. *J. Clin. Invest.* **73:** 1673–1682.

Eikenboom JCJ, Briët E, Reitsma PH, Ploos van Amstel H. (1991) Severe type III von Willebrand's disease in the Dutch population is often associated with the absence of von Willebrand factor messenger RNA. *Thromb. Haemost.* **65:** 1127.

Fojo SS, Gennes J-L de, Chapman J, Parrott C, Lohse P, Kwan SS, Truffert J, Brewer HB. (1989a) An initiation codon mutation in the ApoC-II gene (ApoC-II Paris) of a patient with a deficiency of apolipoprotein C-II. *J. Biol. Chem.* **264:** 20839–20842.

Fojo SS, Lohse P, Parrott C, Baggio G, Gabelli C, Thomas F, Hoffman J, Brewer HB. (1989b) A nonsense mutation in the apolipoprotein C-II Padova gene in a patient with apolipoprotein C-II deficiency. *J. Clin. Invest.* **84:** 1215–1219.

Frangi D, Cicardi M, Sica A, Colotta F, Agostoni A, Davis AE. (1991) Nonsense mutations affect C1 inhibitor messenger RNA levels in patients with type 1 hereditary angioneurotic edema. *J. Clin. Invest.* **88:** 755–759.

Fucharoen S, Kobayashi Y, Fucharoen G, Ohba Y, Miyazono K, Fukumaki Y, Takaku F. (1990) A single nucleotide deletion in codon 123 of the β-globin gene causes an inclusion body β-thalassaemia trait: a novel elongated globin chain β Makabe. *Br. J. Haematol.* **75:** 393–399.

Hamosh A, Trapnell BC, Zeitlin PL, Montrose-Rafizadeh C, Rosenstein BJ, Crystal RG, Cutting GR. (1991) Severe deficiency of cystic fibrosis transmembrane conductance regulator messenger RNA carrying nonsense mutations R553X and W1316X in respiratory epithelial cells of patients with cystic fibrosis. *J. Clin. Invest.* **88:** 1880–1885.

Hattori Y, Yamashiro Y, Ohba Y, Miyaji T, Morishita M, Yamamoto K, Yamamoto K, Narai S, Kimura A. (1991) A new β-thalassemia mutation (initiation codon ATG → GTG) found in the Japanese population. *Hemoglobin* **15:** 317–325.

Hesketh JE, Pryne IF. (1991) Interaction between mRNA, ribosomes and the cytoskeleton. *Biochem. J.* **277:** 1–10.

Higgs DR, Goodbourn SEY, Lamb J, Clegg JB, Weatherall DJ. (1983) α-thalassaemia caused by a polyadenylation signal mutation. *Nature* **306:** 398–400.

Humphries KR, Ley TJ, Anagnou NP, Baur AW, Nienhuis AW. (1984) β⁰-39 thalassaemia gene: a premature termination codon causes β-mRNA deficiency without affecting cytoplasmic β-mRNA stability. *Blood* **64:** 23–32.

Hunt DM, Higgs DR, Winichagoon P, Clegg JB, Weatherall DJ. (1982) Haemoglobin Constant Spring has an unstable α chain messenger RNA. *Br. J. Haematol.* **51:** 405–413.

Jankovic L, Efremov GD, Petkov G, Kattamis C, George E, Yang K-G, Stoming TA, Huisman THJ. (1990a) Two novel polyadenylation mutations leading to β⁺-thalassaemia. *Br. J. Haematol.* **75:** 122–126.

Jancovic L, Efremov GD, Josifovska O, Juricic D, Stoming TA, Kutlar A, Huisman THJ. (1990b) An initiation codon mutation as a cause of β-thalassaemia. *Hemoglobin* **14:** 169–176.

John SW, Rozen R, Laframboise R, Laberge C, Scriver CR. (1989) Novel PKU mutation on haplotype 2 in French-Canadians. *Am. J. Hum. Genet.* **45:** 905–909.

Kazazian HH, Boehm CD. (1988) Molecular basis and prenatal diagnosis of β-thalassemia. *Blood* **72:** 1107–1116.

Kazazian HH, Dowling CE, Hurwitz RL, Coleman M, Adams JG. (1989) Thalassemia mutations in exon 3 of the β-globin gene often cause a dominant form of thalassemia and show no predilection for malarial-endemic regions of the world. *Am. J. Hum. Genet. Suppl.* **25:** 950.

Kinniburgh AJ, Maquat LE, Schedl T, Rachmilewitz E, Ross J. (1982) mRNA-deficient β⁰-thalassaemia results from a single nucleotide deletion. *Nucleic Acids Res.* **10:** 5421–5427.

Kozak M. (1984) Compilation and analysis of sequences upstream from the translational start site in eukaryotic mRNAs. *Nucleic Acids Res.* **12:** 857–872.

Kozak M. (1991) Structural features in eukaryotic mRNAs that modulate the initiation of translation. *J. Biol. Chem.* **266:** 19867–19870.

Lam VMS, Xie SS, Tam JWO, Woo YK, Gu YL, Li AMC. (1990) A new single nucleotide change at the initiation codon (ATG → AGG) identified in amplified genomic DNA of a Chinese β-thalassemic patient. *Blood* **75:** 1207–1208.

Lehrman MA, Schneider WJ, Brown MS, Davis CG, Elhammer A, Russell DW, Goldstein JL. (1987) The Lebanese allele at the low density lipoprotein receptor locus. *J. Biol. Chem.* **262:** 401–410.

Liebhaber SA, Coleman MB, Adams JG, Cash FE, Steinberg MH. (1987) Molecular basis for nondeletion α-thalassaemia in American blacks: α2 116 GAG → UAG. *J. Clin. Invest.* **80:** 154–159.

Lim S-K, Sigmund CD, Gross KW, Maquat LE. (1992) Nonsense codons in human β-globin mRNA result in the production of mRNA degradation products. *Mol. Cell. Biol.* **12:** 1149–1161.

Longo N, Langley SD, Griffin LD, Elsas LJ. (1992) Reduced mRNA and a nonsense mutation in the insulin-receptor gene produce heritable severe insulin resistance. *Am. J. Hum. Genet.* **50:** 998–1007.

Losson R, Lacroute F. (1979) Interference of nonsense mutations with eukaryotic messenger RNA stability. *Proc. Natl. Acad. Sci. USA* **76:** 5134–5137.

Maquat LE, Kinniburgh AJ, Rachmilewitz EA, Ross J. (1981) Unstable β-globin mRNA in mRNA-deficient β⁰-thalassemia. *Cell* **27:** 543–553.

Mashima Y, Murakami A, Weleber RG, Kennaway NG, Clarke L, Shiono T, Inana G. (1992) Nonsense-codon mutations of the ornithine aminotransferase gene with decreased levels of mutant mRNA in gyrate atrophy. *Am. J. Hum. Genet.* **51:** 81–91.

Milner PF, Clegg JB, Weatherall DJ. (1971) Haemoglobin H disease due to a unique haemoglobin variant with an elongated α chain. *Lancet* **i:** 729–732.

Mitchell GA, Brody LC, Looney J, Steel G, Suchanek M, Dowling C, Kaloustian V der, Kaiser-Kupfer M, Valle D. (1988) An initiator codon mutation in ornithine-δ-aminotransferase causing gyrate atrophy of the choroid and retina. *J. Clin. Invest.* **81:** 630–633.

Moi P, Cash FE, Liebhaber SA, Cao A, Pirastu M. (1987) An initiation codon mutation (AUG→GUG) of the human α1-globin gene. *J. Clin. Invest.* **80:** 1416–1421.

Morlé F, Lopez B, Henni T, Godet J. (1985) α-thalassemia associated with the deletion of two nucleotides at position −2 and −3 preceding the AUG codon. *EMBO J.* **4:** 1245–1250.

Mules EH, Hayflick S, Miller CS, Reynolds LW, Thomas GH. (1992) Six novel deleterious and three neutral mutations in the gene encoding the α-subunit of hexosaminidase A in non-Jewish individuals. *Am. J. Hum. Genet.* **50:** 834–841.

Murru S, Loudianos G, Deiana M, Camaschella C, Sciarratta GV, Agosti S, Parodi MI, Cerruti P, Cao A, Pirastu M. (1991) Molecular characterization of β-thalassemia intermedia in patients of Italian descent and identification of three novel β-thalassemia mutations. *Blood* **77:** 1342–1347.

Myers RM, Tilly K, Maniatis T. (1986) Fine structure genetic analysis of a β-globin promoter. *Science* **232:** 613–618.

Neote K, Brown CA, Mahuran DJ, Gravel RA. (1990) Translation initiation in the HEXB gene encoding the β-subunit of human β-hexosaminidase. *J. Biol. Chem.* **265:** 20799–20806.

Orkin SH, Cheng T-C, Antonarakis SE, Kazazian HH. (1985) Thalassemia due to a mutation in the cleavage-polyadenylation signal of the human β-globin gene. *EMBO J.* **4:** 453–456.

Patten JL, Johns DR, Valle D, Eil C, Gruppuso PA, Steele G, Smallwood PM, Levine MA. (1990) Mutation in the gene encoding the stimulatory G protein of adenylate cyclase in Albright's hereditary osteodystrophy. *N. Engl. J. Med.* **322:** 1412–1418.

Peerlinck K, Eikenboom JCJ, Ploos van Amstel HK, Sangtawesin W, Arnout J, Reitsma PH, Vermylen J, Briët E. (1992) A patient with von Willebrand's disease characterized by compound heterozygosity for a substitution of Arg 854 by Gln in the putative factor VIII-binding domain of von Willebrand factor on one allele and very low levels of mRNA from the second allele. *Br. J. Haematol.* **80:** 358–363.

Pirastu M, Saglio G, Chang JC, Cao A, Kan YW. (1984) Initiation codon mutation as a cause of α thalassemia. *J. Biol. Chem.* **259:** 12315–12317.

Ploos van Amstel HK, Diepstraten CM, Reitsma PH, Bertina RM. (1991) Analysis of platelet protein S mRNA suggests silent alleles as a frequent cause of hereditary protein S deficiency type I. *Thromb. Haemost.* **65:** 808.

Ristaldi MS, Pirastu M, Murru S, Casula L, Loudianos G, Cao A, Sciarrata GV, Agosti S, Parodi MI, Leone D, Melesendi C. (1990) A spontaneous mutation produced a novel elongated β-globin chain structural variant (Hb Agnana) with a thalassemia-like phenotype. *Blood* **75:** 1378–1380.

Rund D, Dowling C, Najjar K, Rachmilewitz EA, Kazazian HH, Oppenheim A. (1992) Two mutations in the β-globin polyadenylation signal reveal extended transcripts and new RNA polyadenylation sites. *Proc. Natl. Acad. Sci. USA* **89:** 4324–4328.

Schnabel D, Schröder M, Fürst W, Klein A, Hurwitz R, Zenk T, Weber J, Harzer K,

Paton BC, Poulos A, Suzuki K, Sandhoff K. (1992) Simultaneous deficiency of sphingolipid activator proteins 1 and 2 is caused by a mutation in the initiation codon of their common gene. *J. Biol. Chem.* **267:** 3312–3315.

Sligh JE, Hurwitz MY, Zhu C, Anderson DC, Beaudet AL. (1992) An initiation codon mutation in CD18 in association with the moderate phenotype of leukocyte adhesion deficiency. *J. Biol. Chem.* **267:** 714–718.

Takeshita K, Forget BG, Scarpa A, Benz EJ. (1984) Intranuclear defect in β-globin mRNA accumulation due to a premature translation termination codon. *Blood* **64:** 13–22.

Tarlé SA, Davidson BL, Wu VC, Zidar FJ, Seegmiller JE, Kelley WN, Palella TD. (1991) Determination of the mutations responsible for the Lesch–Nyhan syndrome in 17 subjects. *Genomics* **10:** 499–501.

Thein SL, Wallace RB, Pressley L, Clegg JB, Weatherall DJ, Higgs DR. (1988) The polyadenylation site mutation in the α-globin gene cluster. *Blood* **71:** 313–319.

Thein SL, Hesketh C, Taylor P, Temperley IJ, Hutchinson RM, Old JM, Wood WG, Clegg JB, Weatherall DJ. (1990) Molecular basis for dominantly inherited inclusion body β-thalassemia. *Proc. Natl. Acad. Sci. USA* **87:** 3924–3928.

Trecartin RF, Liebhaber SA, Chang JC, Lee KY, Kan YW, Furbetta M, Angius A, Cao A. (1981) β^{o} thalassemia in Sardinia is caused by a nonsense mutation. *J. Clin. Invest.* **68:** 1012–1017.

Urlaub G, Mitchell PJ, Ciudad CJ, Chasin LA. (1989) Nonsense mutations in the dihydrofolate reductase gene affect RNA processing. *Mol. Cell. Biol.* **9:** 2868–2880.

Winslow RM, Swenberg M-L, Gross E, Chervenick PA, Buchman RR, Anderson WF. (1976) Hemoglobin McKees Rocks ($\alpha_2\beta_2$ 145 Tyr$\rightarrow$Term). A human nonsense mutation leading to a shortened β-chain. *J. Clin. Invest.* **57:** 772–781.

Wong C, Dowling CE, Saiki RK, Higuchi R, Erlich HA, Kazazian HH. (1987) Characterization of β-thalassaemia mutations using direct genomic sequencing of amplified single copy DNA. *Nature* **330:** 384–386.

Yüregir GT, Aksoy K, Çürük MA, Dikmen N, Fei Y-J, Baysal E, Huisman THJ. (1992) Hb H disease in a Turkish family resulting from the interaction of a deletional α-thalassaemia-1 and a newly discovered poly A mutation. *Br. J. Haematol.* **80:** 527–532.

The genotype–phenotype relationship

For the great majority of 'monogenic disorders', it is probable that, even if one could somehow set aside the influence of environmental variables for a moment, knowledge of the pathological lesion alone would still provide insufficient information to be able to determine and define the clinical phenotype precisely. Even a disease with no allelic heterogeneity, sickle cell anaemia, in which all patients are homozygous for the same β-globin (HBB) gene lesion, is no exception to this rule. Indeed, as we shall see below (Section 12.3), the clinical severity of sickle cell disease may be ameliorated by the effects of genetic variation either within the HBB gene regulatory region, in far upstream regions controlling the expression of the linked G–γ (HBG2) and A–γ (HBG1) globin genes, or at the unlinked α-globin locus (or a combination of these). Thus, since no gene can exist in splendid isolation, no gene (or gene product) can be completely insulated from genetic influences emanating either from its immediate sequence environment or from other gene loci. In a sense, therefore, all inherited disease states, including so-called 'single gene defects', must be regarded in some way as multifactorial. This truism should not, however, obscure the fact that those genetic factors which influence the genotype–phenotype relationship in a given disorder can often be studied individually and may even be quantified, thereby improving the accuracy of prognostic predictions.

In this chapter, we set out briefly to explore some of the potential genetic influences on clinical phenotype: those factors which could, at least in principle and often in practice, determine that two individuals with identical genetic lesions at a given locus experience quite different clinical symptoms. The phenotypic effect exerted by a mutant allele may be modified by many factors: the proportion of cells bearing the lesion (mosaicism), the activity state of the chromosome carrying it (X-inactivation and imprinting), the effects of other loci and their products (epistasis), the status of the other allele and the variable expression of the wild-type or mutant allele as a consequence either of alternative mRNA processing or the influence of genetic variation in the gene promoter region. In what follows, coverage is by no means intended to be exhaustive but rather a guide to the factors that may serve to further complicate an already complex relationship between inherited genotype and clinical phenotype.

12.1 Somatic and germline mosaicism

Somatic mosaicism is an important cause of phenotype modification resulting in variation in the clinical expression of an inherited trait or disorder (reviewed by Hall, 1988). The proportion of affected cells in the expressing tissue(s) of the individual concerned is clearly an important factor in determining phenotypic severity. Moreover, if the germline of that individual is also affected, then subsequent progeny will be at risk of developing a much more severe phenotype, e.g. as in cases of osteogenesis imperfecta (Byers et al., 1988) and neurofibromatosis (Riccardi and Lewis, 1988). Mosaicism for a specific gene mutation may be confined to somatic cells or to the germline, or be present in both, depending on the developmental stage at which the lesion occurred. Interestingly, the frequency of particular types of lesion may vary depending on whether they have originated in the germline or the soma (reviewed by Albertini et al., 1990). Germline mosaicism provides an explanation for the inheritance pattern in cases where multiple affected offspring are born to clinically and phenotypically normal parents. It arises through the occurrence of a de novo mutation in a germline cell or one of its precursors during the early embryonic development of the parent. Hall (1988) speculated that since in both male and female there are at least 30 mitoses in germ cells before each meiotic event, most germline mutations are likely to be mitotic rather than meiotic in origin.

The powerful new techniques of molecular genetics have allowed us to probe both the nature and the frequency of occurrence of germline mosaicism. In cases of sporadic X-linked disease (e.g. haemophilia, Duchenne muscular dystrophy) in which a specific causative lesion has been identified in a particular gene of the proband, but where the mother of the affected male is phenotypically normal, it is in practice often difficult to distinguish de novo mutation from the much less frequent maternal mosaicism. The main difference lies in the very real recurrence risk to subsequent progeny in cases of germline mosaicism. Direct demonstration of germline mosaicism is clearly not feasible in these women for practical and/or ethical reasons. However, indirect evidence for germline mosaicism may be inferred from DNA-based studies. Several examples of somatic and/or germline mosaicism will now be described from studies on haemophilia A.

Gitschier et al. (1989) reported a partial deletion of exons 5 and 6 of the factor VIII (F8) gene causing severe haemophilia A: an aberrant SstI fragment associated with the deletion was present in the proband's sister (i.e. she was a carrier) but was not seen in lymphocyte DNA from his mother. Since both children were shown by restriction fragment length polymorphism (RFLP) tracking analysis to have inherited the same F8 allele from their mother, it was inferred that the mother was a germline mosaic for the mutation despite the absence of the diagnostic band from her somatic tissues. Gitschier et al. (1991)

found evidence for maternal mosaicism in three of 13 (20%) haemophilia A families investigated in their laboratory.

Somatic mosaicism has also been demonstrated in haemophilia A (Higuchi *et al.*, 1988). A sporadic severe haemophiliac was found to possess a deletion of ~2 kb encompassing exon 3 and part of the following intron of the F8 gene, resulting in an aberrant 5.4 kb HindIII fragment on a Southern blot. Autoradiographic examination of Southern blots of the mother's DNA derived from either lymphocytes or fibroblasts revealed the faint presence of this same fragment, from which it was inferred that 10–20% of cells in the tissues examined contained the aberrant X-chromosome. Although germline mosaicism was also present (the mutations exhibited by the mother and proband were identical), it is never possible to extrapolate from the proportion of mutant somatic cells observed to the proportion of germline cells affected in order to assess the recurrence risk to future offspring. Another case of germline/somatic mosaicism for a F8 gene deletion was reported by Bröcker-Vriends *et al.* (1990). Microdensitometric analysis of Southern blots indicated that one-third of the mother's fibroblasts/lymphocytes possessed the deletion.

In Duchenne muscular dystrophy (DMD), RFLP tracking has been used to demonstrate that deletions of the DMD gene were transmitted to two or more offspring by parents who themselves showed no evidence of the lesion in their somatic (white blood) cells (Bakker *et al.*, 1987; Darras and Francke *et al.*, 1987; Lanman *et al.*, 1987; Monaco, 1987; Darras *et al.*, 1988; Wood and McGillivray, 1988; Barbujani *et al.*, 1990; Claustres *et al.*, 1990; Lebo *et al.*, 1990; Covone *et al.*, 1991; van Essen *et al.*, 1992; reviewed by Grimm *et al.*, 1990), establishing a frequency of ~7% for the proportion of sporadic cases exhibiting germline mosaicism.

Bakker *et al.* (1989) studied the parental origin of 41 sporadic deletion/duplication-type mutations in the DMD gene causing Duchenne/Becker muscular dystrophy. One case of somatic mosaicism was suspected because a proportion of maternal lymphocytes carried a mutation. Six cases of gonadal mosaicism were inferred in the mothers of patients who had transmitted the mutation to more than one child, yet lacked the mutation in their own lymphocytes. By considering the total of at-risk RFLP haplotypes transmitted in all families with new mutations, these authors calculated a recurrence risk of 14% for the at-risk haplotype, i.e. a 14% risk for brothers of patients with an identified new mutation when the male fetus is shown to possess the at-risk haplotype. A figure of 20% was estimated by van Essen *et al.* (1992), who studied a larger collection of DMD families. Since mosaicism arises as a result of the occurrence of a mutation during development, the stage at which the mutation occurs will determine the proportion of germ cells bearing the lesion; the proportion of germ cells bearing the mutated gene is twice the probability of recurrence of the mutation (Jeanpierre, 1992).

Wallis *et al.* (1990) reported the case of a father with a mild form of osteogenesis imperfecta (OI) who was a somatic/germline mosaic for a potentially lethal mutation, causing a Gly→Arg substitution at codon 550 of the α1(I) collagen (COL1A1) protein. His son had died perinatally from lethal (type II)

OI. The mutant allele accounted for 50% of the COL1A1 alleles in the father's fibroblasts, 27% in his blood and 37% in his sperm. Similar cases of somatic/germline mosaicism in OI have been reported by Cohn et al. (1990), Constantinou et al. (1990), Bonaventure et al. (1992) and Edwards et al. (1992).

Wieland et al. (1991) described the case of a factor X (F10) partial gene deletion (exons 7 and 8) where the father appeared to be a germline mosaic. Abnormal restriction fragments associated with the deletion were present in three siblings but were completely absent from the somatic cells of the father. Other examples of the molecular genetic analysis of somatic/germline mosaicism have been reported in retinoblastoma (Greger et al., 1990), ornithine transcarbamylase deficiency (Maddalena et al., 1988; Legius et al., 1990), adrenoleukodystrophy (Graham et al., 1992), Ehlers–Danlos syndrome (Kontusaari et al., 1992) and X-linked agammaglobulinaemia (Hendriks et al., 1989).

A high proportion of what may initially appear to be 'new' mutations may therefore be due to germline mosaicism. Although the frequency with which germline mosaicism occurs may well differ quite markedly between different disease states, it does provide an important explanation for the recurrence of rare mutations within a single family, and should always be considered when counselling such cases.

12.2 Tumour susceptibility genes and the two-hit hypothesis

Although it is beyond the remit of this volume to explore either somatic mutation or mechanisms of carcinogenesis in any detail, it is important at least to mention the conditions known to be caused by defects in tumour suscepti-bility genes, since these disorders are associated with a hereditary predisposi-tion to tumorigenesis. Retinoblastoma will be used to illustrate the general principles involved.

Retinoblastoma is a malignant tumour of the retina occurring in infancy. It may be unilateral or bilateral, and may in some cases have a positive family history. Non-hereditary retinoblastoma includes 85% of unilateral cases in whom the tumour is unifocal. Hereditary retinoblastoma, which is transmitted as an autosomal dominant trait, includes all bilateral cases, all unilateral cases with multifocal tumours and unilateral cases with a positive family history (Vogel, 1979).

The chromosomal location of the retinoblastoma locus was recognized early on as a result of cytogenetically observable deletions of band 13q14. Knudson (1971) originally proposed the 'two-hit' hypothesis whereby heredi-tary retinoblastoma arises from a germinal mutation followed by a somatic mutation; by contrast, non-hereditary retinoblastoma arises from two succes-sive somatic mutations affecting both homologous chromosomes in the same target cell, the embryonic retinoblast (Figure 12.1). Thus, in hereditary retino-blastoma, the first mutation may be a deletion, point mutation, insertion, rearrangement etc, which alters or abolishes the activity of one of the retino-

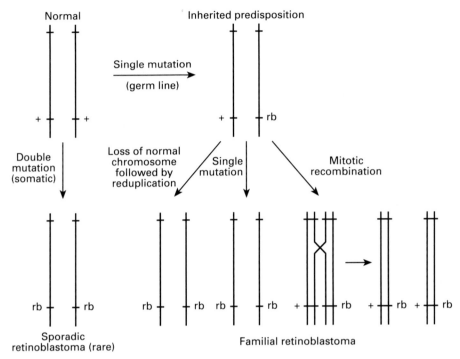

Figure 12.1. Sporadic and familial retinoblastoma. Knudson's (1971) hypothesis distinguished between sporadic retinoblastoma, which required two independent mutations, and a hereditary form, which was due to the inheritance of one (germinal) mutation followed by a somatic mutation. +, wild-type RB1 allele; rb, mutant RB1 allele.

blastoma susceptibility loci on chromosome 13q14. The second mutation affects the same locus on the homologous chromosome, resulting in a 'loss of heterozygosity'. The second mutation may arise as a result of a number of events, including chromosome loss, loss followed by reduplication, mitotic recombination, gene conversion, translocation, deletion or single base-pair substitution (Cavenee et al., 1983; Murphree and Benedict, 1985). The loss of both normal retinoblastoma alleles results in hemizygosity or homozygosity for the mutant allele(s) and the emergence of the retinoblastoma phenotype.

RFLPs associated with DNA segments from the long arm of chromosome 13 were initially used as markers to determine the extent of loss of constitutional heterozygosity at loci on this chromosome in tumour DNAs (Cavenee et al., 1983). The specific mechanism of somatic mutation involved in a given tumour was then inferred from the extent and pattern of loss of heterozygosity observed when compared with that exhibited by constitutional chromosomes 13 from other tissues in the same individual.

Three groups independently identified the retinoblastoma (RB1) gene (Friend et al., 1986; Fung et al., 1987; Lee et al., 1987) by screening single-copy genomic DNA sequences from the 13q14 region. Disease candidacy was tested for on the basis that the RB1 gene should be expressed in retinal cells but not in tumours. Both cDNA and genomic clones from the RB1 gene were isolated and characterized (Lee *et al.*, 1987; Bookstein *et al.*, 1988).

Screening retinoblastoma DNA samples by Southern blotting with the RB1 gene probe demonstrated the existence of fragments of altered size corresponding to partial deletions, fragments of reduced intensity (hetero-zygous deletions) and absent fragments (homozygous deletions). Since these first reports, a considerable number of intragenic lesions have been reported from the RB1 gene (e.g. Bookstein *et al.*, 1988; Dunn *et al.*, 1988; Yandell *et al.*, 1989; see Appendices 2, 3 and 4). Abnormalities in the RB1 gene are associated not only with retinoblastoma but also with other tumours, e.g. sarcomas (Friend *et al.*, 1987), breast cancer (Lee *et al.*, 1988), small cell lung cancer (Yokota *et al.*, 1987), and bladder cancer (Horowitz *et al.*, 1989), as might be expected from the broad range of expression of the RB1 gene. These tumours also appear to arise as a result of the functional loss of both normal RB1 alleles, consistent with a model which invokes a tumour suppressor role for the RB1 locus.

A number of other cancer predisposing conditions are also known to be characterized by a loss of constitutional heterozygosity and appear to be caused by mutation in tumour suppressor genes [e.g. Wilms' tumour (11p), renal carcinoma (3p), phaeochromocytoma (1p, 22), medullary thyroid carcinoma (1p), rhabdomyosarcoma (11p), meningioma (22), acoustic neuroma (22), breast cancer (11p, 13q, 17p, 3p), stomach cancer (13q), colon cancer (several chromosomes), lung/small cell lung cancer (3p, 13q, 17p) etc]. From the recurrence of certain chromosomal locations in these conditions, we may surmise that some loci could well be involved in the causation of several differ-ent tumour states.

12.3 Phenotype modification through regulatory sequence variation

Sickle cell anaemia results from a specific mutation (GAG → GTG) which substitutes valine for glutamic acid at codon 6 of the β-globin (HBB) gene. The phenotype of sickle cell disease is, however, highly variable, some indivi-duals having repeated crises whereas others are relatively symptom-free. It has been known for some time that genetic variation within both the α-and β-globin gene clusters is associated with an amelioration of the pathological symptoms of this disorder. Such epistatic effects may, for example, involve the coinheritance of α-thalassaemia (Embury *et al.*, 1982; Deceular *et al.*, 1983) or high levels of HbF (Nagel *et al.*, 1987; Noguchi *et al.*, 1988) and are thought to exert their effects by potentiating a decrease in the intracellular polymeriza-tion of sickle cell haemoglobin.

There are several examples of an association between genetic variation within the β-globin gene cluster and high levels of HbF in the adult (e.g. Gilman and Huisman, 1984; Labie *et al.*, 1985; Wainscoat *et al.*, 1985). In particular, the $C \rightarrow T$ transition at position -158 upstream of the $G-\gamma$ globin (HBG2) gene (see Section 10.2) has been found to be strongly associated with a high level of HBG2 gene expression and somewhat less strongly with high HbF levels (Nagel et al., 1985; Labie et al., 1985; Kulozik et al., 1987). However, in vitro expression studies have suggested that variation in the $G-\gamma$ (HBG2) and $A-\gamma$ (HBG1) globin promoter regions does not invariably play a role in elevating levels of γ-globin synthesis (Lanclos et al., 1991). In addition, there is now good evidence for the existence of a locus on the X-chromosome which is capable of influencing HbF levels (Miyoshi et al., 1988; Dover et al., 1992).

Öner et al. (1992) have recently provided evidence for a role of DNA sequence variation within the locus control region (LCR; see Section 10.5) some 10–11 kb upstream of the ε-globin (HBE1) gene: One mutational change at $-10\,905$ serves to create a potential Sp1 binding site, whereas other sequence variants at $-10\,924$ and $-10\,390$ occur within motifs that could have the potential to bind erythroid-specific transcription factors. A further $(TA)_n$ copy number polymorphism between $-10\,623$ and $-10\,570$, not unlike that present at the BP1 binding site upstream of the β-globin gene (see below), was also noted. These variants were specific for a β^s chromosome with a particular haplotype (no. 19) known to be associated with a low level of HbF expression. Öner et al. (1992) observed a crossover in a homozygous sickle cell patient which resulted in the placement of the LCR of a haplotype (no. 3) normally associated with high HbF expression, in juxtaposition to sequences derived from haplotype 19; this novel haplotype was associated with high HbF expression (20%) and a mild form of the disease not hitherto seen with haplotype 19. Sequence variation within the LCR may therefore serve to ameliorate the sickle cell disease clinical phenotype by up-regulating γ-globin gene expression.

Additional sources of genetic variation in and around the β-globin (HBB) gene are also likely to be important, as evidenced by the variable clinical severity manifested by individuals bearing the five known independent sickle cell mutations (Senegal, Bantu, Benin, Cameroon, Arabo-Indian) which are distinguished by reference to their different haplotypes (Kan and Dozy, 1980; Pagnier et al., 1984; Kulozik et al., 1986; Lapouméroulie et al., 1992). The Arabo-Indian haplotype is associated with a much milder clinical phenotype. One DNA variant, a tandem repeat $(AT)_x (T)_y$ copy number polymorphism (Spritz, 1981) located between 530 and 526 bp $5'$ to the HBB gene transcriptional initiation site, may be of particular importance since it appears in distinct forms specific to each haplotype (Table 12.1; Chebloune et al., 1988; Lapouméroulie et al., 1992). This polymorphism is located within a region between -610 and -490, upstream of the HBB gene, known to be bound by a protein, BP1, present in nuclear extracts derived from human erythroleukaemia K562 cells, in which fetal γ-globin but not adult β-globin is synthesized (Berg et al., 1989). The increased binding of BP1 to a DNA sequence bearing a mutation at -530 derived from a β-thalassaemia patient correlates with a reduction in β-globin synthesis (Berg et al., 1991). BP1 binding may therefore serve to down-regulate the expression of the HBB gene. Using

Table 12.1. Copy number polymorphism upstream of the β-globin (HBB) gene in β^s alleles from different haplotype backgrounds

Haplotype	-551	-543		-521	-491
Reference	T	C	$(AT)_7 (T)_7$	C	A
Senegal	T	C	$(AT)_8 (T)_4$	C	A
Benin	T	T	$(AT)_8 (T)_4$	C	C
Bantu	C	C	$(AT)_6 (T)_9$	C	A
Cameroon	T	C	$(AT)_8 (T)_5$	C	A
Arabo-Indian	C	C	$(AT)_9 (T)_5$	C	A

Reproduced from Lapouméroulie *et al.*, 1992, by permission of Springer Verlag.

mobility shift (gel retardation) assays, Elion *et al.* (1992) have shown that DNA sequence between -556 and -518 from the Arabo-Indian β^s allele exhibits a six-fold higher affinity for BP1 than does the reference sequence. By contrast, DNA sequences corresponding to the Bantu and Benin β^s alleles exhibit a 2–3-fold and 1.5-fold lower affinity respectively for BP1 as compared to the reference sequence. Further, Elion *et al.* (1992) have shown that the severity of sickle cell disease is directly related to the relative amount of HbS produced, and that this is considerably lower for the Arabo-Indian β^s allele. It may be therefore, that, far from being merely neutral variation, the $(AT)_x (T)_y$ polymorphism in the HBB gene promoter region serves to reduce the expression of the β^s gene, by virtue of its higher affinity for a repressor protein. In so doing, it ameliorates the sickle cell disease phenotype.

Ragusa *et al.* (1992) have, however, reported individuals homozygous for the $(AT)_9 (T)_5$ allele who exhibit a severe clinical phenotype and low HbF expression. These authors proposed that although the $(AT)_x (T)_y$ polymorphism may be a necessary precondition for a mild clinical presentation, it is not sufficient on its own. Interestingly, they suggested that a combination of the HBG2 gene -158 mutation and the Arabo-Indian $(AT)_9 (T)_5$ allele might be associated with a particularly high level of HbF expression and an unusually mild anaemia (Ragusa *et al.*, 1992). If this finding is confirmed, it may be that a combination of low HbS levels and high HbF levels may serve to ameliorate the symptoms of anaemia more successfully than either factor acting alone. Other factors such as the coinheritance of α-thalassaemia, which is frequently found in sickle cell disease patients of Arabo-Indian origin, may of course also play a role in the amelioration of the clinical phenotype.

12.4 Alternative mRNA splicing

Until the dystrophin (DMD) gene was isolated and characterized, the molecular basis for the distinction between the clinically severe form of muscular dystrophy [Duchenne type (DMD)] and its milder form [Becker type (BMD)] could only be guessed at. The major leap forward in understanding came through the analysis of deletions of the DMD gene in both groups of patients (Monaco *et al.*, 1988); deletions in three DMD patients altered the translational reading frame of the protein (presumably leading to premature termination of translation), whereas deletions in three BMD patients maintained the reading frame. It was assumed that the shortened proteins produced in BMD patients had retained some of their biological activity, thus avoiding the most severe clinical symptoms of the disease. This 'reading frame hypothesis' received support from further analyses of DMD and BMD patients (e.g. Liechti-Gallati *et al.*, 1989). However, exceptions to the rule soon emerged: a total of six BMD patients (five unrelated) possessed deletions of exons 3 to 7 of the DMD gene which would disrupt the translational reading frame (Malhotra *et al.*, 1988). Similarly, deletions of exon 45 of the DMD gene, which should result in a frameshift, have been found in both BMD and DMD patients (Gillard *et al.*, 1989; Hodgson *et al.*, 1989).

With the advent of ectopic transcript analysis (Section 4.3.2), the probable explanation for at least some of these anomalous cases emerged. Chelly *et al.* (1991) studied two BMD patients with deletions spanning exons 3–7 and found evidence for alternative transcripts (exon 1 spliced to exon 8 and exon 2 spliced to exon 10) in which the reading frame had been restored; these transcripts occurred at a level of 1–2% of that of the frameshifted mRNA. Roberts *et al.* (1990) analysed the DMD genes of DMD and BMD patients by PCR amplification of DMD mRNA isolated from their peripheral blood lymphocytes. One DMD patient with a deletion of exon 45 possessed a novel PCR fragment which corresponded to an alternatively spliced mRNA skipping exons 44 and 45. This alternative splicing event would further shorten the dystrophin molecule but would at least serve to restore the reading frame of the protein. Alternative splicing therefore has the potential, at least in principle (although not apparently in practice in this DMD patient!), to override the potentially severe effects of a frameshift mutation. This analysis was then extended to a larger series of patients (Roberts *et al.*, 1991). Two examples of alternative splicing of the DMD transcript, involving exons 9 and 71, were observed in normal healthy controls. Alternative splicing was able to account for the phenotype of a mildly affected patient who, with a frameshift deletion of exons 42 and 43, had originally been thought to violate the frameshift rule. The major PCR product isolated from his lymphocytes also lacked exon 44, whose absence restored the translational reading frame. Alternative splicing was observed in a further six patients. In each case, the alternative splicing event was *specific to the patient* and involved the skipping of an exon immediately adjacent to the rearrangement. These two observations are unlikely to be unrelated and probably reflect the importance of the local nucleotide sequence context in splice site selection.

However, at least one anomalous case has been reported: that of a BMD patient with a frameshift deletion of DMD exons 3–7 which, contrary to the findings of Chelly *et al.* (1991) in similar patients, is not obviously associated with an alternative splicing event (Gangopadhyay *et al.*, 1992). Various hypotheses such as mRNA editing and activation of a cryptic promoter were rejected by these workers. However, since dystrophin of slightly reduced size was detectable immunologically, the translational reading frame must have been restored either by a transcriptional or a post-transcriptional mechanism. Gangopadhyay et al. (1992) suggested two possible alternative hypotheses to explain this intriguing observation: reinitiation of protein synthesis from an AUG codon in exon 8, or ribosomal frameshifting.

Exon skipping in the cystic fibrosis transmembrane conductance regulator (CFTR) gene was first reported by Chu et al. (1991). These workers analysed mRNA isolated from the bronchial epithelium of clinically normal adults and demonstrated that all individuals tested possessed some CFTR transcripts lacking exon 9 (exon 9⁻ transcripts). Exons 9–12 of the CFTR gene encode the first nucleotide-binding fold of the protein; this domain is thought to be the primary site of ATP hydrolysis on the CFTR molecule and essential for its postulated role as a chloride channel. Exon 9⁻ transcripts may therefore, if translated, give rise to a non-functional protein product despite the conservation of the reading frame (Zielenski et al., 1991). Whilst exon 9⁻ transcripts usually represented between 9 and 25% of the total transcript population in the bronchial epithelial cells of normal controls, some individuals exhibited a level as high as 66% (Chu et al., 1991). Two individuals with the highest level of exon 9⁻ transcript were shown to possess an identical TT dinucleotide deletion, between 6 and 11 bp upstream of the intron 8/exon 9 acceptor splice site. (The surrounding sequence, a stretch of T residues and a series of TG repeats, also exhibited copy number variation but the latter did not correlate with the exon 9⁻ phenotype.) The proportion of alternatively spliced exon 9⁻ transcripts was reproducible and constant in any given individual. Further studies indicated that some control individuals exhibited levels of exon 9⁻ transcripts as high as 92%, despite normal sweat Cl⁻ values and no obvious clinical manifestation of cystic fibrosis (Chu et al., 1992). Moreover, these individuals did not up-regulate CFTR gene expression in their bronchial epithelial cells. The authors concluded that either exon 9 is unnecessary for normal CFTR structure and function or (more likely in their view) only a small proportion of bronchial epithelial cells need to express full-length CFTR mRNA transcripts to maintain a normal clinical phenotype. During differentiation of colon adenocarcinoma cells, the proportion of exon 9⁻ to exon 9⁺ transcripts increases two-fold (Montrose-Rafizadeh et al., 1992), suggesting that alternative splicing of this exon may be very precisely regulated.

Slomski et al. (1992) reported similar findings for exon 12 of the CFTR gene in both lymphocytes and bronchial epithelial cells of healthy controls: five individuals possessed only exon 12⁺ transcripts, six exhibited proportions of 8, 75, 79, 86, 87 and 87% exon 12⁻ transcript respectively. In one case, no exon 12⁺ transcript appeared to be detectable (implying that a normal clinical phenotype may still be feasible despite a drastically lowered level of wild-type CFTR mRNA). Results were reproducible in all individuals tested. Finally, the skipping of CFTR exon 4 in normal healthy controls has also been reported (Bremer et al., 1992). Several possible clinical implications of these findings may be considered, some of which may yet prove to have a more general significance:

304

(i) As in the case of DMD, the alternative splicing events in the CFTR gene observed in normal healthy controls could in principle provide the means to circumnavigate frameshift deletions and/or in-frame termination codons which would otherwise lead to a severe clinical phenotype in cystic fibrosis patients. Additional exon-skipped mRNA species may also be found to be specific to certain CFTR mutant genotypes (as found in DMD). Since exon skipping appears to involve several CFTR exons, every individual, healthy or otherwise, could in principle possess a CFTR transcript population made up of a patchwork of different exon combinations and permutations and a variable amount of full-length CFTR mRNA. Although as yet untested, this variation could account for the mild pulmonary disease found in some patients homozygous for nonsense mutations in the CFTR gene (Cutting *et al.*, 1990; Bonduelle *et al.*, 1991).

(ii) Individual-specific mRNA splicing patterns could also account for the clinical and phenotypic variability sometimes manifested by different individuals bearing the same CFTR gene lesion (e.g. Cuppens *et al.*, 1990; Kerem *et al.*, 1990; Kalaydjieva *et al.*, 1991). Moreover, if there is a threshold concentration of CFTR protein below which the disease phenotype becomes apparent, an otherwise mild CFTR gene lesion might cause a severe disease state if associated with an alternative splicing pattern yielding predominantly exon-skipped mRNA transcripts. As far as other genetic disorders are concerned, there is little evidence for or against this hypothesis. However, it is not unreasonable to suppose that, for any disorder, the lower the threshold concentration of the protein in question, the lower would be the likely clinical significance of alternative splicing.

Naylor *et al.* (1991) have detected alternatively spliced ectopic transcripts involving exons 4–7 of the F8 gene in the lymphocytes of normal individuals. 'Aberrant alternative splicing' (denoting the production of alternative transcripts lacking any obvious function) is also apparent in the genes for argininosuccinate lyase (ASAL; Walker *et al.*, 1990), platelet glycoprotein IIb (GP2B; Kolodziej *et al.*, 1991) and adenosine deaminase (ADA; Kashii *et al.*, 1991) among others. Since these alternatively spliced mRNA species from the F8 and DMD genes were out-of-frame, and since exon skipping in the ASAL and GP2B genes would be predicted to remove a vital protein binding site or prevent protein export, these transcripts are not thought likely to give rise to a functional protein product. If this phenomenon proves to be a common feature of disease genes, the study of mRNA splicing patterns could become an important tool for the analysis of the genotype–phenotype relationship in many inherited disorders.

12.5 Genomic imprinting

Monk (1988) has defined genomic imprinting as the 'differential modification of the maternal and paternal contributions to the zygote, resulting in the differential expression of parental alleles during development and in the adult'.

This differential modification appears to be essential for normal development since parthenogenetic embryos (whether diploid paternal or diploid maternal) do not survive to term. In diploid maternal embryos, fetal development is normal but development of the extraembryonic membranes is abnormal. In diploid paternal embryos, it is the other way around (reviewed by Monk, 1988). Clearly, maternal and paternal chromosomes must differ epigenetically and in such a way that different developmental programmes are followed.

In principle, imprinting must be established either before or early in gametogenesis, must be stable enough to be retained in somatic cells and must be capable of being erased in the germline at every generation prior to the fresh establishment of the imprinting pattern. The idea that imprinting might involve DNA methylation was proposed by Monk *et al.* (1987) on the grounds that this post-synthetic modification was heritable, reversible and known to play a role in the control of gene expression. This view soon received solid support from the results of studies on transgenic mice (reviewed by Surani *et al.*, 1988; Hall, 1990). In most cases reported, transgenes inherited from the father were less methylated than transgenes inherited from the mother. Further, the expression of the transgene correlated with its methylation status, the less methylated paternally inherited transgenes exhibiting higher levels of expression.

Whether methylation is a primary or secondary event in imprinting is still unclear (Surani, 1991). It does, however, appear by itself to possess all the necessary properties to allow it to fulfil an epigenetic role in development. Monk *et al.* (1987) have shown that, before fertilization, the egg genome is relatively undermethylated by comparison with the sperm genome. The embryo then becomes progressively less methylated until the blastocyst stage, at which time *de novo* methylation is initiated, which establishes the eventual tissue-specific patterns of the modification.

Assuming that imprinting is critical for normal development, it may reasonably be supposed that a failure to modify the maternal and paternal chromosomes differentially would give rise to a clinically recognizable phenotype. A number of possible examples of chromosome disorders are now known which could in principle be explicable in terms of imprinting. In Beckwith–Wiedemann syndrome (BWS) sporadic cases are associated with trisomy of 11p15.5 and the duplicated region is invariably of paternal origin (Henry *et al.*, 1989). By contrast, the familial form of the disease, which maps to the same chromosomal location, is transmitted three times more frequently by mothers than by fathers (Moutou *et al.*, 1992). Observations such as these originally led Koufos *et al.* (1989) to propose that the paternally transmitted allele is always inactivated by imprinting whereas children are affected only if the mutant allele is inherited from their mother. This postulate is now supported by data from 19 published BWS families although the reduced fecundity of affected males also contributes to the excess of transmitting females (Moutou *et al.*, 1992).

Perhaps the clearest example of imprinting is provided by the Angelman (AS) and Prader–Willi syndromes (PWS), two inherited disorders often associated with cytogenetically detectable (and indistinguishable) deletions of chromosome 15q11-q13. In cases of AS, the deletion is exclusively maternal in origin (Knoll *et al.*, 1989; Williams *et al.*, 1990; Clayton-Smith *et al.*, 1992) whereas, in the great majority of cases of PWS, the deletion originates from the father (Nicholls *et al.*, 1989; Robinson *et al.*, 1991). Driscoll *et al.* (1992) have demonstrated that the D15S9 locus (15q11–q12) exhibits paternal and maternal allele-specific differences in DNA methylation, and that AS and PWS patients can be distinguished by virtue of their different patterns of methylation. However, whereas maternal transmission of a deletion encompassing the GABA receptor β3 subunit (GABRB3) gene results in AS, paternal transmission results in a normal phenotype, not PWS (Saitoh *et al.*, 1992), suggesting that the AS and PWS loci may be distinct (albeit closely linked) as well as subject to differential imprinting. This interpretation is further supported by the case of a family with chromosome 15-associated non-deletion AS, which was exclusively transmitted through the maternal line (Wagstaff *et al.*, 1992).

Genomic imprinting may also be important in embryonal tumours. In most sporadic cases of Wilms' tumour (WT), retinoblastoma and osteosarcoma, the paternal chromosome (bearing the initial mutation) is retained while the maternal chromosome is preferentially lost (Schroeder *et al.*, 1987; Dryja *et al.*, 1989; Williams *et al.*, 1989; Zhu *et al.*, 1989; Pal *et al.*, 1990; reviewed by Reik and Surani, 1989). In the case of Wilms' tumour, which is associated with allele loss on chromosome 11p, Wilkins (1988) has sought to explain this finding by proposing that a transforming gene is linked to the WT locus. Inactivation of the WT locus would serve to derepress the transforming gene and would lead to tumour formation. If the maternally inherited allele of the transforming gene is inactivated by imprinting or methylation, only the combination of an inactive Wilms' tumour gene and an active transforming gene on the paternal chromosome would give rise to a tumour. Allele-specific methylation differences at the retinoblastoma locus (RB1), which are dependent on parental origin, have been noted by Blanquet *et al.* (1991).

Genomic imprinting has been implicated in rhabdomyosarcoma, which is associated with losses of maternal alleles in the region of chromosome 11p (Scrable *et al.*, 1989). Van der Mey *et al.* (1989) have shown that familial glomus tumours are transmitted almost exclusively through the paternal line. Similarly, the defective gene underlying hereditary paragangliomas has been localized to the long arm of chromosome 11, and all affected individuals have inherited the disease allele from their fathers (Heutink *et al.*, 1992).

A number of single gene defects exhibiting variable penetrance and expressivity could in principle also be related to genomic imprinting (reviewed by Reik, 1989; Hall, 1990). In Huntington disease (HD), the age of onset is variable and is strongly influenced by the parental origin of the defective gene. Early onset HD is associated with paternal transmission, whereas late onset HD is associated with maternal transmission. Reik (1988) proposed that the earlier onset of symptoms of HD in patients who have inherited the defective gene from their father is due to imprinting of that gene leading to early and/or high-level expression. Conversely, maternal transmission of the HD gene would result in reduced or delayed expression. An inverse relationship between age of onset of HD and paternal age has also been explained in terms of genomic imprinting (Krawczak *et al.*, 1991; Farrer *et al.*, 1992).

In type I neurofibromatosis, maternal transmission of the disease gene (NF1) is associated with a more severe clinical phenotype (Miller and Hall, 1978), whilst the vast majority of new mutations are paternal in origin but do not exhibit a paternal age effect (Jadayel *et al.*, 1990; Stephens *et al.*, 1992). These observations could in principle be accounted for by differential imprinting or methylation of the parental chromosomes: a higher level of methylation of the paternal allele might reduce its capacity for expression, hence the greater clinical severity results when the more highly expressed maternal allele is inactivated due to mutation. A higher level of methylation in the paternal gene would undoubtedly lead to an increase in frequency of methylation-mediated deamination-type mutations; however, it would be very surprising if such a methylation difference alone could satisfactorily explain the very considerable sex difference in the origin of neurofibromatosis mutations.

The means by which imprinting influences disease phenotype probably depends on whether the mutant alleles at a given locus exert their pathological effects through a gain or loss of function. Explanations for phenotypic variability associated with the parental origin of a given inherited defect will be placed upon a much sounder footing once we know more about the mechanism of imprinting, the regions of the human genome involved in the imprinting process and how imprinting exerts its differential effects upon the maternal and paternal alleles of specific genes.

12.6 X-inactivation in female carriers of X-linked disease

Inactivation of one X-chromosome in females is in principle a random affair (reviewed by Lyon, 1988). Thus, in females who are heterozygous carriers of a given X-linked defect our expectation is that about 50% of cells will express the defect, whereas 50% of cells will be normal. However, since inactivation of X chromosomes is believed to follow a multinomial distribution pattern, a given tissue in a specific individual may by chance contain a much higher proportion of cells bearing the mutant gene on the active X chromosome. This will tend to result in a disease phenotype which approaches that of a hemizygous male. Such 'extreme lyonization' of the factor VIII (F8) and IX (F9) genes in liver is one cause of haemophilia in females, and examples of this phenomenon will be drawn from (and confined to) these conditions.

Ingerslev *et al.* (1989) reported the case of a girl with haemophilia A with a phenotypically normal (by clotting assays) mother and an affected maternal grandfather. Use of F8 intragenic and extragenic RFLPs demonstrated the inheritance of the grandpaternal X chromosome through the carrier mother. Using a phosphoglycerate kinase (PGK) gene probe, these authors provided evidence for the hypermethylation (and, by inference, inactivation; see Section 5.6) of the paternal X chromosome in the proband. Although it is difficult to exclude *de novo* mutation of the paternal allele, a much more likely explanation of the haemophilia phenotype is extreme lyonization, the healthy paternal X chromosome being preferentially inactivated in the daughter. Presumably the opposite occurred in the proband's mother, with the mutant X chromosome being preferentially inactivated, resulting in a normal phenotype.

Similar examples of extreme lyonization have also been reported as a cause of haemophilia B in females (Nisen *et al.*, 1986; Nisen and Waber, 1989; Kling *et al.*, 1991) and methylation analysis of the F9 gene has been consistent with this interpretation. Taylor *et al.* (1991) reported female-to-female transmission of haemophilia B; both women possessed two copies of the F9 gene (by RFLP tracking), and only a single heterozygous TGT→TCT transversion at Cys 350, originally identified in the grandfather, could be found in their F9 genes. This suggested that the normal F9 gene had been preferentially inactivated in both women. Since such extreme lyonization in succeeding generations would be exceedingly improbable, Taylor *et al.* (1991) proposed the existence of a second lesion, possibly in the primary inactivation centre on the mutant X chromosome.

12.7 Relative phenotypic effects of nonsense and missense mutations

One aim of direct genetic analysis is predictive: given a particular genotype, what will be the most likely clinical phenotype? Intuitively, a nonsense mutation which abolishes the synthesis of a full-length protein product, might be expected to produce at least as severe a phenotype as a missense mutation producing a structurally or functionally altered protein. In most cases this is probably true (see Section 6.5.2) but there are exceptions, and three such examples will now be explored. These counter examples serve to illustrate the potential complexity of genotype–phenotype predictions.

12.7.1 Thalassaemia-β

In contrast to the typical recessive mode of inheritance manifested by β-thalassaemia, an unusual dominant form of the disease also occurs. This type of β-thalassaemia is often caused by heterozygous mutations in exon 3 of the β-globin (HBB) gene (Kazazian *et al.*, 1989). A total of 16 different mutations (mostly but not exclusively in exon 3 of the HBB gene) causing the dominant form of the disease have recently been collated by Thein (1992), who classified them into three distinct groups:

(i) Highly unstable β-globin chain variants caused either by base substitution or the deletion of intact codons

(ii) Truncated β-globin chain variants caused by premature termination of translation

(iii) Elongated β-globin variants with an altered carboxy terminal resulting from a frameshift mutation

Comparison of these different β-globin variants has suggested mechanisms to explain why exon 3 mutations are sometimes associated with a particularly severe clinical phenotype. Nonsense mutations that occur in the 5' half of the HBB gene (exons 1 and 2) do not give rise to a detectable β-globin product (due to mRNA and/or protein instability) and thus result in a typical hetero- zygous β-thalassaemia phenotype due to a simple reduction in β-globin synthesis. Whilst the most unstable β-globin variants precipitate in the erythro- blasts resulting in imbalanced globin synthesis, less unstable β-chain variants could still be capable of transiently forming tetramers with α-chains, resulting in severe anaemia. β-globin chains truncated by exon 3 nonsense mutations may often be synthesized, since steady-state mRNA levels may be either normal or only slightly reduced (see Section 11.5). Such chains are, however, unlikely to be capable of forming viable tetramers, although they might still retain the ability to bind haem. On the other hand, elongated β-chain variants would possess an abnormal carboxy terminal end, causing instability and the subse- quent aggregation and precipitation of an abnormal globin molecule. Produc- tion of an abnormal β-chain capable of forming dysfunctional tetramers may thus in many instances be clinically more serious than the abolition of β-chain synthesis.

12.7.2 Osteogenesis imperfecta

Type I procollagen contains an extensive triple helical domain comprising two α1(I) chains and a single α2(I) chain encoded by the COL1A1 and COL1A2 loci respectively. The nature of the tightly packed triple helix is only made possible by a very simple repeat structure consisting of Gly–X–Y, where X and Y are often proline and hydroxyproline respectively. Osteogenesis imperfecta (OI) is inherited as either an autosomal dominant or a recessive trait, both types manifesting a considerable degree of variable penetrance and expressiv- ity. The cataloguing of different types of mutation in the COL1A1 and COL1A2 genes has provided us with a good idea of the different types of mutation responsible for the different clinical phenotypes associated with OI (reviewed by Sykes, 1985; Byers, 1990; see Appendix 1). Indeed, OI is a para- digm for the study of the genotype–phenotype relationship manifested by dis- orders in which the defective protein product is either a homodimer or a heterodimer of two or more polypeptide chains.

All mutations in the COL1A1 and COL1A2 genes responsible for OI result in the decreased synthesis of normal type 1 procollagen. Mutations in the axial glycine residues disrupt the inter-chain relationships and propagate an abnormal structure along the entire length of the triple helical domain. Mutations in the α2 chain are usually much less severe clinically than α1 chain mutants. This effect on phenotype appears to be due largely to the stoichiometry of the triple helical type I collagen molecule, which dictates that a mutant α2 chain would be incorporated into 50% type I collagen molecules, whereas only 25% type I collagen molecules would be free of a mutant α1 chain.

When abnormal molecules are synthesized (termed 'included' mutants by Sykes, 1985), the phenotype can range from mild to lethal depending on the nature of the mutation and its effects on the structure, stability and secretion of the collagen molecule. Included mutants may be internal in-frame deletions (e.g. Chu *et al.*, 1983) or missense mutations (e.g. Steinmann *et al.*, 1984). In addition to reducing the production of a given collagen chain, these mutants exert their phenotypic effects by destroying the function of otherwise normal chains into which they have become incorporated. Although 'excluded' mutants are associated with a reduction in the overall amount of protein product from the mutant allele, no mutant chains are incorporated into the type I collagen molecule. Examples of excluded mutants are nonsense and frameshift mutations (e.g. Pihlajaniemi *et al.*, 1984). Thus, as with the β-globin variants described in Section 12.7.1, the abolition of synthesis of a gene product can be less detrimental to the clinical phenotype (at least in the heterozygous state) than the synthesis of a defective product.

12.7.3 Factor XI deficiency

Factor XI deficiency is a rare coagulopathy found predominantly but not exclusively in Ashkenazi Jewish kindreds, where the defective allele occurs at a frequency of at least 4%. This disorder is inherited as an autosomal incompletely recessive trait; homozygous and heterozygous patients are characterized by a severe or partial deficiency of factor XI respectively, but both groups are at risk from an increased bleeding tendency (Bolton-Maggs *et al.*, 1988). The disorder is of particular interest both because of the considerable variability in bleeding severity between affected individuals and because of the absence of any strong correlation between clinical phenotype and the plasma level of factor XI (Ragni *et al.*, 1985). These observations have been considered to reflect either allelic heterogeneity or non-allelic factors.

Factor XI is a serine protease zymogen that links the contact phase of blood coagulation with the intrinsic pathway via the activation of factor IX. Factor XI circulates as a homodimer that is cleaved by factor XIIa between Arg 369 and Ile 370 in each monomer to generate factor XIa. The activated protease thus comprises two N-terminal heavy chains and two C-terminal light chains held together by a disulphide bridge between Cys 321 residues (Meijers *et al.*, 1992). *In vitro*, factor XI activation requires high molecular weight kininogen (HMWK), which binds to a site between residues 56 and 86 in the factor XI heavy chain (Baglia *et al.*, 1989). The substrate binding site for factor IX has been localized to the heavy chain between residues 134 and 172 (Baglia *et al.*, 1991).

Asakai *et al.* (1989) identified the two most common factor XI (F11) gene mutations in the Ashkenazi Jewish population: a Glu 117→Term nonsense mutation in exon 5 (type II) and a Phe 283→Leu misense mutation in exon 9 (type III). Hancock *et al.* (1991) investigated 63 British and Israeli patients with factor XI deficiency. Comparative analysis of phenotype and genotype suggested that patients with a type II/III genotype were significantly more likely to experience moderate bleeding than patients with other genotypes: of the patients with a II/III genotype, approximately 50% had a moderate bleeding tendency and the other 50% had a mild clinical picture. Indeed, six of the seven patients from the sample who exhibited a moderate bleeding tendency possessed this genotype. This result indicated that a knowledge of a factor XI-deficient patient's genotype might be of some use in predicting the likely outcome of an elective haemostatic challenge. These data also demonstrated an association between plasma factor XI:C levels and a patient's genotype. The relatively severe phenotype associated with the type II/III genotype is reminiscent of the effects of 'included' collagen mutations causing osteogenesis imperfecta (Section 12.7.2). It is possible that a stable dysfunctional II/III dimer could sequester either HMWK or factor IX, thereby producing a more severe phenotype than that associated with II/II dimers that would be unlikely to be stable. Confirmation or otherwise of this postulate awaits structural and functional studies of the mutant factor XI proteins *in vitro*.

References

Albertini RJ, Nicklas JA, O'Neill P, Robison SH. (1990) *In vivo* somatic mutations in humans: measurement and analysis. *Ann. Rev. Genet.* **24:** 305–326.

Asakai R, Chung DW, Ratnoff OD, Davie EW. (1989) Factor XI (plasma thromboplastin antecedent) deficiency in Ashkenazi Jews is a bleeding disorder that can result from three types of point mutations. *Proc. Natl. Acad. Sci. USA* **86:** 7667–7671.

Baglia FA, Sinha D, Walsh PN. (1989) Functional domains in the heavy-chain region of factor XI: a high molecular weight kininogen-binding site and a substrate-binding site for factor IX. *Blood* **74:** 244–251.

Baglia FA, Jameson BA, Walsh PN. (1991) Identification and chemical synthesis of a substrate-binding site for factor IX on coagulation factor XIa. *J. Biol. Chem.* **266:** 24190–24197.

Bakker E, Van Broeckhoven C, Bonten EJ, van de Vooren MJ, Veenema H, Van Hul W, Van Ommen GJB, Vandenberghe A, Pearson PL. (1987) Germline mosaicism and Duchenne muscular dystrophy mutations. *Nature* **329:** 554–558.

Bakker E, Veenema H, Den Dunnen JT, Van Broeckhoven C, Grootscholten PM, Bonten EJ, Van Ommen GJB, Pearson PL. (1989) Germinal mosaicism increases the recurrence risk for 'new' Duchenne muscular dystrophy mutations. *J. Med. Genet.* **26:** 553–559.

Barbujani G, Russo A, Danieli GA, Spiegler AWJ, Borkowska J, Hausmanova-Petrusewicz I. (1990) Segregation analysis of 1885 DMD families: significant departure from the expected proportion of sporadic cases. *Hum. Genet.* **84:** 522–526.

Berg PE, Williams DM, Quian RL, Cohen RB, Cao SX, Mittelman M, Schechter AN. (1989) A common protein binds to two silencers 5′ to the human β-globin gene. *Nucleic Acids Res.* **17:** 8833–8852.

Berg PE, Mittleman M, Elion J, Labie D, Schechter A. (1991) Increased protein binding to a −530 mutation of the human β-globin gene associated with decreased β-globin synthesis. *Am. J. Hematol.* **36:** 42–46.

Blanquet V, Turleau C, De Grouchy J, Creau-Goldberg N. (1991) Physical map around the retinoblastoma gene: possible genomic imprinting suggested by NruI digestion. *Genomics* **10:** 350–355.

Bolton-Maggs PHB, Wan-Yin BY, McCraw AH, Slack J, Kernoff PBA. (1988) Inheritance and bleeding in factor XI deficiency. *Br. J. Haematol.* **69:** 521–528.

Bonaventure J, Cohen-Solal L, Lasselin C, Maroteaux P. (1992) A dominant mutation in the COL1A1 gene that substitutes glycine for valine causes recurrent lethal osteogenesis imperfecta. *Hum. Genet.* **89:** 640–646.

Bonduelle M, Lissens W, Liebaers I, Malfroot A, Dab I. (1991) Mild cystic fibrosis in a child homozygous for G542 non-sense mutation in CF gene. *Lancet* **338:** 189.

Bookstein R, Lee EYHP, To H, Young L-H, Sery T, Hayes R, Friedmann T, Lee W-H. (1988) Human retinoblastoma susceptibility gene: genomic organization and analysis of heterozygous intragenic deletion mutants. *Proc. Natl. Acad. Sci. USA* **85:** 2210–2214.

Bremer S, Hoof T, Wilke M, Busche R, Scholte B, Riordan JR, Maass G, Tümmler B. (1992) Quantitative expression patterns of multidrug-resistance P-glycoprotein (MDR1) and differentially spliced cystic fibrosis transmembrane conductance regulator mRNA transcripts in human epithelia. *Eur. J. Biochem.* **206:** 137–149.

Bröcker-Vriends AHJT, Briët E, Dreesen JCFM, Bakker B, Reitsma P, Pannekoek H, van de Kamp JJP, Pearson PL. (1990) Somatic origin of inherited haemophilia A. *Hum. Genet.* **85:** 288–292.

Byers PH. (1990) Brittle bones — fragile molecules: disorders of collagen gene structure and expression. *Trends Genet.* **6:** 293–300.

Byers PH, Tsipouras P, Bonadio JF, Starman BJ, Schwartz RC. (1988) Perinatal lethal osteogenesis imperfecta (OI type II): a biochemically heterogeneous disorder usually due to new mutations in the genes for type 1 collagen. *Am. J. Hum. Genet.* **42:** 237–248.

Cavenee WK, Dryja TP, Phillips RA, Benedict WF, Godbout R, Gallie BL, Murphree AL, Strong LC, White RL. (1983) Expression of recessive alleles by chromosomal mechanisms in retinoblastoma. *Nature* **305:** 779–784.

Chebloune Y, Pagnier J, Trabuchet G, Faure C, Verdier G, Labie D, Nigon V. (1988) Structural analysis of the 5' flanking region of the β-globin gene in African sickle cell anemia patients: further evidence for three origins of the sickle cell mutation in Africa. *Proc. Natl. Acad. Sci. USA* **85:** 4431–4435.

Chelly J, Gilgenkrantz H, Hugnot JP, Hamard G, Lambert M, Récan D, Akli S, Cometto M, Kahn A, Kaplan JC. (1991) Illegitimate transcription: application to the analysis of truncated transcripts of the dystrophin gene in nonmuscle cultured cells from Duchenne and Becker patients. *J. Clin. Invest.* **88:** 1161–1166.

Chu M-L, Williams CJ, Pepe G, Hirsch JL, Prockop DJ, Ramirez F. (1983) Internal deletion in a collagen gene in a perinatal lethal form of osteogenesis imperfecta. *Nature* **304:** 78–80.

Chu C-S, Trapnell BC, Murtagh JJ, Moss J, Dalemans W, Jallat S, Mercenier A, Pavirani A, Lecocq J-P, Cutting GR, Guggino WB, Crystal RG. (1991) Variable deletion of exon 9 coding sequences in cystic fibrosis transmembrane conductance regulator gene mRNA transcripts in normal bronchial epithelium. *EMBO J.* **10:** 1355–1363.

Chu C-S, Trapnell BC, Curristin SM, Cutting GR, Crystal RG. (1992) Extensive posttranscriptional deletion of the coding sequences for part of nucleotide-binding fold 1 in respiratory epithelial mRNA transcripts of the cystic fibrosis transmembrane conductance regulator gene is not associated with the clinical manifestations of cystic fibrosis. *J. Clin. Invest.* **90:** 785–790.

Claustres M, Kjellberg P, Desgeorges M, Bellet H, Demaille J. (1990) Germinal mosaicism from grand-paternal origin in a family with Duchenne muscular dystrophy. *Hum. Genet.* **86:** 241–243.

Clayton-Smith J, Webb T, Pembrey ME, Nichols M, Malcolm S. (1992) Maternal origin of deletion 15q11-13 in 25/25 cases. *Hum. Genet.* **88:** 376–378.

Cohn DH, Starman BJ, Blumberg B, Byers PH. (1990) Recurrence of lethal osteogenesis imperfecta due to parental mosaicism for a dominant mutation in a human type I collagen gene (COL1A1). *Am. J. Hum. Genet.* **46:** 591–601.

Constantinou CD, Pack M, Young SB, Prockop DJ. (1990) Phenotypic heterogeneity in osteogenesis imperfecta: the mildly affected mother of a proband with a lethal variant has the same mutation substituting cysteine for α1-glycine 904 in a type I procollagen gene (COL1A1). *Am. J. Hum. Genet.* **47:** 670–679.

Covone AE, Lerone M, Romeo G. (1991) Genotype–phenotype correlation and germline mosaicism in DMD/BMD patients with deletions of the dystrophin gene. *Hum. Genet.* **87:** 353–360.

Cuppens H, Marynen P, DeBoeck C, DeBaets F, Eggermont E, Van den Berghe H, Cassiman JJ. (1990) A child, homozygous for a stop codon in exon 11, shows milder cystic fibrosis symptoms than her heterozygous nephew. *J. Med. Genet.* **27:** 717–719.

Cutting GR, Kasch LM, Rosenstein BJ, Tsui L-C, Kazazian HH, Antonarakis SE. (1990) Two patients with cystic fibrosis, nonsense mutations in each cystic fibrosis gene, and mild pulmonary disease. *N. Engl. J. Med.* **323:** 1685–1688.

Darras BT, Francke U. (1987) A partial deletion of the muscular dystrophy gene transmitted twice by an unaffected male. *Nature* **329:** 556–558.

Darras BT, Blattner P, Harper JF, Spiro AJ, Alter S, Francke U. (1988) Intragenic deletions in 21 Duchenne muscular dystrophy (DMD)/Becker muscular dystophy (BMD) families studied with the dystrophin cDNA: location of breakpoints on HindIII and BglII exon-containing fragment maps, meiotic and mitotic origin of the mutations. *Am. J. Hum. Genet.* **43:** 620–629.

Deceular K, Higgs DR, Weatherall DJ, Hayes RJ, Serjeant BE, Serjeant GR. (1983) α-thalassaemia reduces the hemolytic rate in homozygous sickle cell disease. *N. Engl. J. Med.* **309:** 189–194.

Dover GJ, Smith KD, Chang YP, Purvis S, Mays A, Meyers DA, Shiels C, Serjeant G. (1992) Fetal hemoglobin levels in sickle cell disease and normal individuals are partially controlled by an X-linked gene located at Xp22.2. *Blood* **80:** 816–824.

Driscoll DJ, Waters MF, Williams CA, Zori RT, Glenn CC, Avidano KM, Nicholls RD. (1992) A DNA methylation imprint, determined by the sex of the parent, distinguishes the Angelman and Prader–Willi syndromes. *Genomics* **13:** 917–924.

Dryja TP, Mukai S, Petersen R, Rapaport JM, Walton D, Wandell DW. (1989) Parental origin of mutations of the retinoblastoma gene. *Nature* **339:** 556–558.

Dunn J, Phillips R, Becker A, Gallie B. (1988) Identification of germline and somatic mutations affecting the retinoblastoma gene. *Science* **241:** 1797–1800.

Edwards MJ, Wenstrup RJ, Byers PH, Cohn DH. (1992) Recurrence of lethal osteogenesis imperfecta due to parental mosaicism for a mutation in the COL1A2 gene of type I collagen: the mosaic parent exhibits phenotypic features of a mild form of the disease. *Hum. Mutat.* **1:** 47–54.

Elion J, Berg PE, Lapouméroulie C, Trabuchet G, Mittelman M, Krishnamoorthy R, Schechter AN, Labie D. (1992) DNA sequence variation in a negative control region 5′ to the β-globin gene correlates with the phenotypic expression of the β^s mutation. *Blood* **79:** 787–792.

Embury SH, Dozy AM, Miller J, Davis JR, Klemen KM, Preisler H, Vichinsky E, Lande WN, Lubin WN, Kan YW, Mentzer WC. (1982) Concurrent sickle-cell anemia and α thalassemia: effect on severity of anemia. *N. Engl. J. Med.* **306:** 270–274.

Essen AJ van, Abbs S, Baiget M, Bakker E, Boileau C, van Broeckhoven C, Bushby K, Clarke A, Claustres M, Covone AE, Ferrari M, Ferlini A, Galluzzi G, Grimm T, Grubben C, Jeanpierre M, Kääriainen H, Liechti-Gallati S, Melis MA, van Ommen GJB, Poncin JE, Scheffer H, Schwartz M, Speer A, Stuhrmann M, Verellen-Dumoulin C, Wilcox DE, ten Kate LP. (1992) Parental origin and germline mosaicism of deletions and duplications of the dystrophin gene: a European study. *Hum. Genet.* **88:** 249–257.

Farrer LA, Cupples LA, Kiely DA, Conneally PM, Myers RH. (1992) Inverse relationship between age at onset of Huntington disease and paternal age suggests involvement of genetic imprinting. *Am. J. Hum. Genet.* **50:** 528–535.

Friend SH, Bernards R, Rogelj S, Weinberg RA, Rapaport JM, Albert DM, Dryja TP. (1986) A human DNA segment with properties of the gene that predisposes to retinoblastoma and osteosarcoma. *Nature* **323:** 643–646.

Friend SH, Horowitz JM, Gerber MR, Wang X-F, Bogenmann E, Li FP, Weinberg RA. (1987) Deletions of a DNA sequence in retinoblastomas and mesenchymal tumors:

organization of the sequence and its encoded protein. *Proc. Natl. Acad. Sci. USA* **84:** 9059–9063.

Fung YK-T, Murphree AL, T'Ang A, Quian J, Hinrichs SH, Benedict WF. (1987) Structural evidence for the authenticity of the human retinoblastoma gene. *Science* **236:** 1657–1661.

Gangopadhyay SB, Sherratt TG, Heckmatt JZ, Dubowitz V, Miller G, Shokeir M, Ray PN, Strong PN, Worton RG. (1992) Dystrophin in frameshift deletion patients with Becker muscular dystrophy. *Am. J. Hum. Genet.* **51:** 562–570.

Gillard EF, Chamberlain JS, Murphy EG, Duff CL, Smith B, Burghes AHM, Thompson MW. (1989) Molecular and phenotypic analysis of patients with deletions within the deletion-rich region of the Duchenne muscular dystrophy (DMD) gene. *Am. J. Hum. Genet.* **45:** 507–520.

Gilman JG, Huisman THJ. (1984) Two independent genetic factors in the β-globin gene cluster are associated with high G–γ levels of HbF of SS patients. *Blood* **64:** 452–457.

Gitschier J, Levinson B, Lehesjoki A-E, De La Chapelle A. (1989) Mosaicism and sporadic haemophilia: implications for carrier determination. *Lancet* **i:** 273–274.

Gitschier J, Kogan S, Diamond C, Levinson B. (1991) Genetic basis of hemophilia A. *Thromb. Haemost.* **66:** 37–39.

Graham GE, MacLeod PM, Lillicrap DP, Bridge PJ. (1992) Gonadal mosaicism in a family with adrenoleukodystrophy: molecular diagnosis of carrier status among daughters of a gonadal mosaic when direct detection of the mutation is not possible. *J. Inherit. Metab. Dis.* **15:** 68–74.

Greger V, Passarge E, Horsthemke B. (1990) Somatic mosaicism in a patient with bilateral retinoblastoma. *Am. J. Hum. Genet.* **46:** 1187–1193.

Grimm T, Müller B, Müller CR, Janka M. (1990) Theoretical considerations on germline mosaicism in Duchenne muscular dystrophy. *J. Med. Genet.* **27:** 683–687.

Hall JG. (1988) Somatic mosaicism: observations related to clinical genetics. *Am. J. Hum. Genet.* **43:** 355–363.

Hall JG. (1990) Genomic imprinting: review and relevance to human diseases. *Am. J. Hum. Genet.* **46:** 857–873.

Hancock JF, Wieland K, Pugh RE, Martinowitz U, Schulman S, Kakkar VV, Kernoff PBA, Cooper DN. (1991) A molecular genetic study of factor XI deficiency. *Blood* **77:** 1942–1948.

Hendriks RW, Mensink EJBM, Kraakman MEM, Thompson A, Schuurman RKB. (1989) Evidence for male X chromosomal mosaicism in X-linked agammaglobulinemia. *Hum. Genet.* **83:** 267–270.

Henry I, Jeanpierre M, Couillin P, Barichard F, Serre J-L, Jourrel H, Lamouroux A, Turleau C, de Grouchy J, Junien C. (1989) Molecular definition of the 11p15.5 region involved in Beckwith–Wiedemann syndrome and probably in predisposition to adrenocortical carcinoma. *Hum. Genet.* **81:** 273–277.

Heutink P, van der Mey AGL, Sandkuijl LA, van Gils APG, Bardoel A, Breedveld GJ, van Vliet M, van Ommen GJ, Cornelisse CJ, Oosta BA, Weber JL, Devilee P. (1992) A gene subject to genomic imprinting and responsible for hereditary paragangliomas maps to chromosome 11q23-qter. *Hum. Mol. Genet.* **1:** 7–10.

Higuchi M, Kochhan L, Olek K. (1988) A somatic mosaic for haemophilia A detected at the DNA level. *Mol. Biol. Med.* **5:** 23–27.

Hodgson S, Hart K, Abbs S, Heckmatt J, Rodillo E, Bobrow M, Dubowitz V. (1989) Correlation of clinical and deletion data in Duchenne and Becker muscular dystrophy. *J. Med. Genet.* **26:** 682–693.

Horowitz J, Yandell D, Park S, Canning S, Whyte P, Buchovich K, Harlow E, Weinberg R, Dryja T. (1989) Point mutational inactivation of the retinoblastoma antioncogene. *Science* **243:** 937–940.

Ingerslev J, Schwartz M, Lamm LU, Kruse TA, Bukh A, Stenbjerg S. (1989) Female haemophilia A in a family with seeming extreme bidirectional lyonization tendency: abnormal premature X-chromosome inactivation? *Clin. Genet.* **35:** 41–48.

Jadayel D, Fain P, Upadhyaya M, Ponder MA, Huson SM, Carey J, Fryer A, Mathew CGP, Barker DF, Ponder BAJ. (1990) Paternal origin of new mutations in Von Recklinghausen neurofibromatosis. *Nature* **343**: 558–559.

Jeanpierre M. (1992) Germline mosaicism and risk calculation in X-linked diseases. *Am. J. Hum. Genet.* **50**: 960–967.

Kalaydjieva L, Angelicheva D, Galeva I, Lalov V, Konstantinova D. (1991) Cystic fibrosis in Bulgaria. *J. Med. Genet.* **28**: 807.

Kan YW, Doxy AM. (1980) Evolution of the hemoglobin S and C genes in world populations. *Science* **209**: 388–391.

Kashii S, Ito K, Monden S, Sasai Y, Tsuchida K, Fujita M, Kawamoto H, Norioka M, Okuma M. (1991) Adenosine deaminase deficiency due to heterozygous abnormality consisting of a deletion of exon 7 and the absence of enzyme mRNA. *J. Cell. Biochem.* **47**: 49–53.

Kazazian HH, Dowling CE, Hurwitz RL, Coleman M, Adams JG. (1989) Thalassemia mutations in exon 3 of the β-globin gene often cause a dominant form of thalassaemia and show no predelection for malarial-endemic regions of the world. *Am. J. Hum. Genet.* **25** (Suppl.): 950.

Kerem E, Corey M, Kerem B, Rommens J, Markiewicz D, Levison H, Tsui L-C, Durie P. (1990) The relationship between genotype and phenotype in cystic fibrosis: an analysis of the most common mutation (δF508). *N. Engl. J. Med.* **323**: 1517–1522.

Kling S, Coffey AJ, Ljung R, Sjörin E, Nilsson IM, Holmberg L, Giannelli F. (1991) Moderate haemophilia B in a female carrier caused by preferential inactivation of the paternal X chromosome. *Eur. J. Haematol.* **47**: 257–261.

Knoll JHM, Nicholls RD, Magenis RE, Graham JM, Lalande M, Latt SA. (1989) Angelman and Prader–Willi syndromes share a common chromosome 15 deletion but differ in parental origin of the deletion. *Am. J. Med. Genet.* **32**: 285–290.

Knudson AG. (1971) Mutation and cancer: statistical study of retinoblastoma. *Proc. Natl. Acad. Sci. USA* **68**: 820–823.

Kolodziej MA, Vilaire G, Rifat S, Poncz M, Bennett JS. (1991) Effect of deletion of glycoprotein IIb exon 28 on the expression of platelet glycoprotein IIb/IIIa complex. *Blood* **78**: 2344–2353.

Kontusaari S, Tromp G, Kuivaniemi H, Stolle C, Pope FM, Prockop DJ. (1992) Substitution of aspartate for glycine 1018 in the type III procollagen (COL3A1) gene causes type IV Ehlers–Danlos syndrome: the mutated allele is present in most blood leukocytes of the asymptomatic and mosaic mother. *Am. J. Hum. Genet.* **51**: 497–507.

Koufos A, Grundy P, Morgan K, Aleck KA, Hadro T, Lampkin BC, Kalbakji A, Cavenee WK. (1989) Familial Wiedemann–Beckwith syndrome and a second Wilms' tumor locus both map to 11p15.5. *Am. J. Hum. Genet.* **44**: 711–719.

Krawczak M, Bockel B, Sandkuijl L, Thies U, Fenton I, Harper PS. (1991) Covariate-dependent age-at-onset distributions for Huntington disease. *Am. J. Hum. Genet.* **49**: 735–745.

Kulozik AE, Wainscoat JS, Serjeant GR, Kar BC, Al-Awamy B, Essan GJF, Falusi AG, Haque SK, Hilali AM, Kate S, Ranasinghe WAEP. (1986) Geographical survey of β^s globin gene haplotypes: evidence for an independent Asian origin of the sickle cell mutation. *Am. J. Hum. Genet.* **39**: 239–244.

Kulozik AE, Kar BC, Satapathy RK, Serjeant BE, Serjeant GR, Weatherall DJ. (1987) Fetal hemoglobin levels and β^s globin haplotypes in an Indian population with sickle cell disease. *Blood* **69**: 1742–1746.

Labie D, Pagnier J, Lapouméroulie F, Rouabhi F, Dunda-Belkhodja O, Chardin P, Beldjord C, Wajcman H, Fabry ME, Nagel RL. (1985) Common haplotype dependency of high G-γ-globin expression and high HBF levels in β-thalassemia and sickle cell anemia patients. *Proc. Natl. Acad. Sci. USA* **82**: 2111–2114.

Lanclos KD, Öner C, Dimovski AJ, Gu Y-C, Huisman THJ. (1991) Sequence variations in the 5' flanking and IVS-II regions of the G-γ and A-γ-globin genes of β^s chromosomes with five different haplotypes. *Blood* **77**: 2488–2496.

Lanman JT, Pericak-Vance MA, Bartlett RJ, Chen JC, Yamaoka L, Koh J, Speer MC,

Hung W-Y, Roses AD. (1987) Familial inheritance of a DXS164 deletion mutation from a heterozygous female. *Am. J. Hum. Genet.* **41**: 138–144.

Lapouméroulie C, Dunda O, Ducrocq R, Trabuchet G, Mony-Lobé M, Carnevale P, Labie D, Elion J, Krishnamoorthy R. (1992) A novel sickle cell mutation of yet another origin in Africa: the Cameroon type. *Hum. Genet.* **89**: 333–337

Lebo RV, Olney RK, Golbus MS. (1990) Somatic mosaicism at the Duchenne locus. *Am. J. Med. Genet.* **37**: 187–190.

Lee W-H, Bookstein R, Hong F, Young L-J, Shew J-Y, Lee EY-HP. (1987) Human retinoblastoma susceptibility gene: cloning, identification and sequence. *Science* **235**: 1394–1399.

Lee EY-H, To H, Shew J-Y, Bookstein R, Scull P, Lee W-H. (1988) Inactivation of the retinoblastoma susceptibility gene in human breast cancers. *Science* **241**: 218–221.

Legius E, Baten E, Stul M, Marynen P, Cassiman JJ. (1990) Sporadic late onset ornithine transcarbamylase deficiency in a boy with somatic mosaicism for an intragenic deletion. *Clin. Genet.* **38**: 155–159.

Liechti-Gallati S, Koenig M, Kunkel LM, Frey D, Boltshauser E, Schneider V, Braga S, Moser H. (1989) Molecular deletion patterns in Duchenne and Becker type muscular dystrophy. *Hum. Genet.* **81**: 343–348.

Lyon MF. (1988) X-chromosome inactivation and the location and expression of X-linked genes. *Am. J. Hum. Genet.* **42**: 8–16.

Maddalena A, Sosnoski DM, Berry GT, Nussbaum RL. (1988) Mosaicism for an intragenic deletion in a boy with mild ornithine transcarbamylase deficiency. *N. Engl. J. Med.* **319**: 999–1003.

Malhotra SB, Hart KA, Klamut HJ, Thomas NST, Bodrug SE, Burghes AHM, Bobrow M, Harper PS, Thompson MW, Ray PN, Worton RG. (1988) Frame-shift deletions in patients with Duchenne and Becker muscular dystophy. *Science* **242**: 755–759.

Meijers JCM, Mulvihill ER, Davie EW, Chung DW. (1992) Apple four in human blood coagulation factor XI mediates dimer formation. *Biochemistry* **31**: 4680–4684.

Miller M, Hall JG. (1978) Possible maternal effect on severity of neurofibromatosis. *Lancet* **ii**: 1071–1073.

Miyoshi K, Kaneto Y, Kawai H, Ohchi H, Niki S, Hasegawa K, Shirakami A, Yamo T. (1988) X-linked dominant control of F-cells in normal adult life: characterization of the Swiss type as hereditary persistence of fetal hemoglobin regulated dominantly by gene(s) on X chromosome. *Blood* **72**: 1854–1860.

Monaco AP, Bertelsen CJ, Colletti-Feener C, Kunkel LM. (1987) Localization and cloning of Xp21 deletion breakpoints involved in muscular dystrophy. *Hum. Genet.* **75**: 221–227.

Monaco AP, Bertelson CJ, Liechti-Gallati S, Moser H, Kunkel LM. (1988) An explanation for the phenotypic differences between patients bearing partial deletions of the DMD locus. *Genomics* **2**: 90–95.

Monk M. (1988) Genomic imprinting. *Genes Dev.* **2**: 921–925.

Monk M, Boubelik M, Lehnert S. (1987) Temporal and regional changes in DNA methylation in the embryonic, extraembryonic and germ cell lineages during mouse embryo development. *Development* **99**: 371–382.

Montrose-Rafizadeh C, Blackmon DL, Hamosh A, Oliva MM, Hawkins AL, Curristin SM, Griffin CA, Yang VW, Guggino WB, Cutting GR, Montrose MH. (1992) Regulation of cystic fibrosis transmembrane conductance regulator (CFTR) gene transcription and alternative RNA splicing in a model of developing intestinal epithelium. *J. Biol. Chem.* **267**: 19299–19305.

Moutou C, Junien C, Henry I, Bonaïti-Pellié C. (1992) Beckwith–Wiedemann syndrome: a demonstration of the mechanisms responsible for the excess of transmitting females. *J. Med. Genet.* **29**: 217–220.

Murphree AL, Benedict WF. (1985) Retinoblastoma: clues to human oncogenesis. *Science* **223**: 1028–1033.

Nagel RL, Fabry ME, Pagnier J, Zohoun I, Wajcman H, Baudin V, Labie D. (1985) Hematologically and genetically distinct forms of sickle cell anemia in Africa: the Senegal type and the Benin type. *N. Engl. J. Med.* **312**: 880–884.

Nagel RL, Rao SK, Dunda-Belkhodja O, Connolly MM, Fabry ME, Georges A, Krishnamoorthy R, Labie D. (1987) The hematological characteristics of sickle cell anemia bearing the Bantu haplotype: the relationship between G–γ and HbF level. *Blood* **69**: 1026–1030.

Naylor JA, Green PM, Montandon AJ, Rizza CR, Giannelli F. (1991) Detection of three novel mutations in two haemophilia A patients by rapid screening of whole essential region of factor VIII gene. *Lancet* **337**: 635–639.

Nicholls RD, Knoll JH, Glatt K, Hersh JH, Brewster TD, Graham JM, Wurster-Hill D, Wharton R, Latt SA. (1989) Restriction fragment length polymorphisms within proximal 15q and their use in molecular cytogenetics and the Prader–Willi syndrome. *Am. J. Med. Genet.* **33**: 66–77.

Nisen P, Stamberg J, Ehrenpreis R, Velasco S, Shende A, Engelberg J, Karayalcin G, Waber L. (1986) The molecular basis of severe hemophilia B in a girl. *N. Engl. J. Med.* **315**: 1139–1142.

Nisen PD, Waber PG. (1989) Nonrandom X chromosome DNA methylation patterns in hemophilic females. *J. Clin. Invest.* **83**: 1400–1403.

Noguchi CT, Rogers GP, Serjeant GR, Schechter AN. (1988) Levels of fetal hemoglobin necessary for treatment of sickle cell disease. *N. Engl. J. Med.* **318**: 96–99.

Öner C, Dimovski AJ, Altay C, Gurgey A, Gu YC, Huisman THJ, Lanclos KD. (1992) Sequence variations in the 5' hypersensitive site-2 of the locus control region of β^s chromosomes are associated with different levels of fetal globin in hemoglobin S homozygotes. *Blood* **79**: 813–819.

Pagnier J, Mears JG, Dunda-Belkhodja O, Schaefer-Rego KE, Beldjord C, Nagel RL, Labie D. (1984) Evidence for the multicentric origin of the hemoglobin S gene in Africa. *Proc. Natl. Acad. Sci. USA* **81**: 1771–1773.

Pal N, Wadey RB, Buckle B, Yeomans E, Pritchard J, Cowell JK. (1990) Preferential loss of maternal alleles in sporadic Wilms' tumour. *Oncogene* **5**: 1665–1668.

Pihlajaniemi T, Dickson LA, Pope FM, Korhonen VR, Nicholls A, Prockop DJ, Myers JC. (1984) Osteogenesis imperfecta: cloning of a pro $\alpha2(1)$ collagen gene with a frameshift mutation. *J. Biol. Chem.* **259**: 12941–12944.

Ragni MV, Sinha D, Seaman F, Lewis JH, Spero JA, Walsh PN. (1985) Comparison of bleeding tendency, factor XI coagulant activity and factor XI antigen in 25 factor XI-deficient kindreds. *Blood* **65**: 719–724.

Ragusa A, Lombardo M, Beldjord C, Ruberto C, Lombardo T, Elion J, Nagel RL, Krishnamoorthy R. (1992) Genetic epidemiology of β-thalassemia in Sicily: do sequences 5' to the G–γ gene and 5' to the β gene interact to enhance HbF expression in β-thalassaemia? *Am. J. Hematol.* **40**: 199–206.

Reik W. (1988) Genomic imprinting: a possible mechanism for the parental origin effect in Huntington's chorea. *J. Med. Genet.* **25**: 805–808.

Reik W. (1989) Genomic imprinting and genetic disorders in man. *Trends Genet.* **5**: 331–336.

Reik W, Surani MA. (1989) Genomic imprinting and embryonal tumours. *Nature* **338**: 112–113.

Riccardi VM, Lewis RA. (1988) Penetrance of von Recklinghausen neurofibromatosis: a distinction between predecessors and descendants. *Am. J. Hum. Genet.* **42**: 284–289.

Roberts RG, Bentley DR, Barby TFM, Manners E, Bobrow M. (1990) Direct diagnosis of carriers of Duchenne and Becker muscular dystrophy by amplification of lymphocyte RNA. *Lancet* **336**: 1523–1526.

Roberts RG, Barby TFM, Manners E, Bobrow M, Bentley DR. (1991) Direct detection of dystrophin gene rearrangements by analysis of dystophin mRNA in peripheral blood lymphocytes. *Am. J. Hum. Genet.* **49**: 298–310.

Robinson WP, Bottani A, Yagang X, Balakrishman J, Binkert F, Machler M, Prader A, Schinzel A. (1991) Molecular, cytogenetic and clinical investigations of Prader–Willi syndrome patients. *Am. J. Hum. Genet.* **49**: 1219–1234.

Saitoh S, Kubota T, Ohta T, Jinno Y, Niikawa N, Sugimoto T, Wagstaff J, Lalande M. (1992) Familial Angelman syndrome caused by imprinted submicroscopic deletion encompassing GABA$_A$ receptor β3-subunit gene. *Lancet* **339**: 366–367.

Schroeder WT, Chao LY, Dao DD, Strong LC, Pathak S, Riccardi V, Lewis WH, Saunders GF. (1987) Non-random loss of maternal chromosomes in Wilms' tumors. *Am. J. Hum. Genet.* **40**: 413–420.

Scrable H, Cavenee W, Ghavimi F, Lowell M, Morgan K, Sapienza C. (1989) A model for embryonal rhabdomyosarcoma tumorigenesis that involves genomic imprinting. *Proc. Natl. Acad. Sci. USA* **86**: 7480–7484.

Slomski R, Schlösser M, Berg L-P, Wagner M, Kakkar VV, Cooper DN, Reiss J. (1992) Omission of exon 12 in CFTR gene transcripts. *Hum. Genet.* **89**: 615–619.

Spritz RA. (1981) Duplication/deletion polymorphism 5′ to the human β-globin gene. *Nucleic Acids Res.* **9**: 5037–5047.

Steinmann B, Rao VH, Vogel A. (1984) Cysteine in the triple-helical domain of one allelic product of the α1(1) gene of type I collagen produces a lethal form of osteogenesis imperfecta. *J. Biol. Chem.* **259**: 11129–11138.

Stephens K, Kayes L, Riccardi VM, Rising M, Sybert VP, Pagon RA. (1992) Preferential mutation of the neurofibromatosis type 1 gene in paternally derived chromosomes. *Hum. Genet.* **88**: 279–282.

Surani MA, Reik W, Allen ND. (1988) Transgenes as molecular probes for genomic imprinting. *Trends Genet.* **4**: 59–62.

Surani MA. (1991) Influence of genome imprinting on gene expression, phenotypic variations and development. *Hum. Reprod.* **6**: 45–51.

Sykes B. (1985) The molecular genetics of collagen. *Bioessays* **3**: 112–117.

Taylor SAM, Deugau KV, Lillicrap DP. (1991) Somatic mosaicism and female-to-female transmission in a kindred with hemophilia B (factor IX deficiency). *Proc. Natl. Acad. Sci. USA* **88**: 39–42.

Thein SL. (1992) Dominant β thalassaemia: molecular basis and pathophysiology. *Br. J. Haematol.* **80**: 273–277.

Van der Mey AGL, Maaswinkel-Mooy PD, Cornelisse CJ, Schmidt PH, Van de Kamp JJP. (1989) Genomic imprinting in hereditary glomus tumours: evidence for new genetic theory. *Lancet* **ii**: 1291–1294.

Vogel F. (1979) Genetics of retinoblastoma. *Hum. Genet.* **52**: 1–54.

Wagstaff J, Knoll JHM, Glatt KA, Shugart YY, Sommer A, Lalande M. (1992) Maternal but not paternal transmission of 15q11-13-linked nondeletion Angelman syndrome leads to phenotypic expression. *Nature Genetics* **1**: 291–294.

Wainscoat JS, Thein SL, Higgs DR, Bell JI, Weatherall DJ, Al-Wamy BH, Serjeant GR. (1985) A genetic marker for elevated levels of haemoglobin F in homozygous sickle cell disease? *Br. J. Haematol.* **60**: 261–268.

Walker DC, McLoskey DA, Simard LR, McInnes RR. (1990) Molecular analysis of human argininosuccinate lyase: mutant characterization and alternative splicing of the coding region. *Proc. Natl. Acad. Sci. USA* **87**: 9625–9629.

Wallis GA, Starman BJ, Zinn AB, Byers PH. (1990) Variable expression of osteogenesis imperfecta in a nuclear family is explained by somatic mosaicism for a lethal point mutation in the α1(I) gene (COL1A1) of type I collagen in a parent. *Am. J. Hum. Genet.* **46**: 1034–1040.

Wieland K, Millar DS, Grundy CB, Mibashan RS, Kakkar VV, Cooper DN. (1991) Molecular genetic analysis of factor X deficiency: gene deletion and germline mosaicism. *Hum. Genet.* **86**: 273–278.

Wilkins RJ. (1988) Genomic imprinting and carcinogenesis. *Lancet* **i**: 329–331.

Williams JC, Brown KW, Mott MG, Maitland NJ. (1989) Maternal allele loss in Wilms' tumour. *Lancet* **i**: 283–284.

Williams CA, Zori RT, Stone JW, Gray BA, Cantú ES, Ostrer H. (1990) Maternal origin of 15q11-q13 deletions in Angelman syndrome suggests a role for genomic imprinting. *Am. J. Med. Genet.* **35**: 350–353.

Wood S, McGillivray BC. (1988) Germinal mosaicism in Duchenne muscular dystrophy. *Hum. Genet.* **78:** 282–284.

Yandell DW, Campbell TA, Dayton SH, Petersen R, Walton D, Little JB, McConkie-Rosell A, Buckley EG, Dryja TP. (1989) Oncogenic point mutations in the human retinoblastoma gene: their application to genetic counselling. *N. Engl. J. Med.* **321:** 1689–1695.

Yokota J, Wada M, Shimosato Y, Terada M, Sugimura T. (1987) Loss of heterozygosity on chromosomes 3, 13 and 17 in small-cell carcinoma and on chromosome 3 in adenocarcinoma of the lung. *Proc. Natl. Acad. Sci. USA* **84:** 9252–9257.

Zhu X, Dunn JM, Phillips RA, Goddard AD, Paton KE, Becker A, Gallie BL. (1989) Preferential germline mutation of the paternal allele in retinoblastoma. *Nature* **340:** 312–313.

Zielenski J, Rozmahel R, Bozon D, Kerem B, Grzelczak Z, Riordan JR, Rommens J, Tsui L-C. (1991) Genomic DNA sequence of the cystic fibrosis transmembrane conductance regulator (CFTR) gene. *Genomics* **10:** 214–228.

13

Mutation rates in humans

13.1 Mutation rates based on incidence/prevalence data

The mutation rate, μ, is conventionally defined as the ratio of the number of germ cells carrying a particular *de novo* mutation to the total number of germ cells being at risk for carrying that mutation (Vogel, 1990). Since humans stem from two different germ cells, μ equals half the number of individuals carrying a new mutation divided by the total number of individuals being at risk for that mutation. For dominant mutations, almost all individuals bearing a *de novo* mutation can be easily identified as so-called 'sporadic cases', i.e. as affected children born to unaffected parents. Occasionally, the same expression is also used for isolated cases of X-linked recessive disorders in which a family history of the disease is lacking. However, with recessive disorders (autosomal as well as X-linked), a major problem lies in the substantial proportion of mutations that first appear in heterozygotes and which therefore go undetected phenotypically. Unless reliable carrier detection techniques are available, mutation rates in recessive disorders can thus only be estimated using indirect approaches.

Indirect estimates of mutation rates rely on the assumption that alleles that are removed from a population's gene pool by selection are continually replaced by new mutations. If the opposing forces of selection and mutation are allowed to act on the gene pool for a sufficient length of time, the population will reach an equilibrium state at which the proportion of lost alleles equals that of newly acquired mutants. To quantify the numerical properties of this equilibrium state, let us first denote the population frequency of an autosomal recessive mutation by q, and the reproductive fitness of homozygotes (relative to others) by f. In the overall population, the mutant allele frequency is, of course

$$q = q^2 + 2q(1-q)/2$$

but among individuals who are able to contribute to the gene pool of the next generation it only makes up

$$q' = fq^2 + 2q(1-q)/2 = q - (1-f)q^2$$

Thus, the frequency of the mutant allele is reduced by $(1-f)q^2$, and this loss must be compensated for by mutation. We may therefore conclude that the mutation rate for an autosomal recessive disorder equals

$$\mu = (1-f)q^2$$

at mutation–selection (i.e. genetic) equilibrium, which is $1-f$ times the incidence of that disorder.

Applying similar arguments, it can be shown that the proportion of lost alleles is $(1-f)q$ for an autosomal dominant mutation. Thus we have

$$\mu = (1-f)q$$

which equals $1-f$ times *half* the incidence of the disease (see also Vogel, 1990).

With X-linked recessive disorders, the mathematical treatment is slightly more complicated. In such cases, selection is acting only on males and a proportion $(1-f)$ of the mutations they bear will be lost. Since males carry only one X chromosome as opposed to two in females, mutations in males make up only one-third of the total, q. Thus, we have

$$\mu = (1-f)q/3$$

which is $1-f$ times *one-third* of the incidence of the disease among males.

Mutation rates for specific disease loci involved in both autosomal dominant and sex-linked recessive conditions appear to vary quite widely within a range spanning 5×10^{-5} (Duchenne muscular dystrophy) to 2×10^{-7} (von Hippel–Lindau syndrome) (Vogel and Motulsky, 1986; Childs *et al.*, 1982) with a median value of $\sim 5 \times 10^{-6}$. One problem with this type of general survey is that genetic conditions with a high incidence/prevalence tend to be studied in the most detail, leading to an inflated estimate of the 'average' mutation rate. Early attempts to allow for this bias have suggested that the true median value may lie between 3×10^{-6} and 1×10^{-7} (Stevenson and Kerr, 1967; Cavalli-Sforza and Bodmer, 1971). However, the 'typical' mutation rate will still be overestimated if the number of individual loci at which mutation is very rare is found to be considerable. Nevertheless, from the point of view of the social impact of human gene mutation, genes that mutate at the highest frequency assume the greatest clinical importance and may well contribute the most to the 'total mutation rate' manifested in human populations. This topic is further discussed by Crow and Denniston (1985).

The indirect estimation of mutation rates for autosomal recessive conditions is impeded by a variety of factors, the most important ones being heterozygote advantage/disadvantage and the effects of inbreeding and genetic drift. Taking into account both the strikingly different incidence/prevalence figures observed for some closely related populations and the theoretical expectation of very slow changes applying to gene frequencies, the assumption of genetic equilibrium appears to be unjustified for most autosomal recessive diseases (Vogel and Motulsky, 1986). The actual gene frequencies are more likely to result from either chance fluctuations or systematic deviations from random mating (or both) rather than from the counterbalancing forces of mutation and selection. Furthermore, it can be shown that minor differences in reproductive fitness between heterozygous carriers and homozygous wild-type individuals may cause serious errors in the estimation of mutation rates (Cavalli-Sforza and Bodmer, 1971). For example, if $q = 10^{-3}$ for a lethal recessive mutation and $f = 1$ for heterozygotes, then $\mu = 10^{-6}$. If however $f = 0.9$, then the equilibrium mutation rate increases by a factor of 100, i.e. $\mu = 10^{-4}$.

A prime example of the arbitrariness of indirect mutation rate estimates for autosomal recessive diseases is provided by cystic fibrosis (CF). CF is very common among Caucasians, with approximately one in 2000 newborns being affected. Since CF patients have in the past been virtually unable to reproduce, the mutation rate should approximately equal $\mu = 5 \times 10^{-4}$. This would represent an exceptionally high mutation rate, being at least one order of magnitude higher than any hitherto observed for dominant or X-linked recessive disorders. Furthermore, the fact that $\simeq 70\%$ of mutant chromosomes bear an identical mutation (the deletion of a Phe residue at position 508 of the CFTR protein), and the observation that this deletion exhibits a considerable degree of association with a specific RFLP haplotype, argues strongly against a high CF mutation rate. In summary, one cannot help but agree with the conclusion drawn by Vogel and Motulsky (1986):

> Depending on more or less arbitrary assumptions, almost any mutation rate estimate can be calculated for a recessive condition using the same data. Hence, such estimates are guessing games without scientific value.

13.2 Mutation rates at the molecular level

Measurement of the base mutation rate in humans has been approached in a variety of different ways (Kimura and Ohta, 1973; Stamatoyannopoulos and Nute, 1982; Neel et al., 1986) but estimates usually lie within the range 2.5×10^{-9} to 9.0×10^{-8} per base-pair per generation. Increasingly, at least for the sex-linked recessive conditions, gene mutation rates will become available which are directly comparable at the nucleotide level. Thus, for example, Koeberl et al. (1990a) have estimated from molecular genetic studies that the total mutation rate for the factor IX (F9) gene is 3.2×10^{-9} per base-pair per generation. Were this mutation rate to be typical of the human genome as a whole, Sommer (1992) has calculated that each individual might be expected on average to contain 16 transitions and 2.4 transversions. However, only 0.38 mutations per generation per diploid genome would be expected to occur within coding sequence, and many of these would be silent or result in minimal clinical dysfunction.

Chakraborty and Neel (1989), using population data on electrophoretic variants of proteins, estimated that the mutation rates for 27 loci studied varied by more than a factor of 20, with an average of 1.1×10^{-5} per locus per generation. From their studies of electrophoretically detectable variants, Kuick et al. (1992) have estimated the rate of spontaneous mutation per cell generation in a human lymphoblastoid cell line to be 7.2×10^{-8} and the rate of spontaneous germline mutation to be 3.3×10^{-8}. The average cell generation times for these cells are 18.5 h and 26 days respectively. These authors have argued that the similarity of in vivo and in vitro mutation rate estimates implies that spontaneous mutation is much more dependent on the number of cell generations than on time.

In Chapter 6, we explored the possible relationship between the underlying DNA sequence of a gene and its mutability. The chromosomal location of a gene may, however, also be important in determining its mutability. Thus, Wolfe et al. (1989) claimed that the rate of silent substitution in mammalian protein-coding genes correlated both with the base composition of the gene (particularly G + C content) and the surrounding chromosomal region. Further, they noted that genes which were physically close to one another in the genome tended to exhibit a similar G + C content and rate of silent substitution. These authors hypothesized that mutational patterns might vary with the timing of replication of different chromosomal regions in the germline. In principle, the frequency and nature of replication-associated gene mutations could vary with the stage of the cell cycle, perhaps because of changes in dNTP precursor pools and/or DNA polymerase activity. Subsequent studies such as that of Ikemura and Wada (1991) have confirmed that genes with a high G + C content at the third codon position are usually embedded in long G + C-rich genomic sequences. Indeed, such G + C-rich gene sequences are known to predominate in T-type R bands and/or terminal R bands whereas A + T-rich genes occur mainly on G bands or non-T-type internal R bands. It is, however, still unclear whether chromosomal position directly influences the mutation rate or whether its influence is merely indirect through the composition of the underlying DNA sequence. For example, Wolfe (1991) and Mathews and Ji (1992) have reviewed the arguments for an imbalance in intranuclear dNTP pool sizes influencing the misincorporation rate: given that dGTP is almost always the least abundant of the four dNTPs (Mathews and Ji, 1992), competition with 'incorrect' dNTPs would tend to increase the mutation frequency in G + C rich regions.

13.3 A sex difference in the mutation rate

In Chapters 6–8, we provided both empirical and theoretical evidence for a substantial proportion of mutations causing human genetic disease being replication associated. It is therefore tempting to speculate that gene mutations are more likely to occur in the germline of males than of females. Such reasoning appears justified by the dramatic difference in the proliferation of germ cells between the two sexes: the number of cell divisions involved in the maturation of a sperm is *on average* 15 times that of an oocyte (Vogel and Motulsky, 1986). We shall now examine whether or not studies of mutation rates for X-linked disorders provide support for this conclusion.

13.3.1 Haemophilia A

Based on the observed rarity of sporadic cases, Haldane (1947) concluded that, in haemophilia, the mutation rate in males could be as much as 10-fold higher than in females. Today, a considerable body of work has accumulated on the mutation rate in this sex-linked condition. This is undoubtedly because of its high prevalence, the high frequency of clinical detection and because molecular genetic data on the origin of mutational lesions in the factor VIII (F8) gene abound.

Using the formulae presented in Section 13.1 we can deduce that (assuming equal mutation rates in males and females) one-third of the F8 gene mutations present in a population must have occurred *de novo*. A lower proportion will, however, be found if the gene is not invariably lethal to males carrying it, if the mutation rate is higher in males than in females, or if the fitness of carrier females is somehow increased. Although no evidence has been put forward for the greater fitness of female carriers of haemophilia A, the fitness of affected males is clearly greater than zero. The latter fitness is currently very difficult to estimate, since it will depend critically on the net influence of such factors as improved treatment, counterbalanced by the effects of HIV infection.

A considerable number of studies have now been carried out to determine the proportion of cases of haemophilia A that are truly sporadic. Although a deficiency of sporadic cases has sometimes been found, a question mark has remained over the possibility of ascertainment bias and the reliability of carrier detection methods. Vogel (1977), reviewing early studies, concluded that a higher mutation rate in male germ cells was nevertheless likely. The largest study to date, of 949 families with haemophilia A (Barrai *et al.*, 1985), estimated the frequency of sporadic cases to be 16% but no evidence for a significantly higher mutation rate in male germ cells (1.7 times that in female germ cells) was found. Another study of 246 families showed that less than 12% of cases could have been due to new mutation (Miller *et al.*, 1987).

Clearly there are many problems associated with this type of study, not the least being the ability to distinguish between a true *de novo* mutation and one that has been transmitted matrilineally over several previous generations. In an attempt to overcome this problem, Winter *et al.* (1983) conducted phenotypic carrier detection tests on 21 mothers of sporadic haemophiliacs. A combination of linear discriminant analysis and prior probabilities calculated from pedigree data suggested that 16 (76%) were carriers. A conservative estimate of the fitness of affected males [0.7; the authors suggested that the true fitness might be as low as 0.3, a figure borne out by recent reproductive pattern data (Miller *et al.*, 1987)] was used to derive a maximum likelihood estimate of the male:female mutation ratio of 9.6 (95% confidence interval 2.2–41.5). A lower value for the fitness of affected males would have increased the size of this ratio still further. This value of the mutation ratio agrees with Haldane's (1947) prediction, and if this sex ratio is correct, then 97.4% of all mothers of haemophiliacs would be expected to be carriers.

Using coagulation assays alone, it is often difficult to establish with certainty the precise origin of an F8 gene mutation. These assays are only 90–95% reliable owing to the wide range of clotting activity values exhibited by both normal and carrier females. Restriction fragment length polymorphism (RFLP) analysis, using both intragenic and extragenic probes, can now be used in concert with coagulation assays to determine the origin of a novel F8 gene mutation in a majority of cases. So, for example, when the chromosome bearing the haemophilia allele is shown to have originated in the haemostatically normal maternal grandfather, a *de novo* mutation either in the proband or in his mother is indicated. Coagulation data from the mother can then be used to distinguish between these two alternatives. This approach has proved successful in demonstrating cases of *de novo* mutation either in the maternal grandfather's gamete (Delpech *et al.*, 1986; Grover *et al.*, 1987; Pecorara *et al.*, 1987; Howard *et al.*, 1988) or in one of the mother's gametes (Grover *et al.*, 1987). The direct demonstration of *de novo* mutations has also been achieved by detection of pathological lesions in the F8 gene (e.g. Gitschier *et al.*, 1985, 1988).

Results from four studies in which the origin of F8 gene mutations could be determined unequivocally are summarized in Table 13.1. Combining these data results in a 23:12 male/female sex ratio of mutation. Allowing for two X chromosomes in females, this would approximate to a four-fold higher frequency of mutation in male as opposed to female sex cells. This figure lies midway between the estimates of Barrai *et al.* (1985) and Winter *et al.* (1983) and, if accurate, may indicate the absence of a linear relationship between the probability of mutation and the number of germline cell divisions. Recalculation using the method of Winter *et al.* (1983), in the light of this new estimate of the sex ratio of the mutation rate, would yield a figure of 83% for the proportion of all possible carrier mothers who would be expected to be carriers. Similar results have been obtained by Rosendaal *et al.* (1990) (80%) and Bröcker-Vriends *et al.* (1991) (86%).

13.3.2 Other diseases

Haemophilia B is a bleeding disorder caused by mutations in the factor IX (F9) gene, located on the long arm of the X chromosome. Recently, Montandon *et al.* (1992) have presented the first direct analysis of *de novo* F9 gene mutations found under complete ascertainment in a predefined population: the molecular nature of the underlying F9 gene mutation was characterized in all Swedish

Table 13.1. Observed number of F8 gene mutations as classified by sex of meiotic origin

Origin of mutation		Reference
Female meiosis	Male meiosis	
2	6	Bernardi *et al.*, 1987
3	7	Bröcker-Vriends *et al.*, 1987
3	2	Higuchi *et al.*, 1989
4	8	Ljung *et al.*, 1989

haemophilia B families of which the index patient was registered at one particular hospital in Malmö. Based on these data, which comprise approximately 60% of all Swedish haemophilia B patients and families, the authors estimated the sex-specific mutation rates to be 1.88×10^{-6} per generation in female meioses, and 2.07×10^{-5} for males. Thus, the sex-ratio of the mutation rates is 11.0 and, if the reproductive fitness of affected males is assumed to be 0.53 (Ferrari and Rizza, 1986), this implies that the mother of a haemophiliac is a carrier in approximately 96% of cases. However, in apparent contradiction to the conclusions drawn by Montandon *et al.* (1992), several other studies have tended to suggest that mutation rates in males and females are similar for the F9 gene (Koeberl *et al.*, 1990b; Taylor *et al.*, 1991; Ludwig *et al.*, 1992).

Ornithine transcarbamylase (OTC) deficiency is a partially dominant X-linked disorder. This disease is characterized by lethal neonatal hyper-ammonaemia in affected males and variable manifestations in heterozygous females, ranging from eating problems to life-threatening coma. Pooling two sets of data from the French population, Bonaïti-Pellié *et al.* (1990) demonstrated that new mutations must occur much more frequently in male than in female germ cells. Since there was no evidence for a single sporadic affected male in their data set (all mothers of male patients were at least mildly affected), the maximum likelihood estimate of the female mutation rate was actually zero. An upper 95% confidence limit for the proportion of male sporadic cases was given as 16%.

X-linked Duchenne muscular dystrophy (DMD) is the most common form of muscular dystrophy. In the Dutch population, DMD has been shown to occur with a prevalence of 2.37×10^{-4} (1:4215) among male live births (Essen *et al.*, 1992). Males affected by DMD have children only rarely, whereas female carriers are free of gross symptoms and can thus be assumed to have the same reproductive fitness as normal individuals. These findings would suggest that, assuming equal mutation rates in males and females, the proportion of sporadic DMD cases should be one-third (see above). However, using a modified sex ratio approach, Essen *et al.* (1992) estimated this figure to be 0.106. Although their estimate is actually more than three times smaller than expected, its 95% confidence interval ranges from 0% to 33.2%, and thus appears to be compatible with the absence of any sex difference of mutation rates for DMD. Apparent familial DMD may also be due to germline mosaicism (see Section 12.1), which could mimic a lack of sporadic cases in a given data set. In another study performed by Müller *et al.* (1992), evidence for a sex difference in mutation rates was expected from the study of grand-maternal and grandpaternal RFLP haplotypes in index patients. The relative frequency of these haplotypes is directly related to the relative ratio of male to female mutation rates. Among the 295 DMD cases analysed, 196 patients (66%) inherited their X chromosome from the maternal grandmother, whereas 99 (34%) carried the grandpaternal X chromosome. These observations suggest a male:female ratio of mutation rates of 1.14 (95% confidence limit 0.31–2.60) and thus argue against a sex difference for DMD.

References

Barrai I, Cann HM, Cavalli-Sforza LL, Barbujani G, De Nicola P. (1985) Segregation analysis of hemophilia A and B. *Am. J. Hum. Genet.* **37**: 680–699.

Bernardi F, Marchetti G, Bertagnolo V, Faggioli L, Volinia S, Patracchini P, Bartolai S, Vannini F, Felloni L, Rossi L, Panicucci F, Conconi F. (1987) RFLP analysis in families with sporadic hemophilia A: estimate of the mutation ratio in male and female gametes. *Hum. Genet.* **76**: 253–256.

Bonaïti-Pellié C, Pelet A, Ogier A, Nelson JR, Largilliere C, Bertholot J, Saudubray JM, Munnich A. (1990) A probable sex difference in mutation rates in ornithine transcarbamylase deficiency. *Hum. Genet.* **84**: 163–166.

Bröcker-Vriends AHJT, Briët E, Dreesen JCFM, Bakker E, van de Kamp JJP, Pearson PL. (1987) The origin of the mutation in families with an isolated case of haemophilia A. *Thromb. Haemost.* **58**: 337.

Bröcker-Vriends AHJT, Rosendaal FR, van Houwelingen JC, Bakker E, van Ommen GJB, van de Kamp JJP, Briët E. (1991) Sex ratio of the mutation frequencies in haemophilia A: coagulation assays and RFLP analysis. *J. Med. Genet.* **28**: 672–680.

Cavalli-Sforza LL, Bodmer WF. (1971) *The Genetics of Human Populations.* Freeman, San Francisco, California.

Chakraborty R, Neel JV. (1989) Description and validation of a method for simultaneous estimation of effective population size and mutation rate from human population data. *Proc. Natl. Acad. Sci. USA* **86**: 9407–9411.

Childs JD. (1982) Dominant and X-linked recessive mutation rates in man. In: *Progress in Medical Research*, Vol. 3. Elsevier, Amsterdam, pp. 163–167.

Crow JF, Denniston C. (1985) Mutation in human populations. *Adv. Hum. Genet.* **14**: 59–123.

Delpech M, Deburgrave N, Baudis M, Maissonneuve P, Bardin JM, Sultan Y, Kaplan J-C. (1986) *De novo* mutation in hemophilia A established by DNA haplotype analysis and precluding prenatal diagnosis. *Hum. Genet.* **74**: 316–317.

Essen AJ van, Busch HF, te Meerman GJ, ten Kate LP. (1992) Birth and population prevalence of Duchenne muscular dystrophy in the Netherlands. *Hum. Genet.* **88**: 258–266

Ferrari N, Rizza CA. (1986) Estimation of the genetic risk of carriership for possible carriers of Christmas disease (haemophilia B). *Braz. J. Genet.* **9**: 87–99

Gitschier J, Wood WI, Tuddenham EGD, Shuman MA, Goralka TM, Chen EY, Lawn RM. (1985) Detection and sequence of mutations in the factor VIII gene of haemophiliacs. *Nature* **315**: 427–430.

Gitschier J, Kogan S, Levinson B, Tuddenham EGD. (1988) Mutations of factor VIII cleavage sites in hemophilia A. *Blood* **72**: 1022–1028.

Grover H, Phillips MA, Lillicrap DP, Giles AR, Garvey MB, Teitel J, Rivard G, Blanchette V, White BN, Holden JJA. (1987) Carrier detection of haemophilia A using DNA markers in families with an isolated affected male. *Clin. Genet.* **32**: 10–19.

Haldane JBS. (1947) The mutation rate of the gene for haemophilia and its segregation ratios in males and females. *Ann. Eugen.* **13**: 262–271.

Higuchi M, Kochhan L, Schwaab R, Egli H, Brackmann H-H, Horst J, Olek K. (1989) Molecular defects in hemophilia A: identification and characterization of mutations in the factor VIII gene and family analysis. *Blood* **74**: 1045–1051.

Howard PL, Hoag JB, Bovill EG, Heintz NH. (1988) Spontaneous mutation in the male gamete as a cause of hemophilia A: clarification of a case using DNA probes. *Am. J. Hematol.* **28**: 167–169.

Ikemura T, Wada K. (1991) Evident diversity of codon usage patterns of human genes with respect to chromosome banding patterns and chromosome numbers: relation between nucleotide sequence data and cytogenetic data. *Nucleic Acids Res.* **19**: 4333–4339.

Kimura M, Ohta T. (1973) Mutation and evolution at the molecular level. *Genetics* **73** (Suppl.): 19–35.

Koeberl DD, Bottema CD, Ketterling RP, Bridge PJ, Lillicrap DP, Sommer SS. (1990a) Mutations causing hemophilia B: direct estimate of the underlying rates of spontaneous germ-line transitions, transversions and deletions in a human gene. *Am. J. Hum. Genet.* **47**: 202–217.

Koeberl DD, Bottema CDK, Sarkar G, Ketterling RP, Chen S-H, Sommer SS. (1990b) Recurrent nonsense mutations at arginine residues cause severe hemophilia B in unrelated hemophiliacs. *Hum. Genet.* **84**: 387–390.

Kuick RD, Neel JV, Strahler JR, Chu EHY, Bargal R, Fox DA, Hanash SM. (1992) Similarity of spontaneous germinal and *in vitro* somatic cell mutation rates in humans: implications for carcinogenesis and for the role of exogenous factors in 'spontaneous' germinal mutagenesis. *Proc. Natl. Acad. Sci. USA* **89**: 7036–7040.

Ljung R, Kling S, Sjörin E, Nilsson IM. (1989) The majority of isolated cases of hemophilia A are caused by a recent mutation. *Thromb. Haemost.* **62**: 202.

Ludwig M, Grimm T, Brackmann HH, Olek K. (1992) Parental origin of factor IX gene mutations and their distribution in the gene. *Am. J. Hum. Genet.* **50**: 164–173.

Mathews CK, Ji J. (1992) DNA precursor asymmetries, replication fidelity and variable genome evolution. *BioEssays* **14**: 295–301.

Miller CH, Hilgartner MW, Aledort LM. (1987) Reproductive choices in hemophilic men and carriers. *Am. J. Med. Genet.* **26**: 591–598.

Montandon AJ, Green PM, Bentley DR, Ljung R, Kling S, Nilsson IM, Giannelli F. (1992) Direct estimate of the haemophilia B (factor IX deficiency) mutation rate and of the ratio of the sex-specific mutation rates in Sweden. *Hum. Genet.* **89**: 319–322

Müller B, Dechant C, Meng G, Liechti-Gallati S, Doherty RA, Hejtmancik JF, Bakker E, Read AP, Jeanpierre M, Fischbeck KH, Romeo G, Francke U, Wilichowski E, Greenberg CR, van Broeckhoven C, Junien C, Müller CR, Grimm T. (1992) Estimation of the male and female mutation rates in Duchenne muscular dystrophy (DMD). *Hum. Genet.* **89**: 204–206

Neel JV, Satoh C, Goriki K, Fujita M, Takahashi N, Asakawa J-I, Hazama R. (1986) The rate with which spontaneous mutation alters the electrophoretic mobility of polypeptides. *Proc. Natl. Acad. Sci. USA* **83**: 389–393.

Pecorara M, Casarino L, Mori PG, Morfini M, Mancuso G, Scrivano AM, Boeri E, Molinari AC, DeBiasi R, Ciavarella N, Bencivelli F, Ripa T, Barbujani G, Loi A, Perseu L, Cao A, Pirastu M. (1987) Hemophilia A: carrier detection and prenatal diagnosis by DNA analysis. *Blood* **70**: 531–535.

Rosendaal FR, Bröcker-Vriends AHJT, van Houwellingen JC, Smit C, Varekamp I, van Dijck H, Suurmeijer TPBM, Vandenbroucke JP, Briët E. (1990) Sex ratio of the mutation frequencies in haemophilia A: estimation and meta-analysis. *Hum. Genet.* **86**: 139–146.

Sommer SS. (1992) Assessing the underlying pattern of human germline mutations: lessons from the factor IX gene. *FASEB J.* **6**: 2767–2774.

Stamatoyannopoulos G, Nute PE. (1982) *De novo* mutations producing unstable Hbs or Hbs M. *Hum. Genet.* **60**: 181–188.

Stevenson AC, Kerr CB. (1967) On the distributions of frequencies of mutation to genes determining harmful traits in man. *Mutat. Res.* **4**: 339–352.

Taylor SAM, Deugau KV, Lillicrap DP. (1991) Somatic mosaicism and female-to-female transmission in a kindred with hemophilia B (factor IX deficiency). *Proc. Natl. Acad. Sci. USA* **88**: 39–42.

Vogel F. (1977) A probable sex difference in some mutation rates. *Am. J. Hum. Genet.* **29**: 312–319.

Vogel F. (1990) Mutation in man. In: *Principles and Practice of Medical Genetics*, Vol I (eds AEH Emery, DL Rimoin). Churchill Livingstone, Edinburgh.

Vogel F, Motulsky AG. (1986) *Human Genetics. Problems and Approaches*, 2nd Edn. Springer, New York.

Winter RM, Tuddenham EGD, Goldman E, Matthews KB. (1983) A maximum likelihood estimate of the sex ratio of mutation rates in haemophilia A. *Hum. Genet.* **64**: 156–159.

Wolfe KH, Sharp PM, Li W-H. (1989) Mutation rates differ among regions of the mammalian genome. *Nature* **337**: 283–285.

Wolfe KH. (1991) Mammalian DNA replication: mutation biases and the mutation rate. *J. Theor. Biol.* **149**: 441–451.

Appendix 1 Direct and indirect analysis of human genetic disease

Human genetic diseases currently amenable to DNA-based diagnosis

The information collated in this table draws primarily from the collection of literature references 'Diagnosis and analysis of human genetic disease by recombinant DNA' (Cooper and Schmidtke, 1991, 1993) and the McKusick catalogue 'Mendelian Inheritance in Man (MIM)' in its printed (McKusick, 1991) and on-line ('OMIM', Welch Medical Library, Baltimore) versions. For the purpose of this compilation, the literature from 1978 until December 1992 has been followed. In order to facilitate access to each entry in MIM or OMIM, the list has been ordered according to the McKusick catalogue number and has also adopted McKusick's disease nomenclature. In accordance with the policy of this catalogue, where disease states are often discussed under the name of the gene locus implicated in their aetiology, we have usually not listed diseases caused by mutations in one and the same locus separately (e.g. haemoglobino-pathies, thalassaemias). If, however, locus heterogeneity is known for a particu-lar clinical entity, the disease is listed repeatedly (e.g. Osteogenesis imperfecta). In addition to the disease names and the MIM number, the symbol specifying the gene locus responsible for the disease is given if an intragenic lesion has been identified. The type of mutation observed is given in the column 'mutation type', where P = point mutation, D = deletion, I = insertion, U = duplication, L = loss of heterozygosity, V = Inversion, R = rearrangement. If reference to a mutation is made without a gene being named, usually a chromosomal deletion or rearrangement is implicated which has been analysed using a DNA probe. Finally, the chromosomal localization of the disease locus is given.

The list currently comprises 440 entries. It should be noted that the true number of clinical entities amenable to DNA-based diagnosis exceeds this number due to their frequent subsumation under a single MIM number. Using the data given in the table, Figure 3.2 depicts the progress made in this field up until 1990. Undoubtedly due to technological improvements in the field of DNA sequence analysis (especially PCR methodology and automated sequencing), both the absolute and relative number of diseases amenable to the direct approach have increased dramatically during the last few years. Of these diseases, almost one half are already known to exhibit heterogeneity with respect to the type of mutation observed; this proportion will almost certainly increase as more patients with these disorders are studied. Indeed, many loci for which only one particular type of mutation has so far been described exhibit variability with respect to the site where a mutation occurs; allelic heterogeneity is clearly the rule rather than the exception. As it has turned out, molecular analysis has sometimes provided evidence for allelism in cases of diseases previously thought to be due to mutation at distinct loci, e.g. gonadal dysgenesis, a disorder of sexual differentiation, and Kennedy disease, a type of spinal and bulbar muscular atrophy, are both associated with specific lesions in one and the same gene, the androgen receptor (AR) gene, and must therefore be formally termed allelic disorders. On the other hand, the present version of this table is likely to underestimate the true extent of locus heterogeneity. For many entries, only a single or a few patients have actually been found to carry a specific mutation and it is possible that other loci will be found to be implicated in the aetiology of the disease in other patients.

References

Cooper DN, Schmidtke J. (1991) Diagnosis of human genetic disease using recombinant DNA. Third edition. *Hum. Genet.* **87**: 519–560.

Cooper DN, Schmidtke J. (1993) Diagnosis of human genetic disease using recombinant DNA. Fourth edition. *Hum. Genet.* **92**: 211–236.

McKusick V. (1991) *Mendelian Inheritance in Man*, 10th edn. Johns Hopkins University Press, Baltimore.

Direct and indirect analysis of human genetic disease (continued)

Disease	MIM number	Gene	Chromosomal localization	Mutation type
Abdominal aortic aneurysma	100070	COL3A1	2q31	P
Acoustic neurinoma (neurofibromatosis type 2)	101000		22q11.21-q13.1	DPIU
APRT deficiency	102600	APRT	16q24	DP
Adenosine deaminase deficiency	102700	ADA	20q13.11	P
AMP deaminase deficiency	102770	AMPD1	1p21-p13	P
Adenylate kinase deficiency	103000	AK1	9q34.1	DP
Albumin deficiency	103600	ALB	4q11-q13	P
Aldolase A deficiency	103850	ALDA	16q22-q24	R
Aldosteronism, sensitive to dexamethasone	103900	GSH	8q22	PR
Alpha-2-macroglobulin deficiency	103950	A2M	12p13.3-p12.3	P
Alpha-galactosidase B deficiency (Schindler disease)	104170	NAGA	22q11	P
Alzheimer disease	104300		19, Mitochondrial	P
Alzheimer disease	104300	APP	21q21.3-q22.05	P
Amyloid of aging and Alzheimer disease	104760	APP	21q21.3-q22.05	P
Amyloidosis V	105120	APP	21q21.3-q22.05	P
Amyloidosis V	105120	GSN	9q34	P
Amyloidosis VI	105150	CST3	20p11	P
Amyotrophic lateral sclerosis	105400		21q22.1-q22.2	DPUR
Angioneurotic edema	106100	C1I	11q11-q13	DPUR
Aniridia	106200		2p25	DI
Aniridia (type 2)	106210	AN2	11p13	DPI
Antithrombin III deficiency	107300	AT3	1q23.1-q23.9	DPI
Alpha-1-antitrypsin deficiency	107400	PI	14q32.1	DPIV
Apolipoprotein A1 deficiency	107660	APOA1	11q23-qter	P
Apolipoprotein A2 deficiency	107670	APOA2	1p21-q23	DP
Amyloidotic polyneuropathy	107680	APOA1	11q23-qter	DPV
Apolipoprotein A1 deficiency	107680	APOA1	11q23-qter	P
Hyperalphalipoproteinemia	107680	APOC3	11q23-qter	D
Apolipoprotein A4 deficiency	107690	APOA4	11q23-qter	

Direct and indirect analysis of human genetic disease (continued)

Disease	MIM number	Gene	Chromosomal localization	Mutation type
Apolipoprotein B deficiency	107730	APOB	2p24	DP
Apolipoprotein E deficiency	107741	APOE	19q13.1	P
Aromatase deficiency	107910	CYP19	15q21.1	P
Arthroophthalmopathy (Stickler syndrome)	108300	COL2A1	12q13.1-q13.3	P
Band 3 of red cell membrane, aberration	109270	EPB3	17q21-q22	DP
Blood group Gerbich deficiency	110750	GPC	2q14-q21	D
Blood group MN deficiency	111300	GYPA	4q28-q31	D
Bullous ichthyosiform erythroderma	113800		12	
Cancer of the breast (Li–Fraumeni syndrome)	114480	TP53	17p13.1	P
Cardiomyopathy, familial idiopathic	115200		Mitochondrial	P
Cardiomyopathy, hypertrophic	115200	MYHCB	14q11.2-q13	DP
Catalase deficiency	115500	CAT	11p13	P
Cell adhesion molecule, leukocyte, deficiency	116920	LCAM	21q22.1-qter	PI
Central core disease	117000		19q13.1	
Charcot–Marie–Tooth disease (type 1a)	118200	PMP22	17p12-p11.2	U
Charcot–Marie–Tooth disease (type 1a)	118220		17p11.2-q23	U
Cholestasis with peripheral pulmonary stenosis (Alagille)	118450	AGS	20p11.1	D
Cholesteryl ester transfer protein deficiency	118470	CETP	16q21	P
Cleft lip/palate with mucous cysts (van de Woude syndrome)	119300		1q32	
Cleft lip with/without cleft palate	119530		6pter-p23	
Epidermolysis bullosa	120120		3p21	
Collagen of cartilage (osteoarthritis)	120140	COL2A1	12q13.1-q13.3	P
Collagen of skin, tendon and bone (osteogenesis imperfecta)	120150	COL1A1	17q21.31-q22.05	P
Collagen of skin, tendon and bone (osteogenesis imperfecta)	120160	COL1A2	7q21.3-q22.1	DP
Complement C3 deficiency	120700	C3	19p13.3-p13.2	DP
Complement C4 deficiency (complete)	120830	C4F	6p21.3	D
Contractural arachnodactyly, congenital (Beals syndrome)	121050		5q23-q31, 15q21.1	
Convulsions, benign familial neonatal	121200		20	
Corneal dystrophy, Lattice type	122200	GSN	9q34	P
Creutzfeldt–Jakob disease	123400	PRNP	20pter-p12	P

Disease	OMIM	Gene	Location	
Crystallin, gamma (Cataract, Coppock-like)	123660		2q33-q35	P
Cytochrome P450C2 deficiency	123960	P450C2	19q13.1-q13.3	P
Corticosterone methyloxidase II deficiency	124080	CYP11B2	8q21	
Deafness, progressive low tone	124900		5q22-q32	P
Delta-aminolevulinate dehydrase deficiency	125270	ALAD	9q34	
Depressive disorders	125480		11p, Xq28, 6p	
Diabetes insipidus, neurohypophyseal	125700	ARVP	20pter-p12.21	P
Immunodeficiency with growth retardation and sun sensitivity	126391	LIG1	19q13.3	P
Dystonia musculorum deformans (Torsion dystonia)	128100		9q32-q34	
Ectopia lentis	129600		15q21.1	DPR
Ehlers–Danlos syndrome (type 4)	130050	COL3A1	2q31	P
Ehlers–Danlos syndrome (type 7)	130060	COL1A1	17q21.31-q22.05	P
Ehlers–Danlos syndrome (type 7)	130060	COL1A2	7q21.3-q22.1	DR
Elliptocytosis (type 1)	130500	EL1	1p36.2-p34	P
Elliptocytosis, Rhesus-linked type (type 1)	130500	SPTA1	1q21	DP
Elliptocytosis, Rhesus-linked type (type 1)	130500	SPTB	14q22-q23.2	PIU
Elliptocytosis (type 2)	130600	SPTA1	1q21	UR
EMG-syndrome (Beckwith–Wiedemann syndrome)	130650	BWS	11pter-p15.4	L
Endocrine adenomatosis (MEN1)	131100	MEN1	11q13	
Epidermolysis bullosa dystrophica, Pasini type	131750		3p21	
Epidermolysis bullosa simplex, Ogna type	131950		8q24	
Esophageal cancer	133239	APC	5q21-q22	L
Esophageal cancer	133239	MCC	5q21-q22	L
Factor XIII deficiency	134570	F13A	6p25-p24	DP
Beta-dysfibrinogenemia	134830	FGB	4q26-q28	P
Fibrinogen deficiency	134850	FGG	4q26-q28	P
Fish-eye disease	136120	LCAT	16q22.1	P
Foveal dystrophy, progressive	136550		6	
Gerstmann–Straeussler syndrome	137440	PRP	12p13.2	PI
Gilles de la Tourette syndrome	137580		18q22.1	
Glioma of brain	137800	RB1	13q14.1-q14.2	D
Glioma of brain	137800	TP53	17p13.1	L
Glucocorticoid receptor deficiency	138040	GR	5q31	P
Diabetes mellitus, non-insulin-dependent (type 2)	138079	GCK	7p15-p14	P

Direct and indirect analysis of human genetic disease (continued)

Disease	MIM number	Gene	Chromosomal localization	Mutation type
Diabetes mellitus (NIDDM)	138190	GLUT4	17p13	P
Glutathione-S-transferase-1 deficiency	138350	GST1	1p31	D
Growth hormone deficiency	139250	GH	17q22-q24	DP
Albright's osteodystrophy	139320	GNAS	20q13.2	D
Epidermolytic hyperkeratosis	139350	KRT1	12q11-q21	P
Hb-disorders,-alpha1 (thalassemia, HbH-disease)	141800	HBA1	16pter-p13.3	DPIR
Hb-disorders,-alpha2 (thalassemia)	141850	HBA2	16pter-p13.3	DP
Hb-disorders,-beta (HbS, HPFH, thalassemia)	141900	HBB	11p15.5	DPIR
Hb-disorders,-delta (thalassemia)	142200	HBD	11p15.5	DPI
Hb-disorders,-gamma1 (HPFH)	142200	HBG1	11p15.5	DPU
Hb-disorders,-gamma2 (HPFH)	142250	HBG2	11p15.5	PU
Heparin cofactor 2 deficiency	142360	HCF2	22q11	P
Huntington disease	143100		4p16.3	
Hypercholesterolemia	143890	LDLR	19p13.2-p13.1	DPUR
Hyperlipidemia, familial combined	144250		11q23-qter	
Hypernephroma	144700	TP53	17p13.105-p12	L
Hypernephroma	144700	RCC	3p14.2	L
Hyperthermia of anesthesia	145600	RYDR	19q13.1	P
Hypocalciuric hypercalcemia	145980		3	
Immunoglobulin G Fc receptor III deficiency	146740	FCG3	1q23-q24	D
Immunoglobulin Am1 (heavy chain disease, alpha)	146900	IGHA1	14q32.33	IR
Immunoglobulin M (heavy chain disease, mu)	147020	IGHM1	14q32.33	DIR
Atopic IgE responsiveness	147050	IGH	11q12-q13	
Immunoglobulin Gm1 (H-chain deficiency)	147100	IGH	14q32.33	D
Immunoglobulin G4 deficiency	147130	IGHG4	14q32.33	D
Immunoglobulin K-chain deficiency	147200	IGK	2p12	DP
Insulin receptor (diabetes mellitus, leprechaunism)	147670	INSR	19p13.3-p13.2	DP
Epidermolysis bullosa	148066	KRT14	14q12-q21	P
Lactate dehydrogenase deficiency	150000	LDHA	11p15.4	DP
Lactate dehydrogenase deficiency	150100	LDHB	12p12.2-p12.1	P

Disease	MIM	Gene	Location	Method
Lactogen, placental, deficiency	150200	CSH1	17q22-q24	D
Langer–Giedion syndrome	150230		8q24.11-q24.13	D
Hepatic lipase deficiency	151670	LIPC	15q21-q23	P
Leukocyte adhesion deficiency	153370	LFA1	16p13.1-p11	P
Macular degeneration, polymorphic vitelline	153700		6q25-qter	
Mandibulofacial dysostosis (Treacher–Collins syndrome)	154500		5q11	
Marfan syndrome	154700	FBN1	15q21.1	DP
Medullary thyroid carcinoma	155240		10q21.1	
Melanoma, malignant	155600		6	L
Muscular dystrophy, facioscapulohumeral (Landouzy)	158900		4q34-qter	
Muscular dystrophy, proximal (limb-girdle)	159000		5	
Myotonic dystrophy	160900	DM	19q13	IUR
Nemaline myopathy	161800		1p21-q23	
Neurofibromatosis (type 1)	162200	NF1	17q11.2	DPI
Neuronal ceroid lipofuscinosis (type 1)	162350		1p35-p33	
Purine nucleoside phosphorylase deficiency	164050	NP	14q13.1	P
Olivopontocerebellar atrophy	164400		6p21.3-p21.2	
Oncocytoma	164601		Mitochondrial	D
Piebaldism	164920	KIT	4q11-q12	P
External ophthalmoplegia	165000		Mitochondrial	D
Kearns–Sayre syndrome	165100		Mitochondrial	D
Osteogenesis imperfecta (type 1)	166200	COL1A1	17q21.31-q22.05	DP
Osteogenesis imperfecta (type 1)	166200	COL1A2	7q21.3-q22.1	DP
Osteogenesis imperfecta (type 2)	166210	COL1A1	17q21.31-q22.05	P
Osteogenesis imperfecta (type 2)	166210	COL1A2	7q21.3-q22.1	PI
Osteogenesis imperfecta (type 4)	166220	COL1A2	7q21.3-q22.1	P
Ovalocytosis, hereditary hemolytic	166900	BND3	17q21-q22	D
Ovarian cancer	167000		17q12-q23	
Paragangliomata	168000		11	
Paramyotonia congenita of von Eulenburg	168300		7q21.1, 17q23.1-q25.3	
Hypoparathyroidism	168450	PTH	11p15	P
Parkinsonism	168600		Mitochondrial	D
Parotid salivary glycoprotein deficiency	168840	PRP3	12p13.2	P
Peptidase D (prolidase) deficiency	170100	PEPD	19cen-q13.11	DP

Direct and indirect analysis of human genetic disease (continued)

Disease	MIM number	Gene	Chromosomal localization	Mutation type
Periodic paralysis (type 2)	170500	SCN4A	17q23.1-q25.3	P
Zellweger syndrome	170995	PMP70	1p22-p21	P
Pheochromocytoma (MEN2A)	171400		10p11.2-q11.2	
Phosphofructokinase(muscle)deficiency	171850	PFKM	1cen-q32	D
Piebald trait	172800	KIT	4q11-q12	P
Pituitary-specific transcription factor deficiency	173110	PIT1	3q	P
Plasminogen deficiency	173350	PLG	6q26-q27	P
Glanzmann's thrombasthenia	173470	GP3A	17q21.1-q21.3	P
Polycystic kidney disease	173900		16p13.31-p13.12	
Polyostotic fibrous dysplasia (McCune–Albright)	174800	GPSA	20	P
Polyposis, adenomatous	175100	APC	5q22-q23	DPIL
Polyposis, adenomatous intestinal	175100	MCC	5q21-q22	D
Polyposis, adenomatous intestinal	175100	TP53	17p13.105-p12	D
Polysyndactyly with peculiar skull (Greig syndrome)	175700	GLI3	7p13	DR
Porphyria, acute intermittent	176000	PBGD	11q23.2-qter	DP
Porphyria cutanea tarda	176100	UROD	1p34	DP
Prader–Willi syndrome	176270	PWS	15q11	DR
Prealbumin amyloidosis	176300	PALB	18q11.2-q12.1	P
Proinsulin (diabetes mellitus) deficiency	176730	INS	11p15.5	P
Leukodystrophy, metachromatic	176801	SAP1	10q21-q22	PI
Sphingolipid activator protein deficiency	176801	SAP1	10q21-q22	P
Gaucher disease, atypical	176801	SAP2	10q21-q22	P
Protein C deficiency	176860	PROC	2q13-q14	DP
Protein S deficiency	176880	PROS	3p11.1-q11.2	D
Protoporphyria, erythropoietic	177000	FECH	18q21.3	P
Anemia, hemolytic	177070	EPB42	15q15	P
Pseudocholinesterase, silent phenotype	177400	CHE1	3q25.2	PIU
Pseudo-von Willebrand disease	177820	GP1BA	17pter-p12	P
Retinitis pigmentosa	179605	RDS	6p21.2-cen	DP
Retinitis pigmentosa	180100	RDS	6p21.3, 8p12, X	DP

Disease	Number	Gene	Location	Code
Retinitis pigmentosa	180100	RHO	3q21-q24	DP
Retinoblastoma	180200	RB1	13q14.1-q14.2	DPR
Retinitis pigmentosa	180380	RHO	3q21-q24	P
Malignant hyperthermia	180901	RYR1	19q13.1	P
Schizophrenia (type 1)	181510		5q11.2-q13.3	
Small-cell cancer of the lung	182280		3p21	D
Smith–Magenis syndrome	182290		17p11.2	D
Spectrin A (elliptocytosis)	182860	SPTA	1q21	P
Spectrin B (elliptocytosis, type 3)	182870	SPTB	14q22-q23.2	PI
Spherocytosis	182900	ANK1	8p11	D
Spondyloepiphyseal dysplasia	183900	COL2A1	12q13.1-q13.3	DU
Thrombasthenia of Glanzmann	187800	GP2B	17q21.32	D
Thymus and parathyroids, absence (Di George syndrome)	188400		22q11	D
Thyroglobulin (Hypothyroidism)	188450		8q24.2-q24.3	
Thyrotropin deficiency	188540	TSHB	1p22	P
Thyroid hormone resistance	188570	ERBA2	3p24.3	DP
Thyroid hormone resistance	188570	PALB	18q11.2-q12.1	P
Thyroid hormone resistance, generalized	190160	ERBA2	3p24.3	DPI
Triose phosphate isomerase deficiency	190450	TPI	12p13	P
Tritanopia	190900	BCP	7q22-qter	P
Tuberous sclerosis (type 2)	191090		11q23	
Tuberous sclerosis	191100		9q33-q34, 12q24.1	
Bladder cancer	191170	P53	17p13.105-p12	L
Ependymoma, intracranial	191170	P53	17p13.105-p12	P
Gastric cancer	191170	P53	17p13.105-p12	DP
Hepatocellular carcinoma	191170	P53	17p13.105-p12	P
Cervical carcinoma	191181		11q13-q23	L
Velocardiofacial syndrome	192430		22	D
Ventricular fibrillation with prolonged Q–T interval	192500		11p15.5	
Von Hippel–Lindau disease	193300		3p25	
Von Willebrand disease	193400	VWF	12pter-p12	DPU
Waardenburg syndrome	193500	HUP2	2q35	DP
Watson syndrome	193520		17q11.2	
Wilms' tumour	194070	WT1	11p13	DP
Wolf–Hirschhorn syndrome	194190		4q	D

Direct and indirect analysis of human genetic disease (continued)

Disease	MIM number	Gene	Chromosomal localization	Mutation type
Abetalipoproteinemia	200100	APOB	2p24	DP
Achondrogenesis-hypochondrogenesis (type 2)	200610	COL2A1	12q13.1-q13.3	P
Acyl-CoA dehydrogenase (M) deficiency	201450	ACADM	1p31	DP
Acyl-CoA dehydrogenase (S) deficiency	201470	ACADS	12q22-qter	P
Adrenal hyperplasia (type 3)	201910	CYP21	6p21.3	DPIUR
Adrenal hyperplasia (type 3)	201910	HSD3B2	1p13.1	P
Adrenal hyperplasia (type 4)	202010	CYP11B1	8q21	P
Adrenal hyperplasia (type 5)	202110	CYP17	10	DPU
Albinism (type 1)	203100	TYR	11q14-q21	DPIU
Aldosterone deficiency (type 2)	203410	P45OC11	8q21	R
Alpha-methylacetoaceticaciduria	203750	ACAT	11q22.3-q23.1	P
Amaurotic family idiocy, juvenile (Batten disease)	204200		16	
Analbuminemia	205300	ALB	4q11-q13	P
Anemia, nonspherocytic hemolytic	206300	G6PD	Xq28	P
Apolipoprotein C2 deficiency	207750	APOC2	19q13.1	DP
Argininemia	207800	ARG1	6q23	DP
Argininosuccinicaciduria	207900	ASL	7cen-q11.2	DPI
Aspartylglucosaminuria	208400	AGA	4q21-qter	
Ataxia-telangiectasia	208900		11q22-q23	
Breast cancer, ductal (type 1)	211410		1, 7, 17	L
Cerebral cholesterinosis	213700	CYP27	2q33-qter	P
Cerebrohepatorenal syndrome (Zellweger)	214100	PAF1		P
Citrullinuria	215700	ASS	9q34	DP
Complement C2 deficiency	217000	C2	6q21.3	D
Crigler–Najjar syndrome	218800	UGT1	2	DP
Cystic fibrosis	219700	CFTR	7q31.3-q32	DPIU
Diaphragmatic hernia	222400		1q32.3-q42.3	D
Diastrophic dysplasia	222600		5q34-qter	
Ehlers–Danlos syndrome (type 7)	225410	COL1A1	17q21.31-q22.05	P
Ehlers–Danlos syndrome (type 7)	225410	COL1A2	7q21.3-q22.1	DP

Disorder	OMIM	Gene	Location	Analysis
Epidermolysis bullosa dystrophy (Hallopeau–Siemens)	226600		3p21	
Factor VII deficiency	227500	F7	13q34	DP
Factor X deficiency	227600	F10	13q34	DP
Fanconi anemia	227650		20q	P
Fanconi pancytopenia (type 1)	227650	FACC	9q22.3	D
Flaujeac factor (Kininogen) deficiency	228960	KNG	3q26-qter	DPR
Friedreich ataxia	229300		9q13-q21.1	R
Fructose intolerance	229600	ALDOB	9q22	P
Fucosidosis	230000	FUCA1	1p34	PU
Galactosemia	230400	GALT	9p13	P
Gangliosidosis generalized GM1 (type 1)	230500	GLB1	3p21-p14.2	PR
Gangliosidosis, GM2, juvenile, A(M)B variant	230710	HEXA	15q22-q25.1	P
Gaucher disease (types 1, 2, 3)	230800	GBA	1q21	P
Giant platelet (Bernard–Soulier) syndrome	231200	GP1BA	17pter-p12	DR
Glutaricaciduria (type 2b)	231680	ETFA	15q23-q25	PR
Glycinemia, ketotic	232000	PCCB	3q13.3-q22	D
Glycogen storage disease II (Pompe disease)	232300	GAA	17q23	P
Granulomatous disease, chronic	233690	CYBA	16q24	DR
Hagemann factor deficiency	234000	F12	5q33-qter	PR
Happy puppet syndrome (Angelman)	234400	GABRB3	15q11.2-q12	D
Hemochromatosis	235200		6p21.2	P
Homocystinuria	236200	CBS	21q22.3	DR
Hyperammonemia (type 2)	237300		2p	P
Hyperglycinemia, isolated non-ketotic	238300	GCS	9p22	DPR
Hyperlipoproteinemia (type 1)	238600	LPL	8p22	DPIUR
Hypophosphatasia, infantile	241500	ALPL	1p36.1-p34	P
Isovaleric acidemia	243500	IVD	15q14-q15	DPI
Krabbe disease	245200		14q11.2-q24.3	PI
LCAT deficiency	245900	LCAT	16q22.1	P
Leprechaunism	246200	INSR	19p13.3-p13.2	D
Lissencephaly syndrome (Miller–Dieker)	247200		17p13.3	DPI
Maple syrup urine disease	248600	BCKDHA	19q13.1-q13.2	R
Mediterranean fever, familial	249100		16pter-p13.3	
Mediterranean fever, familial	249100	SAA	11pter-p12	

Direct and indirect analysis of human genetic disease (continued)

Disease	MIM number	Gene	Chromosomal localization	Mutation type
Metachromatic leukodystrophy	249900	SAP1	10q21-q22	PI
Metachromatic leukodystrophy	249900	SAP2	10q21-q22	P
Metachromatic leukodystrophy, late infantile	250100	ARSA	22q13.31-qter	DPI
Methemoglobinemia (Methemoglobin reductase deficiency)	250800	DIA1	22q13.31-qter	P
Methylmalonicaciduria	251000	MCM	6p21.2-p12	DP
Mevalonicaciduria	251170	MVLK	12	P
Mitochondrial myopathy	251900		Mitochondrial	DP
Mitochondrial myopathy with lactic acidosis	251950		Mitochondrial	P
Mucopolysaccharidosis (type 1)	252800	IDUA	22q11	P
Mucopolysaccharidosis (type 4a)	253000	GALNS	16q24	DP
Mucopolysaccharidosis (type 6)	253200	ARSB	5q11-q13	P
Mucopolysaccharidosis (type 7)	253220	GUSB	7q21.1-q22	P
Muscular atrophy (type 1, Werdnig–Hoffmann)	253300		5q12-q14	
Muscular atrophy (type 3, Kugelberg–Welander)	253400		5q12-q14	
Muscular atrophy (type 2, infantile-chronic)	253550		5q12-q14	
Muscular dystrophy (type 1, limb-girdle)	253600		15	
Myeloperoxidase deficiency	254600	MPO	17q21.3-q23	R
Myoclonus epilepsy (Unverricht–Lundborg)	254800		21	
Myopathy with deficiency of carnitine palmitoyltransferase II	255110	CPT2	Mitochondrial	P
Necrotizing encephalopathy, infantile subacute	256000		Mitochondrial	
Neuraminidase deficiency (galactosialidosis)	256540	CPA1	7q23-qter	P
Neuronal ceroid-lipofuscinosis, infantile Finnish	256730		1	
Niemann–Pick disease (types a,b)	257200	SMPD1	11p15.4-p15.1	DP
Ophthalmoplegia, progressive external	258450		Mitochondrial	DP
Ornithinemia with gyrate atrophy	258870	OAT	10q26	DPI
Osteogenesis imperfecta (type 3)	259420	COL1A1	17q21.31-q22.05	P
Osteopetrosis with renal tubular acidosis	259730	CA2	8q22	P
Osteoporosis, juvenile	259750	CALC1	11p15.4	–
Osteoporosis, juvenile	259750	COL1A2	7q21.3-q22.1	P
Oxalosis (type 1)	259900	AGT	1q42-q43	P

Disease	OMIM	Gene	Location	Code
Oxalosis (type 1)	259900	SPAT	2q36-q37	P
Pearson marrow–pancreas syndrome	260560		Mitochondrial	D
Persistent Müllerian duct syndrome	261550	AMH	19p13.3-p13.2	P
Phenylketonuria (type 1)	261600	PAH	12q24.1	DPI
Phenylketonuria (type 2)	261630	DHPR	4p15.3	I
Pituitary dwarfism (type 2, Laron)	262500	GHR	5p13-p12	DP
Plasmin inhibitor deficiency	262850	PLI	18p11.1-q11.2	DI
Porphyria congenital erythropoietic (Gunther disease)	263700	UROS	10q25.2-q26.3	P
Pseudohermaphroditism, male, with gynecomastia	264300	EDHB17A	17q11-q12	D
Pseudovaginal perineoscrotal hypospadias	264600	SRD5A2	2p23	DP
Pseudo-vitamin D deficiency (type 1)	264700		12q14	
PTA (Factor XI) deficiency	264900	F11	4q35	P
Pyruvate kinase deficiency of erythrocyte	266200	PKR	1q21-q22	P
Sandhoff disease	268800	HEXA	15q22-q25.1	D
Sandhoff disease	268800	HEXB	5q13	DPU
Tay–Sachs disease, AB variant	272750	GM2A	5	P
Tay–Sachs disease, AB variant	272750	HEXB	5q13	P
Tay–Sachs disease	272800	HEXA	15q22-q25.1	DPI
Tay–Sachs disease	272800	HEXB	5q13	DPI
Thrombasthenia (Glanzmann-Naegli)	273800	GP2B	17q21.32	DP
Thyroid hormonogenesis defect (type 5)	274900	TG	8q24.2-q24.3	P
Tyrosine transaminase deficiency	276600	TAT1	16q22.1-q22.3	D
Usher syndrome (type 2)	276901		1q32	
Vitamin D-resistant rickets	277440	VDR	12q12-q14	P
Werner syndrome	277700		8p11	
Wilson disease	277900		13q14-q21	
Xeroderma pigmentosum (type 1)	278700	XPAC	1q41-q42	DP
Adrenoleukodystrophy	300100	RCP	Xq28	DR
Adrenal hypoplasia	300200		Xp21.3-p21.2	D
Agammaglobulinemia, Bruton type	300300		Xq21.3-q22	R
Agammaglobulinemia, Swiss type	300400		Xq13.1-q21.1	
Albinism, ocular (type 1)	300500		Xpter-p22.32	

Direct and indirect analysis of human genetic disease (continued)

Disease	MIM number	Gene	Chromosomal localization	Mutation type
Albinism, ocular (type 2)	300600		Xp11.4-p11.23	D
Albinism, ocular (type 2)	300600		Xp21.3-p21.2	
Albinism-deafness syndrome	300700		Xq26.3-q27.1	DP
Albright hereditary osteodystrophy	300800	GNAS1	20q13.2	
Aldrich (Wiskott–Aldrich) syndrome	301000		Xp11.3-p11	DP
Alport syndrome	301050	COL4A5	Xq22	D
Amelogenesis imperfecta, hypomaturation type	301100	AMG	Xp22.3-p22.1	D
Amelogenesis imperfecta, hypoplastic type	301200	AMG	Xp22.3-p22.1	P
Anemia, hypochromic	301300	ALAS2	Xp21-q21	
Anemia, sideroblastic, and spinocerebellar ataxia	301310		Xq13	
Angiokeratoma, diffuse (Fabry disease)	301500	GLA	Xq22	DP
Ataxia dementia syndrome	301840		Xq21.31	
Borjeson–Forssman–Lehmann syndrome	301900		Xq26-q27	
Cardioskeletal myopathy (Barth syndrome)	302060		X	
Cataract-dental (Nance–Horan) syndrome	302350		Xp22.3-p21.1	
Charcot–Marie–Tooth disease	302800		Xq13	DU
Chondrodysplasia punctata	302950		Xpter-p22.32	PI
Choroideremia	303100	CHM	Xq21.1-q21.3	D
Choroideremia	303100	TCD	Xq21.2	
Clasped thumb and mental retardation	303350		X	
Cleft palate, X-linked	303400		Xq21	
Coffin–Lowry syndrome	303600		Xp22.2-p22.1	
Colorblindness, blue cone	303700	CBP/D	Xq28	DR
Colorblindness, partial, deutan series	303800	CBD	Xq28	DPR
Colorblindness, red cone	303900	CBP	Xq28	D
Cone dystrophy	304020		Xp21.1-p11.3	
Deafness with stapes fixation	304400		Xq13-q21.1	
Diabetes insipidus, nephrogenic	304800	V2R	Xq28	D
Dyskeratosis congenita	305000		Xq28	D
Ectodermal dysplasia, anhidrotic	305100		Xq12.2-q13.1	

Disease	Number	Gene	Location	Code
Endocardial fibroelastosis (Barth syndrome)	305300		Xq28	
G6PD-deficiency	305900	G6PD	Xq28	P
Glycogen storage disease (type 8)	306000		Xq12-q13	
Gonadal dysgenesis, XY female type	306100	SRY	Yp11.3	DP
Granulomatous disease, chronic	306400	CGD	Xp21.1	DP
Hemophilia A	306700	F8	Xq28	DPIU
Hemophilia B	306900	F9	Xq27.1-q27.2	DPIR
Hydrocephalus	307000		Xq28	
Hyperglycerolemia (glycerol kinase deficiency)	307030	GK	Xp21.3-p21.2	D
Hypoparathyroidism	307700		Xq26-q27	
Hypophosphatemia	307800		22	
HPRT-deficiency	308000	HPRT	Xq26-q27.2	DPIUR
Ichthyosis	308100	STS	Xpter-p22.32	DP
Immunodeficiency with hyper-IgM	308230		Xq24-q27	
Immunodeficiency, X-linked progressive	308240		Xq25	
Incontinentia pigmenti	308300		Xp11.2	
Kallmann syndrome	308700	KAL	Xpter-p22.32	DPR
Keratosis follicularis spinulosa decalvans	308800		X	
Leber optic neuropathy	308900		Mitochondrial	P
Lowe oculocerebrorenal syndrome	309000	OCRL	Xq25	R
Manic-depressive psychosis	309200		Xq28	
Megalocornea	309300		Xq21.3-q22	
Menke syndrome	309400		Xq12-q13	
Mental retardation, X-linked, non-specific	309530		Xq26-q27.2	
Mental retardation, X-linked, ass. marXq28 (FRAXA)	309550	FMR1	Xq27.3	DIUR
Mental retardation, X-linked, (Allan–Herndon syndrome)	309600		Xq21	
Mental retardation, X-linked, (Prieto syndrome)	309610		X	
Mental retardation, skeletal dysplasia	309620		Xq28	
Mucopolysaccharidosis (type 2, Hunter syndrome)	309900	IDS	Xq27.3	DPI
Muscular dystrophy, Duchenne and Becker types	310200	DMD	Xp21.2	DPIUR
Muscular dystrophy, Dreyfuss–Emery type	310300		Xq28	
Myopathy, centronuclear	310400		Xq28	
Myopia (Bornholm eye disease)	310460		Xq28	
Neuropathy (type 2)	310490		Xq21.31	

345

Direct and indirect analysis of human genetic disease (continued)

Disease	MIM number	Gene	Chromosomal localization	Mutation type
Night blindness, congenital stationary	310500		Xp11.3	
Norrie disease	310600		Xp11.4	D
Ornithine transcarbamylase deficiency	311250	OTC	Xp21.1	DP
Parkinsonism (Waisman syndrome)	311510		Xq28	
Phosphoglycerate kinase deficiency	311800	PGKA	Xq13	P
Properdin deficiency	312060		Xp11.4	
Pelizaeus–Merzbacher disease	312080	PLP	Xq22	DPR
Pyruvate dehydrogenase E1-alpha deficiency	312170	PDHA1	Xp22.2-p22.1	DPI
Retinitis pigmentosa (type 2)	312600		Xp11.3	D
Retinitis pigmentosa (type 3)	312610		Xp21	D
Retinoschisis	312700		Xp22	
Simpson dysmorphia syndrome	312870			X
Spastic paraplegia	312900		Xq28	
Spinal and bulbar muscular atrophy (Kennedy disease)	313200	AR	Xcen-q13	IU
Spondyloepiphyseal dysplasia tarda	313400		Xp22.1	
Testicular feminization syndrome	313700	AR	Xcen-q13	DP
Thrombocytopenia	313900		Xp11.3-p11	
Thyroxine-binding globulin deficiency	314200	TBG	Xq21-q22	P
Torsion dystonia, X-linked	314250		X	
Wieacker–Wolf syndrome	314580		Xq13-q21	
Xk-Locus (McLeod syndrome)	314850		Xp21.2-p21.1	
Retinitis pigmentosa	316200		Xp21.1	D
Diabetes-deafness syndrome	520000		Mitochondrial	D
Kearns–Sayre syndrome	530000		Mitochondrial	
Encephalomyopathy, progressive	550000		Mitochondrial	D
Respiratory enzyme deficiency (fatal infanticide)	551000		Mitochondrial	P
Pearson/Kearns–Sayre syndrome	557000		Mitochondrial	D
Renal tubulopathy, proximal, diabetes, ataxia	560000		Mitochondrial	U

McKusick (1991) nomenclature has been strictly adhered to.

Abbreviated journal names used in Appendices 2–4

AHG	*Ann. Hum. Genet.*
AJHG	*Am. J. Hum. Genet.*
AJMG	*Am. J. Med. Genet.*
ANN HAEMAT	*Ann. Haematol.*
ANN NEUROL	*Ann. Neurol.*
BBA	*Biochim. Biophys. Acta*
BBRC	*Biochem. Biophys. Res. Commun.*
BIOCHEM	*Biochemistry*
BIOCHEM J	*Biochem. J.*
BJH	*Br. J. Haematol.*
BLOOD	*Blood*
CELL	*Cell*
CFC	*CF Consortium*
CIRCULAT	*Circulation*
CLIN CHEM	*Clin. Chem.*
DIABETES	*Diabetes*
DNA	*DNA*
EMBO J	*EMBO J.*
EXP NEUROL	*Exp. Neurol.*
FEBS LETTS	*FEBS Letts*
GENE	*Gene*
GENOMICS	*Genomics*
HEMOGLOBIN	*Hemoglobin*
HUM GENET	*Hum. Genet.*
HUM MUTAT	*Hum. Mutat.*
J BIOCHEM	*J. Biochem.*
J NCHEM	*J. Neurochem.*
JBC	*J. Biol. Chem.*
JCBS	*J. Cell. Biochem. (Suppl.)*
JCEM	*J. Clin. Endocrinol. Metab.*
JCI	*J. Clin. Invest.*
JEM	*J. Exp. Med.*
JIMD	*J. Inher. Metab. Dis.*
JLR	*J. Lipid Res.*

JMG	*J. Med. Genet.*
LANCET	*Lancet*
MBM	*Mol. Biol. Med.*
MCB	*Mol. Cell. Biol.*
MOL END	*Mol. Endocrinol.*
NAR	*Nucleic Acids Res.*
NATURE	*Nature*
NEJM	*N. Engl. J. Med.*
PNAS	*Proc. Natl. Acad. Sci. USA*
SCIENCE	*Science*
SCMG	*Somatic Cell. Mol. Genet.*
TH	*Thromb. Haemost.*
THR RES	*Thromb. Res.*

Abbreviations used in Appendices 2–4

17 α-Hydrox/lyase	17 α-Hydroxylase/17, 20-lyase
Aa.	Amino acid
ADA	Adenosine deaminase
APRT	Adenine phosphoribosyltransferase
Act.	Activating
Acut. hep.	Acute hepatic
Acut. int.	Acute intermittent
Adenomat. polyp.	Adenomatous polyposis
Adenyl.	Adenylate
Adhes.	Adhesion
Amyloid. polyneur.	Amyloidotic polyneuropathy
Angioneurot.	Angioneurotic
Apo	Apolipoprotein
Argin.succ.	Argininosuccinate
Arylsulphat.	Arylsulphatase
Aspartylglucosamin.	Aspartylglucosaminuria
AT3	Antithrombin III
Atyp	Atypical
Bull.	Bullosa
Carb.	Carbonic
Cardiomyop. hypertro.	Cardiomyopathy, hypertrophic
Centr. diabet. insip.	Central diabetes insipidus
Cerebrot. xanthomat.	Cerebrotendinous xanthomatosis
Cereb. haemors.	Cerebral haemorrhage
Chesterf	Chesterfield
Chr. granulomat.	Chronic granulomatous
Chron. obstr. pulm.	Chronic obstructive pulmonary
Cof.	Cofactor
Cong.	Congenital
Creutzf.–Jakob	Creutzfeldt–Jakob
Defic./def.	Deficiency
Dehydr.	Dehydratase
Dehydrog./dehyd.	Dehydrogenase
Diabetes (MODY)	Maturity-onset diabetes of the young
Diabetes (NIDDM)	Non-insulin-dependent diabetes mellitus
Dis.	Disease
Dnstm.	Downstream

Dwarf.	Dwarfism
Dysbetalipoprotein.	Dysbetalipoproteinaemia
Ellipt. glycoph. C	Elliptocytosis, Glycophorin C
Eryth.	Erythrocytic
Fam.	Familial
G6PD	Glucose-6-phosphate dehydrogenase
Gangliosid.	Gangliosidosis
Gerstmann–Str.	Gerstmann–Sträussler
Granulom.	Granulomatous
HPRT	Hypoxanthine guanine phosphoribosyltransferase
Horm.	Hormone
Hypercholesterol.	Hypercholesterolaemia
Hyperchylomicronaem.	Hyperchylomicronaemia
Hyperkal. per. paral.	Hyperkalemic periodic paralysis
Hyperlipoprotein.	Hyperlipoproteinaemia
Hyperproinsulin.	Hyperproinsulinaemia
Hypobetalipoprotein.	Hypobetalipoproteinaemia
Hyp. thyr.	Hyperthyroxinaemia
Immunoglob.	Immunoglobulin
Imp.	Imperfecta
Insens.	Insensitivity
Ins. res.	Insulin resistant
LCAM	Leukocyte cell adhesion molecule
LCAT	Lecithin cholesterol acetyltransferase
LDH	Lactate dehydrogenase
LDLR	Low density lipoprotein receptor
Lipoprotein.	Lipoproteinaemia
Lipoprt.	Lipoprotein
LongIsl.	Long Island
LosAng	Los Angeles
MCAD	Medium chain acyl coenzyme A dehydrogenase
Malign.	Malignant
Metachrom. leukodys.	Metachromatic leukodystrophy
Methaemoglobin.	Methaemoglobinaemia
Methylmalonicacid.	Methylmalonicaciduria
Mod.	Moderate
Mucopolysacch.	Mucopolysaccharidosis
Müll.	Müllerian
Musc. dystr.	Muscular dystrophy
NK.	Non-ketotic
Nt.	Nucleotides
OTC	Ornithine transcarbamylase
Oculocut./ocul.	Oculocutaneous
Osteodys.	Osteodystrophy
PDH	Pyruvate dehydrogenase

PNP	Purine nucleoside phosphorylase
Pelizaeus–Merzb.	Pelizaeus–Merzbacher
Pigm.	Pigmentosa
Phosphoglyc. kin.	Phosphoglycerokinase
Prealb.	Prealbumin
Presbyt.	Presbyterian
Prot.	Protein
Pseud.	Pseudodeficiency
Resist./res.	Resistance
Retinit. pigm. (aut.)	Retinitis pigmentosa, autosomal
SAP	Sphingolipid activator protein
Sen. sys.	Senile systemic
Spondylo. dysp. con.	Spondyloepiphyseal dysplasia congenita
Ster.11β-hydrox.	Steroid 11β-hydroxylase
Ster.17α-hydrox.	Steroid 17α-hydroxylase
Ster.21-hydrox.	Steroid 21-hydroxylase
Stnvil.	Stanleyville
Syn.	Syndrome
Temp.-dep.	Temperature-dependent
TPI	Triose phosphate isomerase
TSH	Thyroid-stimulating hormone
Thrombast.	Thrombasthenia
Thyr.-bind. glob.	Thyroxine-binding globulin
Upstm.	Upstream
Ur.	Urine
VWD	von Willebrand disease
Vit.D-res.	Vitamin D-resistant
Von Willebrand 2a	von Willebrand disease type 2a
Von Willebrand 2b	von Willebrand disease type 2b
Wt.	Wild-type

Appendix 2 Single base-pair substitution database

Single base-pair substitutions causing human genetic disease

No.	Disease state	Gene symbol	Base change	Amino acid	Codon	Author	Journal	Vol.	Page	Year	CG
1	ADA deficiency	ADA	cCGG–TGG	Arg–Trp	76	Hirschhorn	PNAS	87	6171	90	*
2	ADA deficiency	ADA	AAA–AGA	Lys–Arg	80	Valerio	EMBO J	5	113	86	
3	ADA deficiency	ADA	CGG–CAG	Arg–Gln	101	Bonthron	JCI	76	894	85	*
4	ADA deficiency	ADA	gCGG–TGG	Arg–Trp	101	Akeson	JBC	263	16291	88	*
5	ADA deficiency	ADA	CTG–CCG	Leu–Pro	107	Hirschhorn	PNAS	87	6171	90	
6	ADA deficiency	ADA	CGG–CAG	Arg–Gln	149	Hirschhorn	PNAS	87	6171	90	*
7	ADA deficiency	ADA	CGT–CAT	Arg–His	211	Akeson	JBC	263	16291	88	*
8	ADA deficiency	ADA	cCGT–TGT	Arg–Cys	211	Hirschhorn	PNAS	87	6171	90	*
9	ADA deficiency	ADA	cGCC–ACC	Ala–Thr	215	Hirschhorn	PNAS	87	6171	90	*
10	ADA deficiency	ADA	cGGG–AGG	Gly–Arg	216	Hirschhorn	AJHG	49	878	91	*
11	ADA deficiency	ADA	CCG–CTG	Pro–Leu	274	Hirschhorn	PNAS	87	6171	90	*
12	ADA deficiency	ADA	CCG–CAG	Pro–Gln	297	Hirschhorn	JCI	83	497	89	
13	ADA deficiency	ADA	CTG–CGG	Leu–Arg	304	Valerio	EMBO J	5	113	86	
14	ADA deficiency	ADA	GCG–GTG	Ala–Val	329	Akeson	PNAS	84	5947	87	*
15	APRT deficiency	APRT	GAC–GTC	Asp–Val	65	Chen	AJHG	49	1306	91	
16	APRT deficiency	APRT	TGGg–TGA	Trp–Term	98	Sakota	NAR	18	5915	90	
17	APRT deficiency	APRT	ATG–ACG	Met–Thr	136	Hidaka	JCI	81	945	88	
18	Acyl CoA Dehydr. def.	SCAD	cCGT–TGT	Arg–Cys	107	Naito	JCI	85	1575	90	*
19	Acyl CoA Dehydr. def.	SCAD	cCGG–TGG	Arg–Trp	319	Naito	JCI	85	1575	90	*
20	Adenomat. polyp. coli	APC	TCA–TGA	Ser–Term	280	Nishisho	SCIENCE	253	665	91	
21	Adenomat. polyp. coli	APC	tCGA–TGA	Arg–Term	284	Groden	CELL	66	589	91	*
22	Adenomat. polyp. coli	APC	tCGA–TGA	Arg–Term	302	Nishisho	SCIENCE	253	665	91	*
23	Adenomat. polyp. coli	APC	aCGC–TGC	Arg–Cys	414	Nishisho	SCIENCE	253	665	91	*
24	Adenomat. polyp. coli	APC	TATg–TAG	Tyr–Term	482	Groden	CELL	66	589	91	

#	Disease	Gene	Codon change	Amino acid	Codon no.	Author	Journal	Vol	Page	Year	*
25	Adenomat. polyp. coli	APC	TCA-TGA	Ser-Term	713	Nishisho	SCIENCE	253	665	91	
26	Adenyl. kinase defic.	AK1	cCGG-TGG	Arg-Trp	128	Matsuura	JBC	264	10148	89	*
27	Adrenal hyperplasia	CA21HB	ATC-AAC	Ile-Asn	172	Amor	PNAS	85	1600	88	
28	Adrenal hyperplasia	CA21HB	cGTG-CTG	Val-Leu	211	Speiser	NEJM	319	19	88	
29	Adrenal hyperplasia	CA21HB	AGC-ACC	Ser-Thr	269	Rodrigues	EMBO J	6	1653	87	
30	Adrenal hyperplasia	CA21HB	cGTG-TTG	Val-Leu	281	Speiser	NEJM	319	19	88	
31	Adrenal hyperplasia	CA21HB	gCAG-TAG	Gln-Term	318	Globerman	JCI	82	139	88	
32	Adrenal hyperplasia	CA21HB	CCC-CGC	Pro-Arg	426	Matteson	PNAS	84	5858	87	
33	Adrenal hyperplasia	CA21HB	AAC-AGC	Asn-Ser	494	Rodrigues	EMBO J	6	1653	87	
34	Albinism, ocul. (1)	TYR	GAC-GGC	Asp-Gly	42	King	MBM	8	19	91	
35	Albinism, ocul. (1)	TYR	TGT-TAT	Cys-Tyr	55	King	MBM	8	19	91	
36	Albinism, ocul. (1)	TYR	CGG-CAG	Arg-Gln	59	Takeda	JBC	265	17792	90	*
37	Albinism, ocul. (1)	TYR	CGG-CAG	Arg-Gln	77	Kikuchi	HUM GENET	85	123	90	*
38	Albinism, ocul. (1)	TYR	CCT-CTT	Pro-Leu	81	Giebel	PNAS	87	3255	90	
39	Albinism, ocul. (1)	TYR	TGG-TAG	Trp-Term	178	Giebel	JMG	28	464	91	
40	Albinism, ocul. (1)	TYR	aGCT-ACT	Ala-Thr	206	King	MBM	8	19	91	
41	Albinism, ocul. (1)	TYR	tGTC-TTC	Val-Phe	275	Giebel	AJHG	48	1159	91	
42	Albinism, ocul. (1)	TYR	ACA-AAA	Thr-Lys	355	Spritz	NEJM	322	1724	90	
43	Albinism, ocul. (1)	TYR	cGAT-AAT	Asp-Asn	365	Spritz	NEJM	322	1724	90	
44	Albinism, ocul. (1)	TYR	CCT-CTT	Pro-Leu	406	Giebel	AJHG	48	1159	91	
45	Albinism, ocul. (1)	TYR	gGGA-AGA	Gly-Arg	419	King	MBM	8	19	91	*
46	Albinism, ocul. (1)	TYR	CGG-CAG	Arg-Gln	422	Giebel	JCI	87	1119	91	
47	Albright's osteodys.	GSA	cATG-GTG	Met-Val	-1	Patten	NEJM	322	1412	90	
48	Albumin Iowa2	ALB	GAT-GTT	Asp-Val	1	Madison	PNAS	88	9853	91	*
49	Albumin B	ALB	gGAG-AAG	Glu-Lys	570	Madison	PNAS	88	9853	91	
50	Albumin Christchurch	ALB	CGA-CAA	Arg-Gln	-1	Madison	PNAS	88	9853	91	
51	Albumin Iowa1	ALB	GAT-GTT	Asp-Val	365	Madison	PNAS	88	9853	91	*
52	Albumin Komagome2	ALB	CAT-CGT	His-Arg	128	Madison	PNAS	88	9853	91	
53	Albumin Lille	ALB	CGT-CAT	Arg-His	-2	Madison	PNAS	88	9853	91	*
54	Albumin Naskapi	ALB	cAAA-GAA	Lys-Glu	372	Madison	PNAS	88	9853	91	
55	Albumin Redhill	ALB	tCGT-TGT	Arg-Cys	-2	Brennan	PNAS	87	26	91	*
56	Aldolase A defic.	ALDA	GAT-GGT	Asp-Gly	128	Kishi	PNAS	84	8623	90	
57	Aldolase B defic.	ALDB	tGCT-CCT	Ala-Pro	149	Cross	CELL	53	881	88	
58	Alport syndrome	COL4A5	TGT-TCT	Cys-Ser	108	Zhou	GENOMICS	9	10	91	
59	Alzheimer disease	APP	cGTC-TTC	Val-Phe	717	Murrell	SCIENCE	254	97	91	
60	Alzheimer disease	APP	GTC-GGC	Val-Gly	717	Chartier	NATURE	353	844	91	*
61	Alzheimer disease	APP	cGTC-ATC	Val-Ile	717	Goate	NATURE	349	704	91	*
62	Amyloidosis	GLS	cGAC-AAC	Asp-Asn	187	Maury	FEBS LETTS	276	75	90	

Human gene mutation

Single base-pair substitutions causing human genetic disease (continued)

No.	Disease state	Gene symbol	Base change	Amino acid	Codon	Author	Journal	Vol.	Page	Year	CG
63	Amyloid. polyneur.	APOA1	cGGC-CGC	Gly-Arg	26	Nichols	GENOMICS	8	318	90	
64	Amyloid. polyneur.	PALB	cGTG-ATG	Val-Met	30	Furuya	JCI	80	1706	87	*
65	Amyloid. polyneur.	PALB	gGCT-CCT	Ala-Pro	36	Jones	AJHG	48	979	91	
66	Amyloid. polyneur.	PALB	CTC-CAC	Leu-His	58	Nichols	GENOMICS	5	535	89	
67	Amyloid. polyneur.	PALB	CTC-CGC	Leu-Arg	58	Saeki	BBRC	180	380	91	
68	Amyloid. polyneur.	PALB	TCT-TAT	Ser-Tyr	77	Wallace	JCI	81	189	88	
69	Amyloid. polyneur.	PALB	ATC-AGC	Ile-Ser	84	Wallace	AJHG	43	182	88	
70	Amyloid. polyneur.	PALB	TAC-TGC	Tyr-Cys	114	Ueno	BBRC	169	143	90	
71	Amyloid. polyneur.	PALB	cGTC-ATC	Val-Ile	122	Jacobsen	AJHG	47	127	90	*
72	Amyloid. prealbumin	PALB	GTG-GCG	Val-Ala	30	Jones	CLIN GENET	41	70	92	
73	Amyloidosis, prealb.	PALB	tGGG-CGG	Gly-Arg	47	Murakami	BBRC	182	520	92	
74	Androgen insens. syn.	AR	gAAA-TAA	Lys-Term	588	Marcelli	MOL END	4	1105	90	
75	Androgen insens. syn.	AR	CGT-CCT	Arg-Pro	615	Marcelli	JCI	87	1123	91	
76	Androgen insens. syn.	AR	TGGg-TGA	Trp-Term	717	Sai	AJHG	46	1095	90	
77	Androgen insens. syn.	AR	TAC-TGC	Tyr-Cys	761	McPhaul	JCI	87	1413	91	
78	Androgen insens. syn.	AR	cCGC-TGC	Arg-Cys	774	Brown	MOL END	4	1759	90	*
79	Androgen insens. syn.	AR	TGGc-TGA	Trp-Term	794	Marcelli	JCI	85	1522	90	
80	Androgen insens. syn.	AR	CGA-CAA	Arg-Gln	831	Brown	MOL END	4	1759	90	* *
81	Androgen insens. syn.	AR	cGTG-ATG	Val-Met	866	Lubahn	PNAS	86	9534	89	* *
82	Androgen insens. syn.	AR	cAAG-TAG	Lys-Term	882	Trifiro	AJMG	40	493	91	
83	Angioneurotic oedema	C1I	tGCA-ACA	Ala-Thr	436	Levy	PNAS	87	265	90	
84	Angioneurotic oedema	C1I	CGC-CAC	Arg-His	444	Skriver	JBC	264	3066	89	* *
85	Angioneurotic oedema	C1I	gCGC-TGC	Arg-Cys	444	Skriver	JBC	264	3066	89	* *
86	Angioneurotic oedema	C1I	CGC-CTC	Arg-Leu	444	Frangi	FEBS LETTS	301	34	92	
87	Antithrombin III def.	AT3	GTG-GAG	Val-Glu	-3	Daly	FEBS LETTS	273	87	90	
88	Antithrombin III def.	AT3	ATC-AAC	Ile-Asn	7	Perry	MBM	6	239	89	
89	Antithrombin III def.	AT3	cCGC-TGC	Arg-Cys	24	Perry	MBM	6	239	89	* *
90	Antithrombin III def.	AT3	CCG-CTG	Pro-Leu	41	Chang	JBC	261	1174	86	*
91	Antithrombin III def.	AT3	gCGT-TGT	Arg-Cys	47	Duchange	NAR	14	2408	86	* *
92	Antithrombin III def_	AT3	CGT-CAT	Arg-His	47	Perry	MBM	6	239	89	* *
93	Antithrombin III def.	AT3	CGA-CAA	Arg-Gln	129	Gandrille	JBC	265	18997	90	* *
94	Antithrombin III def.	AT3	cCGA-TGA	Arg-Term	129	Gandrille	BJH	78	414	91	*

Significance markers (top of table): * *   *   * *   * * *   *   *   * *

No.	Disorder	Gene	Codon change	Amino acid	Codon	Author	Journal	Vol	Page	Year
95	Antithrombin III def.	AT3	cAAC-GAC	Asn-Asp	187	Perry	TH	65	838	91
96	Antithrombin III def.	AT3	gTCC-CCC	Ser-Pro	349	Grundy	HUM GENET	88	707	92
97	Antithrombin III def.	AT3	aGCA-ACA	Ala-Thr	382	Devraj-K.	BLOOD	72	1518	88
98	Antithrombin III def.	AT3	tGCA-CCA	Ala-Pro	384	Perry	MBM	6	239	89
99	Antithrombin III def.	AT3	tGCA-TCA	Ala-Ser	384	Blajchman	TH	65	838	91
100	Antithrombin III def.	AT3	GGC-GAC	Gly-Asp	392	Thein	TH	65	913	91
101	Antithrombin III def.	AT3	cCGT-TGT	Arg-Cys	393	Thein	BLOOD	72	1817	88
102	Antithrombin III def.	AT3	CGT-CAT	Arg-His	393	Lane	BLOOD	72	1817	88
103	Antithrombin III def.	AT3	CGT-CCT	Arg-Pro	393	Olds	JBC	264	10200	89
104	Antithrombin III def.	AT3	TCG-TTG	Ser-Leu	394	Olds	NAR	17	10511	89
105	Antithrombin III def.	AT3	TTC-TGC	Phe-Cys	402	Olds	TH	65	670	91
106	Antithrombin III def.	AT3	TTC-TCC	Phe-Ser	402	Olds	TH	65	670	91
107	Antithrombin III def.	AT3	gGCC-ACC	Ala-Thr	404	Bock	TH	62	494	89
108	Antithrombin III def.	AT3	AGG-ATG	Arg-Met	406	Tsuji	TH	65	913	91
109	Antithrombin III def.	AT3	CCT-CTT	Pro-Leu	407	Bock	BIOCHEM	27	6171	88
110	Antithrombin III def.	AT3	CCT-CTT	Pro-Leu	429	Olds	BLOOD	79	1206	92
111	Antitrypsin α1 def.	PI	TCG-TTG	Ser-Leu	−19	Graham	HUM GENET	85	537	90
112	Antitrypsin α1 def.	PI	cCGC-TGC	Arg-Cys	39	Graham	HUM GENET	84	55	89
113	Antitrypsin α1 def.	PI	CTG-CCG	Leu-Pro	41	Takahashi	JBC	263	15528	88
114	Antitrypsin α1 def.	PI	TCC-TTC	Ser-Phe	53	Seyama	JBC	266	12627	91
115	Antitrypsin α1 def.	PI	GGG-GAG	Gly-Glu	67	Curiel	MCB	10	47	90
116	Antitrypsin α1 def.	PI	ATC-AAC	Ile-Asn	92	Fraizer	JCI	86	1878	90
117	Antitrypsin α1 def.	PI	CGT-CAT	Gly-His	101	Faber	AJHG	46	1158	90
118	Antitrypsin α1 def.	PI	cGGC-AGC	Gly-Ser	115	Graham	HUM GENET	85	537	90
119	Antitrypsin α1 def.	PI	cGGG-AGG	Gly-Arg	148	Matsunaga	AJHG	46	602	90
120	Antitrypsin α1 def.	PI	GTG-GCG	Val-Ala	213	Nukiwa	JBC	261	15989	86
121	Antitrypsin α1 def.	PI	gAAG-TAG	Lys-Term	217	Satoh	AJHG	42	77	88
122	Antitrypsin α1 def.	PI	GAT-GTT	Asp-Val	256	Graham	HUM GENET	84	55	89
123	Antitrypsin α1 def.	PI	cGAG-AAG	Glu-Lys	342	Kidd	NATURE	304	230	83
124	Antitrypsin α1 def.	PI	CCT-CTT	Pro-Leu	369	Hofker	HUM GENET	81	264	89
125	Antitrypsin α1 def.	PI	GAAa-GAC	Glu-Asp	376	Graham	HUM GENET	85	381	90
126	Anti-Müll. horm. (Brx)	AMH	tGAA-TAA	Glu-Term	358	Knebelman	PNAS	88	3767	91
127	Aortic aneurysm	COL3A1	cGGA-AGA	Gly-Arg	619	Kontusaari	JCI	86	1465	90
128	ApoA1 deficiency	APOA1	CGA-CTA	Arg-Leu	34	Ladias	HUM GENET	84	439	90
129	ApoA1 deficiency	APOA1	gCAG-TAG	Gln-Term	84	Matsumaga	PNAS	88	2793	91
130	ApoA1 deficiency	APOA1	GAGc-GAT	Glu-Asp	120	Law	JBC	260	12810	85
131	ApoB deficiency	APOB	tCGA-TGA	Arg-Term	1306	Collins	NAR	16	8361	88
132	ApoB deficiency	APOB	tCGA-TGA	Arg-Term	2058	Young	NEJM	320	1604	89

Single base-pair substitutions causing human genetic disease (continued)

No.	Disease state	Gene symbol	Base change	Amino acid	Codon	Author	Journal	Vol.	Page	Year	CG
133	ApoB deficiency	APOB	aCAA-TAA	Gln-Term	2153	Hospatta.	BBRC	148	279	87	
134	ApoB deficiency	APOB	CGG-CAG	Arg-Gln	3500	Soria	PNAS	86	587	89	*
135	ApoC2 deficiency	APOC2	tATG-GTG	Met-Val	-1	Fojo	JBC	264	20842	89	
136	ApoC2 deficiency	APOC2	TACg-TAA	Tyr-Term	37	Fojo	JCI	84	1215	89	
137	ApoC2 deficiency	APOC2	TACg-TAG	Tyr-Term	59	Crecchio	BBRC	168	1118	90	
138	ApoC3 deficiency	APOC3	tAAG-GAG	Lys-Glu	58	v.Eckards.	JCI	87	1724	91	
139	ApoE deficiency	APOE	gCGC-AGC	Arg-Ser	136	Emi	GENOMICS	3	373	88	
140	ApoE deficiency	APOE	gCGC-TGC	Arg-Cys	142	Rall	JCI	83	1095	89	*
141	ApoE deficiency	APOE	gCGT-TGT	Arg-Cys	145	Emi	GENOMICS	3	373	88	*
142	ApoE deficiency	APOE	gCGC-TGC	Arg-Cys	158	Funke	CLIN CHEM	32	1285	86	*
143	ApoE deficiency	APOE	gGAG-AAG	Glu-Lys	244	Tajima	J BIOCHEM	105	249	89	
144	ApoE4 Philadelphia	APOE4	cGAG-AAG	Glu-Lys	13	Lohse	JBC	266	10479	91	*
145	Apobetalipoprotein.	APOB	cCAG-TAG	Gln-Term	2252	Hardman	JCI	88	1722	91	
146	Argin. succ. lyase def.	ASAL	cCGC-TGC	Arg-Cys	95	Walker	PNAS	87	9625	90	*
147	Arylsulphat. A def.	ARSA	AAT-AGT	Asn-Ser	350	Gieselmann	PNAS	86	9436	89	
148	Arylsulphat. A pseud.	ARSAPD	TCC-TTC	Ser-Phe	96	Gieselman	AJHG	49	407	91	
149	Aspartylglucosamin.	AGA	GGC-GAC	Gly-Asp	60	Ikonen	PNAS	88	11222	91	*
150	Aspartylglucosamin.	AGA	CGG-CAG	Arg-Gln	61	Mononen	PNAS	88	2941	91	
151	Aspartylglucosamin.	AGA	GCA-GTA	Ala-Val	101	Ikonen	PNAS	88	11222	91	
152	Aspartylglucosamin.	AGA	CGG-CAG	Arg-Gln	161	Fisher	JBC	266	12105	91	*
153	Aspartylglucosamin.	AGA	TGC-TCC	Cys-Ser	163	Fisher	JBC	266	12105	91	
154	Aspartylglucosamin.	AGA	tGGG-AGG	Gly-Arg	302	Ikonen	PNAS	88	11222	91	
155	Aspartylglucosamin.	AGA	aTGT-CGT	Cys-Arg	306	Ikonen	PNAS	88	11222	91	
156	Bernard Soulier syn.	GP1BA	cCTC-TTC	Leu-Phe	57	Miller	BLOOD	79	439	92	
157	Bernard Soulier syn.	GP1BA	TGGa-TGA	Trp-Term	343	Ware	PNAS	87	2026	90	
158	Carb. anhydrase def.	CA2	gCAT-TAT	His-Tyr	107	Venta	AJHG	49	1082	91	
159	Cardiomyop. hypertro.	MYHCB	CGA-CAA	Arg-Gln	249	Rosenzweig	NEJM	325	1754	91	*
160	Cardiomyop. hypertro.	MYHCB	CGG-CAG	Arg-Gln	403	Geistrf.L.	CELL	62	999	90	*
161	Cardiomyop. hypertro.	MYHCB	aCGC-TGC	Arg-Cys	453	Watkins	NEJM	326	1108	92	*
162	Cardiomyop. hypertro.	MYHCB	cGGC-CGC	Gly-Arg	584	Watkins	NEJM	326	1108	92	
163	Cardiomyop. hypertro.	MYHCB	cGTG-ATG	Val-Met	606	Watkins	NEJM	326	1108	92	*
164	Cardiomyop. hypertro.	MYHCB	cGAG-AAG	Glu-Lys	924	Watkins	NEJM	326	1108	92	*

No.	Disease	Gene	DNA change	AA change	Codon	Author	Journal	Vol	Page	Year	
165	Cardiomyop. hypertro.	MYHCB	aGAG-AAG	Glu-Lys	949	Watkins	NEJM	326	1108	92	*
166	Centr. diabet. insip.	NP2	cGGG-AGC	Gly-Ser	57	Ito	JCI	87	725	91	
167	Cerebrot. xanthomat.	CYP27	gCGT-TGT	Arg-Cys	362	Cali	JBC	266	7779	91	*
168	Cerebrot. xanthomat.	CYP27	cCGC-TGC	Arg-Cys	446	Cali	JBC	266	7779	91	*
169	Chron. obstr. pulm. dis.	A2M	TGT-TAT	Cys-Tyr	972	Poller	HUM GENET	88	313	92	
170	Chron. obstr. pulm. dis.	A2M	gGTC-ATC	Val-Ile	1000	Poller	HUM GENET	88	313	92	
171	Chr. granulomat. dis.	CYBB	CCC-CAC	Pro-His	415	Dinauer	JCI	84	2012	89	*
172	Chr. granulomat. dis.	CYBB91	tCGA-TGA	Arg-Term	73	Bolscher	BLOOD	77	2482	91	
173	Chr. granulomat. dis.	CYBB91	CAT-CGT	His-Arg	101	Bolscher	BLOOD	77	2482	91	
174	Chr. granulomat. dis.	CYBB22	tGCT-ACT	Ala-Thr	156	Bolscher	BLOOD	77	2482	91	
175	Chr. granulomat. dis.	CYBB91	CCG-CAG	Pro-Gln	156	Dinauer	PNAS	88	11231	91	
176	Chr. granulomat. dis.	CYBB91	aCAT-TAT	His-Tyr	209	Bolscher	BLOOD	77	2482	91	
177	Chr. granulomat. dis.	CYBB91	TGT-TCT	Cys-Ser	244	Bolscher	BLOOD	77	2482	91	
178	Chr. granulomat. dis.	CYBB91	GGG-GCG	Gly-Ala	389	Bolscher	BLOOD	77	2482	91	
179	Chylomicronaemia	LPL	CCG-CTG	Pro-Leu	207	Ma	NEJM	324	1761	91	
180	Citrullinaemia	ASS	cGGC-AGC	Gly-Ser	14	Kobayashi	JBC	265	11361	90	*
181	Citrullinaemia	ASS	TCG-TTG	Ser-Leu	18	Kobayashi	MBM	8	95	91	*
182	Citrullinaemia	ASS	cCGC-TGC	Arg-Cys	86	Kobayashi	MBM	8	95	91	*
183	Citrullinaemia	ASS	CGC-CAC	Arg-His	157	Kobayashi	JBC	265	11361	90	*
184	Citrullinaemia	ASS	AGC-AAC	Ser-Asn	180	Kobayashi	JBC	265	11361	90	*
185	Citrullinaemia	ASS	cCGG-TGG	Arg-Trp	304	Kobayashi	JBC	265	11361	90	*
186	Citrullinaemia	ASS	cGGT-AGT	Gly-Ser	324	Kobayashi	JBC	265	11361	90	*
187	Citrullinaemia	ASS	cCGG-TGG	Arg-Trp	363	Kobayashi	JBC	265	11361	90	*
188	Citrullinaemia	ASS	cGGG-AGG	Gly-Arg	390	Kobayashi	JBC	265	11361	90	*
189	Corneal dystrophy(2)	GSN	cGAC-AAC	Asp-Asn	187	Gorevic	NEJM	325	1780	91	*
190	Creutzf.-Jakob syn.	PRP	cGAC-AAC	Asp-Asn	178	Goldfarb	LANCET	337	425	91	*
191	Creutzf.-Jakob syn.	PRP	cGAG-AAG	Glu-Lys	200	Goldgaber	EXP NEUROL	106	204	89	
192	Cystic fibrosis	CFTR	GGA-GAA	Gly-Glu	85	Zielenski	GENOMICS	10	229	91	
193	Cystic fibrosis	CFTR	tGAC-CAC	Asp-His	110	Dean	CELL	61	863	90	
194	Cystic fibrosis	CFTR	CGC-CAC	Arg-His	117	Dean	CELL	61	863	90	
195	Cystic fibrosis	CFTR	tGGA-AGA	Gly-Arg	178	Zielenski	GENOMICS	10	229	91	
196	Cystic fibrosis	CFTR	CGC-CCC	Arg-Pro	327	Dean	CELL	61	863	90	
197	Cystic fibrosis	CFTR	cCGG-TGG	Arg-Trp	334	Gasparini	GENOMICS	10	193	91	
198	Cystic fibrosis	CFTR	GCG-GAG	Ala-Glu	455	Kerem	PNAS	87	8447	90	
199	Cystic fibrosis	CFTR	tCAG-TAG	Gln-Term	493	Kerem	PNAS	87	8447	90	
200	Cystic fibrosis	CFTR	tATC-GTC	Ile-Val	506	Kobayashi	AJHG	47	611	90	*
201	Cystic fibrosis	CFTR	TTT-TGT	Phe-Cys	508	Kobayashi	AJHG	47	611	90	
202	Cystic fibrosis	CFTR	cGTC-TTC	Val-Phe	520	Jones	HMG	1	11	92	*

Single base-pair substitutions causing human genetic disease (continued)

No.	Disease state	Gene symbol	Base change	Amino acid	Codon	Author	Journal	Vol.	Page	Year	CG
203	Cystic fibrosis	CFTR	TGCc-TGA	Cys-Term	524	Jones	HMG	1	11	92	
204	Cystic fibrosis	CFTR	tGGa-TGA	Gly-Term	542	Kerem	PNAS	87	8447	90	
205	Cystic fibrosis	CFTR	AGT-ATT	Ser-Ile	549	Kerem	PNAS	87	8447	90	
206	Cystic fibrosis	CFTR	AGT-AAT	Ser-Asn	549	Cutting	NATURE	346	366	90	
207	Cystic fibrosis	CFTR	AGTg-AGG	Ser-Arg	549	Kerem	PNAS	87	8447	90	
208	Cystic fibrosis	CFTR	gAGT-CGT	Ser-Arg	549	Sangiuolo	GENOMICS	9	788	91	
209	Cystic fibrosis	CFTR	GGT-GAT	Gly-Asp	551	Kerem	PNAS	87	8447	90	
210	Cystic fibrosis	CFTR	tCAA-TAA	Gln-Term	552	Devoto	AJHG	48	1127	91	
211	Cystic fibrosis	CFTR	aCGA-TGA	Arg-Term	553	Cutting	NATURE	346	366	90	*
212	Cystic fibrosis	CFTR	aGCA-ACA	Ala-Thr	559	Cutting	NATURE	346	366	90	
213	Cystic fibrosis	CFTR	AGA-ACA	Arg-Thr	560	Kerem	PNAS	87	8447	90	
214	Cystic fibrosis	CFTR	aTAC-AAC	Tyr-Asn	563	Kerem	PNAS	87	8447	90	
215	Cystic fibrosis	CFTR	CCT-CAT	Pro-His	574	Kerem	PNAS	87	8447	90	
216	Cystic fibrosis	CFTR	TGGa-TGA	Trp-Term	846	Vidaud	HUM GENET	85	446	90	*
217	Cystic fibrosis	CFTR	tCGA-TGA	Arg-Term	851	White	GENOMICS	11	778	91	
218	Cystic fibrosis	CFTR	TAT-TGT	Tyr-Cys	913	Vidaud	HUM GENET	85	446	90	* *
219	Cystic fibrosis	CFTR	gCGA-TGA	Arg-Term	1158	Ronchetto	GENOMICS	12	417	92	* *
220	Cystic fibrosis	CFTR	cCGA-TGA	Arg-Term	1162	Gasparini	GENOMICS	10	193	91	
221	Cystic fibrosis	CFTR	GGA-GAA	Gly-Glu	1244	Devoto	AJHG	48	1127	91	
222	Cystic fibrosis	CFTR	TGGa-TGA	Trp-Term	1282	Kerem	PNAS	87	8447	90	
223	Cystic fibrosis	CFTR	CAGa-CAC	Gln-His	1291	Jones	HMG	1	11	92	
224	Cystic fibrosis	CFTR	AACt-AAG	Asn-Lys	1303	Osborne	AJHG	48	608	91	
225	Diabetes insipidus	ARVP	GGC-GTC	Gly-Val	17	Bahnsen	EMBO J	11	19	92	* *
226	Diabetes (ins. res.)	INSR	AGGt-AGT	Arg-Ser	735	Yoshimasa	SCIENCE	240	784	88	
227	Diabetes (ins. res.)	INSR	TGG-TCG	Trp-Ser	1200	Moller	NEJM	319	1526	88	
228	Diabetes (MODY)	INS	TTC-TCC	Phe-Ser	24	Haneda	PNAS	80	6366	83	
229	Diabetes (NIDDM)	GLUT4	cGTC-ATC	Val-Ile	383	Kusari	JCI	88	1323	91	
230	Diabetes (NIDDM)	INSR	cGTG-ATG	Val-Met	985	O'Rahilly	DIABETES	40	777	91	
231	Diabetes (NIDDM)	INSR	GGC-GTC	Gly-Val	996	Odawara	SCIENCE	245	66	89	
232	Diabetes (NIDDM)	INSR	cAAG-GAG	Lys-Glu	1068	O'Rahilly	DIABETES	40	777	91	
233	Duchenne musc. dystr.	DMD	aGAG-TAG	Glu-Term	931	Roberts	PNAS	89	2331	92	
234	Duchenne musc. dystr.	DMD	aCAG-TAG	Gln-Term	1851	Roberts	PNAS	89	2331	92	

No.	Disorder	Gene	Codon change	Amino acid	Position	Author	Journal	Vol	Page	Year	*
235	Duchenne musc. dystr.	DMD	tCGA-TGA	Arg-Term	2982	Roberts	PNAS	89	2331	92	*
236	Duchenne musc. dystr.	DMD	tCGA-TGA	Arg-Term	3370	Roberts	PNAS	89	2331	92	*
237	Duchenne musc. dystr.	DMD	gGAG-TAG	Glu-Term	3677	Bulman	GENOMICS	10	457	91	
238	Dysbetalipoprotein.	APOE	gTGC-CGC	Cys-Arg	112	Smit	JLR	31	45	90	
239	Dysbetalipoprotein.	APOE	tAAG-CAG	Lys-Gln	146	Smit	JLR	31	45	90	
240	Ehlers-Danlos	COL3A1	GGC-GAC	Gly-Asp	883	Tromp	JBC	264	19313	89	
241	Ehlers-Danlos IV	COL3A1	gGGT-AGT	Gly-Ser	790	Tromp	JBC	264	1349	89	
242	Ehlers-Danlos IV	COL3A1	GGT-GTT	Gly-Val	910	Richards	JMG	28	458	91	
243	Ehlers-Danlos VII	COL1A1	ATGg-ATA	Met-Ile	159	Weil	EMBO J	8	1705	89	
244	Elliptocytosis	SPTA	CGT-CAT	Arg-His	22	Garbarz	BLOOD	75	1691	90	*
245	Elliptocytosis	SPTA	gCGT-AGT	Arg-Ser	28	Floyd	BLOOD	78	1364	91	
246	Elliptocytosis	SPTA	gCGT-TGT	Arg-Cys	28	Coetzer	JCI	88	743	91	*
247	Elliptocytosis	SPTA	CGT-CTT	Arg-Leu	28	Floyd	BLOOD	78	1364	91	
248	Elliptocytosis	SPTA	gCGG-TGG	Arg-Trp	35	Morle	BLOOD	74	828	89	*
249	Elliptocytosis	SPTA	AGGg-AGT	Arg-Ser	39	Lecomte	BLOOD	74	1126	89	
250	Elliptocytosis	SPTA	GGT-GTT	Gly-Val	40	Morle	JCI	86	548	90	
251	Elliptocytosis	SPTA	gCTT-TTT	Leu-Phe	43	Morle	JCI	86	548	90	
252	Elliptocytosis	SPTA	AAG-AGG	Lys-Arg	48	Floyd	BLOOD	78	1364	91	
253	Elliptocytosis	SPTA	CTG-CCG	Leu-Pro	207	Gallagher	JCI	89	892	92	
254	Elliptocytosis	SPTA	CAG-CCG	Gln-Pro	465	Sahr	JCI	84	1243	89	
255	Elliptocytosis	SPTA2	gGCT-CCT	Ala-Pro	2053	Tse	JCI	86	909	90	*
256	Epidermolysis bull.	KRT14	cCGC-TGC	Arg-Cys	125	Coulombe	CELL	66	1301	91	*
257	Epidermolysis bull.	KRT14	CGC-CAC	Arg-His	125	Coulombe	CELL	66	1301	91	
258	Epidermolysis bull.	KRT14	CTG-CCG	Leu-Pro	384	Bonfias	SCIENCE	254	1202	91	
259	Erythropoietic prot.	FECH	gGGT-TGT	Gly-Cys	55	Lamoril	BBRC	181	594	91	
260	Erythropoietic prot.	FECH	ATGt-ATA	Met-Ile	267	Lamoril	BBRC	181	594	91	*
261	Euthyroid hyp. thyr.	PALB	cGCC-ACC	Ala-Thr	109	Moses	JCI	86	2025	90	
262	Fabry disease	GLA	gCCT-TCT	Pro-Ser	40	Koide	FEBS LETTS	259	353	90	
263	Fabry disease	GLA	TGG-TAG	Trp-Term	44	Sakuraba	AJHG	47	784	90	
264	Fabry disease	GLA	cATG-GTG	Met-Val	296	v.Scheidt	NEJM	324	395	91	*
265	Fabry disease	GLA	CGA-CAA	Arg-Gln	301	Sakuraba	AJHG	47	784	90	*
266	Fabry disease	GLA	cCGG-TGG	Arg-Trp	356	Berstein	JCI	83	1390	89	
267	Factor VII defic.	F7	CGG-CAG	Arg-Gln	79	Chaing	BLOOD	76	417a	90	*
268	Factor VII defic.	F7	AGG-AAG	Arg-Lys	152	Chaing	TH	65	1262	91	
269	Factor VII defic.	F7	CGG-CAG	Arg-Gln	304	O'Brien	BLOOD	78	132	91	*
270	Factor X defic.	F10	cGAA-AAA	Glu-Lys	14	Watzke	JBC	265	11982	90	*
271	Factor X defic.	F10	tCCC-TCC	Pro-Ser	343	James	BLOOD	77	317	90	
272	Factor X defic.	F10	gCGC-TGC	Arg-Cys	366	Reddy	BLOOD	74	1486	89	*

Single base-pair substitutions causing human genetic disease (continued)

No.	Disease state	Gene symbol	Base change	Amino acid	Codon	Author	Journal	Vol.	Page	Year	CG
273	Factor XI defic.	F11	aGAA-TAA	Glu-Term	117	Asakai	PNAS	86	7667	89	
274	Factor XI defic.	F11	tTTC-CTC	Phe-Leu	283	Asakai	PNAS	86	7667	89	
275	Fibrinogen defic.	FGG	GGC-GTC	Gly-Val	292	Bantia	BLOOD	76	2279	90	
276	Fibrinogen defic.	FGG	AATg-AAG	Asn-Lys	308	Muramatsu	TH	65	821	91	
277	Fibrinogen defic.	FGG	ATG-ACG	Met-Thr	310	Yamazumi	pers.comm.				
278	Fibrinogen defic.	FGG	gGAT-TAT	Asp-Tyr	330	Terukina	BLOOD	74	2681	89	
279	Fish-eye disease	LCAT	ACA-ATA	Thr-Ile	123	Funke	PNAS	88	4855	91	
280	Fish-eye disease	LCAT	ACG-ATG	Thr-Met	347	Klein	JCI	89	499	92	*
281	Fructose intolerance	ALDB	GCC-GAC	Ala-Asp	174	Cross	LANCET	335	306	90	
282	Fructose intolerance	ALDB	TGCa-TGA	Cys-Term	240	Kajihara	AJHG	47	562	90	
283	Fructose intolerance	ALDB	AACt-AAG	Asn-Lys	334	Cross	NAR	18	1925	90	
284	G6PD deficiency	G6PD	CAC-CGC	His-Arg	32	Chao	NAR	19	6056	91	
285	G6PD deficiency	G6PD	cGCC-ACC	Ala-Thr	33	Vulliamy	PNAS	85	5171	88	*
286	G6PD deficiency	G6PD	gGAT-AAT	Asp-Asn	57	Vulliamy	PNAS	85	5171	88	
287	G6PD deficiency	G6PD	cGTG-ATG	Val-Met	67	Vulliamy	PNAS	85	5171	88	*
288	G6PD deficiency	G6PD	gAAT-GAT	Asn-Asp	125	Vulliamy	PNAS	85	5171	88	
289	G6PD deficiency	G6PD	cGAG-AAG	Glu-Lys	156	Vulliamy	PNAS	85	5171	88	*
290	G6PD deficiency	G6PD	aGGC-AGC	Gly-Ser	163	Vulliamy	NAR	17	5868	89	
291	G6PD deficiency	G6PD	gAAC-GAC	Asn-Asp	165	Tang	BLOOD	79	2135	92	
292	G6PD deficiency	G6PD	TCC-TTC	Ser-Phe	188	Vulliamy	PNAS	85	5171	88	*
293	G6PD deficiency	G6PD	cCGC-TGC	Arg-Cys	198	Corcoran	HUM GENET	88	688	92	
294	G6PD deficiency	G6PD	gGTG-CTG	Val-Leu	213	Beutler	JBC	266	4145	91	
295	G6PD deficiency	G6PD	aGAT-CAT	Asp-His	282	De Vita	AJHG	44	233	89	
296	G6PD deficiency	G6PD	AACg-AAA	Asn-Lys	363	Beutler	JBC	266	4145	91	
297	G6PD deficiency	G6PD	CGC-CAC	Arg-His	393	Beutler	JBC	266	4145	91	
298	G6PD deficiency	G6PD	cGAG-AAG	Glu-Lys	416	Hirono	HUM GENET	88	347	92	
299	G6PD deficiency	G6PD	cGGG-AGG	Gly-Arg	446	Vulliamy	PNAS	85	5171	88	
300	G6PD deficiency	G6PD	CGT-CTT	Arg-Leu	459	Chiu	BBRC	180	988	91	
301	G6PD deficiency	G6PD	CGT-CAT	Arg-His	463	Chiu	BBRC	180	988	91	
302	G6PD deficiency	G6PD	CGC-CAC	Arg-His	533	Vives-Cor.	AJHG	47	575	90	* *
303	G6PD deficiency	G6PD	CGG-CTG	Arg-Leu	680	Beutler	BLOOD	74	2550	89	* *
304	G6PD deficiency	G6PD	CTG-CCG	Leu-Pro	968	Beutler	BLOOD	74	2550	89	* *

No.	Disease	Gene	DNA	Amino acid	Codon	Author	Journal	Vol	Page	Year	*
305	Galactosaemia	GALT	gGTG-ATG	Val–Met	44	Reichardt	PNAS	88	2633	91	*
306	Galactosaemia	GALT	ATG-AAG	Met–Lys	142	Reichardt	PNAS	88	2633	91	
307	Galactosaemia	GALT	cCGG-TGG	Arg–Trp	148	Reichardt	GENOMICS	12	596	92	
308	Galactosaemia	GALT	CAG-CGG	Gln–Arg	188	Reichardt	AJHG	49	860	91	*
309	Galactosaemia	GALT	CTG-CCG	Leu–Pro	195	Reichardt	GENOMICS	12	596	92	
310	Galactosaemia	GALT	cCGG-TGG	Arg–Trp	333	Reichardt	AJHG	49	860	91	*
311	Galactosialidosis	CPSA	cTTC-GTC	Phe–Val	412	Zhou	EMBO J	10	4041	91	
312	Gangliosidosis GM1	GLB1	tCGC-TGC	Arg–Cys	49	Nishimoto	AJHG	49	566	91	*
313	Gangliosidosis GM1	GLB1	ATC-ACC	Ile–Thr	51	Yoshida	AJHG	49	435	91	
314	Gangliosidosis GM1	GLB1	tGGG-AGG	Gly–Arg	123	Yoshida	AJHG	49	435	91	
315	Gangliosidosis GM1	GLB1	gCGC-TGC	Arg–Cys	201	Yoshida	AJHG	49	435	91	
316	Gangliosidosis GM1	GLB1	TAT-TGT	Tyr–Cys	316	Yoshida	AJHG	49	566	91	*
317	Gangliosidosis GM1	GLB1	gCGA-TGA	Arg–Term	457	Nishimoto	AJHG	49	435	91	*
318	Gangliosidosis GM2	GLB1	CGA-CAA	Arg–Gln	457	Yoshida	AJHG	49	435	91	
319	Gangliosidosis GM2	GLB1	cTGT-CGT	Cys–Arg	107	Schroeder	FEBS LETTS	290	1	91	*
320	Gangliosidosis GM2	HEXB	CGC-CAC	Arg–His	178	Ohno	AJHG	41	A231	87	*
321	Gangliosidosis GM2	HEXB	aGGT-AGT	Gly–Ser	269	Paw	PNAS	86	2413	89	
322	Gangliosidosis GM2	HEXB	CGT-CAT	Arg–His	499	Paw	JBC	265	9452	90	*
323	Gangliosidosis GM2	HEXB	CGC-CAC	Arg–His	504	Paw	JBC	265	9452	90	
324	Gaucher's disease	GBA	TTC-TAC	Phe–Tyr	255	Beutler	AHG	54	149	90	
325	Gaucher's disease	GBA	tGCT-CCT	Ala–Pro	456	Latham	AJHG	47	79	90	*
326	Gaucher's disease	GBA	cCGC-TGC	Arg–Cys	463	Hong	DNA	9	233	90	*
327	Gaucher's disease	GBA	CGG-CAG	Arg–Gln	119	Graves	DNA	7	521	88	
328	Gaucher's disease (1)	GBA	tGAT-CAT	Asp–His	140	Eyal	HUM GENET	87	328	91	
329	Gaucher's disease (1)	GBA	GCT-GTT	Ala–Val	309	Latham	DNA	10	15	91	
330	Gaucher's disease (1)	GBA	TGGt-TGT	Trp–Cys	312	Latham	DNA	10	15	91	
331	Gaucher's disease (1)	GBA	gGAG-AAG	Glu–Lys	326	Eyal	HUM GENET	87	328	91	
332	Gaucher's disease (1)	GBA	AGC-ACC	Ser–Thr	364	Latham	DNA	10	15	91	
333	Gaucher's disease (1)	GBA	AAC-AGC	Asn–Ser	370	Tsuji	PNAS	85	2349	88	
334	Gaucher's disease (1)	GBA	cAAG-CAG	Lys–Gln	157	Latham	DNA	10	15	91	
335	Gaucher's disease (2)	GBA	aGGG-AGG	Gly–Arg	325	Eyal	GENE	96	277	90	
336	Gaucher's disease (2)	GBA	cTGT-GGT	Cys–Gly	342	Eyal	GENE	96	277	90	
337	Gaucher's disease (2)	GBA	gGAC-CAC	Asp–His	409	Eyal	GENE	96	277	90	
338	Gaucher's disease (2)	GBA	CCC-CGC	Pro–Arg	415	Widgerson	AJHG	44	365	89	
339	Gaucher's disease (2)	GBA	CTG-CCG	Leu–Pro	444	Tsuji	NEJM	316	570	87	
340	Gaucher's disease (3)	GBA	cTTT-ATT	Phe–Ile	213	Kawame	AJHG	49	1378	91	
341	Gaucher's dis. (atyp)	SAP2	TGC-TTC	Cys–Phe	385	Schnabel	FEBS LETTS	284	57	91	
342	Gerstmann-Str. syn.	PRP	CCG-CTG	Pro–Leu	102	Hsiao	NATURE	338	342	89	*

Single base-pair substitutions causing human genetic disease (continued)

No.	Disease state	Gene symbol	Base change	Amino acid	Codon	Author	Journal	Vol.	Page	Year	CG
343	Gerstmann-Str. syn.	PRP	GCA-GTA	Ala-Val	117	Doh-Ura	BBRC	163	974	89	
344	Gerstmann-Str. syn.	PRP	cATG-GTG	Met-Val	129	Doh-Ura	BBRC	163	974	89	*
345	Glanzmann thrombast.	GP3A	CGG-CAG	Arg-Gln	214	Bajt	JBC	267	3789	92	
346	Glucocorticoid res.	GR	GAC-GTC	Asp-Val	641	Hurley	JCI	87	680	91	
347	Glutaric acidaemia 2	ETF	GTG-GGG	Val-Gly	157	Indo	AJHG	49	575	91	*
348	Glycogenesis 2	GAA	cGAG-AAG	Glu-Lys	521	Hermans	BBRC	179	919	91	
349	Günther's disease	CPS	CCT-CTT	Pro-Leu	53	Deybach	BLOOD	75	1763	90	
350	Günther's disease	CPS	aTGT-CGT	Cys-Arg	73	Deybach	BLOOD	75	1763	90	
351	Gyrate atrophy	OAT	ATGt-ATA	Met-Ile	-1	Mitchell	JCI	81	630	88	
352	Gyrate atrophy	OAT	ATGt-ATA	Met-Ile	1	Brody	JBC	267	3302	92	
353	Gyrate atrophy	OAT	AACt-AAA	Asn-Lys	54	Ramesh	PNAS	85	3777	88	
354	Gyrate atrophy	OAT	cTAC-CAC	Tyr-His	55	Brody	JBC	267	3302	92	
355	Gyrate atrophy	OAT	AACc-AAA	Asn-Lys	89	Brody	JBC	267	3302	92	
356	Gyrate atrophy	OAT	TGT-TTT	Cys-Phe	93	Brody	JBC	267	3302	92	
357	Gyrate atrophy	OAT	CGT-CTT	Arg-Leu	154	Brody	JBC	267	3302	92	
358	Gyrate atrophy	OAT	AGG-ACG	Arg-Thr	180	Mitchell	PNAS	86	197	89	*
359	Gyrate atrophy	OAT	CCA-CAA	Pro-Gln	199	Kaufman	GENOMICS	8	656	90	
360	Gyrate atrophy	OAT	CCG-CTG	Pro-Leu	241	Brody	JBC	267	3302	92	
361	Gyrate atrophy	OAT	TAC-TGC	Tyr-Cys	245	Brody	JBC	267	3302	92	
362	Gyrate atrophy	OAT	CGA-CCA	Arg-Pro	250	Brody	JBC	267	3302	92	
363	Gyrate atrophy	OAT	ACA-ATA	Thr-Ile	267	Brody	JBC	267	3302	92	
364	Gyrate atrophy	OAT	gGCC-CCC	Ala-Pro	270	Brody	JBC	267	3302	92	
365	Gyrate atrophy	OAT	AGA-AAA	Arg-Lys	271	Brody	JBC	267	3302	92	
366	Gyrate atrophy	OAT	gCAT-TAT	His-Tyr	319	Inana	JBC	264	17432	89	
367	Gyrate atrophy	OAT	aGTG-ATG	Val-Met	332	Ramesh	PNAS	85	3777	88	
368	Gyrate atrophy	OAT	GGC-GAC	Gly-Asp	353	Brody	JBC	267	3302	92	
369	Gyrate atrophy	OAT	GGA-GCA	Gly-Ala	375	Brody	JBC	267	3302	92	
370	Gyrate atrophy	OAT	gTGT-CGT	Cys-Arg	394	Brody	JBC	267	3302	92	*
371	Gyrate atrophy	OAT	aCGA-TGA	Arg-Term	396	Brody	JBC	267	3302	92	*
372	Gyrate atrophy	OAT	tGGA-TGA	Gly-Term	401	Brody	JBC	267	3302	92	
373	Gyrate atrophy	OAT	CTT-CCT	Leu-Pro	402	Mitchell	PNAS	86	197	89	
374	Gyrate atrophy	OAT	CCG-CTG	Pro-Leu	417	Brody	JBC	267	3302	92	*

No.	Disease	Gene	Change	AA change	Codon	Author	Journal	Vol	Page	Year
375	Gyrate atrophy	OAT	TTGt-TTT	Leu-Phe	437	Brody	JBC	267	3302	92
376	HPRT deficiency	HPRT	ATGg-ATA	Met-Ile	-1	Tarle	GENOMICS	10	499	91
377	HPRT deficiency	HPRT	GGC-GAC	Gly-Asp	6	Davidson	AJHG	48	951	91
378	HPRT deficiency	HPRT	aGGT-AGT	Gly-Ser	16	Sculley	HUM GENET	87	688	91
379	HPRT deficiency	HPRT	GAT-GTT	Asp-Val	19	Davidson	AJHG	48	951	91
380	HPRT deficiency	HPRT	CTA-CCA	Leu-Pro	40	Davidson	JCI	84	342	89
381	HPRT deficiency	HPRT	ATT-ACT	Ile-Thr	41	Davidson	AJHG	48	951	91
382	HPRT deficiency	HPRT	AGG-AAG	Arg-Lys	44	Gibbs	GENOMICS	7	235	90
383	HPRT deficiency	HPRT	GCT-GTT	Ala-Val	49	Tarle	GENOMICS	10	499	91
384	HPRT deficiency	HPRT	tCGA-GGA	Arg-Gly	50	Wilson	JCI	72	767	83
385	HPRT deficiency	HPRT	tCGA-TGA	Arg-Term	50	Fujimori	HUM GENET	84	483	90
386	HPRT deficiency	HPRT	CGA-CCA	Arg-Pro	50	Davidson	AJHG	48	951	91
387	HPRT deficiency	HPRT	GAT-GGT	Asp-Gly	52	Lightfoot	HUM GENET	88	695	92
388	HPRT deficiency	HPRT	ATG-ACG	Met-Thr	56	Skopeck	HUM GENET	85	111	90
389	HPRT deficiency	HPRT	gGGA-AGA	Gly-Arg	58	Sculley	HUM GENET	87	688	91
390	HPRT deficiency	HPRT	GGG-GAG	Gly-Glu	69	Davidson	JCI	84	342	89
391	HPRT deficiency	HPRT	gGGC-CGC	Gly-Arg	70	Fujimori	JCI	83	11	89
392	HPRT deficiency	HPRT	TTCt-TTA	Phe-Leu	73	Gibbs	PNAS	86	1919	89
393	HPRT deficiency	HPRT	TTCt-TTA	Phe-Leu	74	Sculley	HUM GENET	87	688	91
394	HPRT deficiency	HPRT	cCTG-GTG	Leu-Val	78	Sculley	HUM GENET	87	688	91
395	HPRT deficiency	HPRT	GAT-GTT	Asp-Val	79	Davidson	JCI	84	342	89
396	HPRT deficiency	HPRT	AGCt-AGA	Ser-Arg	103	Cariello	AJHG	42	726	88
397	HPRT deficiency	HPRT	cCAG-TAG	Gln-Term	108	Gibbs	GENOMICS	7	235	90
398	HPRT deficiency	HPRT	TCA-TTA	Ser-Leu	109	Davidson	JCI	82	2164	88
399	HPRT deficiency	HPRT	GTC-GAC	Val-Asp	129	Davidson	GENE	68	85	88
400	HPRT deficiency	HPRT	TTG-TCG	Leu-Ser	130	Gibbs	PNAS	86	1919	89
401	HPRT deficiency	HPRT	ATTg-ATG	Ile-Met	131	Fujimori	HUM GENET	79	39	88
402	HPRT deficiency	HPRT	ATT-ACT	Ile-Thr	131	Davidson	AJHG	48	951	91
403	HPRT deficiency	HPRT	cGCA-TCA	Ala-Ser	160	Gibbs	PNAS	86	1919	89
404	HPRT deficiency	HPRT	AGCt-AGG	Ser-Arg	161	Davidson	AJHG	48	951	91
405	HPRT deficiency	HPRT	ACC-ATC	Thr-Ile	168	Gordon	JIMD	13	692	90
406	HPRT deficiency	HPRT	cCGA-TGA	Arg-Term	169	Gibbs	PNAS	86	1919	89
407	HPRT deficiency	HPRT	CCA-CTA	Pro-Leu	175	Davidson	AJHG	48	951	91
408	HPRT deficiency	HPRT	aGAC-TAC	Asp-Tyr	176	Gibbs	GENOMICS	7	235	90
409	HPRT deficiency	HPRT	ATT-ACT	Ile-Thr	182	Tarle	GENOMICS	10	499	91
410	HPRT deficiency	HPRT	tGAC-AAC	Asp-Asn	193	Gibbs	GENOMICS	7	235	90
411	HPRT deficiency	HPRT	cTTC-GTC	Phe-Val	198	Gibbs	PNAS	86	1919	89
412	HPRT deficiency	HPRT	GAT-GGT	Asp-Gly	200	Davidson	JBC	264	520	89

Single base-pair substitutions causing human genetic disease (continued)

No.	Disease state	Gene symbol	Base change	Amino acid	Codon	Author	Journal	Vol.	Page	Year	CG
413	HPRT deficiency	HPRT	tCAT-GAT	His-Asp	203	Gibbs	PNAS	86	1919	88	
414	HPRT deficiency	HPRT	CAT-CGT	His-Arg	203	Tarle	GENOMICS	10	499	91	
415	HPRT deficiency	HPRT	TGT-TAT	Cys-Tyr	205	Gibbs	PNAS	86	1919	89	
416	Haemoglobin A2-Wrens	HBD	cGTG-ATG	Val-Met	98	Codrington	BBA	1009	87	89	*
417	Haemoglobin Chesterf	HBB	CTG-CGG	Leu-Arg	28	Thein	BLOOD	77	2791	91	
418	Haemoglobin D Los Ang	HBB	aGAA-CAA	Glu-Gln	121	Schnee	HUM GENET	84	365	90	
419	Haemoglobin J Mexico	HBA2	cCAG-GAG	Gln-Glu	54	Dode	BJH	76	275	90	
420	Haemoglobin LongIsl.	HBB	CAC-CCC	His-Pro	2	Prchal	PNAS	83	24	86	
421	Haemoglobin Malta	HBB	CAT-CGT	His-Arg	117	Kutlar	HUM GENET	86	591	91	
422	Haemoglobin Neapolis	HBB	GTG-GGG	Val-Gly	126	Pagano	BLOOD	78	3070	91	
423	Haemoglobin Presbyt.	HBB	AACg-AAG	Asn-Lys	108	Schnee	HUM GENET	84	365	90	
424	Haemoglobin Stnvil.2	HBA2	AACg-AAA	Asn-Lys	78	Dode	BJH	76	275	90	
425	Haemoglobin Westmead	HBA2	CACg-CAG	His-Gln	122	Jiang	HEMOGLOBIN	15	291	91	
426	Haemoglobin Yahata	HBB	TGT-TAT	Cys-Tyr	112	Harano	HEMOGLOBIN	15	109	91	
427	Haemolytic anaemia	P42	cGCT-ACT	Ala-Thr	142	Bouhassira	BLOOD	79	1848	92	*
428	Haemolytic anaemia	PGK	CTG-CCG	Leu-Pro	88	Maeda	BLOOD	77	1348	91	
429	Haemolytic anaemia	PKR	cCGC-TGC	Arg-Cys	132	Neubauer	BLOOD	77	1871	91	*
430	Haemolytic anaemia	PKR	ACG-ATG	Thr-Met	353	Neubauer	BLOOD	77	1871	91	*
431	Haemolytic anaemia	PKR	ACG-ATG	Thr-Met	384	Kanno	PNAS	88	8218	91	*
432	Haemolytic anaemia	PKR	gCAG-AAG	Gln-Lys	421	Kanno	BLOOD	79	1347	92	*
433	Haemophilia A	F8	gCGA-TGA	Arg-Term	-5	Pattinson	unpub.res.	76	2242	90	*
434	Haemophilia A	F8	GAA-GTA	Glu-Val	11	Gitschier	unpub.res.				
435	Haemophilia A	F8	AAG-ACG	Lys-Thr	89	Higuchi	PNAS	88	7405	91	
436	Haemophilia A	F8	cATG-GTG	Met-Val	91	Higuchi	PNAS	88	7405	91	
437	Haemophilia A	F8	tGTG-ATG	Val-Met	162	Gitschier	unpub.res.				
438	Haemophilia A	F8	AAA-ACA	Lys-Thr	166	Higuchi	PNAS	88	8307	91	
439	Haemophilia A	F8	TCA-TTA	Ser-Leu	170	Chan	BLOOD	74	2688	89	
440	Haemophilia A	F8	TGGc-TGA	Trp-Term	255	Antonarakis	unpub.res.				
441	Haemophilia A	F8	GTG-GGG	Val-Gly	266	Higuchi	PNAS	88	7405	91	
442	Haemophilia A	F8	GAA-GGA	Glu-Gly	272	Youssoufia	AJHG	42	867	88	
443	Haemophilia A	F8	CGC-CAC	Arg-His	282	Higuchi	PNAS	88	7405	91	
444	Haemophilia A	F8	TTC-TCC	Phe-Ser	293	Higuchi	PNAS	88	7405	91	

#	Disease	Gene	Change	Substitution	Codon	Author	Reference	Vol.	Page	Year	*
445	Haemophilia A	F8	tACT-GCT	Thr-Ala	295	Higuchi	PNAS	88	8307	91	*
446	Haemophilia A	F8	aGTA-CTA	Val-Leu	326	Kogan	PNAS	87	2092	90	*
447	Haemophilia A	F8	cTGT-CGT	Cys-Arg	329	Kogan	PNAS	87	2092	90	*
448	Haemophilia A	F8	aCGA-TGA	Arg-Term	336	Gitschier	BLOOD	72	1022	88	
449	Haemophilia A	F8	CGC-CAC	Arg-His	372	Arai	PNAS	86	4277	89	
450	Haemophilia A	F8	tCGC-TGC	Arg-Cys	372	Shima	BLOOD	74	1612	89	
451	Haemophilia A	F8	TTGa-TTT	Leu-Phe	412	Higuchi	PNAS	88	8307	91	*
452	Haemophilia A	F8	AAA-AGA	Lys-Arg	425	Higuchi	PNAS	88	7405	91	
453	Haemophilia A	F8	cCGA-TGA	Arg-Term	427	Pattinson	BLOOD	76	2242	90	
454	Haemophilia A	F8	TAT-CAT	Tyr-His	473	Higuchi	PNAS	88	8307	91	*
455	Haemophilia A	F8	aTAT-CAT	Tyr-His	473	Higuchi	PNAS	88	7405	91	*
456	Haemophilia A	F8	tCGG-TGG	Arg-Trp	527	Higuchi	PNAS	88	8307	91	
457	Haemophilia A	F8	cCGC-TGC	Arg-Cys	531	Higuchi	PNAS	88	8307	91	
458	Haemophilia A	F8	cCGC-GGC	Arg-Gly	531	Higuchi	PNAS	88	8307	91	
459	Haemophilia A	F8	tAGT-GGT	Ser-Gly	535	Antonarakis	unpub.res.				
460	Haemophilia A	F8	GAT-GGT	Asp-Gly	542	Higuchi	PNAS	88	7405	91	
461	Haemophilia A	F8	cCAG-AAG	Gln-Lys	565	Higuchi	PNAS	88	8307	91	
462	Haemophilia A	F8	ATA-ACA	Ile-Thr	566	Antonarakis	unpub.res.				
463	Haemophilia A	F8	tTCT-CCT	Ser-Pro	577	Antonarakis	unpub.res.				*
464	Haemophilia A	F8	cCGA-TGA	Arg-Term	583	Pattinson	BLOOD	76	2242	90	
465	Haemophilia A	F8	AGC-ATC	Ser-Ile	584	Antonarakis	unpub.res.				*
466	Haemophilia A	F8	aCGC-TGC	Arg-Cys	593	Higuchi	PNAS	88	7405	91	
467	Haemophilia A	F8	AAC-AGC	Asn-Ser	612	Antonarakis	unpub.res.				
468	Haemophilia A	F8	GCA-GTA	Ala-Val	644	Higuchi	PNAS	88	8307	91	*
469	Haemophilia A	F8	cGCC-ACC	Ala-Thr	704	Higuchi	PNAS	88	7405	91	
470	Haemophilia A	F8	gCGA-TGA	Arg-Term	795	Pattinson	BLOOD	76	2242	90	*
471	Haemophilia A	F8	tGAG-AAG	Glu-Lys	1038	Higuchi	PNAS	88	8307	91	
472	Haemophilia A	F8	TAT-TTT	Tyr-Phe	1680	Higuchi	GENOMICS	6	65	90	
473	Haemophilia A	F8	TAT-TGT	Tyr-Cys	1680	Traystman	GENOMICS	6	293	90	
474	Haemophilia A	F8	tCAG-TAG	Gln-Term	1686	Higuchi	GENOMICS	6	65	90	*
475	Haemophilia A	F8	cCGC-TGC	Arg-Cys	1689	Gitschier	BLOOD	72	1022	88	
476	Haemophilia A	F8	cGGA-TGA	Arg-Term	1696	Pattinson	BLOOD	76	2242	90	*
477	Haemophilia A	F8	gGAG-AAG	Glu-Lys	1704	Paynton	HUM GENET	87	397	91	
478	Haemophilia A	F8	ATG-ACG	Met-Thr	1772	Antonarakis	unpub.res.				
479	Haemophilia A	F8	CGT-CAT	Arg-His	1781	Higuchi	PNAS	88	7405	91	
480	Haemophilia A	F8	TCC-TAC	Ser-Tyr	1784	Higuchi	PNAS	88	7405	91	*
481	Haemophilia A	F8	aCCC-TCC	Pro-Ser	1825	Higuchi	PNAS	88	8307	91	
482	Haemophilia A	F8	cACT-CCT	Thr-Pro	1826	Antonarakis	unpub.res.				

Single base-pair substitutions causing human genetic disease (continued)

No.	Disease state	Gene symbol	Base change	Amino acid	Codon	Author	Journal	Vol.	Page	Year	CG
483	Haemophilia A	F8	CTGg–CTA	Leu–Leu	1843	Higuchi	PNAS	88	8307	91	
484	Haemophilia A	F8	CAC–CGC	His–Arg	1848	Higuchi	PNAS	88	8307	91	
485	Haemophilia A	F8	cAAT–GAT	Asn–Asp	1922	Traystman	GENOMICS	6	293	90	
486	Haemophilia A	F8	AAT–AGT	Asn–Ser	1922	Higuchi	PNAS	88	7405	91	
487	Haemophilia A	F8	CGA–CTA	Arg–Leu	1941	Nafa	unpub.res.				
488	Haemophilia A	F8	tCGA–TGA	Arg–Term	1941	Youssoufian	NATURE	324	380	86	*
489	Haemophilia A	F8	CGA–CAA	Arg–Gln	1941	Levinson	AJHG	46	53	90	*
490	Haemophilia A	F8	gCGG–TGG	Arg–Trp	1997	Higuchi	PNAS	88	8307	91	*
491	Haemophilia A	F8	TTTa–TTG	Phe–Leu	2101	Higuchi	PNAS	88	8307	91	
492	Haemophilia A	F8	tCGA–TGA	Arg–Term	2116	Youssoufian	NATURE	324	380	86	*
493	Haemophilia A	F8	CGA–CCA	Arg–Pro	2116	Levinson	NAR	15	9797	87	
494	Haemophilia A	F8	TCC–TAC	Ser–Tyr	2119	Higuchi	PNAS	88	8307	91	*
495	Haemophilia A	F8	tCGA–TGA	Arg–Term	2147	Levinson	NAR	15	9797	87	*
496	Haemophilia A	F8	CGT–CAT	Arg–His	2150	Higuchi	PNAS	88	7405	91	*
497	Haemophilia A	F8	tCGC–TGC	Arg–Cys	2159	Higuchi	PNAS	88	8307	91	*
498	Haemophilia A	F8	CGC–CAC	Arg–His	2163	Antonarakis	unpub.res.				
499	Haemophilia A	F8	TTG–TCG	Leu–Ser	2166	Levinson	AJHG	46	53	90	
500	Haemophilia A	F8	tCGA–TGA	Arg–Term	2209	Gitschier	NATURE	315	427	85	*
501	Haemophilia A	F8	CGA–CAA	Arg–Gln	2209	Youssoufian	AJHG	42	718	88	*
502	Haemophilia A	F8	CGA–CTA	Arg–Leu	2209	Millar	HUM GENET	87	607	91	
503	Haemophilia A	F8	TGGc–TGT	Trp–Cys	2229	Naylor	LANCET	337	635	91	
504	Haemophilia A	F8	aCCG–TCG	Pro–Ser	2300	Paynton	HUM GENET	87	397	91	
505	Haemophilia A	F8	CCG–CTG	Pro–Leu	2300	Higuchi	PNAS	88	8307	91	*
506	Haemophilia A	F8	tCGC–TGC	Arg–Cys	2304	Higuchi	PNAS	88	7405	91	*
507	Haemophilia A	F8	tCGA–TGA	Arg–Term	2307	Gitschier	NATURE	315	427	85	*
508	Haemophilia A	F8	CGA–CAA	Arg–Gln	2307	Gitschier	SCIENCE	232	1415	86	*
509	Haemophilia A	F8	CGA–CTA	Arg–Leu	2307	Inaba	HUM GENET	81	335	89	
510	Heparin cof. 2 def.	HCF2	CGC–CAC	Arg–His	189	Blinder	JBC	264	5128	89	*
511	Hepatic lipase def.	HL	AAT–AGT	Asn–Ser	193	Hegele	BBRC	179	78	91	
512	Hepatic lipase def.	HL	TCC–TTC	Ser–Phe	267	Hegele	BBRC	179	78	91	
513	Hered. cereb. haemors.	APP	aGAA–CAA	Glu–Gln	22	Levy	SCIENCE	248	1124	90	
514	Hyperammonaemia	OTC	CCG–CTG	Pro–Leu	225	Hentzen	HUM GENET	88	153	91	*

	Disease	Gene	Codon	AA change	Codon no.	Author	Journal	Vol	Page	Year
515	Hyperarginaemia	ARG	ACT–AGT	Thr–Ser	290	Klein	SCMG	17	369	91
516	Hypercholesterolaem.	LDLR	cTGG–GGG	Trp–Gly	66	Leitersd.	JCI	85	1014	90
517	Hypercholesterolaem.	LDLR	GACt–GAG	Asp–Glu	206	Leitersd.	JCI	84	954	89
518	Hypercholesterolaem.	LDLR	aGAG–AAG	Glu–Lys	207	Leitersd.	JCI	85	1014	90
519	Hypercholesterolaem.	LDLR	cGTG–ATG	Val–Met	408	Leitersd.	JCI	84	954	89
520	Hypercholesterolaem.	LDLR	TGT–TAT	Cys–Tyr	646	Leitersd.	JCI	85	1014	90
521	Hypercholesterolaem.	LDLR	CCG–CTG	Pro–Leu	664	Soutar	PNAS	86	4166	89
522	Hypercholesterol.	LDLR	TACg–TAG	Tyr–Term	167	Landsberger	AJHG	50	427	92
523	Hyperkal. per. paral.	NAC2	cATG–GTG	Met–Val	704	Rojas	NATURE	354	387	91
524	Hyperkal. per. paral.	SCN4A	ACG–ATG	Thr–Met	704	Ptacek	CELL	67	1021	91
525	Hyperlipidaemia (1)	LPL	TCA–TGA	Ser–Term	447	Kobayashi	BBRC	182	70	92
526	Hyperlipoprotein.	LPL	GGA–GAA	Gly–Glu	142	Ameis	JCI	87	1165	91
527	Hyperoxaluria	AGT	GGGa–GGA	Gly–Glu	82	Purdue	GENOMICS	13	215	92
528	Hyperoxaluria (1)	SPT	cTCG–CCG	Ser–Pro	205	Nishiyama	BBRC	176	1093	91
529	Hyperproinsulinaemia	INS	tGTG–TTG	Val–Leu	3	Awata	DIABETES	37	1068	88
530	Hyperproinsulinaemia	INS	aCAC–GAC	His–Asp	10	Chan	PNAS	84	2194	87
531	Hyperproinsulinaemia	INS	TTct–TTG	Phe–Leu	24	Kwok	BBRC	98	844	81
532	Hyperproinsulinaemia	INS	CGT–CAT	Arg–His	65	Shibasaki	JCI	76	378	85
533	Hypobetalipoprotein.	ALPL	GGT–GTT	Gly–Val	1424	Young	JCI	85	933	90
534	Hypoparathyroidism	PTH	tTGT–CGT	Cys–Arg	18	Arnold	JCI	86	1084	90
535	Hypophosphatasia	ALPL	cGCC–ACC	Ala–Thr	162	Weiss	PNAS	85	7666	88
536	Hypothyroidism	TSHB	cGAA–TAA	Glu–Term	12	Dacou-V.	AJHG	46	988	90
537	Ichthyosis	STS	TCG–TTG	Ser–Leu	1226	Basler	AJHG	50	483	92
538	Ichthyosis	STS	gTGG–AGG	Trp–Arg	1320	Basler	AJHG	50	483	92
539	Ichthyosis	STS	TGC–TAC	Cys–Tyr	1543	Basler	AJHG	50	483	92
540	Immunoglob. K def.	IGK	gTGG–CGG	Trp–Arg	148	Stavnezer	SCIENCE	230	458	85
541	Immunoglob. K def.	IGK	cTGC–GGC	Cys–Gly	194	Stavnezer	SCIENCE	230	458	85
542	Insulin resistance	INSR	CTG–CCG	Leu–Pro	233	Klinkham.	EMBO J	8	2503	89
543	Insulin resistance	INSR	cTTC–GTC	Phe–Val	382	Accili	EMBO J	8	2509	89
544	Insulin resistance A	INSR	gGCA–ACA	Ala–Thr	1134	Moller	JBC	265	14979	90
545	Isovaleric acidaemia	IVD	CTA–CCA	Leu–Pro	13	Vockley	AJHG	49	147	91
546	Isovaleric acidaemia	IVD	GGC–GTC	Gly–Val	170	Vockley	AJHG	49	147	91
547	Ketothiolase (3)-def.	KT3	cGGC–AGG	Gly–Arg	150	Fukao	JCI	89	474	92
548	Ketothiolase (3)-def.	KT3	aGCT–ACT	Ala–Thr	347	Fukao	BBRC	179	124	91
549	LCAT deficiency	LCAT	gCGG–TGG	Arg–Trp	147	Taramelli	HUM GENET	85	195	90
550	LCAT deficiency	LCAT	ATGt–ATA	Met–Ile	293	Maeda	BBRC	178	460	91
551	LDH deficiency	LDHA	gGAG–TAG	Glu–Term	328	Maekawa	BBRC	180	1083	91
552	LDH deficiency	LDHB	CGC–CAC	Arg–His	173	Sudo	BBRC	168	672	90

Single base-pair substitutions causing human genetic disease (continued)

No.	Disease state	Gene symbol	Base change	Codon	Amino acid	Author	Journal	Vol.	Page	Year	CG
553	LDLR deficiency	LDLR	TGCc-TGA	660	Cys-Term	Lehrmann	JBC	262	401	87	
554	LDLR deficiency	LDLR	TGGc-TGA	792	Trp-Term	Lehrmann	CELL	41	735	85	
555	LDLR deficiency	LDLR	TAT-TGT	807	Tyr-Cys	Davis	CELL	45	15	86	
556	Laron dwarfism	GHR	TGCc-TGA	38	Cys-Term	Amselem	JCI	87	1098	91	
557	Laron dwarfism	GHR	gCGA-TGA	43	Arg-Term	Amselem	JCI	87	1098	91	*
558	Laron dwarfism	GHR	TTT-TCT	96	Phe-Ser	Amselem	NEJM	321	989	89	
559	Leprechaunism	INSR	AACa-AAA	15	Asn-Lys	Kadowaki	JCI	86	254	90	
560	Leprechaunism	INSR	aGGA-AGA	31	Gly-Arg	V.d. Vorm.	JBC	267	66	92	
561	Leprechaunism	INSR	CAC-CGC	209	His-Arg	Kadowaki	JCI	86	254	90	
562	Leprechaunism	INSR	gAAG-GAG	460	Lys-Glu	Kadowaki	SCIENCE	240	787	88	
563	Leprechaunism	INSR	cCAG-TAG	672	Gln-Term	Kadowaki	SCIENCE	240	787	88	
564	Leprechaunism	INSR	gCGA-TGA	897	Arg-Term	Kadowaki	PNAS	87	658	90	*
565	Leukocyte adhes. def.	CD18	ATG-AAG	1	Met-Lys	Sligh	JBC	267	714	92	
566	Leukocyte adhes. def.	LFA1	CTA-CCA	149	Leu-Pro	Wardlaw	JEM	172	335	90	
567	Leukocyte adhes. def.	LFA1	cGGG-AGG	169	Gly-Arg	Wardlaw	JEM	172	335	90	*
568	Lipoprt. lipase def.	LPL	TATg-TAA	61	Tyr-Term	Gotoda	JCI	88	1856	91	
569	Lipoprt. lipase def.	LPL	aCAG-TAG	106	Gln-Term	Emi	AJHG	47	107	90	
570	Lipoprt. lipase def.	LPL	GAT-GGT	156	Asp-Gly	Ma	JBC	267	1918	92	
571	Lipoprt. lipase def.	LPL	cGAT-AAT	156	Asp-Asn	Ma	JBC	267	1918	92	*
572	Lipoprt. lipase def.	LPL	tGCA-ACA	176	Ala-Thr	Beg	PNAS	87	3474	90	
573	Lipoprt. lipase def.	LPL	GGG-GAG	188	Gly-Glu	Emi	JBC	265	5910	90	
574	Lipoprt. lipase def.	LPL	ATT-ACT	194	Ile-Thr	Henderson	JCI	87	2005	91	
575	Lipoprt. lipase def.	LPL	GACa-GAG	204	Asp-Glu	Gotoda	JCI	88	1856	91	
576	Lipoprt. lipase def.	LPL	aTGT-AGT	216	Cys-Ser	Ma	JBC	267	1918	92	
577	Lipoprt. lipase def.	LPL	CGC-CAC	243	Arg-His	Gotoda	JCI	88	1856	91	*
578	Lipoprt. lipase def.	LPL	cTCC-ACC	244	Ser-Thr	Hata	AJHG	47	721	90	
579	Lipoprt. lipase def.	LPL	TGGa-TGA	382	Trp-Term	Gotoda	JCI	88	1856	91	
580	Lipoprt. lipase def.	LPL	TCA-TGA	590	Ser-Term	Hata	NAR	18	5407	90	
581	Li-Fraumeni syndrome	P53	GGC-GAC	245	Gly-Asp	Srivastava	NATURE	243	747	90	
582	LCAM deficiency	LCAM	AAT-AGT	351	Asn-Ser	Nelson	JBC	267	3351	92	
583	LCAM deficiency	LCAM	AAA-ACA	196	Lys-Thr	Arnaout	JCI	85	977	90	
584	LCAM deficiency	LCAM	tCGT-TGT	593	Arg-Cys	Arnaout	JCI	85	977	90	*

*	No.	Disease	Gene	Codon change	Substitution	Codon	Author	Journal	Vol	Page	Year
*	585	MCAD deficiency	MCAD	ATGa–ATA	Met–Ile	149	Yokota	AJHG	49	1280	91
	586	MCAD deficiency	MCAD	aTGT–CGT	Cys–Arg	244	Yokota	AJHG	49	1280	91
	587	MCAD deficiency	MCAD	cGGA–AGA	Gly–Arg	267	Yokota	AJHG	49	1280	91
	588	MCAD deficiency	MCAD	gAAA–GAA	Lys–Glu	304	Kelly	PNAS	87	9236	90
	589	MCAD deficiency	MCAD	gAAA–GAA	Lys–Glu	329	Matsubara	BBRC	171	498	90
*	590	MCAD deficiency	MCAD	ATA–ACA	Ile–Thr	375	Yokota	AJHG	49	1280	91
	591	Malign. hyperthermia	RYDR	aCGC–TGC	Arg–Cys	614	Gillard	GENOMICS	11	751	91
	592	Maple syrup ur. dis.	BCKDH	TTT–TGT	Phe–Cys	215	Chuang	MBM	8	49	89
	593	Maple syrup ur. dis.	BCKDH	cTAC–AAC	Tyr–Asn	394	Zhang	JCI	83	1425	89
	594	Marfan syndrome	COL1A2	CAG–CGG	Gln–Arg	618	Phillips	JCI	86	1723	90
*	595	Marfan syndrome	FIB1	CGC–CCC	Arg–Pro	239	Dietz	NATURE	352	337	91
*	596	McCune–Albright syn.	GPSA	tCGT–TGT	Arg–Cys	201	Weinstein	NEJM	325	1688	91
	597	McCune–Albright syn.	GPSA	CGT–CAT	Arg–His	201	Weinstein	NEJM	325	1688	91
	598	Metachrom. leukodys.	ARSA	GGC–GAC	Gly–Asp	99	Kondo	AJHG	48	971	91
	599	Metachrom. leukodys.	ARSA	ATC–AGC	Ile–Ser	266	Fluharty	AJHG	49	1340	91
	600	Metachrom. leukodys.	ARSA	ACT–AGT	Thr–Ser	391	Polten	NEJM	324	18	91
	601	Metachrom. leukodys.	SAP1	ACC–ATC	Thr–Ile	216	Rafi	BBRC	116	1017	90
*	602	Metachrom. leukodys.	SAP1	TGC–TCC	Cys–Ser	241	Holtschmid	JBC	266	7556	91
	603	Methaemoglobin. (1)	DIA1	CGG–CAG	Arg–Gln	57	Katsube	AJHG	48	799	91
	604	Methaemoglobin. (3)	DIA1	CTG–CCG	Leu–Pro	148	Katsube	AJHG	48	799	91
*	605	Methylmalonicacid.	MCM	ACG–ATG	Thr–Met	17	Ledley	PNAS	87	3147	90
*	606	Methylmalonicacid.	MCM	CGT–CAT	Arg–His	93	Raff	JCI	87	203	91
	607	Methylmalonicacid.	MCM	cTGG–CGG	Trp–Arg	105	Jansen	AJHG	47	808	90
	608	Methylmalonicacid.	MCM	GCA–GAA	Ala–Glu	378	Jansen	AJHG	47	808	90
	609	Methylmalonicacid.	MCM	CAT–CGT	His–Arg	532	Crane	JCI	89	385	92
*	610	Methylmalonicacid.	MCM	cGTA–ATA	Val–Ile	671	Crane	JCI	89	385	92
	611	Methylmalonicacid.	MCM	GGT–GTT	Gly–Val	717	Crane	JCI	89	385	92
*	612	Morquio B disease	GLB1	CGT–CAT	Arg–His	482	Oshima	AJHG	49	1091	91
	613	Morquio B disease	GLB1	TGGa–TGT	Trp–Cys	509	Oshima	AJHG	49	1091	91
	614	Motor neuron disease	HEXB	cATT–GTT	Ile–Val	207	Banerjee	BBRC	181	108	91
	615	Motor neuron disease	HEXB	TAT–TCT	Tyr–Ser	456	Banerjee	BBRC	181	108	91
*	616	Mucopolysacch. (VII)	GUSB	cCGT–TGT	Arg–Cys	382	Fukuda	JIMD	14	800	91
*	617	Mucopolysacch. (VII)	GUSB	GCG–GTG	Ala–Val	619	Fukuda	JIMD	14	800	91
*	618	Mucopolysacch. (VII)	GUSB	CCG–CTG	Pro–Leu	649	Fukuda	JIMD	14	800	91
	619	Mucopolysacch. (VI)	ARSB	GGT–GTT	Gly–Val	137	Wicker	JBC	266	21386	91
	620	Neurofibromatosis (1)	NF1	CTG–CCG	Leu–Pro		Cawthon	CELL	62	193	90
	621	Neurofibromatosis (1)	NF1	aCGA–TGA	Arg–Term		Cawthon	CELL	62	193	90
*	622	Niemann–Pick disease	SMPD1	CGT–CTT	Arg–Leu	496	Levran	PNAS	88	3748	91

Single base-pair substitutions causing human genetic disease (continued)

No.	Disease state	Gene symbol	Base change	Amino acid	Codon	Author	Journal	Vol.	Page	Year	CG
623	Niemann–Pick dis. (A)	SMPD1	gGGC-AGC	Gly-Ser	577	Ferlinz	BBRC	179	1187	91	
624	OTC deficiency	OTC	tCGA-TGA	Arg-Term	23	Grompe	AJHG	48	212	91	*
625	OTC deficiency	OTC	CGG-CAG	Arg-Gln	26	Grompe	AJHG	48	212	91	*
626	OTC deficiency	OTC	CTA-CCA	Leu-Pro	45	Grompe	AJHG	48	212	91	
627	OTC deficiency	OTC	tCGA-TGA	Arg-Term	92	Grompe	AJHG	48	212	91	*
628	OTC deficiency	OTC	CGA-CAA	Arg-Gln	92	Grompe	AJHG	48	212	91	*
629	OTC deficiency	OTC	CGA-CAA	Arg-Gln	109	Maddalena	JCI	82	1353	88	*
630	OTC deficiency	OTC	tCGA-TGA	Arg-Term	109	Hata	AJHG	45	123	89	*
631	OTC deficiency	OTC	CTT-CCT	Leu-Pro	111	Grompe	AJHG	48	212	91	
632	OTC deficiency	OTC	tCGA-TGA	Arg-Term	141	Grompe	AJHG	48	212	91	*
633	OTC deficiency	OTC	aGAA-TAA	Glu-Term	154	Grompe	PNAS	86	5888	89	
634	OTC deficiency	OTC	gCAG-GAG	Gln-Glu	216	Grompe	PNAS	86	5888	89	
635	OTC deficiency	OTC	gCGG-TGG	Arg-Trp	277	Finkelst.	GENOMICS	7	167	90	*
636	OTC deficiency	OTC	CGA-CTA	Arg-Leu	320	Grompe	AJHG	48	212	91	*
637	Osteoarthritis	COL2A1	cCGT-TGT	Arg-Cys	519	Ala-Kokko	PNAS	87	6565	90	
638	Osteogenesis imp. 2A	COL1A1	tGGT-TGT	Gly-Cys	691	Steinmann	BIOCHEM J	279	747	91	
639	Osteogenesis imp. 3/4	COL1A1	cGGC-TGC	Gly-Cys	415	Nicholls	JMG	28	757	91	
640	Osteogenesis imp. (2)	COL1A1	GGT-GTT	Gly-Val	256	Patterson	JBC	264	10083	89	
641	Osteogenesis imp. (2)	COL1A1	gGGA-AGA	Gly-Arg	550	Wallis	AJHG	46	1034	90	
642	Osteogenesis imp. (2)	COL1A1	GGT-GAT	Gly-Asp	550	Zhuang	AJHG	48	1186	91	
643	Osteogenesis imp. (2)	COL1A1	cGGA-AGA	Gly-Arg	664	Bateman	JBC	263	11627	88	*
644	Osteogenesis imp. (2)	COL1A1	tGGA-AGA	Gly-Arg	847	Wallis	JBC	265	18628	90	
645	Osteogenesis imp. (2)	COL1A1	GGC-GAC	Gly-Asp	883	Cohn	AJHG	46	591	90	
646	Osteogenesis imp. (2)	COL1A1	tGGC-TGC	Gly-Cys	904	Costanti.	JCI	83	574	88	
647	Osteogenesis imp. (2)	COL1A1	GGT-GCT	Gly-Ala	928	Lamande	JBC	264	15809	89	
648	Osteogenesis imp. (2)	COL1A1	GGC-GTC	Gly-Val	973	Lamande	JBC	264	15809	89	
649	Osteogenesis imp. (2)	COL1A1	tGGT-CGT	Gly-Arg	976	Lamande	JBC	264	15809	89	
650	Osteogenesis imp. (2)	COL1A1	GGT-GTT	Gly-Val	1006	Lamande	JBC	264	15809	89	
651	Osteogenesis imp. (2)	COL1A2	GGT-GAT	Gly-Asp	805	Grange	NAR	18	4227	90	
652	Osteogenesis imp. (3)	COL1A1	cGGG-AGG	Gly-Arg	154	Pruchno	HUM GENET	87	33	91	*
653	Osteogenesis imp. (3)	COL1A1	cGGC-AGC	Gly-Ser	1003	Pruchno	HUM GENET	87	33	91	*
654	Osteogenesis imp. (4)	COL1A1	tGGT-AGT	Gly-Ser	832	Marini	JBC	264	11893	89	

*	No.	Disorder	Gene	Codon change	Amino acid change	Codon	Author	Journal	Vol.	Page	Year
	655	Osteogenesis imp. (4)	COL1A2	GGT–GTT	Gly–Val	586	Bateman	BIOCHEM J	276	765	91
	656	Osteogenesis imp. (1)	COL1A1	tGGT–TGT	Gly–Cys	748	Vogel	JBC	262	14737	87
*	657	Osteogenesis imp. (1)	COL1A1	tGGT–TGT	Gly–Cys	1017	Labhard	MBM	5	197	88
	658	Osteogenesis imp. (1)	COL1A2	GGT–GAT	Gly–Asp	907	Baldwin	JBC	264	3002	89
	659	Osteogenesis imp. (?)	COL1A1	tGGT–AGT	Gly–Ser	598	Westerhsn.	JBC	265	13995	90
	660	Osteogenesis imp. (?)	COL1A1	cGGC–AGC	Gly–Ser	631	Westerhsn.	JBC	265	13995	90
	661	Osteogenesis imp. (?)	COL1A1	GGC–GTC	Gly–Val	637	Tsuneyoshi	JBC	266	15608	91
	662	Osteogenesis imp. (?)	COL1A1	tGGT–CGT	Gly–Arg	694	Tsuneyoshi	JBC	266	15608	91
	663	Osteogenesis imp. (?)	COL1A1	aGGT–AGT	Gly–Ser	844	Pack	JBC	264	19694	89
	664	Osteogenesis imp. (?)	COL1A1	aGGT–TGT	Gly–Cys	43	Shapiro	JCI	89	567	92
	665	Osteogenesis imp. (1)	COL1A1	GGA–AGA	Gly–Arg	85	Deak	JBC	266	21827	91
*	666	Osteogenesis imp. mod	COL1A1	tGGT–TGT	Gly–Cys	178	Valli	JBC	266	1872	91
	667	Osteoporosis	COL1A2	cGGT–AGT	Gly–Ser	661	Spotila	PNAS	88	5423	91
	668	PNP deficiency	PNP	tGAA–AAA	Glu–Lys	89	Williams	JBC	262	2332	87
	669	Pelizaeus–Merzb. dis.	PLP	CCC–CTC	Pro–Leu		Troffatter	PNAS	86	9427	89
	670	Pelizaeus–Merzb. dis.	PLP	cCCT–TCT	Pro–Ser	215	Gencic	AJHG	45	435	89
	671	Pelizaeus–Merzb. dis.	PLP	gGTT–TTT	Val–Phe	218	Pham–Dinh	PNAS	88	7562	91
	672	Phenylketonuria	PAH	cATG–GTG	Met–Val	−1	John	AJHG	45	905	89
	673	Phenylketonuria	PAH	TTct–TTG	Phe–Leu	39	Forrest	AJHG	49	175	91
*	674	Phenylketonuria	PAH	TTG–TCG	Leu–Ser	48	Konecki	HUM GENET	87	389	91
	675	Phenylketonuria	PAH	CGG–CAG	Arg–Gln	158	Dworniczak	HUM GENET	84	95	89
	676	Phenylketonuria	PAH	TAT–TGT	Tyr–Cys	204	Wang	GENOMICS	10	449	91
*	677	Phenylketonuria	PAH	GAA–GGA	Glu–Gly	221	Konecki	HUM GENET	87	389	91
	678	Phenylketonuria	PAH	cCGA–TGA	Arg–Term	243	Wang	SCMG	16	85	90
	679	Phenylketonuria	PAH	CGA–CAA	Arg–Gln	243	Okano	GENOMICS	10	449	91
*	680	Phenylketonuria	PAH	tCGG–TGG	Arg–Trp	252	Hofman	GENOMICS	9	96	91
	681	Phenylketonuria	PAH	TTG–TCG	Leu–Ser	255	Labrune	AJHG	48	791	91
	682	Phenylketonuria	PAH	GCC–GTC	Ala–Val	259	Dworniczak	AJHG	48	1115	91
	683	Phenylketonuria	PAH	cCGA–TGA	Arg–Term	261	Dianzani	HUM GENET	87	731	91
*	684	Phenylketonuria	PAH	CGA–CAA	Arg–Gln	261	Svensson	AJHG	48	631	91
	685	Phenylketonuria	PAH	tGGA–TGA	Gly–Term	272	Melle	HUM GENET	85	300	90
	686	Phenylketonuria	PAH	TCC–TTC	Ser–Phe	273	Forrest	JMG	28	38	91
	687	Phenylketonuria	PAH	ATGt–ATT	Met–Ile	276	Labrune	AJHG	49	175	91
*	688	Phenylketonuria	PAH	gTAT–GAT	Tyr–Asp	277	Lynnet	AJHG	48	1115	91
	689	Phenylketonuria	PAH	cGAA–AAA	Glu–Lys	280	Okano	AJHG	44	511	89
	690	Phenylketonuria	PAH	CCT–CTT	Pro–Leu	281		GENOMICS	9	96	91
	691	Phenylketonuria	PAH	TTT–TGT	Phe–Cys	299	Eiken	HUM GENET	88	608	92
	692	Phenylketonuria	PAH	CTG–CCG	Leu–Pro	311	Licht.-K.	BIOCHEM	27	2881	88

Single base-pair substitutions causing human genetic disease (continued)

No.	Disease state	Gene symbol	Base change	Amino acid	Codon	Author	Journal	Vol.	Page	Year	CG
693	Phenylketonuria	PAH	tCGG-TGG	Arg-Trp	408	Dilella	NATURE	327	333	87	*
694	Phenylketonuria	PAH	CGG-CAG	Arg-Gln	408	Eiken	HUM GENET	88	608	92	*
695	Phenylketonuria	PAH	TAC-TGC	Tyr-Cys	414	Okano	NEJM	324	1232	91	
696	Phosphoglyc. kin. def.	PGK	GGG-GTG	Gly-Val	157	Fujii	BLOOD	79	1582	92	
697	Piebaldism	KIT	TTTc-TTG	Phe-Leu	584	Spritz	AJHG	50	261	92	
698	Piebaldism	KIT	aGGT-AGT	Gly-Ser	664	Giebel	PNAS	88	8696	91	
699	Plasminogen defic.	PLG	gGTC-TTC	Val-Phe	355	Ichinose	PNAS	88	115	91	
700	Plasminogen defic.	PLG	tGCT-ACT	Ala-Thr	601	Ichinose	PNAS	88	115	91	
701	Pompe disease	GAA	ATG-ACG	Met-Thr	318	Zhong	AJHG	49	635	91	
702	Porphyria	ALAD	cGGG-AGG	Gly-Arg	133	Plewinska	AJHG	49	167	91	*
703	Porphyria	ALAD	cGCC-ACC	Ala-Thr	274	Ishida	BBRC	172	237	90	*
704	Porphyria	ALAD	cGTG-ATG	Val-Met	275	Plewinska	AJHG	49	167	91	*
705	Porphyria	UROD	GGG-GAG	Gly-Glu	281	De Verne.	SCIENCE	234	732	86	
706	Porphyria	UROD	GGG-GTG	Gly-Val	281	Garey	BLOOD	73	892	89	
707	Porphyria acut. int.	PBGD	CGA-CAA	Arg-Gln	131	Delfau	AJHG	49	421	91	*
708	Porphyria acut. int.	PBGD	gCAG-TAG	Gln-Term	137	Scobie	HUM GENET	85	631	90	
709	Porphyria acut. int.	PBGD	CGG-CAG	Arg-Gln	149	Delfau	JCI	86	1511	90	*
710	Porphyria acut. int.	PBGD	CGG-CAG	Arg-Gln	155	Delfau	JCI	86	1511	90	*
711	Porphyria acut. int.	PBGD	TGG-TAG	Trp-Term	198	Lee	PNAS	88	10912	91	
712	Porphyria acut. int.	PBGD	CTT-CGT	Leu-Arg	226	Delfau	AJHG	49	421	91	
713	Porphyria cong. eryth	UROS	tCTT-TTT	Leu-Phe	4	Boulechfar	HUM GENET	88	320	92	
714	Porphyria eryth.	UROS	tACC-GCC	Thr-Ala	62	Warner	JCI	89	693	92	*
715	Porphyria eryth.	UROS	GCA-GTA	Ala-Val	66	Warner	JCI	89	693	92	*
716	Porphyria eryth.	UROS	aTGT-CGT	Cys-Arg	73	Warner	JCI	89	693	92	*
717	Porphyria eryth.	UROS	ACG-ATG	Thr-Met	228	Warner	JCI	89	693	92	*
718	Prolidase deficiency	PROL	cGAC-AAC	Asp-Asn	276	Tanoue	AJHG	47	351	90	
719	Proline-rich prot. de	PRP3	aCGT-TGT	Arg-Cys	15	Azen	AJHG	47	686	90	*
720	Protein C deficiency	PROC	gCGG-TGG	Arg-Trp	15	Goossens	pers.comm.				
721	Protein C deficiency	PROC	CGG-CAG	Arg-Gln	15	Goossens	pers.comm.				
722	Protein C deficiency	PROC	GAG-GCG	Glu-Ala	20	Long	pers.comm.				
723	Protein C deficiency	PROC	tGTG-ATG	Val-Met	34	Long	BLOOD	79	1456	92	
724	Protein C deficiency	PROC	cTTC-CTC	Phe-Leu	76	Reitsma	BLOOD	78	890	91	

No.	Disease	Gene	Codon change	Substitution	Codon	Author	Journal	Vol	Page	Year	*
725	Protein C deficiency	PROC	TGCa–TGA	Cys–Term	105	Reitsma	BLOOD	78	890	91	
726	Protein C deficiency	PROC	TGC–TAC	Cys–Tyr	105	Reitsma	BLOOD	78	890	91	
727	Protein C deficiency	PROC	AGCt–AGG	Ser–Arg	119	Reitsma	BLOOD	78	890	91	
728	Protein C deficiency	PROC	gCAG–TAG	Gln–Term	132	Reitsma	BLOOD	78	890	91	
729	Protein C deficiency	PROC	tTGT–CGT	Cys–Arg	141	Reitsma	BLOOD	78	890	91	
730	Protein C deficiency	PROC	gCGC–TGC	Arg–Cys	152	Goossens	pers.comm.				
731	Protein C deficiency	PROC	aCGA–TGA	Arg–Term	157	Goossens	pers.comm.				
732	Protein C deficiency	PROC	CCG–CTG	Pro–Leu	168	Goossens	pers.comm.				
733	Protein C deficiency	PROC	gCGG–TGG	Arg–Trp	169	Matsuda	NEJM	319	1265	88	
734	Protein C deficiency	PROC	CGG–CAG	Arg–Gln	178	Reitsma	BLOOD	78	890	91	
735	Protein C deficiency	PROC	gCGG–TGG	Arg–Trp	178	Reitsma	BLOOD	78	890	91	
736	Protein C deficiency	PROC	gCTT–TTT	Leu–Phe	223	Reitsma	BLOOD	78	890	91	
737	Protein C deficiency	PROC	gCGC–TGC	Arg–Cys	230	Reitsma	BLOOD	78	890	91	*
738	Protein C deficiency	PROC	CCC–CTC	Pro–Leu	247	Grundy	HUM GENET	89	683	92	*
739	Protein C deficiency	PROC	GCA–GTA	Ala–Val	259	Grundy	LANCET	338	575	91	*
740	Protein C deficiency	PROC	cGCC–ACC	Ala–Thr	267	Conard	LANCET	339	743	92	*
741	Protein C deficiency	PROC	cCGG–AGC	Gly–Ser	292	Reitsma	BLOOD	78	890	91	*
742	Protein C deficiency	PROC	gGGG–AGC	Gly–Ser	301	Conard	LANCET	339	743	92	*
743	Protein C deficiency	PROC	cCGA–TGA	Arg–Term	306	Romeo	PNAS	84	2829	87	
744	Protein C deficiency	PROC	TGGa–TGC	Trp–Cys	402	Romeo	PNAS	84	2829	87	
745	Protein C deficiency	PROC	ATCc–ATG	Ile–Met	403	Reitsma	BLOOD	78	890	91	*
746	Protein S deficiency	PROS	TAAg–TAT	Term–Tyr	636	Ploos v.Am.	pers.comm.				
747	Pseudo-VWD	GP1BA	GGT–GTT	Gly–Val	233	Miller	PNAS	88	4761	91	
748	Pyruvate dehyd. def.	PDH	CGT–CAT	Arg–His	378	Hansen	JIMD	14	140	91	*
749	Retinitis pigmentosa	RDS	CTG–CCG	Leu–Pro	185	Kajiwara	NATURE	354	480	91	*
750	Retinitis pigmentosa	RDS	CCT–CTT	Pro–Leu	216	Kajiwara	NATURE	354	480	91	
751	Retinitis pigmentosa	RHO	ACG–ATG	Thr–Met	17	Sheffield	AJHG	49	699	91	*
752	Retinitis pigmentosa	RHO	CCC–CAC	Pro–His	23	Dryja	NATURE	343	364	90	
753	Retinitis pigmentosa	RHO	CCC–CTC	Pro–Leu	23	Dryja	PNAS	88	9370	91	
754	Retinitis pigmentosa	RHO	gTTT–CTT	Phe–Leu	45	Sung	PNAS	88	6481	91	*
755	Retinitis pigmentosa	RHO	GGC–GTC	Gly–Val	51	Dryja	PNAS	88	9370	91	
756	Retinitis pigmentosa	RHO	CCC–CGC	Pro–Arg	53	Inglehearn	HMG	1	41	92	
757	Retinitis pigmentosa	RHO	ACG–AGG	Thr–Arg	58	Dryja	NEJM	323	1302	90	*
758	Retinitis pigmentosa	RHO	GTC–GAC	Val–Asp	87	Sung	PNAS	88	6481	91	
759	Retinitis pigmentosa	RHO	GGT–GAT	Gly–Asp	89	Sung	PNAS	88	6481	91	
760	Retinitis pigmentosa	RHO	cGGG–TGG	Gly–Trp	106	Sung	PNAS	88	6481	91	
761	Retinitis pigmentosa	RHO	cGGG–AGG	Gly–Arg	106	Inglehearn	HMG	1	41	92	
762	Retinitis pigmentosa	RHO	CTG–CGG	Leu–Arg	125	Dryja	PNAS	88	9370	91	*

Single base-pair substitutions causing human genetic disease (continued)

No.	Disease state	Gene symbol	Base change	Amino acid	Codon	Author	Journal	Vol.	Page	Year	CG
763	Retinitis pigmentosa	RHO	gCGG-TGG	Arg-Trp	135	Sung	PNAS	88	6481	91	*
764	Retinitis pigmentosa	RHO	cTGC-CGC	Cys-Arg	167	Dryja	PNAS	88	9370	91	
765	Retinitis pigmentosa	RHO	CCA-CTA	Pro-Leu	171	Dryja	PNAS	88	9370	91	*
766	Retinitis pigmentosa	RHO	TAC-TGC	Tyr-Cys	178	Sung	PNAS	88	6481	91	
767	Retinitis pigmentosa	RHO	cGAG-AAG	Glu-Lys	181	Dryja	PNAS	88	9370	91	
768	Retinitis pigmentosa	RHO	gGGC-AGC	Gly-Ser	182	Sheffield	AJHG	49	699	91	
769	Retinitis pigmentosa	RHO	cTCG-CCG	Ser-Pro	186	Dryja	PNAS	88	9370	91	
770	Retinitis pigmentosa	RHO	tGGA-AGA	Gly-Arg	188	Dryja	PNAS	88	9370	91	
771	Retinitis pigmentosa	RHO	GAC-GGC	Asp-Gly	190	Sung	PNAS	88	6481	91	*
772	Retinitis pigmentosa	RHO	cGAC-AAC	Asp-Asn	190	Keen	GENOMICS	11	199	91	
773	Retinitis pigmentosa	RHO	CAC-CCC	His-Pro	211	Kenn	GENOMICS	11	199	91	
774	Retinitis pigmentosa	RHO	CCC-CTC	Pro-Leu	267	Sheffield	AJHG	49	699	91	
775	Retinitis pigmentosa	RHO	cAAG-GAG	Lys-Glu	296	Akli	GENOMICS	11	199	91	*
776	Retinitis pigmentosa	RHO	cCAG-TAG	Gln-Term	344	Sung	PNAS	88	6481	91	
777	Retinitis pigmentosa	RHO	gGTG-ATG	Val-Met	345	Dryja	PNAS	88	9370	91	
778	Retinitis pigmentosa	RHO	CCG-CTG	Pro-Leu	347	Dryja	NEJM	323	1302	90	*
779	Retinitis pigmentosa	RHO	cCCG-TCG	Pro-Ser	347	Dryja	NEJM	323	1302	90	
780	Retinitis pigmentosa	RHO	CCG-CGG	Pro-Arg	347	Gal	GENOMICS	11	468	91	*
781	Retinoblastoma	RB1	cCGA-TGA	Arg-Term	358	Yandell	NEJM	321	1689	90	*
782	Retinoblastoma	RB1	TCA-TTA	Ser-Leu	567	Yandell	NEJM	321	1689	90	*
783	Retinoblastoma	RB1	TGT-TTT	Cys-Phe	706	Kaye	PNAS	87	6922	90	*
784	Retinoblastoma	RB1	gGAG-TAG	Glu-Term	748	Yandell	NEJM	321	1689	90	
785	Retinoblastoma	RB1	tCGA-TGA	Arg-Term	787	Yandell	NEJM	321	1689	90	*
786	Rickets (vit.D-res.)	VDR	CGA-CAA	Arg-Gln	47	Hughes	SCIENCE	242	1702	89	
787	Rickets (vit.D-res.)	VDR	CGA-CAA	Arg-Gln	49	Saijo	AJHG	49	668	91	*
788	Rickets (vit.D-res.)	VDR	CGC-CAC	Arg-His	77	Sone	MOL END	4	623	90	
789	Rickets (vit.D-res.)	VDR	TACc-TAA	Tyr-Term	292	Ritchie	PNAS	86	9783	89	
790	SAP deficiency	SAP1	tATG-TTG	Met-Leu	1	Schnabel	JBC	267	3312	92	
791	Sandhoff disease	HEXB	tCGC-TGC	Arg-Cys	178	Tanaka	AJHG	46	329	90	*
792	Saposin B deficiency	SAPB	ACC-ATC	Thr-Ile	23	Kretz	PNAS	87	2541	90	
793	Schindler disease	AGS	cAGA-AAA	Glu-Lys	325	Wang	JCI	86	1752	90	*
794	Short-limbed dwarf.	COL2A1	cGGC-AGC	Gly-Ser	943	Vissing	JBC	264	18265	89	*

No.	Disorder	Gene	Sequence	AA change	Codon	Author	Journal	Vol	Page	Year	*
795	Sickle cell anaemia	HBB	GAG-GTG	Glu-Val	6	Engelke	PNAS	85	544	88	*
796	Spondylo. dysp. con.	COL2A1	cGGC-AGC	Gly-Ser	997	Chan	JBC	266	12487	91	*
797	Ster.11β-hydrox. def.	CYP11B1	CGC-CAC	Arg-His	448	White	JCI	87	1664	91	
798	Ster.17α-hydrox. def.	CYP17	gTCC-CCC	Ser-Pro	106	Lin	JBC	266	15992	91	
799	Ster.18-hydrox. def.	CYP18	GTG-GCG	Val-Ala	386	Mitsuuchi	BBRC	182	974	92	
800	Ster.21-hydrox. def.	CYP21B	ATC-AAC	Ile-Asn	172	Chiou	JBC	265	3549	90	*
801	Ster.21-hydrox. def.	CYP21B	cCGG-TGG	Arg-Trp	356	Chiou	JBC	265	3549	90	*
802	Stickler syndrome	COL2A1	tCGA-TGA	Arg-Term	732	Ahmad	PNAS	88	6624	91	
803	TPI deficiency	TPI	GAGt-GAC	Glu-Asp	104	Daar	PNAS	83	7903	86	*
804	TPI deficiency	TPI	cGGA-AGA	Gly-Arg	122	Perry	HUM GENET	88	634	92	
805	TSH deficiency	TSHB	tGGA-AGA	Gly-Arg	29	Hayashiz.	EMBO J	8	2291	89	
806	Tay-Sachs disease	HEXA	TGGc-TGA	Trp-Term	26	Triggs-Raine	AJHG	49	1041	91	*
807	Tay-Sachs disease	HEXA	cCGA-TGA	Arg-Term	137	Akli	GENOMICS	11	124	91	*
808	Tay-Sachs disease	HEXA	CGC-CAC	Arg-His	178	Ohno	J NCHEM	50	316	88	
809	Tay-Sachs disease	HEXA	CGC-CTC	Arg-Leu	178	Triggs-Raine	AJHG	49	1041	91	
810	Tay-Sachs disease	HEXA	TCC-TTC	Ser-Phe	210	Akli	GENOMICS	11	124	91	
811	Tay-Sachs disease	HEXA	aGGT-AGT	Gly-Ser	269	Navon	SCIENCE	243	1471	89	*
812	Tay-Sachs disease	HEXA	gCGA-TGA	Arg-Term	393	Akli	GENOMICS	11	124	91	
813	Tay-Sachs disease	HEXA	TGGt-TGC	Trp-Cys	420	Tanaka	AJHG	47	567	90	*
814	Tay-Sachs disease	HEXA	cGAA-AAA	Glu-Lys	482	Nakano	J NCHEM	51	984	88	*
815	Tay-Sachs disease	HEXA	CGC-CAC	Arg-His	499	Triggs-Raine	AJHG	49	1041	91	*
816	Tay-Sachs disease	HEXA	cCGC-TGC	Arg-Cys	504	Akli	GENOMICS	11	124	91	
817	Thalassaemia α	HBA1	gATG-GTG	Met-Val	-1	Moi	JCI	80	1416	87	
818	Thalassaemia α	HBA2	ATG-ACG	Met-Thr	-1	Piratsu	JBC	259	12315	84	
819	Thalassaemia α	HBA2	CTG-CCG	Leu-Pro	125	Goossens	NATURE	296	864	82	
820	Thalassaemia β	HBB	ATG-AGG	Met-Arg	-1	Lam	BLOOD	75	1207	90	
821	Thalassaemia β	HBB	cATG-GTG	Met-Val	1	Hattori	HEMOGLOBIN	15	317	91	
822	Thalassaemia β	HBB	TGGg-TGA	Trp-Term	15	Aelehla	HUM GENET	84	195	90	
823	Thalassaemia β	HBB	cAAG-TAG	Lys-Term	17	Chang	PNAS	76	2886	79	
824	Thalassaemia β	HBB	tGAG-AAG	Glu-Lys	26	Orkin	NATURE	300	768	82	
825	Thalassaemia β	HBB	TACc-TAA	Tyr-Term	35	Thein	AJHG	47	369	90	
826	Thalassaemia β	HBB	TGGa-TGA	Trp-Term	37	Boehm	BLOOD	67	1185	86	
827	Thalassaemia β	HBB	cCAG-TAG	Gln-Term	39	Trecartin	JCI	68	1012	81	
828	Thalassaemia β	HBB	tGAG-TAG	Glu-Term	43	Atweh	JCI	82	557	88	
829	Thalassaemia β	HBB	tGAG-TAG	Glu-Term	90	Fucharoen	BJH	74	101	90	
830	Thalassaemia β	HBB	CTG-CCG	Leu-Pro	110	Kobayashi	BLOOD	70	1688	87	
831	Thalassaemia β	HBB	aGAA-TAA	Glu-Term	121	Kazazian	AJHG	38	860	86	
832	Thalassaemia β	HBB	gCAA-TAA	Gln-Term	127	Hall	BJH	79	342	91	

Single base-pair substitutions causing human genetic disease (continued)

No.	Disease state	Gene symbol	Base change	Amino acid	Codon	Author	Journal	Vol.	Page	Year	CG
833	Thalassaemia δ	HBD	gGCC-TCC	Ala–Ser	27	Trifillis	BLOOD	78	3298	91	*
834	Thalassaemia δ	HBD	cCGC-TGC	Arg–Cys	116	Trifillis	BLOOD	78	3298	91	*
835	Thalassaemia δ	HBD	CTG-CCG	Leu–Pro	141	Trifillis	BLOOD	78	3298	91	
836	Thyroid hormone res.	ERBA2	cGCT-ACT	Ala–Thr	312	Parrilla	JCI	88	2123	91	
837	Thyroid hormone res.	ERBA2	tGGG-AGG	Gly–Arg	327	Parrilla	JCI	88	2123	91	
838	Thyroid hormone res.	ERBA2	GGT-GTT	Gly–Val	340	Parrilla	JCI	88	2123	91	
839	Thyroid hormone res.	ERBA2	GGG-GAG	Gly–Glu	342	Parrilla	JCI	88	2123	91	*
840	Thyroid hormone res.	ERBA2	cATG-GTG	Met–Val	437	Parrilla	JCI	88	2123	91	
841	Thyroid hormone res.	ERBA2	cCCT-ACT	Pro–Thr	448	Parrilla	JCI	88	2123	91	
842	Thyroid hormone res.	ERBA2	CGC-CAC	Arg–His	438	Boothroyd	BBRC	178	606	91	*
843	Thyroid hormone res.	ERBA2	CCT-CAT	Pro–His	448	Usala	JCI	85	93	90	
844	Thyr.-bind. glob. def.	TBG	tGCC-CCC	Ala–Pro	113	Janssen	HUM GENET	87	119	91	
845	Thyr.-bind. glob. def.	TBG	cCAT-TAT	His–Tyr	331	Bertenshaw	AJHG	48	741	91	*
846	Tritanopia	BCP	cGGA-AGA	Gly–Arg	79	Weitz	AJHG	50	498	92	
847	Tritanopia	BCP	cTCC-CCC	Ser–Pro	214	Weitz	AJHG	50	498	92	
848	Tyrosinase defic.	TYR	cTGC-CGC	Cys–Arg	89	Spritz	AJHG	48	318	91	*
849	von Willebrand 1	VWF	CGG-CAG	Arg–Gln	854	Peerlinck	BJH	80	358	92	
850	von Willebrand 2a	VWF	gGTC-TTC	Val–Phe	551	Lavergne	TH	65	738	91	
851	von Willebrand 2a	VWF	GGA-GAA	Gly–Glu	742	Inbal	BLOOD	78S	73a	91	
852	von Willebrand 2a	VWF	TCG-TTG	Ser–Leu	743	Sigihura	pers.comm.				*
853	von Willebrand 2a	VWF	cCGG-TGG	Arg–Trp	834	Ginsburg	PNAS	86	3723	89	
854	von Willebrand 2a	VWF	GTC-GAC	Val–Asp	844	Ginsburg	PNAS	86	3723	89	
855	von Willebrand 2a	VWF	ATT-ACT	Ile–Thr	865	Iannuzzi	AJHG	48	757	91	
856	von Willebrand 2a	VWF	gGAG-AAG	Glu–Lys	875	Lavergne	TH	65	738	91	
857	von Willebrand 2b	VWF	gCGG-TGG	Arg–Trp	543	Randi	JCI	87	1220	91	*
858	von Willebrand 2b	VWF	gCGC-TGC	Arg–Cys	545	Randi	JCI	87	1220	91	*
859	von Willebrand 2b	VWF	TGGg-TGT	Trp–Cys	550	Ware	PNAS	88	2946	91	
860	von Willebrand 2b	VWF	cGTG-ATG	Val–Met	553	Randi	JCI	87	1220	91	*
861	von Willebrand 2b	VWF	cGGG-AGC	Gly–Ser	561	Rabinowitz	BLOOD	78S	179a	91	*
862	von Willebrand 2b	VWF	CCG-CTG	Pro–Leu	574	Kroner	TH	65	763	91	*
863	von Willebrand 2b	VWF	CGG-CAG	Arg–Gln	578	Cooney	JCI	87	1227	91	*
864	von Willebrand 3	VWF	tCGA-TGA	Arg–Term	365	Bahnak	BLOOD	78	1148	91	*

865	von Willebrand 3	VWF	cCGA-TGA	Arg-Term	896	Zhang	HMG	1	61	92	*
866	von Willebrand 3	VWF	cCGA-TGA	Arg-Term	1772	Eikenboom	TH	65	1127	91	*
867	von Willebrand 3	VWF	gAAC-TAC	Asn-Tyr	1783	Eikenboom	TH	65	1127	91	
868	von Willebrand dis.	VWF	gCGG-TGG	Arg-Trp	19	Kroner	BLOOD	78S	178a	91	*
869	von Willebrand dis.	VWF	ACG-ATG	Thr-Met	28	Gaucher	BLOOD	77	1937	91	*
870	von Willebrand dis.	VWF	cCGG-TGG	Arg-Trp	53	Gaucher	BJH	78	506	91	*
871	von Willebrand dis.	VWF	CATg-CAA	His-Gln	54	Kroner	BLOOD	78S	178a	91	
872	von Willebrand dis.	VWF	CGG-CAG	Arg-Gln	91	Gaucher	BJH	78	506	91	*
873	Waardenburg syndrome	PAX3	CCG-CTG	Pro-Leu		Baldwin	NATURE	355	637	92	*
874	Wilms' tumour	WT1	GGT-GTT	Gly-Val		Pelletier	NATURE	353	431	91	
875	Wilms' tumour	WT1	CGT-CAT	Arg-His	366	Pelletier	CELL	67	437	91	*
876	Wilms' tumour	WT1	cCGG-TGG	Arg-Trp	394	Pelletier	CELL	67	437	91	*
877	Wilms' tumour	WT1	cGAC-AAC	Asp-Asn	396	Pelletier	CELL	67	437	91	*
878	Wilms' tumour	WT1	GAC-GGC	Asp-Gly	396	Pelletier	CELL	67	437	91	
879	Xeroderma pigmentosum	XPAC	TGT-TTT	Cys-Phe	108	Satokata	HUM GENET	88	603	92	
880	Zellweger syndrome	PAF1	aCGA-TGA	Arg-Term	119	Shimozawa	SCIENCE	255	1132	92	*

Gene symbol: McKusick symbol for disease gene; base change: nucleotides flanking the altered codon (denoted by lower case letters) are given when the mutation occurs in the first or third position in the codon; amino acid: amino acid substitution using symbols as listed in Appendix 5; codon: number of amino acid residue in which substitution has occurred. No entry in the Codon column denotes codon number unknown; CG: CG → TG and CG → CA substitutions, which are consistent with a model of methylation-mediated deamination, are marked with a *. Only the first example of each single base-pair substitution has been included in order to avoid multiple inclusion of identical-by-descent mutations. Not included in the above database are single base-pair substitutions in the factor IX (F9) gene causing haemophilia B, mutations in the mitochondrial genome and somatic mutations in oncogenes (see p. 123).

Appendix 3　Deletion database (<20 bp)

Deletions of <20 bp causing human genetic disease

No.	Disease	Gene	Deletion and flanking sequence	Codon	Author	Journal	Vol.	Page	Year
1	APRT deficiency	APRT	TCCTGTA^CCCttcTTCTCTCTCC	172	Hidaka	JCI	80	1409	87
2	Adenomat. polyp. coli	APC	TAATGAAACTtTCATTTGATG	?	Groden	CELL	66	589	91
3	Adenomat. polyp. coli	APC	AAAGAA^ATAGatagTCTTCCTTTA	169	Fodde	GENOMICS	13	1162	92
4	Adenomat. polyp. coli	APC	CACAAG^CAAAgTCTCTATGGT	793	Miyashi	PNAS	89	4452	92
5	Adenomat. polyp. coli	APC	ACCAAT^CGACatGATGATAATA	805	Miyashi	PNAS	89	4452	92
6	Adenomat. polyp. coli	APC	AGAGAA^CGCGgaattGGTCTAGGCA	856	Miyashi	PNAS	89	4452	92
7	Adenomat. polyp. coli	APC	CCCAAA^CACAtaataGAAGATGAAA	1054	Miyashi	PNAS	89	4452	92
8	Adenomat. polyp. coli	APC	ATGAA^ATAAAaacaaaGTGAGCAAAG	1060	Miyashi	PNAS	89	4452	92
9	Adenomat. polyp. coli	APC	CATGAA^GAAGaagaGAGACCAACA	1155	Miyashi	PNAS	89	4452	92
10	Adenomat. polyp. coli	APC	CTTCA^TCACAgAAAACAGTCAT	1190	Miyashi	PNAS	89	4452	92
11	Adenomat. polyp. coli	APC	GCCACT^TGCAaaGTTTCTTCTA	1249	Miyashi	PNAS	89	4452	92
12	Adenomat. polyp. coli	APC	AAATA^AAAGGaaagaTTGGAACTAG	1308	Miyashi	PNAS	89	4452	92
13	Adenomat. polyp. coli	APC	CCAGAT^AGCCcTGGACAAACC	1426	Miyashi	PNAS	89	4452	92
14	Adenomat. polyp. coli	APC	AAAGAGA^GAGagTGGACCTAAG	1464	Miyashi	PNAS	89	4452	92
15	Adenomat. polyp. coli	APC	AAGAA^TCAAAtgaaaACCAAGAGAA	1546	Miyashi	PNAS	89	4452	92
16	Adenomat. polyp. coli	APC	CAGCC^CAGACtGCTTCAAAAT	1596	Miyashi	PNAS	89	4452	92
17	Adenomat. polyp. coli	APC	AGACT^CTAATttatCAAAATGGCAC	2643	Miyashi	PNAS	89	4452	92
18	Albinism, ocul. (1A)	TYR	CACTG^CTTGGgGGATCTGAAA	189	Oetting	AJHG	49	199	91
19	Albinism, ocul. (1A)	TYR	CAGAA^AAGTGtgACATTTGCAC	243	Oetting	AJHG	49	199	91
20	Albright's osteodys.	GNAS1	ATCAAG^CAGGgctgaCTATGTGCCG	187	Weinstein	GENOMICS	13	1319	92
21	Albright's osteodys.	GSA	GGCTCTG^AACcTCTCAAGAG	271	Weinstein	PNAS	87	8287	90
22	Angioneurot. edema (1)	C1I	CTTCGAT^TTtcTTTATGACCT	399	Frangi	JCI	88	755	91
23	Antiplasmin α2 def.	PLI	TCCCATC^AAAgaaGATTTCCTGG	136	Miura	JBC	264	18213	89
24	Antithrombin III def.	AT3	CCACC^AACCGgCGTGTCTGGG	45	Carrell	pers.comm.			
25	Antithrombin III def.	AT3	CTGTCAC^CCCtGAGTATCTCC	80	Olds	BJH	78	408	91
26	Antithrombin III def.	AT3	TGGAGGTA^TTTaagtttGACACCATAT	106	Olds	pers.comm.			
27	Antithrombin III def.	AT3	TCTGAT^CAGAtCCACTTCTTC	118	Olds	BLOOD	76	2182	91
28	Antithrombin III def.	AT3	AGGAA^CTGTTctACAAGGCTGA	238	Carrell	pers.comm.			

#	Disease	Gene	Sequence	Pos	Author	Journal	Vol	Page	Year
29	Antithrombin III def.	AT3	GCTGAT*GGAGaGTCGTGTTCA	244	Grundy	BLOOD	78	1027	91
30	Antithrombin III def.	AT3	GCTGAT*GGAGagTCGTGTTCAG	244	Grundy	BLOOD	78	1027	91
31	Antithrombin III def.	AT3	AAGCCT*GAGAagAGCCTGGCCA	289	Vidaud	BLOOD	78	2305	91
32	Antithrombin III def.	AT3	CAGGAG*TGGCtggaTGAATTGGAG	307	Vidaud	BLOOD	78	2305	91
33	Antithrombin III def.	AT3	TGCATTC*CATaAGGCATTCT	369	Carrell	pers.comm.			
34	Antitrypsin α1 def.	PI	CAATATC*TTCttcTCCCCAGTGA	51	Curiel	JBC	264	13938	89
35	Antitrypsin α1 def.	PI	TCAAC*GATTAcGTGGAGAAGG	159	Nukiwa	JBC	262	11999	87
36	Antitrypsin α1 def.	PI	GGGGCT*GACCtcTCCGGGGTC	317	Sifers	JBC	263	7330	88
37	Antitrypsin α1 def.	PI	CTATCCC*CCCcGAGGTCAAGT	361	Fraizer	HUM GENET	83	377	89
38	ApoA1 deficiency	APOA1	ATCTG*AGCACgCTCAGCGAGA	201	Funke	JCI	87	371	91
39	ApoC2 deficiency	APOC2	CCTCACC*CAGgTGAAGGAATC	37	Fojo	JBC	263	17913	88
40	ApoC2 deficiency	APOC2	GCATT*TTTACtGACCAAGTTC	67	Cox	JMG	25	649	88
41	Argininaemia	ARG	GGGTG*GAAGAaGGCCTACAG	26	Haraguchi	JCI	86	347	90
42	Argininaemia	ARG	GCAGCAA*GTCaagaAGAACGGAAG	87	Haraguchi	JCI	86	347	90
43	Aspartylglucosamin.	AGA	TCAAC*ACTTGgccctttAAGAATGCAA	33	Ikonen	PNAS	88	11222	91
44	Aspartylglucosamin.	AGA	AAAAT*GCTATtGGTGTGGCAC	111	Ikonen	PNAS	88	11222	91
45	Chorioderaemia	CHM	CAGAG*GAACCaGGAACTTTTG	144	van d.Hurk	AJHG	50	1195	92
46	Chorioderaemia	CHM	AGAAA*TTGTTtgttCCATATACTG	190	van d.Hurk	AJHG	50	1195	92
47	Crigler–Najjar syn.1	UGT1	ATTTGAA*GCCtacattaatgcttcTGGAGAACAT	293	Ritter	JCI	90	150	92
48	Cystic fibrosis	CFTR	ATTGTCA*GACatATACCAAATC	36	Fanen	GENOMICS	13	770	92
49	Cystic fibrosis	CFTR	TACTG*GGAAGaATCATAGCTT	103	White	GENOMICS	10	266	91
50	Cystic fibrosis	CFTR	ACACCCA*GCCaTTTTTGGCCT	141	Zielenski	GENOMICS	10	229	91
51	Cystic fibrosis	CFTR	CCCAGCC*ATTtTTGGCCTTCA	142	Graham	GENOMICS	12	854	92
52	Cystic fibrosis	CFTR	CCTTCAT*CACaTTGGAATGCA	147	Fanen	GENOMICS	13	770	92
53	Cystic fibrosis	CFTR	CTCAGGG*TTCtTTGTGGTGTT	315	Claustres	GENOMICS	13	907	92
54	Cystic fibrosis	CFTR	TGTACAA*ACAtGGTGATGACTC	360	Iannuzzi	AJHG	48	227	91
55	Cystic fibrosis	CFTR	CATGG*TATGActCTCTTGGAGC	362	Ferec	NATURE GEN	1	188	92
56	Cystic fibrosis	CFTR	ATTCTGT*TCTcagTTTTCCTGG	492	Chillon	HUM MUTAT	1	75	92
57	Cystic fibrosis	CFTR	AGAAAAT*ATCatcTTTGGTGTTT	506	Kerem	PNAS	87	8447	90
58	Cystic fibrosis	CFTR	AAAAT*ATCATcttTGGTGTTTCC	506	Riordan	SCIENCE	245	1066	89
59	Cystic fibrosis	CFTR	ATGAGT*GAATAtaGATACAGAAG	514	Ivaschenko	GENOMICS	10	298	91
60	Cystic fibrosis	CFTR	CTGAGT*GGAGgTCAACGAGCA	550	Devoto	AJHG	48	1127	91
61	Cystic fibrosis	CFTR	AAAAT*CTACAcGCAGACTTTA	636	Fanen	GENOMICS	13	770	92
62	Cystic fibrosis	CFTR	CAGAA*ACAAAaaAAACAATCTT	682	Tsui	CFC			91
63	Cystic fibrosis	CFTR	GCCGAC*ACTTtGCTTGCTATG	925	Devoto	AJHG	48	1127	91
64	Cystic fibrosis	CFTR	GGTAAA*CCTAcCAAGTCAACC	1175	Kerem	PNAS	87	8447	90
65	Cystic fibrosis	CFTR	AAACCT*ACCaaGTCAACCAAA	1176	Cutting	CFC			91
66	Cystic fibrosis	CFTR	GAGAAT*TCAAaGTCAACCAAA	1196	Cutting	AJHG	50	1185	92

Deletions of <20 bp causing human genetic disease (continued)

No.	Disease	Gene	Deletion and flanking sequence	Codon	Author	Journal	Vol.	Page	Year
67	Cystic fibrosis	CFTR	ACGTG*AAGAAaGATGACATCT	1199	Fanen	GENOMICS	13	770	92
68	Cystic fibrosis	CFTR	TAGAG*AACATtTCCTTCTCAA	1229	White	GENOMICS	10	266	91
69	Duchenne musc. dystr.	DMD	GACTCC*CCCCtGAGCCAGCCT	3484	Roberts	PNAS	89	2331	92
70	Elliptocytosis	GPC	TCTGG*ATGGCcGGATGGCAGA	41	Telen	BLOOD	78	1603	91
71	Factor VII defic.	F7	CATGTG*GTGCcCCTCTGCCTG	259	Millar	LANCET	339	1359	92
72	Factor VII defic.	F7	GCTGCTG*GACcGTGGCGCCAC	289	Millar	LANCET	339	1359	92
73	Factor X defic.	F10	AGTTC*TACATcCTAACGGCAG	270	Reddy	BLOOD	74	1486	89
74	Fructose intolerance	ALDB	ATGCA*GGAACaaacAAAGAAACCA	117	Dazzo	AJHG	46	1194	90
75	Fructose intolerance	ALDB	TGCTATC*AAcCTTTGCCCTCT	287	Cross	LANCET	355	306	90
76	Fructose intolerance	ALDB	TCCCACCATAg*gtaCCATGGGGAA	I2E3	Cross	AJHG	47	101	90
77	Gangliosidosis GM2	HEXA	CAGCTT*GTTTgGAAATCTGCT	145	Mules	AJHG	50	834	92
78	Gangliosidosis GM2	HEXA	TCATCTT*GGAggaGATGAGGTTG	319	Mules	AJHG	50	834	92
79	Glanzmann thrombast.	GP2B	GGCCCTTTCag*gcctgcgcccCCTGGCAGCA	I3E4	Newman	PNAS	88	3160	91
80	Glanzmann thrombast.	GP3A	CTGGC*AGGAtgcagtgaattGTACCTATAA	650	Newman	PNAS	88	3160	91
81	Gyrate atrophy	OAT	AGGACACAATg*TTTTCCAAAC	2	Brody	JBC	267	3302	92
82	Gyrate atrophy	OAT	CCCTG*GAGAGagGAAAAGGTAC	63	Mashima	AJHG	51	81	92
83	Gyrate atrophy	OAT	GACGTTG*TCTgctATCTCCAGTT	183	Brody	JBC	267	3302	92
84	Gyrate atrophy	OAT	ATTAAG*CCAGgGGAGCATGGG	316	Brody	JBC	267	3302	92
85	Gyrate atrophy	OAT	TAGAA*GAAGaAACCTTGCTG	342	Brody	JBC	267	3302	92
86	Gyrate atrophy	OAT	TTTCTCCTgatag*gagtGGAGGCTGGA	I4E5	McClatchey	AJHG	47	790	90
87	HPRT deficiency	HPRT	CCGCGCGCGgcgcgctcgttaTG*GCGACCCG	2	Gibbs	PNAS	86	1919	89
88	HPRT deficiency	HPRT	TATGGA*CTAATtATGGACAGG	40	Gibbs	GENOMICS	7	253	90
89	HPRT deficiency	HPRT	ATGACT*GTAGattTTATCAGACT	79	Tarle	GENOMICS	10	499	91
90	HPRT deficiency	HPRT	TCCTATG*ACTgtAGATTTTATC	95	Gibbs	PNAS	86	1919	89
91	HPRT deficiency	HPRT	AAGAGC*TATTgtGTGAGTA	104	Gibbs	GENOMICS	7	253	90
92	HPRT deficiency	HPRT	AAAGAAT*GTCtGATTGTGGA	129	Gibbs	GENOMICS	7	253	90
93	HPRT deficiency	HPRT	CCCACGA*AGTgttGGATATAAGC	170	Gibbs	GENOMICS	7	253	90
94	HPRT deficiency	HPRT	CCAGAC*TTTGttgGATTGAAAT	177	Gibbs	PNAS	86	1919	89
95	HPRT deficiency	HPRT	AATCAT*GTTTgtGTCATTAGTG	203	Davidson	AJHG	48	951	91
96	Haemophilia B	F9	TCAGGT*AAATtGGAAGAGTTT	5	Green	EMBO J	8	1067	89
97	Haemophilia B	F9	AAACAT*GAAagaACAGTGAGTA	36	Green	EMBO J	8	1067	89
98	Haemophilia B	F9	GGAACTG*GACgaaccttAGTGCTAAAC	276	Green	EMBO J	8	1067	89
99	Haemophilia B	F9	TGGGGA*AGAGtcTTCCACAAAG	312	Green	EMBO J	8	1067	89

100	Haemophilia A	F8	AATGAAA*AATaatgAAGAAGCGGA	Kogan	PNAS	339	87	2092	90
101	Haemophilia A	F8	GAAAAAT*AATgaAGAAGCGGAAG	Higuchi	GENOMICS	340	6	65	90
102	Haemophilia A	F8	CAAGGA*GCCaAAAAAATAAC	Tuddenham	NAR	1438	19	4821	91
103	Haemophilia A	F8	CGATT*AAGTGgaATGAAGCAAA	Tuddenham	NAR	1534	19	4821	91
104	Haemophilia A	F8	ATCTGGG*ATAaaACACAATAT	Tuddenham	NAR	2135	19	4821	91
105	Haemophilia A	F8	GCCACC*TGGTctcCTTCAAAAGC	Tuddenham	NAR	2203	19S	2193	91
106	Haemophilia B	F9	CAGTGCT*GAAtgtacaggtTGTTTCCTTT	Giannelli	NAR	−20	19S	2193	91
107	Haemophilia B	F9	AAATTG*GAAGagTTTGTTCAAG	Giannelli	NAR	7	19S	2193	91
108	Haemophilia B	F9	TGGAA*GAGTTtgttcAAGGGAACCT	Giannelli	NAR	8	19S	2193	91
109	Haemophilia B	F9	CAAGGG*AACCttGAGAGAGAAT	Giannelli	NAR	13	19S	2193	91
110	Haemophilia B	F9	AGCACGA*GAAgTTTTGAAAA	Giannelli	NAR	30	19	1172	91
111	Haemophilia B	F9	GAAAGA*ACAGtgagTATTTCCACA	Chen	NAR	38	19S	2193	91
112	Haemophilia B	F9	CTTTATAG*ACtgAATTTTGGAA	Giannelli	NAR	39	19S	2193	91
113	Haemophilia B	F9	GTGAA*TTAGGtaagTAACTATTTT	Giannelli	NAR	84	19S	2193	91
114	Haemophilia B	F9	TGTTTCA*CAAaCTTCTAAGCT	Giannelli	NAR	139	19S	2193	91
115	Haemophilia B	F9	CTGAA*GCTGAaaccatttggATAACATCAC	Koeberl	AJHG	161	45	448	89
116	Haemophilia B	F9	AGCACC*CAATcATTTAATGAC	Giannelli	NAR	173	19S	2193	91
117	Haemophilia B	F9	TCATTT*AATGaCTTCACTCGG	Giannelli	NAR	176	19S	2193	91
118	Haemophilia B	F9	TCGGGT*GTTggtGGAGAAGATG	Giannelli	NAR	182	19S	2193	91
119	Haemophilia B	F9	GTTGTT*GGTGgagAAGATGCCAA	Giannelli	NAR	183	19S	2193	91
120	Haemophilia B	F9	GCCCTT*CTGGaAACTGGACGA	Giannelli	NAR	273	19S	2193	91
121	Haemophilia B	F9	GATCA*GCTTTagttcttCAGTACCTTA	Giannelli	NAR	320	19S	2193	91
122	Haemophilia B	F9	AGAGT*CCACttgTTGACCGAGC	Giannelli	NAR	329	19S	2193	91
123	Haemophilia B	F9	TAACAAC*ATGtTCTGTGCTGG	Giannelli	NAR	348	19S	2193	91
124	Haemophilia B	F9	GCTTC*TTAACtGGAATTATTA	Giannelli	NAR	379	19S	2193	91
125	Haemophilia B	F9	AGGCAAA*TATggaatatataccaaGGTATCCCGG	Giannelli	NAR	395	19S	2193	91
126	Haemophilia B	F9	GTCAAC*TGGatTAAGGAAAAA	Giannelli	NAR	407	19S	2193	91
127	Haemophilia B	F9	TGTCTTCTTTtattctttataAG*ACTGAATT	Giannelli	NAR	I2E3	19S	2193	91
128	Haemophilia B	F9	TCTATTT*GCttctTTTA*GATGTA	Koeberl	AJHG	I4E5	45	448	89
129	Haemophilia B	F9	CTTCTTTTA*GaTGTAACATGTAAC	Schach	JCI	I4E5	80	1023	87
130	Haemophilia B	F9	CACTTTCACAaTCTGCTAGCA	Reitsma	CIRCULAT	5'UTR	78S2	118	88
131	Hypercholesterol.	LDLR	TTGGGTC*TGCgatgcAGCGCTGAGT	Leitersdorf	PNAS	25	85	7912	88
132	Hypercholesterol.	LDLR	AGCGACA*ATCaccGCCGGGGTCG	Meiner	AJHG	196	49	443	91
133	Hypercholesterol.	LDLR	GGTCA*GATGAaccatcAAAGAGTGCG	Koivisto	JCI	286	90	219	92
134	Hyperglycinaemia (NK)	GLD	TCACAAG*ACCttcTGCATTCCCC	Kure	BBRC	755	174	1176	91
135	Hypobetalipoprotein.	APOB	CCCTG*AAGCTgCATGTGGCTG	Collins	NAR	1793	16	8369	88
136	Hypobetalipoprotein.	APOB	AGCAGAC*ACTgtCTGTAAGGCT	Talmud	JLR	1828	30	1773	92
137	Hypobetalipoprotein.	APOB	ATTAACA*GGGaAGATAGACTT	Welty	JCI	3039	87	1748	91

Deletions of <20 bp causing human genetic disease (continued)

No.	Disease	Gene	Deletion and flanking sequence	Codon	Author	Journal	Vol.	Page	Year
138	Hypobetalipoprotein.	APOB	TTGGGAA`GAAaGAGGCAGCTTC	4033	Talmud	JLR	30	1773	92
139	Isovaleric acidaemia	IVD	ATGGGC`CGCTtTCTTCGAGAT	392	Vockley	AJHG	49	147	91
140	LDH deficiency	LDHB	GGGCT`ATTGGactctgtagcagatttggCAGAGAGTAT	251	Maekawa	BBRC	168	677	90
141	Lactic acidosis	PDHA1	TTAAG`TCAGTcagtTAAGGGGAGG	383	Endo	AJHG	44	358	89
142	Lipoprt. lipase def.	LPL	CATTGGA`GAAgCTATCCGCGT	220	Takagi	JCI	89	581	92
143	MCAD deficiency	MCAD	TGCAAAT`CAGttagCTACTGATGC	336	Ding	AJHG	50	229	92
144	Maple syrup ur. dis.	BCKDH	CGCGG`CTTCCtgggcgcggggcTGGCGCGGGG	26	Nobukuni	JCI	87	1862	91
145	Maple syrup ur. dis.	BCKDH	AACATATAAG`gTTGGCTATGC	E111	Mitsubishi	JCI	87	1207	91
146	Metachrom. leukodys.	ARSA	CCCAG`TTAGAcgacgtgaCCTTCCGGCC	466	Bohne	HUM GENET	87	155	91
147	Neurofibromatosis (1)	NF1	CTACCTGCTGccaccTTGGCTTTAG	?	Stark	HUM GENET	87	685	91
148	Niemann–Pick disease	ASM	GAACATC`TCTttGCCTACTGTG	177	Takahashi	JBC	267	12552	92
149	Niemann–Pick dis. (B)	SMPD1	CTGCT`CTGTGccgCCACCTGATG	606	Levran	JCI	88	806	91
150	Osteogenesis imp.	COL1A2	GTCAAACT`GTaagtatttactCTTAAGCACT	E919	Nicholls	HUM GENET	88	627	92
151	Osteogenesis imp. (2)	COL1A2	CCCAGAC`CAGgaattCGGCTTCGAC	13	Willing	JCI	85	282	90
152	Osteogenesis imp. (2a)	COL1A1	CCCTGGT`GCTcctggtgctCTGGTGCCC	869	Hawkins	JBC	266	22370	91
153	PDH deficiency	PDH1A	AAATT`CAGGAagtaagaAGTAAGAGTGA	303	Dahl	AJHG	47	286	90
154	Phenylketonuria	PAH	TTGCGC`TTATtTGAGGAGAAT	54	Eigel	HUM GENET	87	739	91
155	Phenylketonuria	PAH	TCTGACA`AACatcATCAAGATCT	93	Caillaud	JBC	266	9351	91
156	Phenylketonuria	PAH	GAAGCCA`AAGcttCTCCCCTGG	363	Svensson	HUM GENET	85	300	90
157	Piebaldism	KIT	TCTGAA`CTCAaaGTCCTGAGTT	641	Spritz	AJHG	50	261	92
158	Porphyria acut. int.	PBG	CTACCAT`CCAtGTCCCTGCCC	282	Delfau	AJHG	49	421	91
159	Propionic acidaemia	PCCB	ATACGGGGGCatcATCCGGCATG	?	Lamhonwah	GENOMICS	8	249	90
160	Protein C deficiency	PROC	CGGCAGC`TTCagctgcgactgccgcagcGGCTGGGAGG	76	Tsuda	TH	65	647	91
161	Protein C deficiency	PROC	CAGCTTC`AGCtgcgactgccgcagcggcTGGGAGGGCC	77	Tsuda	TH	65	647	91
162	Protein C deficiency	PROC	GCAGTGT`CACcccgcAGGTGAGAAG	134	Sugahara	BLOOD	80	126	92
163	Protein C deficiency	PROC	CCTGG`AAGCGgATGGAGAAGG	146	Grundy	THR RES	61	335	91
164	Protein C deficiency	PROC	GACGGGC`TGGGgCTACCACAG	300	Bernardi	BJH	81	277	92
165	Protein C deficiency	PROC	GTGAGC`TGGGgTGAGGGCTGT	380	Yamamoto	TH	65	646	91
166	Pyruvate dehydrog. def.	PDH	AGTAAGA`AGTaagAGTCGACCCT	312	Hansen	JIMD	14	140	91
167	Pyruvate dehydrog. def.	PDH	GATCAAG`TTTaaGTCAGTCAGT	386	Hansen	JIMD	14	140	91
168	Retinitis pigmentosa	RDS	TGTGGCT`CTCgcTGCTTTCTGC	117	Farrar	NATURE	354	478	91
169	Retinitis pigmentosa	RDS	TCCTAGC`TCGcacaCGCCCTGCA	218	Kajiwara	NATURE	354	480	91
170	Retinit. pigm. (aut.)	RHO	GCACAAG`AAGctgcgcacgcctCTCAACTACA	67	Keen	GENOMICS	11	199	91

No.	Disease	Gene	Sequence		Author	Journal			
171	Retinit. pigm. (aut.)	RHO	CCGCATG'GTCatcATCATGGTCA	254	Ingelhearn	AJHG	48	26	91
172	Retinoblastoma	RB1	CTTCTG'AATGacaACATTTTCA	478	Lohmann	HUM GENET	89	49	92
173	Retinoblastoma	RB1	CTGGACC'CTTtTCCAGCACAC	683	Lohmann	HUM GENET	89	49	92
174	Retinoblastoma	RB1	CAAGTTT'CCTagttcacctTACGGATTCC	793	Lohmann	HUM GENET	89	49	92
175	Serum albumin def.	ALB	TGCTGC'AAGTcAAGCTGCCTT	613	Watkins	PNAS	88	5959	91
176	Ster.17α-hydrox. def.	CYP17	GCATAAC'AACttcTTCAAGCTGC	52	Yanase	JBC	264	18076	89
177	Ster.21-hydrox. def.	CYP21	TGCAGC'CCCCggGGGATGGGGG	483	Wedell	PNAS	89	7232	92
178	Tay–Sachs disease	HEXA	TCAAC'AAGACtgaGATTGAAGA	157	Triggs-Raine	AJHG	49	1041	91
179	Tay–Sachs disease	HEXA	AGACACTTCCtctccTCTCCAG'GCT	I9E10	Triggs-Raine	AJHG	49	1041	91
180	Tay–Sachs disease	HEXB	GAGCACA'TTCttcTTAGAAGTCA	304	Akli	GENOMICS	11	124	91
181	Tay–Sachs disease	HEXB	TGTCA'CACTtcCGCTGTGAGT	502	Lau	JBC	264	21376	89
182	Thalassaemia α	HBA	GGCCCTG'GAGagGTGAGGCTCC	30	Safaya	JBC	263	4328	88
183	Thalassaemia α	HBA	CCTGGAG'AGGtgaggCTCCCTCCCC	31	Orkin	PNAS	78	5041	81
184	Thalassaemia β	HBA	AGACACC'ATGgtGCACCTGACT	−1	Rosatelli	AJHG	50	422	92
185	Thalassaemia β	HBB	CACCTG'ACTCctGAGGAGAAG	4	Kollia	HEMOGLOBIN	13	597	89
186	Thalassaemia β	HBB	CTGACT'CCTGaGGAGAAGTCT	5	Kazazian	AJHG	35	1028	83
187	Thalassaemia β	HBB	CCTGACT'CCTgaggagAAGTCTGCCG	5	Efstradiad	CELL	21	653	80
188	Thalassaemia β	HBB	TCCTGAG'GAGaaGTCTGCCGTT	7	Kollia	HEMOGLOBIN	13	597	89
189	Thalassaemia β	HBB	AAGTCT'GCCGtTACTGCCCTG	10	Economou	GENOMICS	11	474	91
190	Thalassaemia β	HBB	CCTGTGG'GGCaagtgAACGTGGATG	16	Efstradiad	CELL	21	653	80
191	Thalassaemia β	HBB	CGTGGAT'GAAgttGGTGAGGCCC	22	Efstradiad	CELL	21	653	80
192	Thalassaemia β	HBB	GGCTG'CTGGTggtCTACCCTGG	32	Park	BJH	78	581	91
193	Thalassaemia β	HBB	TCTAC'CCTTGgaccagAGGTTCTTTG	36	Schnee	BLOOD	73	2224	89
194	Thalassaemia β	HBB	ACCCT'TGGACcCAGAGGTTCT	37	Indrak	ANN HAEMAT	63	111	91
195	Thalassaemia β	HBB	GACCCAG'AGGttcTTGAGTCCTTT	40	Kimura	JBC	258	2748	83
196	Thalassaemia β	HBB	CCCAG'AGGTTctttgagtcCTTTGGGGAT	40	Efstradiad	CELL	21	653	80
197	Thalassaemia β	HBB	AGGTTC'TTTGagtctttgGGGATCTGTC	42	Efstradiad	CELL	21	653	80
198	Thalassaemia β	HBB	TCTTT'GAGTCcTTTGGGGATC	43	Kinniburgh	NAR	10	5421	82
199	Thalassaemia β	HBB	TGCTGTT'ATGgcaacctaagGTGAAGGCTC	55	Efstradiad	CELL	21	653	80
200	Thalassaemia β	HBB	CTTTAGT'GATggcctgGCTCACCTGG	73	Efstradiad	CELL	21	653	80
201	Thalassaemia β	HBB	CAACCTC'AAGgGCACCTTTGC	82	Schwartz	NAR	17	3997	89
202	Thalassaemia β	HBB	ACACTG'AGTGagctgcactgtgacaAGCTGCACGT	89	Efstradiad	CELL	21	653	80
203	Thalassaemia β	HBB	GACAAG'CTGCacgTGGATCCTGA	96	Wilson	BLOOD	75	1883	90
204	Thalassaemia β	HBB	TCATG'TCATAgGAAGGGGAGA	108	Kazazian	AJHG	25S	950	92
205	Thalassaemia β	HBB	CAAAGAA'TTCaCCCCACCAGT	122	Fucharoen	BJH	75	393	90
206	Thalassaemia β	HBB	ACCCCA'CCAGtGCAGGCTGCC	125	Murru	BLOOD	77	1342	91
207	Thalassaemia β	HBB	CCACCA'GTGCaggCTGCCTATCA	126	Hattori	HEMOGLOBIN	13	657	89
208	Thalassaemia β	HBB	GCTAAT'GCCCtggccacaAGTATCACTA	140	Wilson	BLOOD	75	1883	90

Human gene mutation

Deletions of <20 bp causing human genetic disease (continued)

No.	Disease	Gene	Deletion and flanking sequence	Codon	Author	Journal	Vol.	Page	Year
209	Thalassaemia β	HBB	GGCTAAT^GCCctgGCCCACAAGT	140	Efstradiad	CELL	21	653	80
210	Thalassaemia β	HBB	ATTCTGCCTAataaaAAACATTTAT	3'UTR	Rund	PNAS	89	4324	92
211	Thalassaemia β	HBB	CTAGCAACCTcaaaCAGACACCAT	5'UTR	Huang	BJH	78	125	91
212	Thalassaemia β	HBB	AAAAAATTAagcaGCAGTATCCT	5'UTR	Gilman	BJH	68	455	88
213	Thyroid hormone res.	THR	AGGGGC^GTGAcacGGGGCCAGCT	331	Usala	MOL END	5	327	91
214	Thyr.-bind. glob. def.	TBG	TGCTGCC^CATaAGGCTGTGCT	351	Yamamori	JCEM	73	262	91
215	Waardenburg syndrome	PAX3	ATAGTGGAGAtggcccaccacggcatccGGCCCTGCGT	?	Tassabehji	NATURE	355	635	92
216	Waardenburg syndrome	PAX3	ATCCTG^TGCAggtaccaggagactGGCTCCATAC	157	Morell	HMG	1	243	92
217	Wilms' tumour	WT1	AACAGTGACAatttataccaaatgacaTCCCAGCTTG	?	Peletier	NATURE	353	431	91
218	Xeroderma pigmentosum	XPAC	GGATTCT^TATcttatGAACCACTTT	116	Satokata	HUM GENET	88	603	92
219	Xeroderma pigmentosum	XPAC	GATTTG^CCAacTTGTGATAAC	124	Satokata	HUM GENET	88	603	92

Deleted bases are denoted by lower-case letters; the number of the triplet following the circumflex is given in the Codon column; IxEy denotes boundary between intron x and exon y; 5' UTR denotes 5' untranslated region; 3' UTR denotes 3' untranslated region; PROM denotes promoter region.

Appendix 4 Examples of splice site mutations

Single base-pair substitutions within mRNA splice sites causing human genetic disease

Table 1

(a) Mutations of the invariant g(+1) at the 5' splice site

No.	Gene	Disease	Exons	Author	Journal	Vol.	Page	Year	I	Mutation	CVN	CVM	Comments
1	APOA2	ApoA2 deficiency	4	Deeb	AJHG	46	822	90	3	AA(g→a)taagt	0.876	0.693	
2	APOC2	ApoC2 deficiency	4	Fojo	JCI	82	1489	88	2	TG(g→c)tgagt	0.889	0.706	
3	AR	Androgen insensit.	8	Ris-Stalp.	PNAS	87	7866	90	4	TG(g→t)taagg	0.876	0.693	Cryptic, 123 nt. upstm. (AGgtgta7)
4	ARSA	Leukodystrophy	8	Polten	NEJM	324	18	91	2	AG(g→a)taagga	0.836	0.653	
5	C3	Complement C3 def.	41	Botto	JCI	86	1158	90	18	GG(g→a)taagg	0.876	0.693	Cryptic, 61 nt. upstm. (77gtgagt)
6	CETP	Lipid transfer def.	16	Brown	NATURE	342	448	89	14	TC(g→a)taagt	0.786	0.604	
7	CFTR	Cystic fibrosis	27	Zielenski	GENOMICS	10	229	91	4	AG(g→t)taata	0.799	0.617	
8	CFTR	Cystic fibrosis	27	Zielenski	GENOMICS	10	229	91	5	AA(g→t)tatgt	0.763	0.580	
9	COL1A2	Ehlers–Danlos VII	49	Weil	JBC	265	16007	90	6	TG(g→a)tatgc	0.750	0.568	100% exon skipping
10	COL3A1	Ehlers–Danlos IV	>45	Cole	JBC	265	17070	90	41	AG(g→a)tgagt	0.967	0.785	100% exon skipping
11	COL3A1	Aortic aneurism	>45	Kontusaari	AJHG	47	112	90	20	GC(g→a)taagt	0.786	0.604	1% exon skipping; 38% cryptic, 24 nt. dnstm.
12	COL3A1	Ehlers–Danlos IV	>45	Kuivaniemi	JBC	265	12067	90	20	GC(g→a)taagt	0.786	0.604	1% exon skipping; 53% cryptic (TGgttatt)
13	COL3A1	Ehlers–Danlos IV	>45	Kuivaniemi	JBC	265	12067	90	16	AG(g→a)taaac	0.797	0.615	70% exon skipping; 21% cryptic (GGgtataa)
14	COL3A1	Ehlers–Danlos IV	>45	Kuivaniemi	JBC	265	12067	90	42	AT(g→a)tgagt	0.839	0.657	100% cryptic, 30 nt. dnstm. (AGgtagaa)
15	F9	Haemophilia B	8	Giannelli	NAR	19S	2193	91	5	AG(g→t)tcata	0.699	0.558	
16	F9	Haemophilia B	8	Rees	NATURE	316	643	85	6	AG(g→t)tactt	0.741	0.558	
17	F9	Haemophilia B	8	Giannelli	NAR	19S	2193	91	6	AG(g→a)tactt	0.741	0.558	
18	F11	Factor XI deficiency	15	Asakai	PNAS	86	7667	89	14	AG(g→a)taaca	0.801	0.619	
19	GNAS	Osteodystrophy	13	Weinstein	PNAS	87	8287	90	10	AG(g→c)tttgt	0.786	0.604	
20	HBB	Thalassaemia β	3	Treisman	NATURE	302	591	83	1	AG(g→a)ttggt	0.792	0.609	No wt. or exon skipped RNA, some cryptic
21	HBB	Thalassaemia β	3	Treisman	CELL	29	903	82	2	GG(g→a)tgagt	0.889	0.706	Cryptic, 47 nt. dnstm.; some exon skipping
22	HEXA	Tay–Sachs disease	14	Ohnu	JBC	34	18563	88	12	TG(g→c)taagg	0.876	0.693	50% exon skipping; 50% cryptic

Table 1 Continued

No.	Gene	Disease	Exons	Author	Journal	Vol.	Page	Year	I	Mutation	CVN	CVM	Comments
23	PAH	Phenylketonuria	13	Dianzani	AJHG	48	631	91	7	CC(g→a)tgagt	0.750	0.568	100% exon skipping
24	PAH	Phenylketonuria	13	Marvit	NAR	15	5613	87	12	CA(g→a)taagt	0.794	0.611	
25	PBGD	Porphyria, acute	15	Grandchamp	PNAS	86	661	89	1	CG(g→a)tgagt	0.885	0.703	
26	PROC	Protein C deficiency	9	Reitsma	pers.comm.					AG(g→a)tggga	0.803	0.703	
27	RB1	Retinoblastoma	27	Dunn	MCB	9	4596	89	12	AC(g→a)taagc	0.807	0.624	100% exon skipping
28	RB1	Retinoblastoma	27	Yandell	NEJM	321	1689	89	10	AG(g→t)tattg	0.697	0.515	100% exon skipping
29	UROD	Porphyria, cutaneous	>7	Garey	JCI	86	1416	90	6	AG(g→c)tgagt	0.967	0.785	100% exon skipping
(b) Mutations of the invariant t(+2) at the 5' splice site													
1	COL1A2	Ehlers–Danlos VIIB	49	Weil	JBC	263	8561	88	6	TGg(t→c)atgc	0.750	0.568	100% exon skipping
2	F9	Haemophilia B	8	Giannelli	NAR	19S	2193	91	3	TGg(t→g)aagc	0.863	0.681	
3	HBB	Thalassaemia β	3	Chibani	HUM GENET	78	190	88	1	AGg(t→g)tggt	0.792	0.609	
4	HBB	Thalassaemia β	3	Gonzalez	BJH	71	113	89	1	AGg(t→c)tggt	0.792	0.609	
5	HBB	Thalassaemia β	3	Bouhass	BLOOD	76	1054	90	1	AGg(t→a)tggt	0.828	0.646	
6	OTC	OTC deficiency	10	Carstens	AJHG	48	1105	91	7	AGg(t→c)atgc	0.828	0.646	
7	RB1	Retinoblastoma	27	Yandell	NEJM	321	1689	89	19	AGg(t→c)tagt	0.900	0.717	
8	SPTB	Elliptocytosis	?	Yoon	JBC	266	8490	91	X	CGg(t→a)gagc	0.827	0.644	Some exon skipping
(c) Other mutations at the 5' splice site													
1	AT3	AT3 deficiency	7	Berg	pers.comm.				3a	A(G→A)gtgagt	0.967	0.843	100% exon skipping, temp.-dep.; aa. change
2	COL1A2	Ehlers–Danlos VII	49	Weil	JBC	264	16804	89	6	T(G→A)gtgatgc	0.750	0.626	
3	F8	Haemophilia A	26	Antonarakis	pers.comm.				16	T(G→A)gtaagc	0.863	0.739	7% exon skipping; 3% wt. RNA; no aa. change
4	HEXA	Tay–Sachs disease	14	Akli	JBC	265	7324	90	5	T(G→A)gtaacc	0.721	0.597	100% exon skipping; aa. change, little wt. RNA, 4 cryptic species
5	PBGD	Porphyria, acute	15	Grandchamp	NAR	17	6637	89	12	T(G→A)gtaggg	0.768	0.644	100% exon skipping
6	HBB	Thalassaemia β	3	Vidaud	PNAS	86	1041	89	1	A(G→C)gttggt	0.792	0.657	100% exon skipping
7	LCAMB	LCAM deficiency	?	Kishimoto	JBC	264	3588	89	B	ATgt(g→c)agt	0.839	0.772	97% exon skipping; 3% wt. RNA
8	OTC	OTC deficiency	10	Carstens	AJHG	48	1105	91	7	AGgta(g→g)tgc	0.828	0.796	100% exon skipping
9	SPTB	Elliptocytosis	?	Garbarz	JCI	88	76	91	Y	GGgt(g→t)agt	0.889	0.821	Exon skipping (frequency not determined)
10	CAT	Acatalasaemia	13	Wen	JMB	211	383	90	4	TGgtag(g→a)t	0.814	0.670	100% exon skipping
11	COL1A1	Osteogenesis imp. II	51	Bonadio	JBC	265	2262	90	14	CTgtaa(g→a)t	0.790	0.646	100% exon skipping, temp.-dep.
12	COL3A1	Ehlers–Danlos IV	>45	Lee	JBC	266	5256	91	25	ATgtga(g→a)t	0.839	0.695	100% exon skipping, temp.-dep.
13	F8	Haemophilia A	26	Antonarakis	pers.comm.				12	CAgtga(g→a)t	0.761	0.617	
14	HBB	Thalassaemia β	3	Treisman	NATURE	302	591	83	1	AGgtt(g→c)t	0.792	0.650	50% wt RNA, 3 cryptic species*
15	HBB	Thalassaemia β	3	Lapoumeroul	BBRC	139	709	86	1	AGgtt(g→a)t	0.792	0.648	
16	HBB	Thalassaemia β	3	Atweh	BLOOD	70	147	87	1	AGgtt(g→a)t	0.792	0.648	
17	HPRT	Lesch–Nyhan syndrome	9	Gibbs	GENOMICS	7	235	90	8	ATgtaa(g→a)t	0.872	0.728	15% wt RNA, 85% cryptic species
18	F9	Haemophilia B	8	Green	BJH	78	390	91	1	AGgttt(g→a)t	0.786	0.642	
19	PROS	Protein S deficiency	15	Ploos v.Am.	pers.comm.				2	CGgtaa(g→a)c	0.859	0.715	

Table 1   Continued

No.	Gene	Disease	Exons	Author	Journal	Vol.	Page	Year	I	Mutation	CVN	CVM	Comments
20	PROC	Protein C deficiency	9	Reitsma	BLOOD	78	890	91	4	CGgtga(g→a)t	0.885	0.703	
21	PROC	Protein C deficiency	9	Reitsma	BLOOD	78	890	91	4	CGgtga(g→c)t	0.885	0.703	
22	PROC	Protein C deficiency	9	Reitsma	BLOOD	78	890	91	4	CGgtga(g→t)t	0.885	0.703	
23	F9	Haemophilia B	8	Bottema	AJHG	47	835	90	2	CAgtaag(t→c)	0.761	0.703	
24	HBB	Thalassaemia β	3	Treisman	NATURE	302	591	83	1	AGgttggt(t→c)	0.792	0.734	Almost normal wt RNA amount
25	F9	Haemophilia B	8	Koeberl	AJHG	47	202	90	4	AGgtaagt(a→g)			

*Exon1/105, AGgtgaac, Exon1/127, TGgttgagg, IVS1/13: AGgttaca.

The Exons column provides the number of exons contained within the gene in question. I denotes the number of the intron in whose vicinity the mutation was found. The Mutation column provides the single base-pair substitution in parentheses; bases within exons and introns are denoted by upper- and lower-case letters respectively. The Comments column includes data on the relative proportion (if known) of mRNA species generated either by exon skipping or by the use of cryptic splice sites. CVN, Shapiro–Senapathy consensus value of normal (wild-type) splice site; CVM, Shapiro–Senapathy consensus value of mutated splice site; CVA, Shapiro–Senapathy consensus value of activated cryptic splice site.

Table 2

No.	Gene	Disease	Exons	Author	Journal	Vol.	Page	Year	I	Mutation	CVN	CVM	Comments
(a) Mutations of the invariant a(−2) at the 3′ splice site													
1	ALB	Analbuminaemia	15	Ruffner	PNAS	85	2125	88	6	tttt(a→g)gGG	0.836	0.598	Five different RNAs including wt.
2	APOE	ApoA deficiency	4	Cladaras	JBC	262	2310	87	3	ccg(a→g)gGG	0.921	0.683	Cryptic, minor 53 nt. upstm.
3	COL1A2	Osteogenesis imp. II	49	Tromp	PNAS	85	5254	88	27	tttc(a→g)gGG	0.960	0.721	Exon skipping
4	F8	Haemophilia A	26	Naylor	LANCET	337	635	91	5	catc(a→g)gGG	0.843	0.605	Ectopic lymphocyte RNA (exon skipping)
5	F9	Haemophilia B	8	Koeberl	AJHG	47	202	90	4	tttt(a→g)gAT	0.814	0.576	Faint cryptic, 271 nt. upstm.
6	HBB	Thalassaemia β	3	Atweh	NAR	13	777	85	2	ccac(a→g)gCT	0.864	0.626	No aberrant RNA detected
7	HBB	Thalassaemia β	3	Padanilam	AJH	22	259	86	2	ccac(a→c)gCT	0.864	0.626	
8	HPRT	Lesch-Nyhan syndrome	9	Gibbs	GENOMICS	7	235	90	1	tttc(a→t)gAT	0.938	0.700	Cryptic 12 nt. dnstm. (gtctagCA)
9	OTC	OTC deficiency	10	Carstens	AJHG	48	1105	91	4	ccac(a→g)gTG	0.829	0.590	Exon skipping
10	RB1	Retinoblastoma	27	Horowitz	SCIENCE	243	937	89	20	tact(a→g)gAT	0.731	0.493	
(b) Mutations of the invariant g(−1) at the 3′ splice site													
1	ASS	Citrullinemia	16	Su	JBC	265	19716	90	15	ttaca(g→c)GC	0.950	0.712	Cryptic, 7 nt dnstm.
2	CFTR	Cystic fibrosis	27	Guillermit	HUM GENET	85	450	90	16	taata(g→a)GA	0.719	0.481	
3	F8	Haemophilia A	26	Antonarakis	pers.comm.					catca(g→c)GG	0.843	0.605	
4	F9	Haemophilia B	8	Koeberl	AJHG	47	202	90	3	tcaaa(g→a)AT	0.752	0.514	
5	F9	Haemophilia B	8	Green	BJH	78	390	91	4	tttta(g→c)AT	0.814	0.576	
6	F9	Haemophilia B	8	Chen	NAR	19	1172	91	7	taata(g→a)GT	0.767	0.529	
7	HEXA	Tay-Sachs disease	14	Mules	AJHG	48	1181	91	4	gcaca(g→t)TT	0.779	0.540	
8	LPL	LPL deficiency	10	Hata	AJHG	47	721	90	2	cttca(g→a)GT	0.976	0.729	
9	PAH	Phenylketonuria	13	Wang	AJHG	48	628	91	4	tcctа(g→a)GG	0.833	0.595	
10	RB1	Retinoblastoma	27	Dunn	MCB	9	4596	89	21	cctca(g→a)AC	0.867	0.629	100% exon skipping
(c) Other mutations at the 3′ splice site													
1	HBB	Thalassaemia β	3	Wong	BLOOD	73	914	89	1	cct(t→g)agGC	0.793	0.743	
2	HBB	Thalassaemia β	3	Wong	BLOOD	73	914	89	2	ccac(t→a)agCT	0.864	0.695	90% wt; 10% cryptic upstream
3	LPL	LPL deficiency	10	Gotoda	BBRC	164	1391	89	6	tag(c→t)agCT	0.805	0.681	
4	CA21HB	Adrenal hyperplasia	10	Hijashi	PNAS	85	7486	88	2	cccca(c→g)ctcctctgcagAC			Several cryptic species
5	HBB	Thalassaemia β	3	Beldjord	NAR	16	4927	88	2	c(t→g)ccacagCT			
6	HBB	Thalassaemia β	3	Murru	BLOOD	77	1342	91	2	ct(c→g)ccacagCT			

The Exons column provides the number of exons contained within the gene in question. I denotes the number of the intron in whose vicinity the mutation was found. The Mutation column provides the single base-pair substitution in parentheses; bases within exons and introns are denoted by upper- and lower-case letters respectively. The Comments column includes data on the relative proportion (if known) of mRNA species generated either by exon skipping or by the use of cryptic splice sites. CVN, Shapiro–Senapathy consensus value of normal (wild-type) splice site; CVM, Shapiro–Senapathy consensus value of mutated splice site; CVA, Shapiro–Senapathy consensus value of activated cryptic splice site.

Table 3

No.	Gene	Disease	Exons	Author	Journal	Vol.	Page	Year	I	Mutation	CVN	CVA	Comments
(a) Creation of novel 5' splice sites													
1	F8	Haemophilia A	26	Youssoufian	GENOMICS	2	32	88	4	(G→A)AAgtgagt			Silent
2	F9	Haemophilia B	8	Koeberl	AJHG	47	202	90	2	AGGTAAAT→AGgtaagt		1.000	
3	F9	Haemophilia B	8	Koeberl	AJHG	47	202	90	5	AG/GTCATAATCTGA(a→g)taaga	0.700	0.741	5-8% cryptic*
4	HBB	Thalassaemia β	3	Orkin	NATURE	300	768	82	1	TGgt(g→a)aggnnnnnnncag/gttggt	0.792	0.876	Silent, 25% wt.
5	HBB	Thalassaemia β	3	Goldsmith	PNAS	80	2318	83	1	(T→A)Ggtgaagccctgggcag/gttggt	0.792	0.992	Minor RNA cryptic
6	HBB	Thalassaemia β	3	Orkin	BLOOD	64	311	84	1	TGgtag(g→t)		0.887	Activates new 3' site†
7	HBB	Thalassaemia β	3	Treisman	NATURE	302	591	83	2	AG(c→g)tacca		0.686	
(b) Creation of novel 3' splice sites													
8	ERCC3	Xeroderma pigm. B	24	Weeda	CELL	62	777	90	?	ttcc(c→a)gCAG/GC	0.838	0.964	Major RNA new site
9	HBB	Thalassaemia β	3	Spritz	PNAS	78	2455	81	1	tatt(g→a)gTCTATTTTCCCACCCTTAG/GC	0.793	0.640	Six of seven identical to wt.
10	HBB	Thalassaemia β	3	Westawa	NAR	9	1777	81	1	tatt(g→a)gTCTATTTTCCCACCCTTAG/GC	0.793	0.640	Branch site involved?
11	HEXB	Sandhoff disease	14	Nakano	JBC	264	5155	89	12	ttgc(g→a)gGGN(16)TTTTAG/GC	0.829	0.957	100% use of new site
12	PAH	Phenylketonuria	13	Kalaydjeva	LANCET	337	865	91	10	actt(g→a)gGGCCTACAG/TA	0.824	0.721	
13	SAP1	Leukodystrophy	?	Zhang	HUM GENET	87	211	91	?	cctc(c→a)gAT		0.902	

*CV of cryptic site before mutation: 0.843(i); †new 3' site upstm. CTTTCTTTCAG/G→extra exon (164 bp), more than wt.; /, original splice site.
The Exons column provides the number of exons contained within the gene in question. I denotes the number of the intron in whose vicinity the mutation was found. The Mutation column provides the single base-pair substitution in parentheses; bases within exons and introns are denoted by upper- and lower-case letters respectively. The Comments column includes data on the relative proportion (if known) of mRNA species generated either by exon skipping or by the use of cryptic splice sites. CVN, Shapiro–Senapathy consensus value of normal (wild-type) splice site; CVM, Shapiro–Senapathy consensus value of mutated splice site; CVA, Shapiro–Senapathy consensus value of activated cryptic splice site.

Appendix 5   Amino acid symbols and the genetic code

Amino acid symbols

A	Ala	Alanine	N	Asn	Asparagine
B	Asp/Asn	Aspartic acid/asparagine	P	Pro	Proline
C	Cys	Cysteine	Q	Gln	Glutamine
D	Asp	Aspartic acid	R	Arg	Arginine
E	Glu	Glutamic acid	S	Ser	Serine
F	Phe	Phenylalanine	T	Thr	Threonine
G	Gly	Glycine	V	Val	Valine
H	His	Histidine	W	Trp	Tryptophan
I	Ile	Isoleucine	X	Term	Termination
K	Lys	Lysine	Y	Tyr	Tyrosine
L	Leu	Leucine	Z	Glu/Gln	Glutamic acid/glutamine
M	Met	Methionine			

Genetic code (nuclear genome of vertebrates)

Phe	UUU	Ser	UCU	Tyr	UAU	Cys	UGU
	UUC		UCC		UAC		UGC
Leu	UUA		UCA	Term	UAA	Term	UGA
	UUG		UCG		UAG	Trp	UGG
Leu	CUU	Pro	CCU	His	CAU	Arg	CGU
	CUC		CCC		CAC		CGC
	CUA		CCA	Gln	CAA		CGA
	CUG		CCG		CAG		CGG
Ile	AUU	Thr	ACU	Asn	AAU	Ser	AGU
	AUC		ACC		AAC		AGC
	AUA		ACA	Lys	AAA	Arg	AGA
Met	AUG		ACG		AAG		AGG
Val	GUU	Ala	GCU	Asp	GAU	Gly	GGU
	GUC		GCC		GAC		GGC
	GUA		GCA	Glu	GAA		GGA
	GUG		GCG		GAG		GGG

Addendum
Cancer-associated
somatic mutations in
the human TP53 gene

The TP53 gene, located on the short arm of chromosome 17, is perhaps the most widely mutated gene in human tumourigenesis (Zambetti and Levine, 1993). It encodes a 53 kDa nuclear protein (p53) which is capable of binding to DNA and activating the transcription of responsive genes. One function of p53 is to act as a (recessive) tumour suppressor which, when inactivated, no longer exerts its protective influence through a DNA damage control pathway (Levine et al., 1991, Ullrich et al., 1992, Zambetti and Levine, 1993). Consistent with this model, primary mutation in one TP53 allele often appears to be associated with the loss of the other allele (Prives and Manfredi, 1993). However, knock-out of both TP53 alleles does not always occur, and a number of cancers may be due to dominant gain-of-function mutations (Dittmer et al., 1993) which typically have a much longer half-life than the wild-type protein and may inactivate it. That some types of cancer manifest TP53 gene mutations earlier in tumour development than others serves to indicate that a variety of cancer pathways may result from lesions in this key gene (Prives and Manfredi, 1993).

Some 83% of TP53 mutations are missense mutations (Harris and Holstein, 1993), a much higher proportion than that found in other tumour suppressor genes. The majority of these lesions have been observed within exons 5–8 of the TP53 gene, probably reflecting the importance of this region for the function of the protein. However, within exons 5–8, point mutations are not uniformly distributed. Rather, they are clustered in particular regions or even codons. This is illustrated in Figure 1 which shows the distribution of 955 somatic TP53 point mutations characterized in either primary tumours, metastases or cell lines from different types of human cancer. [These data represent 308 different single base-pair substitutions and comprise the results of an extensive survey of the literature; this TP53 mutation database is available from Eivind Hovig (Institute for Cancer Research, Oslo, Norway) on request.]

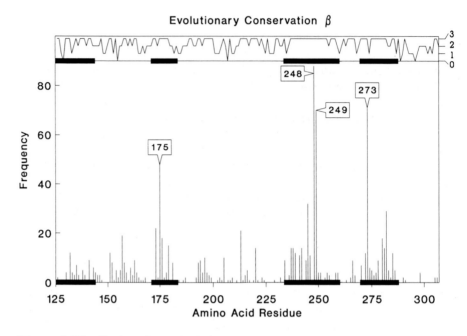

Figure 1. Distribution of 955 single base-pair substitutions within exons 5–8 of the TP53 gene. Exceptional mutation hotspots (over 40 examples known) are indicated by the corresponding amino acid residue number. The line diagram on top depicts the extent of evolutionary conservation, β, based on an amino acid sequence alignment for eight different vertebrates. Conserved regions as previously defined (Soussi *et al.*, 1990) are indicated by horizontal bars.

The analysis of somatic and germline mutational spectra

The determination of the spectrum of TP53 gene mutations detected in human cancer has led to the recognition of mutational hotspots and tissue-specific base substitution patterns (Brash *et al.*, 1991; Holstein *et al.*, 1991; Levine *et al.*, 1991; Ozturk *et al.*, 1991; Caron de Fromentel and Soussi, 1992; Crook and Vousden, 1992, Sato *et al.*, 1993, Ziegler *et al.*, 1993), some of which have suggested the involvement of exogenous mutagens in carcinogenesis. It was unclear, however, whether this mutational spectrum was unique either specifically to TP53 or generally to cancer-associated mutagenesis in somatic cells. Since negative controls had been lacking, extrapolation from mutations induced *in vitro* to causative mechanisms acting *in vivo* may have been premature in some instances. Indeed, Biggs *et al.* (1993) emphasized this point by demonstrating that the spectrum of TP53 single base-pair substitutions found in sporadic colorectal cancer is similar to that of their inherited counterparts in the human factor IX (F9) gene causing haemophilia B. The latter type of lesion must have originated in germ cells and may have been passed down through many generations before coming to clinical attention.

The conclusion by Biggs *et al.* (1993) of causative similarity for somatic and germline mutations was, however, based upon the analysis of only one specific disease gene. In order to avoid interpretational sampling errors that might result from these limitations, Krawczak *et al.* (1994) compared the somatic (*in vivo*) spectrum of single base-pair substitutions of the human TP53 gene with that of over 2000 germline mutations observed in a large collection of 279 different human genes other than TP53 and unrelated to cancer.

As already mentioned above, a number of tissue-specific (i.e. somatic) mutation hotspots and patterns have been identified in the TP53 gene, so that any inferences made concerning the mechanism(s) underlying the remaining mutations would have been confounded by the inclusion of these lesions. Krawczak *et al.* (1994) therefore excluded from their analysis some 12% of TP53 gene mutations that were over-represented at particular nucleotides in particular tissues. The most dramatic examples were 48 G→T transversions at position 249 in liver, 19 G→T tranversions at positions 157 and 273 in lung, and 11 and 13 G→A transitions, respectively, at positions 175 and 248 in colon and blood. The latter two mutations were both CG→CA and are thus potentially explicable by methylation-mediated deamination of 5-methylcyto-sine on the antisense strand (Section 6.2). That these mutations were tissue-specific was to some extent surprising since the CG dinucleotides at positions 175 and 248 have been shown to be similarly methylated in a number of different tissues (Rideout *et al.*, 1990; Felley-Bosco *et al.*, 1993).

The refined spectra of somatic TP53 base substitutions and of germline mutations in other genes obtained by Krawczak *et al.* (1994) are summarized in Table 1. When compared by a χ^2 test, two significant differences emerged:

Table 1. Spectra of (i) somatic single base-pair substitutions within the TP53 gene, and (ii) inherited single base-pair substitutions in 279 different genes causing human inherited disease

Original nucleotide		Newly introduced nucleotide				
		T	C	A	G	Totals
T	(i)	–	32	30	33	95
	(ii)	–	194	73	87	354
C	(i)	163[a]	–	21	37	221
	(ii)	519[b]	–	105	92	716
A	(i)	28	18	–	79	125
	(ii)	58	43	–	155	256
G	(i)	141	54	204[a]	–	399
	(ii)	191	131	576[b]	–	898
Totals	(i)	332	104	255	149	840
	(ii)	768	368	754	334	2224

Mutations of TP53 that were site- and tissue-specific have been excluded. The numbers of CpG→TpG and CpG→CpA transitions, compatible with deamination of 5-methylcytosine to thymine on one of the two DNA strands, are 120 (14.5%) and 108 (12.9%) for TP53 (a), and 338 (15.2%) and 276 (12.4%) for germline mutations (b).

T→C transitions were rarer ($\chi^2 = 21.6$) and G→T transversions more frequent ($\chi^2 = 42.4$) in TP53 than among germline mutations. [Note: The appropriate threshold allowing for multiple testing was 8.2, 1 df, 12 comparisons.] The observed excess of G→T substitutions may indicate that the influence of some exogenous carcinogens had not been completely eliminated by the aforementioned removal of highly frequent, tissue- and site-specific TP53 mutations: benzo[a]pyrene and aflatoxin B1, for example, are known to induce this type of lesion (Caron de Fromentel and Soussi, 1992). Cytosine to thymine (and G→A) transitions were slightly under-represented in the TP53 spectrum but, when tested individually, were found at a significantly higher frequency in skin cancer than in cancers of other tissues ($10/13 = 76.9\%$ vs $357/827 = 43.2\%$, Fisher's $P = 0.015$). This finding was compatible with the mutagenic action of sunlight, a major risk factor for basal cell carcinomas of the skin (Brash et al., 1991, Sato et al., 1993, Ziegler et al., 1993). When only C→T transitions at dipyrimidines on either strand of TP53 were considered (i.e. mutations that are highly specific to UV-irradiation), the difference was even more significant ($8/13 = 61.5\%$ vs $213/827 = 25.8\%$, $P = 0.007$).

Relative mutabilities and clinical observation likelihoods

In addition to the mutation rate, the frequency with which a particular type of base substitution is observed in a clinical sample is determined by (i) the severity of its consequences for protein structure and function, and (ii) the composition of the underlying DNA sequence(s). In Section 6.5, we introduced an analytical model that allows for these determinants and yields maximum likelihood estimates of the parameters involved. Krawczak et al. (1994) applied this methodology to the somatic TP53 gene and germline mutation data, and estimates of the relative mononucleotide substitution rates that emerged from this analysis are depicted in Figure 2. As is evident, the datasets yielded strikingly similar results, and significant discrepancies were noted for only 4/12 substitutions (T→C, C→A, A→G, and G→T). Similar findings were apparent from a nearest neighbour analysis of single base-pair substitutions (Figure 3). Significant differences were observed for only 5/16 dinucleotides, the most notable discrepancies concerning the mutability of CG and AG. Although similar proportions of CG mutations were observed in both datasets (Table 1), this dinucleotide was found to be approximately 30% less mutable in somatic TP53 than in the germline. This result was due to an almost twofold higher CG frequency within exons 5–8 of TP53 as compared with the average human gene coding sequence (Wada et al., 1991). Perhaps the most interesting finding concerned the relative clinical observation likelihoods, C(G). These estimates were strictly correlated with chemical difference for germline mutations, and differed by a factor of three between chemical difference class G = I and mutations creating termination codons. With somatic TP53 mutations, however, no obvious trend or pattern was

(a)

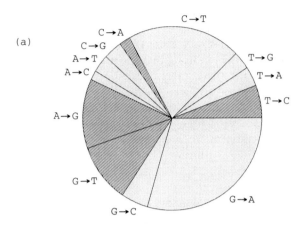

Figure 2. Relative mononucleotide substitution rates estimated from somatic, cancer-associated mutations in the TP53 gene (a) and germline mutations in other human genes (b). The size of each segment is proportional to the rate at which a given nucleotide is replaced by another. Significant differences are indicated by dark hatching. (For details concerning significance testing, see Krawczak *et al.*, 1994.)

(b)

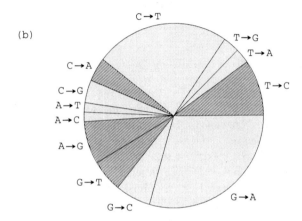

discernible, and as much as 5/11 relative likelihoods differed significantly between the germline and somatic spectra (Figure 4). However, only moderate chemical changes were over-represented among the TP53 mutation data, and no dramatic excess of termination codons was apparent.

Also depicted in Figure 1 is the extent of evolutionary conservation, β, of each amino acid residue. For the definition of β values, each amino acid residue within the human p53 sequence was classified by Krawczak *et al.* (1994) as either $\beta = 0$ (no conservation), $\beta = 1$ (conserved between primates), $\beta = 2$ (conserved between mammals) or $\beta = 3$ (conserved between vertebrates). Inspection of Figure 1 confirms that mutation clusters coincide with the evolutionarily conserved regions of the protein (Soussi *et al.*, 1990). As an additional parameter determining the observed mutational spectrum in TP53, relative likelihoods of clinical observation of particular types of amino acid substitution have been introduced, each depending on the level of evolutionary conserva.ion β. These parameters were estimated for TP53 as 0.8 ($\beta = 1$), 1.7 ($\beta = 2$), and 6.7 ($\beta = 3$), respectively, relative to $\beta = 0$. This implies that

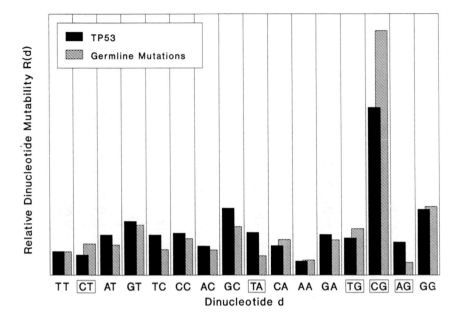

Figure 3. Estimates of relative dinucleotide mutabilities. Within each sample, the length of a vertical bar is proportional to the rate at which a given dinucleotide is affected by point mutation. Both spectra were scaled to a constant sum in order to permit their comparison. Significant differences between germline and TP53 mutations are indicated by squares. (For details concerning significance testing, see Krawczak *et al.*, 1994.)

substitutions at highly conserved p53 amino acid residues are 6.7 times more likely to result in a tumour than those at non-conserved residues.

A tissue-specific comparison of somatic and germline mutations

Sufficient data were available for five tissues, namely blood, breast, colon plus gastrointestinal tract, lung and liver, to allow a more specific analysis of relative mutabilities and clinical observation likelihoods. It should be remembered that highly tissue-specific substitutions at mutation hotspots had already been excluded from the set of TP53 mutations. Thus, differences with respect to the germline spectrum that emerged from the remainder applied more or less to the TP53 gene as a whole, and were therefore likely to reflect mutational and selectional effects in a broader sense rather than merely the specific function of single amino acid residues.

The different types of TP53 mutation in the colon and gastrointestinal tract arise at virtually the same relative rates as germline mutations. This result of Krawczak *et al.* (1994) confirmed findings of Biggs *et al.* (1993) who observed a close resemblance of the colon cancer TP53 and inherited F9 gene mutational spectra. With respect to clinical observation likelihoods, however,

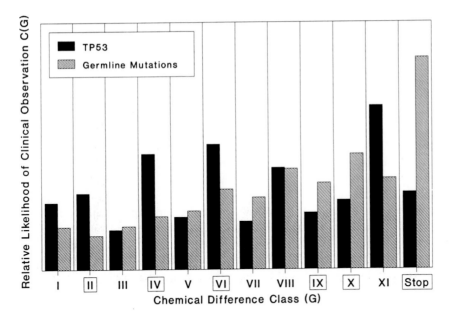

Figure 4. Estimates of the relative observation likelihood of single base-pair substitutions, depending on chemical difference. Relative observation likelihoods for mutations resulting in termination codons ('Stop') have been included. Both spectra were scaled to a constant sum in order to permit their comparison. Significant differences between germline and TP53 mutations are indicated by squares. (For details concerning significance testing, see Krawczak *et al.*, 1994.)

amino acid substitutions in the colon and gastrointestinal tract were notably different from germline mutations. Substitutions in p53 falling into two relatively low-ranking chemical difference classes were over-represented (G = II and G = VI), whereas mutations resulting in termination codons were depleted by a factor larger than three.

In association with lung cancer, G→T transversions have arisen in TP53 at a threefold higher rate as compared with germline mutations, and it is tempting again to invoke polycyclic aromatic hydrocarbons, the constituents of many air pollutants, to explain this difference. Transitions CG→TG and CG→CA, compatible with the deamination of 5-methylcytosine, were found three times less frequently than expected in TP53, thus providing indirect evidence for a lung-specific lack of methylation in this particular gene.

In accord with the data of Biggs *et al.* (1993), G→T transversions of TP53 were also found to be strongly associated with breast cancer, whereas CG→CA substitutions were depleted. The pattern of clinical observation likelihoods depending on chemical difference closely resembled that of colon cancer, and a threefold reduction of nonsense mutations was again apparent.

Two tissues not studied by Biggs *et al.* (1993) were analysed in more detail by Krawczak *et al.* (1994). In cancers related to blood, A→G and G→A transitions in TP53 were over-represented and this was due mainly to mutation at sites with 3'-flanking cytosines. No differences between the blood and germline spectra were observed with respect to clinical observation likelihoods depending on chemical difference.

A similar result was obtained for liver cancer. On the other hand, however, T→A and A→T transversions occurred in hepatocellular carcinomas at four times the expected frequency, and a nearest neighbour analysis revealed that these substitutions corresponded mainly to CT→CA and AG→TG events. The carcinogenic action of polycyclic aromatic hydrocarbons may serve to explain this finding as well. Carothers et al. (1990), for example, were able to induce adenine/thymine exchanges in the dihydrofolate reductase gene of Chinese hamster ovary cells specifically by treatment with benzo[c]phenanthrene; all A→T transversions were at sites with a 3'-flanking guanine residue (AGG, CAG and AAG). Further, in experiments to identify carcinogen-induced initiation events in cell transformation, Nakazawa et al. (1992) observed an A→T substitution at codon 61 of the Ki-ras gene in all (42 of 42) transformed foci of cells induced by benzo[a]anthracene. These mutations could not be induced by any other carcinogen tested.

Spectral similarity as evidence of causative similiarity

Such findings notwithstanding, Krawczak et al. (1994) demonstrated that the bulk of the spectrum of somatic single base-pair substitutions in the TP53 gene strongly resembles that of their germline counterparts seen in other human genes. The latter set of mutations have, however, arisen in a tissue that is usually well protected against exogenous mutagens and carcinogens: the germ cells. Since spectral similarity is strongly suggestive of the involvement of similar mutational mechanisms, it would appear that many TP53 mutations in the soma have arisen directly or indirectly as a consequence of endogenous cellular mechanisms (perhaps including those involved in DNA repair and replication) rather than through the action of exogenous mutagens. Even the (comparatively rare) liver-specific transitions mentioned above were explicable by alternative mutational pathways. Adenine to thymine and T→A transversions can also result from depurination events (i.e. the removal of purines from the phosphodiester backbone of the DNA; see p. 132), because DNA polymerases are known to incorporate deoxyadenosine preferentially opposite abasic sites (the so-called 'A-rule'). Depurination, on the other hand, can result from either endogenous (e.g. spontaneous hydrolysis of the N-glycosylic bond, DNA glycosylase activity during DNA repair) or exogenous (e.g. exposure of DNA to a chemical agent) mechanisms.

The data presented by Krawczak et al. (1994) also revealed that different modes of selection are likely to operate at the cellular (TP53) and individual/population level (germline mutations), determining whether a mutation survives to manifest itself clinically. Point mutations in TP53 have the highest chance of resulting in a tumour when they occur in conserved residues and change the encoded amino acid only moderately. This category of missense mutation may well include gain-of-function p53 variants. Such variants may possess a different conformation, exhibit a longer half-life and display an altered transcription-modulating specificity than wild-type p53 (Dittmer *et al.*, 1993). They may also down-regulate expression of the wild-type TP53 gene product.

Whereas less severe changes of p53 structure are likely to be inconsequential and would therefore go unnoticed, drastic changes resulting in complete inactivation of the protein may well still be compatible with life (certain null mice, although highly susceptible to tumours, appear able to survive in the absence of p53; Donehower *et al.*, 1992). Alternatively, severe aberrations of p53 structure/function may simply kill the mutant cell before it can become malignant. Taken together, these data were consistent with the view that selection, operating at the cellular level, is an important influence on the likelihood that a TP53 mutation will eventually cause human cancer.

The similarity noted between the cancer-associated mutational spectrum of TP53 and germline gene mutations was consistent with the idea that cancer is a critical mediator of negative selection against excessive germline mutation. Sommer (1994) has speculated that for such a mediator function to work, there must be a correlation between germline and somatic mutation rates. If specific mutations were to occur that enhanced the rates of both germline and somatic mutation, a consequent increase in the incidence of cancer before the end of the normal reproductive period would serve to militate against their survival. It follows that TP53 may act as a critical sensor that is built into the genome's molecular warning system and which, through carcinogenesis, "kills the individual and saves the species" (Sommer, 1994).

References

Biggs PJ, Warren W, Venitt S, Stratton MR. (1993) Does a genotoxic carcinogen contribute to human breast cancer? The value of mutational spectra in unravelling the aetiology of cancer. *Mutagenesis* 8: 275–283.

Brash DE, Rudolph JA, Simon JA, Lin A, McKenna GJ, Baden HP, Halperin AJ, Ponten J. (1991) A role for sunlight in skin cancer: UV-induced p53 mutations in squamous cell carcinoma. *Proc. Natl. Acad. Sci. USA* 88: 10124–10128.

Caron de Fromentel C, Soussi T. (1992) TP53 tumor suppressor gene: a model for investigating human mutagenesis. *Genes Chrom. Cancer* 4: 1–15.

Carothers AM, Urlaub G, Mucha J, Harvey RG, Chasin LA, Grunberger D. (1990) Splicing mutations in the CHO DHFR gene preferentially induced by $(+/-)$-3 α, 4 β-dihydroxy-1α, 2α-epoxy-1,2,3,4-tetrahydrobenzo[c]phenanthrene. *Proc. Natl. Acad. Sci. USA* 87: 5464–5468.

Crook T, Vousden KH. (1992) Properties of p53 mutations detected in primary and secondary cervical cancers suggest mechanisms of metastasis and involvement of environmental carcinogens. *EMBO J.* 11: 3935–3940.

Dittmer D, Pati S, Zambetti G, Chu S, Teresky AK, Moore M, Finlay C, Levine AJ. (1993) Gain of function mutations in p53. *Nature Genet.* 4: 42–45.

Donehower LA, Harvey M, Slagle BL, McArthur MJ, Montgomery CA, Butel JS, Bradley A. (1992) Mice deficient for p53 are developmentally normal but susceptible to spontaneous tumors. *Nature* 356: 215–221.

Felley-Bosco E, Mirkovitch J, Keefer L, Harris CC. (1993) Investigation of 5-methylcytosine deamination in codon 248 of the p53 gene in human cells. *Proc. Am. Assoc. Cancer Res.* 34: 118.

Harris CC, Holstein M. (1993) Clinical implications of the p53 tumor-suppressor gene. *N. Engl. J. Med.* **329:** 1318–1327.

Holstein M, Sidransky D, Vogelstein B, Harris CC. (1991) p53 mutations in human cancers. *Science* **253:** 49–53.

Krawczak M, Smith-Sorensen B, Schmidtke J, Kakkar VV, Cooper DN, Hovig E. (1994) The somatic spectrum of cancer-associated single base-pair substitutions in the TP53 gene is determined mainly by endogenous mechanisms of mutation and by selection. *Hum. Mutation,* in press.

Levine AJ, Momand J, Finlay CA. (1991) The p53 tumor suppressor gene. *Nature* **351:** 453–456.

Nakazawa H, Aguelon AM, Yamasaki H. (1992) Identification and quantification of a carcinogen-induced molecular initiation event in cell transformation. *Oncogene* **7:** 2295–2301.

Ozturk M and collaborators. (1991) p53 mutation in hepatocellular carcinoma after aflatoxin exposure. *Lancet* **338:** 1356–1359.

Prives C, Manfredi JJ. (1993) The p53 tumor suppressor protein: meeting review. *Genes Devel.* **7:** 529–534.

Rideout WM, Coetzee GA, Olumi AF, Jones PA. (1990) 5-Methylcytosine as an endogenous mutagen in the human LDL receptor and p53 gene. *Science* **249:** 1288–1290.

Sato M, Nishigori C, Zgahl M, Yagi T, Takebe H. (1993) Ultraviolet-specific mutations in p53 gene in skin tumors in xeroderma pigmentosum patients. *Cancer Res.* **53:** 2944–2946.

Sommer S. (1994) Does cancer kill the individual and save the species? *Hum. Mutation* **3:** 166–169.

Soussi T, Caron de Fromentel C, May P. (1990) Structural aspects of the p53 protein in relation to gene evolution. *Oncogene* **5:** 945–952.

Ullrich SJ, Anderson CW, Mercer WE, Appella E. (1992) The p53 tumor suppressor protein, a modulator of cell proliferation. *J. Biol. Chem.* **267:** 15259–15262.

Wada K, Wada Y, Doi H, Ishibashi F, Gojibori T, Ikemura T. (1991) Codon usage tabulated from the GenBank genetic sequence data. *Nucleic Acids Res. Suppl.* **19:** 1981–1986.

Zambetti GP, Levine AJ. (1993) A comparison of the biological activities of wild-type and mutant p53. *FASEB J.* **7:** 855–865.

Ziegler A, Leffell DJ, Kunala S, Sharma HW, Gailani M, Simon JA, Halperin AJ, Baden HP, Shapiro PE, Bale AE, Brash DE. (1993) Mutation hotspots due to sunlight in the p53 gene of nonmelanoma skin cancers. *Proc. Natl. Acad. Sci.* USA **90:** 4216–4220.

Index

From Genotype to Phenotype

S.E. Humphries & S. Malcolm
respectively University College Medical School, London, UK; and Institute of Child Health, University of London, UK

The study of how the effects of different mutations - the 'genotype' of the individual - are modified by other genetic factors and by the environment to produce variable clinical symptoms - the 'phenotype' - is one of the fastest growing areas of human molecular genetics. *From Genotype to Phenotype* provides a unique review of the mechanisms of interaction between genotype and phenotype, for both common and rare genetic disorders. A detailed understanding of common human phenotypes will improve disease diagnosis and help determine specific therapeutic measures for the future.

"The excitement that comes from making new, often unexpected, observations in the area of clinical genetics is conveyed superbly by the editors and individual authors throughout this book. It is a pleasure to read a book that describes these recent advances so well and which is also so full of novelty." Prof. Kare Berg, Institute of Medical Genetics, Oslo.

Contents

Mutations and human disease, *S.Malcolm*; Cystic fibrosis, *P.F.Pignatti*; Mutations in type I and type III collagen genes, *R.Dalgleish*; Genotype-phenotype correlation in Gaucher disease, *M.Horowitz & A.Zimran*; Familial hypercholesterolaemia, *A.K.Soutar*; The molecular basis of Charcot-Marie-Tooth disease, *F.Baas et al*; The genetics of Wilms' tumour, *J.K.Cowell*; How a dynamic mutation manifests in myotonic dystrophy, *C.L.Winchester & K.J.Johnson*; Length variation in fragile X, *M.C.Hirst*; Somatic mosaicism, chimerism and X inactivation, *A.O.M.Wilkie*; Mitochondrial DNA-associated disease, *S.R.Hammans*; Diabetes - from phenotype to genotype and back to phenotype, *G.A.Hitman et al*; Coronary artery disease and the variability gene concept - the effect of smoking on plasma levels of high density lipoprotein and fibrinogen, *S.E.Humphries*; Genetic predisposition to dyslipidaemia and accelerated atherosclerosis - environmental interactions and modification by gene therapy, *E.Boerwinkle & L.Chan*.

Of interest to:

Clinicians; researchers in molecular genetics; genetic counsellors.

Hardback; 310 pages;   1-872748-62-7; 1994

Autoimmune Disease
Focus on Sjögren's Syndrome

D.A. Isenberg & A.C. Horsfall (Eds)
respectively University College, London, UK; and Kennedy Institute of
Rheumatology, London, UK

This book is a comprehensive guide to the factors involved in the aetiology of
autoimmune diseases in general, and of Sjögren's syndrome in particular. A
wide range of topics is covered, including advances in serological
assessment and therapy, links between autoimmunity and malignancy,
animal models of Sjögren's syndrome, and the role of the T-cell receptor
and cell adhesion molecules.

The book represents the cutting edge of research into understanding the
initiation, perpetuation, consequences and control of autoimmunity. In
particular, it focusses on advances made by the application of molecular
biological techniques.

Contents

Autoimmunity and the clinical spectrum of Sjögren's syndrome,
D.Kausmann et al; The molecular pathology of Sj ögren's syndrome,
P.Speight & R.Jordan; Cell adhesion in autoimmune rheumatic disease,
J.C.W.Edwards & L.S.Wilkinson; Experimental models of Sj ögren's
syndrome, *A.C.Horsfall et al*; Autoantibodies in Sj ögren's syndrome: their
origins and pathological consequences, *P.J.Maddison*; Use of peptides for
the mapping of B-cell epitopes recognized by anti-Ro (SS-A) antibodies,
V.Ricchiuti & S.Muller; Glycosylation abnormalities in Sj ögren's syndrome,
P.Youinou et al; T-cell receptor usage in the autoimmune rheumatic
diseases, *P.M.Lydyard et al*; Immunogenetics: a tool to analyze
autoimmunity, *F.C.Arnett*; Viruses in the initiation and perpetuation of
autoimmunity of Sjögren's syndrome, *P.J.W.Venables et al*; Autoimmunity
and malignancy, *P.Isaacson & J.Spencer*; The therapy of autoimmunity,
M.L.Snaith.

Of interest to:

Clinicians, researchers and postgraduates.

Hardback; 240 pages;   1-872748-23-6; 1994

From Genetics to Gene Therapy
The Molecular Pathology of Human Disease

D.S. Latchman (Ed.)
University College and Middlesex School of Medicine, London, UK

In this book a team of distinguished scientists provide an overview of the molecular pathology of human disease. Each chapter provides an analysis of the molecular biology approaches to individual diseases, such as leukaemia, cardiovascular disease and cancer, and includes a discussion on the likely impact of gene therapy.

Contents

What is molecular pathology? *D.S.Latchman*; Apolipoprotein B and coronary heart disease, *J.Scott*; Prospects for gene therapy of X-linked immunodeficiency diseases, *C.Kinnon*; Duchenne muscular dystrophy, *S.C.Brown & G.Dickson*; Molecular genetics of leukaemia, *M.F.Greaves*; The molecular pathology of endocrine tumours, *A.E.Bishop & J.M.Polak*; Genetic predisposition to breast cancer, *M.R.Stratton*; Gene therapy for cancer, *M.K.L.Collins*; Retrovirus receptors on human cells, *R.A.Weiss*; Viral vectors for gene therapy, *G.W.G.Wilkinson et al*; Direct gene transfer for the treatment of human disease, *G.J.Nabel & E.G.Nabel*; Processing of membrane proteins in neurodegenerative diseases, *R.J.Mayer et al*; Herpes simplex - once bitten, forever smitten? *D.S.Latchman*.

Of interest to:

Medical researchers and clinicians.

Hardback; 272 pages;   1-872748-36-8; 1994

DNA Fingerprinting

M. Krawczak & J. Schmidtke
Medizinische Hochschule, Hannover, Germany

DNA fingerprinting is used to identify individuals and determine family relationships by analysing DNA samples obtained from blood, hair and other biological specimens. It is widely used for paternity testing, to identify rapists and other criminals, and in genetic research.

This book is a comprehensive and easy-to-read review of the theoretical and practical aspects of this important technique. It explains the nature of DNA polymorphisms, the techniques by which they are studied and the evolutionary forces which maintain them within populations. The authors go on to examine the applications of DNA fingerprinting in medicine, to kinship testing, and to the conviction or exoneration of crime suspects. It is an essential reference for all those interested in the genetic, forensic, legal and ethical issues raised by this powerful new technique.

Contents

The genetic background; Studying DNA polymorphism; Origin and maintenance of DNA polymorphism; DNA typing to identify suspects; DNA typing to establish relationships; Further development - technical and ethical issues.

Of interest to:

Undergraduates studying medical genetics or forensic science; Medical students; Lawyers.

Paperback; 118 pages; 1-872748-43-0; 1994

The Human Genome

T. Strachan
St Mary's Hospital, Manchester, UK

If you have any interest in the Human Genome Project, this book is a must!
A clear introduction to the structure of the human genome and the ways in
which recent knowledge is influencing medical research and practice.

"...an easy to read, up to date and complete treatment of the human
genome from biochemistry to medical genetics." *Endocrinologist*

"...a crash course on the ways in which classical human genetics is being
revised and extended by the methods of applied molecular biology" *Biologist*

Contents

Organization and expression of the human genome; Evolution and
polymorphism of the human genome; Analyzing human DNA; Mapping the
human genome; Human disease genes - isolation and molecular pathology;
The human genome - clinical and research applications.

Of interest to:

Undergraduates; Postgraduates; Researchers; Medical students.

Paperback; 170 pages; 1-872748-80-5; 1992

ORDERING DETAILS

Main address for orders

BIOS Scientific Publishers Ltd
St Thomas House, Becket Street,
Oxford OX1 1SJ, UK
Tel: +44 1865 726286
Fax: +44 1865 246823

Australia and New Zealand
DA Information Services
648 Whitehorse Road, Mitcham, Victoria 3132, Australia
Tel: (03) 873 4411
Fax: (03) 873 5679

India
Viva Books Private Ltd
4346/4C Ansari Road, New Delhi 110 002, India
Tel: 11 3283121
Fax: 11 3267224

Singapore and South East Asia
(Brunei, Hong Kong, Indonesia, Korea, Malaysia, the Philippines,
Singapore, Taiwan, and Thailand)
Toppan Company (S) PTE Ltd
38 Liu Fang Road, Jurong, Singapore 2262
Tel: (265) 6666
Fax: (261) 7875

USA and Canada
Books International Inc
PO Box 605, Herndon, VA 22070, USA
Tel: (703) 435 7064
Fax: (703) 689 0660

Payment can be made by cheque or credit card (Visa/Mastercard, quoting number and expiry date). Alternatively, a *pro forma* invoice can be sent.

Prepaid orders must include £2.50/US$5.00 to cover postage and packing for one item and £1.25/US$2.50 for each additional item.